40 Years of Tropical Medicine Research

A History of the
Gorgas Memorial Institute of Tropical
and Preventive Medicine, Inc.
and the
Gorgas Memorial Laboratory

By

Willard H. Wright, D.V.M., M.S., Ph.D.
//

Washington

1970

Library of Congress Catalog Card No. 73-171590

Printed by Reese Press, Baltimore, Maryland

Major General William Crawford Gorgas, Medical Corps,
United States Army, 1854-1920

IN MEMORIAM
WILLIAM CRAWFORD GORGAS
1854-1920

Gorgas, William Crawford, Surgeon General, U.S. Army, born Mobile, Alabama, October 3, 1854; son of General Josiah Gorgas (C.S.A.) and Amelia (Gayle) Gorgas, A.B., University of the South, 1875; M.D. Bellevue Hospital Medical College (New York University), 1879; interne Bellevue Hospital, 1878-80; honorary Sc.D., University of Pennsylvania, 1903; University of the South, 1904; Harvard, 1908; Brown, 1909; Jefferson Medical College, 1909; LL.D., University of Alabama, 1910; Tulane, 1911; married Marie Cook Doughty, Sept. 15, 1885.

Appointed Surgeon, U.S. Army, June 16, 1880; Captain Assistant Surgeon, June 16, 1885; Major brigade surgeon volunteers, June 4—July 6, 1898; Major Surgeon, July 6, 1898; Chief Sanitary Officer Havana and in charge of sanitary work there, 1898-1902; applied methods of combating yellow fever which eliminated that disease in Havana; Colonel assistant surgeon general by special act of Congress, for yellow fever work in Havana, March 3, 1903; Surgeon General, U.S. Army with rank of Brigadier General, January 16, 1914; Major General, Surgeon General, U.S. Army, March 4, 1915; retired December 1, 1918; Director, Yellow Fever Research Rockefeller Foundation. Appointed chief sanitary officer Panama Canal, March 1, 1904; member, Isthmian Canal Commission, March 4, 1907-1914; permanent director, International Health Division, Rockefeller Foundation.

Recipient of Mary Kingsley Medal from Liverpool School of Tropical Medicine, May 27, 1907; Gold Medal, American Museum of Safety, 1914; Harbin Gold Medal, 1920, awarded D.S.M., 1918; Commander, Legion of Honor (French), 1919; Grand Officer, Order of the Crown of Italy, 1918; Knight Commander of the Most Distinguished Order of St. Michael and St. George, 1920; died July 4, 1920.

—WHO WAS WHO IN AMERICA 1897-1942.

GORGAS

God's own Samaritan, intrepid, true;
   With Christly sympathy and love for all,
And wisely skilled,—he wrote Health's page anew;
   And lifted from the Earth its foulest pall.
Where pestilence and plague took direst toll,
   His magic touch brought life and strength and joy;
In Isthmian realms, where rival oceans roll,
   His blessed arts for good he did employ,—
And lo! the link that joins the waters twain
   (The way to Ind, through all the ages hid!)
Grew into form, and stretched from main to main,
   By reasons of the deathless work he did:
And more than this—the wondrous deeds he wrought,
The texts became whereby the World is taught!

             —Maurice H. Thatcher

DEDICATION

This volume is affectionately dedicated to the Honorable Maurice H. Thatcher, distinguished public servant, Governor of the Panama Canal Zone 1910-1913, friend and wise counselor to Major General William Crawford Gorgas, member of the United States House of Representatives from the State of Kentucky 1923-1933, author and sponsor of the legislation which provided the first appropriation for the Gorgas Memorial Laboratory, Honorary President and General Counsel of the Gorgas Memorial Institute, Vice President 1948-1969, member of the Executive Committee, and strong advocate and staunch supporter of the Gorgas Memorial Institute and the Gorgas Memorial Laboratory for over 40 years.

INTRODUCTION

*"One small step for a man, one giant
leap for mankind." Neal A. Armstrong*

The Gorgas Memorial Laboratory is a living memorial to a great physician and his professional accomplishments. It is a living memorial to a great president, jurist, legislator, scholar and compassionate leader. It is a living memorial to those dedicated scientists who have directed the day to day accumulation of the scientific data essential to our understanding of the complex ecology of disease as seen in a tropical environment.

The four decades encompassed by this history mark the early years of organized medical research. They mark its evolution and recognition as a discipline essential to the health progress of mankind. They mark the identification of etiological agents, the development of serological methods for the recognition of disease experience, the advent of ultra microscopy and the availability of a broad biomedical approach to the disease process. Yellow fever and malaria, the major diseases of the canal construction days, have yielded to the press of organized medical research.

Chagas' disease, leishmaniasis, intestinal parasitism, infantile diarrhea, and viral diseases are major causes of morbidity and mortality in the Republics of Central America. The Gorgas research programs emphasize a broad multi-disciplinary approach to the biology of these diseases and the application of current disease prevention public health technology to the health and welfare of the individual.

The importance of nutrition in the physical growth of the infant has been recognized for centuries. The effects of maternal undernutrition and malnutrition on the offspring have been recognized more recently as specific biochemical and cognitive deficits.

If the ideals, the hopes and the dreams of President Porras and General Gorgas are to be realized, the course of tropical disease research must be directed toward the role of nutrition in the total growth and intellectual development of the individual.

Doctor Willard H. Wright has compiled a fascinating history of the Gorgas Memorial Institute and the Gorgas Memorial Laboratory. The efforts and accomplishments of the men and women of Gorgas are now memorialized.

> Calvin B. Galloway
> Rear Admiral MC, USN (Ret.)
> President and Chairman of the Board,
> Gorgas Memorial Institute of Tropical
> and Preventive Medicine, Inc.

Pendennis Mount
Annapolis, Maryland
July 20, 1969

FOREWORD

The idea for the establishment of a memorial to Major General William Crawford Gorgas in the form of an international center for the study of diseases of the tropics originated with Dr. Belisario Porras, eminent jurist, distinguished diplomat and three times President of the Republic of Panama. For nearly a decade, the concept remained only a dream. Then, in 1928, the Gorgas Memorial Laboratory came into being when the Republic of Panama donated the land and the original building and the Congress of the United States provided the initial financial support.

The Laboratory has had a major role in the area of tropical disease research. It has been an outstanding example of excellent cooperation between nations and organizations to produce information for the common good of all.

Physically located in Panama and with the excellent cooperation of the Panama government, it has been able to capitalize on the availability of numerous biomedical problems in the tropics. Under the broad charter of its parent organization, the Gorgas Memorial Institute, the Laboratory was given a wide scope for its activities. A large variety of subject areas have been investigated. All have advanced knowledge in the particular field. Many have been pioneering. While tropical disease research has waxed and waned in many other countries, support has been regular and information has been produced steadily at the Gorgas Memorial Laboratory. The results of research have been of benefit not only to Panama but to other countries of the world. Although in the tropics, significant research also has been done on diseases of importance in cooler climates. Some of these diseases because of being transmitted throughout the year can be studied more intensively in warm climates.

The Laboratory has ranged far and wide in its activities. It has always maintained its international character. Its staff members have served many national and international agencies and governments throughout the world. Also, scientists from many countries have visited to learn, to exchange information, or to do special investigations. It has been a valuable resource for the training of persons of varied backgrounds and disciplines.

Much of the character of the Institute has been formed by the body of distinguished men who make up the directorate and advisory board. These men who are outstanding in their fields of research and administration have given generously of their time and constructive thought to the affairs of the organization. Their broad visions and keen judgments have resulted in the formulation of wise policies. Their altruistic endeavors constitute an intellectual philanthropy of a high order.

This story of the first forty years portrays the major research endeavors and results year by year and epoch by epoch. The present staff members of the Laboratory are proud of their contributions to the elucidation of important health problems and are proud of the accomplishments of their eminent precursors. I share their pride and believe that this history provides an unusual record of achievement.

These achievements were possible only because of the interest, goodwill, and support of many people and organizations to whom we are all deeply indebted.

Martin D. Young, Sc.D.
Director
Gorgas Memorial Laboratory

TABLE OF CONTENTS

List of Illustrations*

* Thanks are due the Pan American Health Organization for the photographs in Figures 7, 8 and 16. The National Geographic Society kindly supplied the photograph in Figure 15 and the Panama Canal Company the one in Figure 4.

Chapter 1.

The Early Years
1921-1928

Establishment; Organization; Fund Raising; Scientific Programs;
Other Activities

"There is properly no history; only biography"
—RALPH WALDO EMERSON

The death of General Gorgas on July 4, 1920, in the Queen Alexandra
Military Hospital at Millbank, England, led to a clearer perspective and an
increased appreciation of his unprecedented contributions to the health of
the Americas. Efforts were soon initiated by a number of organizations to
establish a suitable memorial to this great physician and sanitarian, the
first to effectively control yellow fever.

The Southern Society of Washington, D.C. was one of the leaders in
this movement. In a report of the Committee on Program for a memorial
service for General Gorgas, the Congress of the United States was petitioned
"to set apart a site and erect a monument to the late General Gorgas,
commemorative of his service to humanity."

However, the initiative was assumed by the country which witnessed
his most remarkable achievements. The Southern Society sponsored memorial services for General Gorgas in Washington on January 16, 1921.
In a cablegram read at those ceremonies, Dr. Belisario Porras, President
of the Republic of Panama, stated in part, as follows:

> "I shall always retain happy recollections and genuine veneration
> for Dr. Gorgas, who was full of energy, firmness, goodness, and
> exquisite accomplishments. In acknowledgement of this noble
> character and meritorious work on the Isthmian soil, Panama has
> begun, under my Government, the establishment of an Institute
> for Tropical Medicine which will be called "Gorgas Institute,"
> and which we hope to carry to successful conclusion with the aid
> of men of science and American philanthropists, which I hope to
> obtain, because I know the veneration of Americans for their
> great men."

In an address at the memorial exercises the Honorable José E. Lefevre,
Chargé d'Affaires of the Republic of Panama, brought a similar message
from President Porras.

1

Following closely on President Porras' proposal and at his request, the Honorable José E. Lefevre called a meeting in Washington, D.C. on January 31, 1921. Present at this meeting, in addition to Señor Lefevre, were Dr. L. S. Rowe, Director General of the Pan American Union, the Honorable John Bassett Moore, Major General M. W. Ireland, USA, Rear Admiral E. R. Stitt, USN, Surgeon General H. S. Cumming, U.S. Public Health Service, and Rear Admiral W. C. Braisted, USN.

After a general discussion, a Provisional Committee was constituted with Dr. Belisario Porras as President and Founder, Rear Admiral Braisted as Chairman, and others in attendance as members. The Chairman, Admiral Braisted, was directed to draw up a provisional scheme of organization and it was directed that President Porras be informed of the formation of the committee and the contemplated work.

It was hoped that suitable space could be obtained in the Santo Tomás Hospital in Panama for the initial research program and it was contemplated that the Superintendent of the Hospital would act as the Director of the Institute. Initial staffing of the project was to be made with commissioned officers from the Army, Navy and Public Health Service, with the hope that research individuals from universities and medical schools might be attracted for short term tours of duty. It was suggested that Central and South American countries be notified of the movement with the idea that country representatives might be appointed to assist in the research program and make suitable suggestions with regard to health problems which required attention in the various countries. Initial financing to the extent of $1,000 was provided by the Government of Panama for organizational expenses and secretarial services.

Following its organization, the Provisional Committee continued its activities with increasing vigor. Subsequent meetings of the Committee were held on April 9, June 30, July 20 and September 19, 1921.

It was stated that President Porras had approved the organization and plans of the Committee. The proposals still contemplated the use of the Santo Tomás Hospital as temporary headquarters for the Laboratory. An office was established in the Panama Legation. A publicity campaign and mechanisms of fund raising were discussed. It was decided to offer the position of Director of the Laboratory to Dr. Richard P. Strong, Professor of Tropical Medicine at Harvard.

As a result of these meetings, the Gorgas Memorial Institute of Tropical and Preventive Medicine was incorporated in Delaware on October 25, 1921.

The incorporators were as follows:

Dr. Belisario Porras, President of the Republic of Panama;

Hon. José E. Lefevre, Chargé d'Affaires of Panama in the United States, representing the Panama National Health Board;

2

served as Fleet Surgeon of the Atlantic Fleet from 1912 to 1914. From 1914 to 1921 he was Surgeon General of the Navy. Admiral Braisted was President of the American Medical Association from 1920 to 1921. He retired on November 20, 1921, and died on January 17, 1941. In addition to the Distinguished Service Medal, Admiral Braisted was the recipient of several foreign decorations.

Initial Fund Raising— Contract with Ward Systems Company— Campaign in Alabama   At the meeting on October 26, 1921, the President was authorized to sign a contract with the Ward Systems Company of Chicago, Illinois, for the solicitation of funds.

This contract, which appeared at the time to be a favorable one, was signed on October 26, 1921. It provided that fund raising was to begin on September 26, 1921, and continue for 1 year. The Ward Systems Company was to advance funds as needed but not in excess of $100,000 to cover expenses of the campaign, the funds to be expended with approval of the Finance Committee of the Institute. The Company was to receive a fee of $30,000 for raising the first million dollars, a fee of $35,000 for the second million, and for each succeeding million a fee of $40,000, due on completion of the goal of each million dollars. The Institute was to provide a Treasurer to receive all funds. Mr. E. C. Loucks was Director of Organization for the Ward Systems Company and Mr. A. F. Robbins served as Executive Secretary. Other company employees were also involved in the campaign.

As indicated previously, other efforts were being made to memorialize General Gorgas. One of these movements, known as the Claxton Committee of the Southern Gorgas Memorial, had secured the support of the Southern Medical Association, whereas the American Medical Association had appointed a committee to cooperate with the Gorgas Memorial Institute.

The situation became rather a delicate one and it was decided at a meeting of the Board of Directors on December 2, 1921, that a conference should be held with representatives of the competing agency to coordinate efforts.

On December 9, 1921, the Executive Committee of the Gorgas Memorial Institute met with a committee from an organization stated to be the Gorgas School of Sanitation of the South. It developed that this school was designed for training sanitarians to assist the medical profession and public health officials in disease control. Its purposes, therefore, were intended to carry into actual practice the principles underlying the program of the Gorgas Memorial Institute.

At an adjourned meeting on December 10, 1921, it was decided that the

Merritt W. Ireland, Surgeon General, United States Army;

Edward R. Stitt, Surgeon General, United States Navy;

Hugh S. Cumming, Surgeon General, United States Public Health Service;

Dr. Leo S. Rowe, Director General of the Pan American Union;

Dr. Franklin H. Martin, Director General, American College of Surgeons, Chicago, Illinois;

William C. Braisted, Rear Admiral, United States Navy;

Honorable John Bassett Moore, member, Permanent International Court of Justice.

A meeting of the incorporators was held in Philadelphia, Pa. on October 26, 1921, at which time the following organization was effected and By-Laws adopted.

President: Rear Admiral William C. Braisted;

Vice President: Dr. Franklin H. Martin;

Treasurer: Edward J. Stellwagen, President, Union Trust Co., Washington, D.C.;

Assistant Treasurer: Edson B. Olds;

Executive Secretary: Arthur F. Robbins;

Director of Organization: E. C. Loucks;

Director of Publicity: Edwin L. Zudeck;

Chairman, Board of Scientific Directors: Dr. Richard P. Strong;

Executive Committee: Messrs: Braisted, Rowe, Ireland, Stitt and Cumming.

The Corporation was given legal status in the Republic of Panama by the registration of the Certificate of Incorporation in Escritura Pública No. 1413 on December 6, 1921.

The election of Rear Admiral William C. Braisted as the first President of the Gorgas Memorial Institute was a natural outcome of his close association with General Gorgas during World War I and his stature in the medical profession at the time. Admiral Braisted was born in Toledo, Ohio, on October 9, 1864. He received a Ph.B. degree from the University of Michigan in 1883 and his medical degree from the Medical Department of Columbia University in 1886. He interned and was resident physician at Bellevue Hospital for 2½ years, following which he practiced in Detroit from 1888 to 1890. He entered the Medical Corps of the U.S. Navy on September 26, 1890 as an Assistant Surgeon; rose to Passed Assistant Surgeon on September 26, 1893; Surgeon on March 3, 1893 and Medical Inspector on October 20, 1913. In 1904, he fitted out and equipped the hospital ship "Relief." He served as an observer in the Russo-Japanese War. Dr. Braisted became Assistant Chief of the Navy Bureau of Medicine and Surgery in 1906 and served in that capacity until 1912. During 1906 and 1907, he was attending physician, along with Dr. Rixey, at the White House during the administration of President Theodore Roosevelt. He

Fig. 1. Dr. Belisario Porras, three times *President of Panama, and founder of the Gorgas Memorial Institute of Tropical and Preventive Medicine.*

two memorial movements were in effect complementary and that it would be advisable and desirable to join forces for fund raising, the funds to be distributed "impartially and adequately" between the two organizations after consultation with the Scientific Committee and with the full approval of the Board of Directors. The statement of intent was agreed to and signed on December 10, 1921, by Dr. Seale Harris, Chairman, Gorgas Memorial School of Sanitation. Four representatives from the Gorgas School of Sanitation were added to the Board of Directors of the Gorgas Memorial Institute, which was then constituted as follows:

Dr. Belisario Porras, President of the Republic of Panama;

Dr. Augusto S. Boyd, Chief of Surgical Service, Santo Tomás Hospital;

Hon. John Bassett Moore, New York City;

Dr. Leo S. Rowe, Director General, Pan American Union;

Admiral E. R. Stitt, Surgeon General, United States Navy;

General M. W. Ireland, Surgeon General, United States Army;

Dr. Hugh S. Cumming, Surgeon General, United States Public Health Service;

Dr. Franklin H. Martin, Chicago, Illinois;

Rear Admiral W. C. Braisted, Washington, D.C.;

Dr. Seale Harris, Birmingham, Alabama;

Dr. Oscar Dowling, New Orleans, Louisiana;

Dr. E. J. Williams, Richmond, Virginia;

Dr. Frank Billings, Chicago, Illinois.

A goal of $6,000,000 was set as a desirable one for the combined purposes, now designated as the "Gorgas Memorial."

It would seem that the Alabama movement to memorialize General Gorgas actually predated the decision of the Gorgas Memorial Institute to raise funds for this purpose. On May 23, 1921, the Alumni Association of the University of Alabama presented a resolution to the Board of Trustees of the University meeting on that date asking the Board to support efforts to provide a suitable memorial to General Gorgas and to merge any such effort with that begun in 1914, to honor his mother, Amelia Gayle Gorgas, who had served as Librarian of the University from 1883 to 1907. The resolution expressed gratitude to Dr. Seale Harris, who had agreed to serve as chairman of a fund raising committee, and called for the appointment of a University Provost to supervise arrangements for the campaign and other projects under consideration. The Board of Trustees on the above-mentioned date unanimously adopted a resolution creating the Gorgas School of Sanitation with the understanding that it would be put into effect at some later date when the resources of the University "shall justify it." Apparently, action was taken later to create the post of University Provost; Dr. Philander P. Claxton was appointed to this position and the fund raising committee was known as the Claxton Committee.

Regardless of the origins of the two memorial movements, the Alabama group cooperated actively in the solicitation of funds, and the newspapers of the State gave strong support in publicizing the campaign.

The campaign was launched at Tuscaloosa on February 14, 1922, at a luncheon attended by many prominent men of the State. The Gorgas Memorial Institute also had a part in the launching since the meeting was attended and addressed by Mr. A. F. Robbins, Executive Secretary, and Rear Admiral W. C. Braisted, USN (Ret.), President. A goal of $750,000 was set for collection in Alabama.

Following the initial activity in Tuscaloosa, other rallies were held in several cities in Alabama. Participating in ceremonies at Birmingham on March 3, 1922, were Sir Auckland Geddes, the British Ambassador, the Honorable Leander McCormick Goodhart, First Secretary of the British Embassy, Dr. Franklin H. Martin, Brig. Gen. Robert E. Noble, USA, Mrs. Helen Katherine Gould, President of the International Women's Chamber of Commerce, the Honorable José E. Lefevre, Chargé d'Affaires of the Republic of Panama, Dr. Seale Harris, and Mr. A. F. Robbins. One newspaper, the Birmingham News, sponsored a Gorgas Essay Contest, and Charles H. Colvin of Sheffield, winner of the contest, was present at the ceremonies in question.

Newspaper reports of the period indicated that the fund raising campaign was being pursued with vigor. The State of Alabama had been divided into districts each of which was given a quota. Committees were being organized in other Southern States. The Tuscaloosa (Alabama) News and Times-Gazette reported on March 3, 1922, that Tuscaloosa had raised $25,628 and had been the first district in the State to reach its quota.

In the meantime, the officers of the Gorgas Memorial Institute were increasingly concerned with financial matters. In a meeting of the Board of Directors held on January 16, 1922, the By-Laws were modified to provide for a Board of Finance. On April 1, 1922, the following appointments to this Board were confirmed:

E. J. Stellwagen, President, Union Trust Co., Washington;

Eliot Wadsworth, Assistant Secretary of the Treasury;

W. P. G. Harding, Governor, Federal Reserve Board;

Allen Forbes, President, State Street Trust Company, Boston;

George Reynolds, President, Continental and Commercial Bank, Chicago.

At the above-mentioned meeting, the Executive Secretary, Mr. A. F. Robbins, reported that to date the sum of $86,000 had been raised in Alabama. Questions arose concerning authority over the direction of the campaign. The President, Admiral Braisted, stated that the campaign was under the direction of the Ward Systems Company, in accordance with the contract executed with that group.

The Board of Directors on May 3, 1922, was faced with the decision of financing the fund raising drive in the South. It was revealed that the Alabama campaign had to date netted in cash not over $25,000 with an additional $100,000 in pledges and notes. Expenses to date had been $15,700 of which about $9,000 had been spent in Alabama. The records indicate that from October 1, 1922 to February 19, 1923, the sum of $711.57 was received at the Washington headquarters of the Gorgas Memorial Institute from the Ward Systems Company. Of this amount, all but $49.08 was disbursed by that Company.

It developed that Mr. R. H. Ward of the Ward Systems Company, in accordance with the contract with the Gorgas Memorial Institute, had advanced various sums of money and that Mr. Ward now wished to be reimbursed. It was unanimously voted to reimburse the claimant from any funds received or "which might be received" from any source as a result of the campaign in the South.

At the annual meeting of the Corporation on October 20, 1922, consideration was given to relations with the Ward Systems Company, reports from which were read and placed on file. Proposals were made to settle claims with the above organization, such proposals to be considered in detail at an adjourned meeting on November 11, 1922. At that meeting, Mr. Walter S. Penfield, the attorney for the Institute, submitted a resolution agreed to by a representative of the Ward Systems Company. On the basis of this resolution, a contract dated December 29, 1922, was signed by General Noble and Admiral Stitt for the Institute and Mr. R. H. Ward for the Company. This contract provided that the Institute was to pay to the Ward Systems Company the sum of $15,700 with interest at 6% per annum from November 11, 1922, the payment being contingent on the collection and covering in the treasury of the Institute the sum of $50,000. The contract of October 26, 1921, was terminated.

At that same meeting, it was reported that on February 3, 1922, the Board of Trustees of the American Medical Association had appointed a committee to act in an advisory capacity to the Gorgas Memorial Institute in its efforts to solicit funds to memorialize General Gorgas. This action was approved by the House of Delegates (J. Am. Med. Ass., August 26, 1922). A year later, the Committee reported that its efforts to raise funds for the Institute among State Medical Societies had been a distinct disappointment as only $7.00 had been collected.

Dr. Franklin H. Martin persisted in his attempts to enlist the aid of the American Medical Association but such efforts met with failure (J. Am. Med. Ass., November 29, 1924, p. 1772).

At a meeting of the Board of Directors on August 27, 1923, it developed that the funds collected in Alabama had been retained in that State and that there was a great reluctance to transfer these funds to the Gorgas Memorial Institute. Various efforts had been made to secure release of the

7

funds or for the Alabama Committee to assume the cost of the fund raising campaign which amounted to $9,475.91. All of these efforts were fruitless.

At a meeting of the Board of Trustees of the University of Alabama on November 10, 1923, Dr. Seale Harris appeared and stated that Dr. Franklin H. Martin had requested permission to use $5,000 of the amount subscribed for the Gorgas School of Sanitation for the purpose of financing a new campaign to raise funds for the Gorgas Memorial Institute. Dr. Harris stated that Dr. Martin proposed to give to the School of Sanitation at the University 90 percent of all funds raised in Alabama. Dr. Harris recommended that the amounts raised to date and any subsequent funds be paid to the University for the benefit of the Gorgas School of Sanitation. The Board of Trustees then adopted a resolution to this effect.

The record indicates that the Gorgas School of Sanitation was never established. It was not until 1943, that any further move was made to utilize the monies raised in the campaign of 1922. On July 8, 1943, the Alabama Legislature passed an Act [Title 55, Section 373 (7), Code of Alabama (1940) (Recomp. 1958)] creating the Gorgas Memorial Board "to honor and commemorate the memory of General Josiah Gorgas, former president of the University of Alabama and Amelia Gayle Gorgas, daughter of Governor John Gayle, for many years in charge of the student hospital and library of the University, and William Crawford Gorgas whose fight against yellow fever and tropical diseases made possible the building of the Panama Canal."

At a meeting of the Executive Committee of the Board of Trustees of the University of Alabama held on September 6, 1943, it was resolved that the Gorgas Memorial Commission, composed of Dr. George H. Denny, Dr. Seale Harris and Hon. Hill Ferguson, be discharged and that the responsibility of the Commission be transferred to the Board of Trustees of the University of Alabama. On September 10, 1943, the members of the Gorgas Memorial Commission acceded to the request implied in the above-mentioned resolution and requested that the Board of Trustees of the University assume responsibility for the administration of the amount of money then on deposit to the credit of Mr. Frank M. Moody (deceased), as Treasurer of the Gorgas Memorial Fund, in the First National Bank of Tuskaloosa of Tuscaloosa, Alabama, who functioned as such Treasurer up to the time of his death, under appointment by the above-mentioned members of the Commission. The amount of said deposit at the time was stated to be approximately $5,200.

Under date of March 7, 1969, the Honorable J. Rufus Bealle, Attorney, Land Commissioner and Secretary of the Board of Trustees of the University of Alabama, advised that the amount of money transferred to the Board of Trustees by the members of the Gorgas Memorial Commission was actually $5,585.55 and that the corpus of the fund is still intact, and, with earnings, amounted on the above date to $7,522.84.

Although the record is not clear, it would appear that the lack of co-operation on the part of the Alabama participants was due to a number of factors. It was alleged, for instance, that employees of the Ward Systems Company alienated the regard of supporters of the campaign. Furthermore, one of the objections to transferring funds to the Gorgas Memorial Institute was based on the premise that the donors had understood that their contributions would be retained in the State to be applied to the development of the Gorgas School of Sanitation and that no part of the contributions would go to a money raising organization. In any event, there is no record that the Gorgas Memorial Institute received any of the funds. On the other hand, the Institute was obligated to reimburse the Ward Systems Company for expenses incurred in the operation of the fund raising campaign, an obligation which was met years later at a considerable sacrifice.

In retrospect, it is not possible to evaluate the factors responsible for the unsatisfactory, if not sorry, experience in the initial endeavor to provide funds for the Gorgas Memorial Institute. The campaign in Alabama was launched with great fanfare, the publicity was well handled and the initial organization appeared to provide a favorable atmosphere. It would seem, however, that guidelines were not clearly defined, that agreements were not legally constituted, that management of the fund raising organization lacked a certain degree of business acumen and that certain frictions and disaffections developed which limited the success of the efforts and provided an atmosphere unfriendly to the Gorgas Memorial Institute. Thus the Institute failed to profit from this initial venture and in fact was left shouldered with a considerable debt.

Reorganization of Executive Committee—Removal of Office to Chicago from Washington—New Fund Raising Plans

The initial failure to secure financial support led the Board of Directors to explore other avenues of approach. Discussions of various plans were held during meetings in late 1922 and early 1923. On April 21, 1923, Dr. Franklin H. Martin submitted a plan for a fund raising campaign to be managed by the Institute itself. The plan included the addition of a number of prominent and influential men to the Board of Directors, changes in the personnel of the Executive Committee, removal of the Institute office from Washington to Chicago and proposals for the solicitation of funds. The plan was approved and a new Executive Committee was elected with the following members: Chairman, Dr. Franklin H. Martin,

Mr. F. W. Upham, General Charles G. Dawes, Colonel W. H. G. Logan, Dr. Frank Billings and Dr. Gilbert FitzPatrick.

The affairs of the Institute were apparently in a state of flux during 1922 and 1923. At the annual meeting held in Washington on October 20, 1922, Col. Theodore Roosevelt was elected President and Dr. Franklin H. Martin, reelected Vice President. Pending the acceptance by Col. Roosevelt, Brig. Gen. Robert E. Noble was appointed President pro tem.

The Committee appointed to notify Col. Roosevelt of his election as President, reported on December 29, 1922 that Col. Roosevelt was unable to accept the presidency.

Apparently Admiral Braisted remained as President until the acceptance of his resignation on April 21, 1923.

Removal of the Institute office from Washington to Chicago was accomplished on or about June 11, 1923, although it was not until August 27, 1923 that Dr. Martin was given authority to open a bank account and sign checks. In the meantime, Dr. Martin assumed charge of the campaign for the solicitation of funds and vigorously pursued its objectives. (Dr. Martin was first elected Vice President on October 26, 1921; Chairman of the Board of Directors on August 27, 1923, and President and Chairman of the Board of Directors on October 23, 1925.)

Franklin H. Martin was a man of many talents and boundless energy. Born in Ixonia, Wisconsin, on July 13, 1857, he received his M.D. degree in 1880 from the Chicago Medical College (later the Medical School of Northwestern University). His post-graduate studies led him to Queens University in Belfast, Ireland, the University of Wales and the University of Pittsburgh. He received a Doctor of Public Health degree from the Detroit College of Medicine and Surgery and a Doctor of Science from Northwestern. In 1888, he organized with Dr. W. F. Coleman the Chicago Post Graduate Medical School and founded Charity Hospital. He was the founder in 1905 of "Surgery, Gynecology and Obstetrics" and served as its Editor in Chief for many years. In 1913 he organized the American College of Surgeons and was its Director General for a considerable period. In its behalf, he traveled extensively both at home and abroad and organized many of its foreign affiliates. From 1916 to 1921, Dr. Martin was a member of the Advisory Commission of the Council of National Defense and served actively as a Colonel in the Medical Corps of the United States Army from 1917 to 1919. He was a trustee of Northwestern University. The many honors accorded him included the Distinguished Service Medal, Companion of the Order of St. Michael and St. George, and Commander of the Order of the Crown of Italy. Dr. Martin was the author of many works on surgery and gynecology, as well as several travel books. He died on March 7, 1935.

Dr. Martin plunged enthusiastically into the task of providing the Gorgas

Memorial Institute with an adequate endowment. He strove indefatigably toward this end and the Institute was indeed fortunate in having an advocate with so many capabilities and such an unalterable determination to reach the desired goal. His continued efforts to raise funds must have consumed a great deal of his time and energy but there is no evidence that he ever shirked the task or for the briefest time took his eye off the ultimate goal. Furthermore, he had developed a considerable degree of business acumen and apparently possessed a certain perspicuity not only in the collection of monies but in their conservation. The affairs of the Gorgas Memorial Institute prospered under his aegis.

Dr. Martin conceived the idea of organizing State Governing Committees to assist in the solicitation of funds and for supporting other programs of the Institute. On December 1, 1925, he reported that these Committees had enrolled nearly 2,000 physicians and laymen.

A financial report of June 10, 1924, indicated a bank balance of $9,603.16. The campaign continued to gain momentum and the Executive Committee on November 23, 1925, was concerned with the matter of investing the sum of $30,000. In a report dated October 29, 1926, Dr. Martin noted that a campaign was under way in the Canal Zone to raise $10,000. Of this amount, $2,116.46 had been received at the Chicago headquarters. In the statement of receipts and expenditures for the period October 1, 1926 to September 30, 1927, an additional sum of $3,865 was noted to have been invested in bonds.

At a special meeting of the Executive and Finance Committees on June 8, 1928 in Chicago, the matter of the Ward Systems Company claim was again considered. Mr. Ward was still pressing for payment of the amount due him and threatened to enter suit. It was pointed out in the discussion that such a suit would have a disastrous effect on the prestige of the Institute and would result in great embarrassment, especially because the Congress had recently enacted a bill providing a permanent annual appropriation of $50,000 for the maintenance of the Gorgas Memorial Laboratory in Panama. Dr. Martin, then President and Chairman of the Board of the Gorgas Memorial Institute, was empowered to deal with the situation. A compromise was effected by which Mr. Ward agreed to accept $7,500 in full compensation for his claim. The final agreement was signed on June 25, 1928.

The financial affairs of the Institute were now in a more flourishing condition. Up to June 8, 1928, the sum of $41,000 had been invested in securities and the appropriation from Congress assured operating funds for the Gorgas Memorial Laboratory as soon as it could be established. With this satisfactory state of affairs, it was decided to move the Institute office back to Washington, which was accomplished on August 5, 1928.

Efforts to gain the support of the United States Government in the program of the Gorgas Memorial Laboratory were initiated by the introduction in the Senate of the United States by Senator James Wadsworth of S. 5449 on January 25, 1927 (calendar day January 26, 1927), which bill was referred to the Committee on Foreign Relations. The bill (S. 5449) provided authorization of $50,000 a year to the Gorgas Memorial Institute "for the maintenance of the Gorgas Memorial Laboratory" on certain conditions. No hearing on bill S. 5449 was held. On February 17, 1927, Senator William E. Borah, Chairman of the Committee on Foreign Relations, favorably reported the bill without amendment (Report No. 1504, as recorded in the Congressional Record—Senate, page 4020 of February 17, 1927, showing the filing of the indicated report to the Senate).

On February 28, 1927, the bill without amendment (S. 5449) was passed by the Senate and sent to the House (Congressional Record—Senate, page 5065). On March 1, 1927, the bill (S. 5449) as passed by the Senate, was received by the House but no reference to any Committee is shown (Congressional Record—House, pages 358-359 of March 1, 1927). These proceedings were taken in the 69th Congress, 2nd session, which expired on March 3, 1927, and was succeeded on March 4, 1927, by the 70th Congress. Hence, no action was taken by the House in the 69th Congress because the bill came from the Senate too late for any House consideration before final adjournment. In consequence, no enactment of the bill (S. 5449) was made at the 69th Congress.

The failure of enactment of the above-mentioned bill led Dr. Franklin H. Martin, President and Chairman of the Board of the Gorgas Memorial Institute, to approach Congressman Maurice H. Thatcher for assistance. Congressman Thatcher had been a member of the Isthmian Canal Commission during the construction era of the Panama Canal and in charge of the civil administration of the Canal Zone. He had thus served as a fellow commissioner with General Gorgas and had officially assisted and supported his health and sanitation policies. Consequently, the Congressman was thoroughly cognizant of the health needs of the area and the necessity for additional research on diseases of the tropics. He proceeded, with the proper parliamentary skill and effort, to obtain the desired legislation.

Congressman Thatcher examined S. 5449 of the 69th Congress and found that it was inadequately drafted. After redrafting, he introduced in the 70th Congress the bill (H.R. 8128) in the House on December 20, 1927 and arranged for a hearing thereon. The hearing was held by the House Committee on Foreign Affairs on January 20, 1928, and testimony in support of the bill was given by many prominent persons, selected by Dr. Martin and Congressman Thatcher. The Committee at the beginning appeared to be cool and indifferent to the proposed legislation but the dramatic presentations in its support led to an enthusiastic endorsement with a technical amendment which was accepted by Congressman Thatcher.

Fig. 2. Hon. Maurice H. Thatcher, Honorary President and General Counsel, Gorgas Memorial Institute, Vice President 1948-1969, and sponsor of the legislation providing for the establishment of the Gorgas Memorial Laboratory.

The latter drafted the favorable report of the Committee which was accepted without amendment or change, and filed.

After passage of H.R. 8128 on March 28, 1928, it was referred to the Senate on March 29, 1928 and sponsored by Senator Royal S. Copeland. The Senate Committee on Foreign Relations accepted as sufficient the hearings before the House Committee on Foreign Affairs and the House Report; therefore, no Senate Committee hearings were held on the measure. The bill without change or amendment by the Senate Committee was reported favorably to the Senate on April 11, 1928 and passed the Senate by unanimous vote on April 24, 1928. Thereupon, the bill (H.R. 8128) was sent to the White House and signed by President Coolidge on May 7, 1928 to become Public Law No. 350—70th Congress.

The complete story of the Hearings and the House proceedings on H.R. 8128 are set forth in a brochure entitled "Gorgas Memorial Laboratories—Research Work Touching Causes and Prevention of Tropical Diseases—Panama." This brochure was sponsored by Sir Henry Wellcome and published at his own expense.

Scientific Programs— Mosquito Control—Health Education—Publicity— State Committees

In the 1920's the Gorgas Memorial Institute was engaged in a number of activities other than fund raising and attempts to establish a research institute. One of these activities consisted of an educational campaign to develop cooperation between scientific medicine and the laity to the end that personal health standards might be improved and preventable illness and premature death avoided. This campaign was launched in January 1925 on a modest scale when a signed health release prepared by one of the members of the Board of Directors was sent to the editors of 1,000 newspapers together with a statement that it was the first of a series of authoritative health articles to be distributed by the Gorgas Memorial Institute for the proper guidance of the public in the care of personal health.

This initial venture met with an enthusiastic response as judged by the hundreds of press clippings received in the Gorgas office. Many of these consisted of editorials praising the idea of dispensing timely and reliable health hints to combat misinformation and the false allurements of quackery and cultism. Many letters were received urging that the release of health articles be established on a permanent basis.

With this encouraging beginning, the releases were steadily increased in number until it was estimated that by the end of 1925 they were reaching a total audience of 20 million regular readers. Effective cooperation was furnished by the United Press, the Associated Press and other press agencies.

The same cordial reception was accorded the Gorgas radio programs. Nearly 100 radio talks were broadcast from the principal stations of the country from the Atlantic to the Pacific in 1925. These talks were made by medical members of the State Governing Committees. Certain studios included the Gorgas talks as a regular feature of their programs.

Additional publicity was being given the Gorgas Memorial movement and the health educational campaign through magazine articles, some of which appeared in 1925 in such periodicals as the Literary Digest, World's Work, McClure's and the Saturday Evening Post. Additional coverage was obtained through the medium of state medical journals and county medical society bulletins.

Close liaison was maintained with the medical profession and state and special medical societies, nearly all of which had endorsed the programs of the Gorgas Memorial Institute. A number made contributions to the Institute Endowment Fund; these included during 1925 the state societies of New Hampshire, Maine, and Kentucky, the Medical Society of Hawaii, the American Dental Association, the Medical Veterans of the World War and 18 county medical societies.

It was proposed to make 1926 Health Conservation Year, during which an intensive campaign would be conducted through newspapers, magazines, radio, moving pictures, clubs and other organizations to promote increased interest in better personal health. Every citizen of the United States was to be urged to set aside one day during the year—preferably his birthday—to go to his personal physician for a health examination.

The Gorgas Memorial Institute became initially involved in mosquito control campaigns by reason of a request by the Cook County (Illinois) Commissioners and various village boards in the vicinity of Chicago for advice concerning the elimination of mosquitoes in those localities. The Institute recommended that Mr. Joseph LePrince, who had served with General Gorgas in Panama and who was a recognized authority on mosquito eradication, be called to Chicago to make a survey of local conditions. Mr. LePrince responded and suggested that a Director of Mosquito Control be engaged by the various governing boards within the area. This recommendation was acted upon favorably and the Metropolitan-Chicago District Anti-Mosquito Committee was appointed to operate under the supervision of the Gorgas Memorial Institute with a fund of $5,000 appropriated by the various towns involved. As a result of this activity, the Gorgas Memorial Institute received inquiries from many other communities requesting information and assistance in mosquito control. A mimeographed brochure was drawn up covering methods of control and eradication in the home, city, farm and community with information concerning species of mosquitoes which were disease vectors and those which were simply pestiferous. This brochure was given wide distribution. In 1926, a national mosquito abatement campaign was scheduled to be conducted.

In the spring of 1926, President Martin visited Panama and received assurances from President Rodolfo Chiari of Panama that his Government would do its part toward financing the expense of a laboratory as soon as the Gorgas Memorial Institute was ready to inaugurate research.

The Health Education campaign gained momentum during 1926. It was estimated that publicity reached 22 million people. Daily newspaper coverage was started on August 1. News articles were written and signed by members of the State Governing Committees and not only provided authentic information but were of high quality. A total of 193 physicians and surgeons contributed articles. During 1926, 181 radio talks were given in major cities.

The publicity campaign was broadened to include articles on malaria and the necessity for its control. In cooperation with the National Malaria Committee, an educational campaign of 10 weeks' duration was conducted in malarious areas of the South.

Increasing emphasis was being placed on the anti-mosquito campaign in the Chicago Metropolitan Area. A complete survey was made of the area to map breeding places and control measures were outlined for local authorities. As the result of the campaign, there was a noticeable decrease in mosquito breeding.

It is apparent that the objectives of the Gorgas Memorial Institute were being pursued vigorously. In the annual report of President Martin on December 1, 1927, he classified the year as having been especially significant in growth and achievements. The State Chapters had been strong in their support of the fund raising activity. Arizona, Florida, Idaho, Oregon, Rhode Island, and Washington were listed as having completely filled or oversubscribed their quota. The following States had reached one-half or more of their quota: California, Connecticut, District of Columbia, Michigan, New York, and Utah. One-fourth or more of the respective quotas had been met by Colorado, Delaware, Illinois, Kentucky and Ohio.

During the period, President Martin attended organization meetings in 13 cities ranging from New York to San Diego. The dispatch of 30,000 form letters had resulted in 218 new pledges, 56 for the Endowment and 162 for the Educational and Organization Fund. Editorials were supplied to 475 newspapers in 100 cities commemorating the birthday anniversary of General Gorgas on October 3, and describing the activities of the Gorgas Memorial Institute.

The Health Educational Campaign seems to have gone forward at an increasing pace. Material furnished by the Institute appeared in over 1,000 newspapers during the year and was estimated to have reached approximately 40 million readers. Newspaper publicity was supplemented, as in past years, by radio talks by members of Governing Committees; a total of 301 such programs were given during the year. Many physicians reported an increasing number of requests for health examinations as a result of the publicity.

The Mosquito Control Campaign was continued in Chicago and vicinity and new requests for survey assistance were received from points as far distant as Seattle, Washington, and Bar Harbor, Maine, as well as from the Dutch East Indies. Fifty thousand copies of the booklet entitled "Mosquito Facts for Mosquito Fighters" were printed and distributed. A Gorgas Health Calendar was issued during 1927.

During 1927, a bronze medal, a replica of the one conferred in 1923 at the dedication of the site in Panama of the Gorgas Memorial Institute, was produced for distribution to school superintendents. This medal was to be awarded to the student of the graduating class of any high school in the United States who submitted the best essay on the general topic "The Life and Achievements of Gorgas, and their Relation to our Health." This activity was continued for a number of years and subsequently met with widespread acceptance and public acclaim. Prizes for national winners for the first three contests were donated by Mr. Charles R. Walgreen, President of the Walgreen Company, Chicago, Illinois, who had been a victim of yellow fever during the Spanish-American War. Later, Mr. Henry L. Doherty, President of the Henry L. Doherty Company, New York, N. Y., assumed the role of donor.

Each State winner received a prize of $20. The second national prize was $250. The winner of the first national prize was given a travel allowance for a trip to Washington, D.C. to receive the award of $500 which was presented by the President of the United States at the White House, in his capacity of Honorary President of the Gorgas Memorial Institute.

Chapter 2.

The Formative Years
1928-1935

The Gorgas Memorial Laboratory; Gift of the Republic of Panama; Its Belated Establishment; The First Director, Dr. Herbert C. Clark; The Beginnings of the Research Program; Activities of the Gorgas Memorial Institute.

"How oft the darkest hour of ill
Breaks brightest into dawn"

—EURIPIDES

Although it was the expressed desire of the incorporators that research work would be inaugurated at Santo Tomás Hospital, there is no record that such ever took place. The hope seems to have been maintained for some time. Major Edgar A. Bocock, Superintendent of the Hospital, was interested in this development, and Dr. Richard P. Strong, Chairman of the Board of Scientific Directors, apparently made a number of trips to Panama looking to the possibility of beginning the studies.

After President Porras' original suggestion for a memorial to General Gorgas, the Republic of Panama was not long in granting further support for the Gorgas Memorial Laboratory. In 1922, the Republic purchased a plot of land at Pinel's Point, adjoining the site of the Santo Tomás Hospital, at a cost of $75,000 gold, upon which was to be constructed a building to house the laboratory. The cornerstone of this building was laid with colorful ceremonies on February 18, 1923. The date coincided with a visit of representatives of the American College of Surgeons to various Latin American countries. The reception committee representing the Gorgas Memorial Institute was composed of the following members:

Franklin H. Martin, M.D., Chicago, Illinois, Acting President, Gorgas Memorial Institute of Tropical and Preventive Medicine;

Oscar Dowling, M.D., New Orleans, Louisiana, Director, Gorgas Memorial Institute of Tropical and Preventive Medicine;

John Osborn Polak, M.D., Brooklyn, New York; Samuel Jason Mixter, M.D., Boston, Massachusetts; and Richard R. Smith, M.D., Grand Rapids, Michigan, representing the American Medical Association;

Gilbert FitzPatrick, M.D., Chicago, Illinois, Governor, American College of Surgeons, representing the American Institute of Homeopathy;

17

John George MacDougall, M.D., Halifax, Nova Scotia, Acting President, American College of Surgeons;

Hugh Young, M.D., Baltimore, Maryland, Governor, American College of Surgeons, United States representative;

F. N. G. Starr, M.D., Toronto, Canada, Governor, American College of Surgeons, Canadian representative.

President Porras of Panama, the prime mover in the establishment of the Gorgas Memorial Institute, gave the principal address (see appendix), followed by an address by Dr. Augusto S. Boyd, a prominent Panamanian surgeon and Chairman of the Panamanian Reception Committee, and a reply by Dr. Franklin H. Martin of the Gorgas Memorial Institute (see appendix).

At the laying of the cornerstone, President Porras and Dr. Martin took turns in wielding the trowel. A bronze medal was then pinned on the lapel of each delegate and participating official. The medal contained on one side a bas-relief of a bust of General Gorgas and on the other side a relief of the proposed building with the following inscription:

"CONMEMORATIVA DE LA INICIACION DE LOS TRABAJOS DEL INSTITUTO GORGAS, PANAMA, 1923"

Following the gift of land by the Republic of Panama and the laying of the cornerstone of the proposed laboratory building on February 18, 1923, events proceeded at a snail's pace. A bond issue in the sum of $750,000 had been planned to provide necessary financing for the construction of the laboratory building. However, owing to unforeseen difficulties, the plan did not reach fruition. Five years elapsed before any further activity.

In order to reestablish cooperative arrangements with the Government of Panama, President Martin and Colonel Joseph F. Siler, member of the Scientific Board, departed from New Orleans on August 17, 1928, and arrived at Cristobal on August 22. As a result of negotiations with President Rodolfo Chiari, the Panamanian Government agreed to turn over to the Gorgas Memorial Institute, for a period of 3 years, pending the construction of permanent quarters, an edifice which had been designed and constructed to house a proposed School of Medicine. The plot of land occupied an entire block between the Santo Tomás Hospital and the Hospital Panamá, and was part of the site of the Panama-Pacific Exposition grounds.

On August 23, 1928, President Martin in a letter to President Chiari entered a formal request for the use of the building in question. Promptly, on August 24, 1928, President Chiari replied to Dr. Martin's letter making the building available. The next day, August 25, President Chiari, accompanied by his official staff, met with the representatives of the Gorgas

Fig. 3. Laying the cornerstone of the Gorgas Memorial Institute, Panama, Republic of Panama, February 18, 1923.

Memorial Institute and formally presented the building. Thus, at long last, the Gorgas Memorial Laboratory had found a home.

Formal contract was executed on April 5, 1929, under President Florencio Harmodio Arosemena, approved by the National Assembly of Panama on October 16, 1930, and the property ceded by registered title (Escritura Pública) No. 360 of April 9, 1931.

In the meantime, the Scientific Board of the Institute had been busy considering plans for a research program and selecting a director for the laboratory. After careful consideration and study, it was unanimously agreed to offer the position to Dr. Herbert C. Clark of the United Fruit Company. Initial negotiations with Dr. Clark took place during the visit to Panama of Dr. Martin and Colonel Siler. In a letter dated September 7, 1928, Dr. Martin discussed the appointment with Dr. William E. Deeks, Medical Director of the United Fruit Company, with a view to having Dr. Clark released from his obligation with that organization. At a meeting of the Executive Committee of the Institute on November 13, 1928, Dr. Martin was authorized to draw up a contract for Dr. Clark's employment. The contract was signed by both parties on December 8, 1928.

In retrospect, it is somewhat anomalous to note in the minutes of the above-mentioned meeting that Dr. Clark was hesitant about accepting the appointment because he felt that the permanency of the position was not assured and that the Congress might fail to continue the necessary support.

Dr. Clark was born in Economy, Indiana, on November 11, 1877, and attended Earlham College for 3 years before matriculating in the University of Pennsylvania Medical School from which he graduated in 1906. He interned in the University of Pennsylvania Hospital and later became resident physician. His long tour of duty as Pathologist of the Board of Health Laboratory of the Panama Canal at Ancon, Canal Zone, from 1909 to 1917 provided an unusual opportunity for becoming thoroughly inculcated in tropical medicine. Dr. Clark entered military service as a Captain in the Medical Reserve Corps of the Army on October 25, 1917, served overseas for 18 months, and was discharged as Lieutenant Colonel on September 15, 1919. He returned to his old position with the Panama Canal Board of Health Laboratory and remained until November 1, 1922, when he became Director of Laboratories and Preventive Medicine for the United Fruit Company.

As history has amply confirmed, the selection of Dr. Clark as director was a happy choice. He was not only highly qualified in tropical medicine but was familiar with the Latin American scene and already had an entree into Panamanian medical circles. He possessed an inherent medical curiosity and an inquiring mind which led him to probe for the causes of disease processes as well as, a pathologist, to observe their effects. At times, Dr. Clark seemed to be more of a naturalist and biologist than a physician.

He had an abiding interest in all living things as indicated by his broad research interests and the variety of his publications.

Herbert Clark was an affable, friendly individual and a delightful companion. He was always ready with an appropriate story. On his jungle expeditions, he took great delight in playing sly tricks on unsophisticated visiting scientists. His staff was extremely loyal to him and during his long tenure of office the atmosphere at the Gorgas Memorial Laboratory was friendly and inspiring.

Dr. Clark assumed directorship of the Laboratory on January 1, 1929, and received the keys to the building from the Government of Panama during the second week of that month. It was necessary to install water, sewage, gas, electricity and telephone services. A number of temporary buildings were removed from the grounds while a new building was constructed to provide space for animal quarters, a garage and storage.

Dedication of the Laboratory—First Research Program The Gorgas Memorial Laboratory was dedicated on April 2, 1929. The Honorable Luis F. Clement, Secretary of Agriculture and Public Works, presented the building on behalf of His Excellency Florencio Harmodio Arosemena, President of the Republic of Panama, with remarks in part as follows:

> "This tribute of admiration and recognition we offer today to the memory of the Great Gorgas, in consecrating the building which is to house the Laboratory of scientific investigation of tropical diseases, honors Panama and indirectly all the nations of the continent.
>
> "Our gratitude to the eminent Benefactor is as great, as sincere, and as pure, as are our earnest desires that his name be perpetuated eternally through this institution as a just tribute to the grandeur of his spirit.
>
> "This institution, from this day forward, is opened to men of science, to facilitate their investigations, especially to those physicians of all races and of all peoples of the earth, who wish to cooperate in this humanitarian cause with their knowledge and their able counsel. We are confident that this institution will be rich in the results of its research, and fertile in great scientific achievements, as was the labor of the worthy Gorgas, to whom we most respectfully dedicate this Temple of Science.
>
> "Do us the honor, Doctor Martin, to accept in the name of the Institute of which you are president, this building and the land upon which it stands, as the contribution of the Government of

Panama, so that from this time forward it may serve as the permanent site of the Gorgas Institute."

Dr. Franklin H. Martin, Chairman of the Board of Directors of the Gorgas Memorial Institute of Tropical and Preventive Medicine, gratefully accepted the gift, saying in part as follows:

"Mr. President, Mr. Secretary: I am sure that my distinguished Board of Directors would wish me, as its Chairman, to express to you and to your people our enthusiasm in receiving the gift as one more expression of your friendship for our people, and your special interest in the work of the Memorial which commemorates the great benefactor, Gorgas. Therefore, in their behalf, I formally accept this generous proffer of gift in the spirit in which it is given.

"We have met in the presence of these friends of Gorgas, and distinguished citizens of the Americas to dedicate this Temple of Science. Its future work is in the hands of scientists; its jurisdiction extends to the tropics and semitropics of all the world; its authorizations under the Charter are unlimited; its research and clinical opportunities are unbounded; its prestige in tropical medicine is supported by the name and reputation of the greatest practical sanitarian of the age—Gorgas.

"In behalf of the Gorgas Memorial Institute of Tropical and Preventive Medicine, its Board of Directors and Executive Committee, over which I have the honor to preside as Chairman, may I acknowledge my sense of deep responsibility to you for the sympathetic and generous manner in which the Government of Panama has cooperated in establishing these laboratories, and providing for its permanency.

"Since the inception of the Gorgas Memorial, three administrations in Panama have lent their enthusiastic and statesmanlike cooperation—first Dr. Belisario Porras, then Dr. Rodolfo Chiari, and now we are met with this culminating generous beneficence from your present distinguished President, His Excellency, Señor Don Florencio Harmodio Arosemena."

With alterations and other renovations out of the way, Dr. Clark could turn his entire attention to developing a research program. The Scientific Committee of the Institute had previously agreed that initial attention should be devoted to malaria because of its great health importance not only to Latin America but to the United States as well. With this in view, the appointment to the staff of Medical Entomologist L. H. Dunn was approved on December 20, 1928. The annual report for 1929 indicated that the following problems were under investigation or were proposed for study in the immediate future.

1. Study of human carriers of malaria immediately following the treatment of an acute attack of malaria fever. Mosquito biting experiments during the course of the patient's treatment with quinine, plasmochin, etc.

2. Transfer experiments with monkey and human species of malaria to determine whether the monkey is an animal reservoir for human malaria.

3. Mosquito biting experiments to test infectibility of other anophelines than the three commonly incriminated species in our tropics.

4. A study of anopheline flight habits thoroughout the day and night under various seasonal conditions both in the wild and domestic regions.

5. A study bearing on the number of egg mats that anopheline mosquitoes may deposit. There is some reason to believe that they survive more than one egg batch.

6. Established mosquito indices of malarial infection on anopheline catches indoors and outdoors, both in wild and domestic regions.

7. Some experiments bearing on possible sandfly vectors or unexplained fever epidemics that occasionally occur on the Atlantic side of the Canal Zone.

8. Experiments with two species of human ticks as possible carriers of relapsing fever.

9. Experiments with horse flies in connection with equine trypanosomiasis. Our entomological surveys have shown where the larval stage of two species of horse flies are passed. As far as we can learn this information is entirely new.

10. Texas cattle fever (piroplasmosis) will receive some attention in connection with imported non-immune dairy stock.

1930   During 1930 the research program gained increasing momentum. Initial malaria surveys indicated higher prevalence and parasitemia rates in children, who constituted the main source of mosquito infection and therefore transmission. Mosquito traps with different baits were evaluated.

Species of malaria in Panama monkeys resembled morphologically quartan human parasites. Many young *Ateles* and *Cebus* monkeys were found to succumb to the disease. Experimental transmission of monkey malaria was attempted in eight human volunteers without success. It was concluded that Panama monkeys do not constitute a reservoir for human malaria but can serve as excellent research tools.

A new species of spirochaete was discovered in a marmoset monkey and was transmitted to a human volunteer who became acutely ill as a result.

Fig. 4. *Administration Building of the Gorgas Memorial Laboratory, a gift of the Republic of Panama in 1928. (A 1930 photograph).*

Subsequently, this relapsing fever strain was transmitted through ticks from monkeys to man.

An outbreak of equine trypanosomiasis due to *Trypanosoma hippicum* was studied among horses of the Quartermaster Corps of the United States Army. Treatment with tryparsamide and Bayer 205 (Suramin) was encouraging but failed to provide consistent cures or to prevent relapses. Evidence was obtained that the Capybara is susceptible to the trypanosome but is probably not a carrier of the horse disease.

The warble fly, *Dermatobia hominis,* was found to occur abundantly in Panama and in addition to man was observed to attack certain wild and domestic animals. It was considered to be of economic importance because of the damage to cattle hides. While on a field trip on October 9, 1929, Mr. Dunn captured a fly, a species of *Limnophora,* which had several times alighted on his right knee. A number of eggs were attached to the abdomen of the fly and proved to be those of *D. hominis.* Mr. Dunn placed two of the emerged larvae on the flexor surface of his left forearm. Within 1½ hours both larvae had penetrated the skin. On October 11, a sharp itching was experienced on the forearm and also at four other sites, two on the right forearm and two on the right leg. These latter areas were found also to contain larvae, apparently deposited by the fly without being observed by Mr. Dunn. During the ensuing month, reactions to the larvae became increasingly severe. The lesions exuded blood, serum and pus and it was necessary to keep them bandaged at all times. Symptoms included a pricking sensation in each area, intense pruritis, fever, lassitude and frequent bouts of pain which were especially excruciating during the night and resulted in interrupted sleep. The first larva emerged after a period of 46 days and 15 hours and the last 55 days after penetration. The lesions healed promptly, although the scars occasioned by one of the larvae remained for several months. The emerged larvae were allowed to pupate; the adult flies emerged in 22 to 24 days. The experiment, voluntary and involuntary, provided the first specific data on the life cycle of *D. hominis.*

During the year, Dr. Ernest Carroll Faust of Tulane University Medical School assisted by Dr. William Martínez and Dr. Alberto Prieto, conducted surveys for intestinal parasites on several population groups in Panama with headquarters at the Gorgas Memorial Laboratory. Significant results included a series of 1,662 native patients in the Santo Tomás Hospital, of whom 348 were positive for *Strongyloides stercoralis.* In 29 cases (8.3 percent), the infection was considered of clinical importance. A survey of over 2,000 individuals in groups representing all social and economic levels disclosed prevalence rates varying between 2.8 and 72.7 percent for *Entamoeba histolytica.* The highest rates were encountered in inhabitants of river villages. It was noted that clinical manifestations were infrequent and it was considered that in most cases the host and the parasite were essentially in complete equilibrium. In five autopsies, however, extensive ulceration was noted in two cases. *Ascaris lumbricoides* and *Necator americanus* were relatively common. Prevalence rates of *Trichuris trichiura* ranged from 1.0 to 21.0 percent. *Giardia lamblia* was found in 4.5 to 9.0 percent of various population groups.

In connection with the Gorgas program, Mr. C. H. Bath, Sanitary Inspector of the Panama Canal, conducted studies on the value of several types of mosquito traps in the collection of various species of *Anopheles*.

1931 During 1931 the Miraflores Veterinary Station was established and active work was in progress on equine trypanosomiasis and strongylidosis. Work was also inaugurated at the Santa Rosa Field Station on the Chagres River. Five villages near the site of the proposed Madden Dam were kept under observation for malaria as regards prevalence, transmission patterns, clinical manifestations and treatment. In 772 permanent inhabitants of these villages examined at least once each the infection rate was 54.0 percent. One hundred and eighty-one permanent inhabitants examined at least 8 times gave a rate of 92.3 percent, showing that presumably the entire population at one time or another during its lifetime became infected with malaria. The occurrence of various species of malaria was, as follows: *Plasmodium falciparum* 67.6 percent, *P. vivax* 25.4 percent, *P. malariae* 5.7 percent, and mixed infections 1.2 percent. Positive individuals were placed on voluntary quinine treatment; the results were encouraging but it was evident that mass treatment under thorough discipline would be necessary to bring the parasite index down to a satisfactorily low level.

Human cases of Chagas' disease in Panama were diagnosed for the first time. The first case was recognized by Dr. John W. Miller, part-time pathologist of the Gorgas Memorial Laboratory. The three cases came from the village of Aguas Buenas or its immediate vicinity. Two additional cases were detected during the year. A preliminary survey disclosed spontaneous or naturally acquired infections in dogs, squirrels, armadillos, opossums and bats. The trypanosome of the bats was readily transmitted to dogs, guinea pigs, white rats and white mice. Observations on reduviid bugs indicated that the most common species were *Triatoma geniculata* (= *Panstrongylus geniculatus*) and *Rhodnius prolixus*. Infected specimens of the former were collected from the Chilibrillo Caves, from which an infected opossum and infected bats had been taken. *Trypanosoma cruzi* infections were studied in several laboratory animals. The guinea pig proved to be the most satisfactory animal for laboratory experiments.

Dr. D. P. Curry, Assistant Health Officer of the Canal Zone, and Honorary Assistant Director of the Gorgas Memorial Laboratory, continued his investigations on anopheline vectors of malaria.

Dr. William H. Taliaferro and associates conducted studies on quartan malaria caused by *Plasmodium brasilianum* in Panamanian monkeys. The type of infection encountered with this parasite was considered to be the result of a differential mortality of the parasites which reproduce at a constant rate throughout. During the acute rise of infection, approximately 7.5 out of each brood of about nine merozoites died, whereas at the time of the crisis and thereafter, even more died. Before the crisis, this mortality represented a natural resistance of the host, whereas at the time of the crisis and thereafter, it represented a true acquired immunity which resulted from infection. It could be correlated with the cellular responses of the host. The events responsible for the acquired immunity against malaria of monkeys paralleled so closely those which were found in bird malaria, it would seem not unreasonable to suppose that they might also hold for malaria in man.

The same workers conducted experiments on the transmission of human malaria (*Plasmodium falciparum*) to monkeys. The parasite from nine infected humans was injected in large numbers intravenously. The longest infection was for 8 days, with a peak of 187 parasites per 10,000 red cells 92 hours after infection. The most intense infection was characterized by a peak of 915 parasites per 10,000 red cells 88 hours after infection. Most infections were extremely transitory. They were characterized by the occurrence of sexual stages morphologically indistinguishable from *P. falciparum* in man. Tissue reactions were slight.

Tests were also conducted on two herds of horses and mules some of each of which had been infected with *Trypanosoma hippicum*. One herd contained 103 animals which had never been treated and the other contained 122 animals which had received treatment at various times. The tests employed included complement fixation, precipitin, adhesion, mercuric chloride and Wassermann. The untreated herd showed a striking correlation between the infection of the animal and the positiveness of all tests. Complement fixation, precipitin and adhesion tests were more specific than the mercuric chloride and the Wassermann techniques. The treated herd, on the contrary, showed no correspondence between past infection of the animal and the reactivity of the tests. On the whole, all the specific tests on the treated herd tended to be non-reactive, whereas the non-specific mercuric chloride test tended to be reactive.

In a survey of a group of patients in Santo Tomás Hospital, Dr. Hamilton H. Anderson found only 13.9 percent carrying *Entamoeba histolytica,* a rate comparable with that encountered in California surveys. Experimental therapy with carbarsone was administered to 88 cases. Of 37 which could be followed for a month after treatment, all were cleared of the infection.

During the year, Doctors Robert W. Hegner, Carl M. Johnson and Robert M. Stabler conducted extensive investigations on the host-parasite relations in experimental amoebiasis in Panamanian monkeys. Sources of material included trophozoites of *E. histolytica* from human cases of intestinal amoebiasis and cysts from human carriers. Monkeys belonging to seven species were utilized, of which 10 brown howler monkeys, one red spider monkey and one marmoset were successfully infected, the spider monkey and four brown howler monkeys with cysts per os, and the marmoset and six brown howler monkeys with trophozoites per rectum. On the basis of location and morphology, the authors recognized certain types, as follows: (1) Tissue dwelling amoebae in the wall of the intestine; (2) lumen amoebae which do not invade the wall; (3) precystic amoebae which either become cysts or are evacuated; (4) amoebae evacuated with the stools; and (5) degenerate forms which may occur in the tissues, the lumen or the stools.

The observations indicated that the enormous numbers of trophozoites in the lumen do not come from the tissues, as generally believed, but are the descendants of amoebae living only in the lumen.

The process of excystation was observed as was the method of penetration of the tissues. Infections with trophozoites administered per rectum were more severe and developed more rapidly than was the case of infections produced by cysts per os. It was suggested that trophozoites from acute human cases are more virulent than those which emerge from cysts obtained from carrier cases.

During 1931 the following visiting scientists spent varying periods of time at the Gorgas Memorial Laboratory:

Dr. Edwin O. Jordan, University of Chicago.

Dr. William H. Taliaferro, Dr. Lucy G. Taliaferro and Mr. L. A. Stauber, University of Chicago.

Professor Robert W. Hegner, Dr. Carl M. Johnson and Dr. Robert M. Stabler, The Johns Hopkins University.

Dr. Hamilton H. Anderson, University of California.

Miss Dorothy A. Koch, University of California and the George William Hooper Foundation.

Dr. Ralph W. Nauss, Cornell University.

Also during 1931 the following Service people were assigned to the Laboratory:

Sanitary Engineer W. H. W. Komp, U. S. Public Health Service.

Commander G. F. Clark, Medical Corps, U. S. Navy.

Major H. S. Eakins, Veterinary Corps, U. S. Army.

1932   Malaria investigations were continued in the five Chagres River villages. All positive inhabitants were treated with quinine sulphate and in addition all those in four villages received 1 centigram of plasmochin* twice a week. The average of 12 monthly surveys showed a reduction of the malaria rate to approximately one-third its primary incidence. Dissection of 952 *Anopheles albimanus* from the villages in which plasmochin treatment was being administered indicated an infection rate of 1.7 percent. The results with plasmochin were not considered sufficiently promising to recommend its use as a control procedure, especially in view of its high cost and the labor necessary to administer it. Hospital and field studies were instituted with a new antimalarial drug, atebrin.

Studies were continued on the intravenous treatment of *Trypanosoma hippicum* infections in horses with Bayer 205 (Suramin) and Tartar emetic. Results were encouraging but the drugs were not specific. The vampire bat, *Desmodus rotundus murinus,* was shown to transmit equine trypanosomiasis. The incubation period in the bat varied between 6 and 8 days. The disease proved fatal to all infected bats. *T. hippicum* was transmitted by the bites of the vampire bat to 25 of 55 guinea pigs and 3 of 11 horses and mules.

Infection experiments in various animals indicated that cattle are light carriers of *T. hippicum*. The strain recovered from cattle produced fatal infections in two horses; when introduced into a calf, trypanosomes were later isolated from the blood but the calf failed to develop any symptoms. Other susceptible animals capable of carrying a light infection for long periods with spontaneous recovery included the hog, sheep and goat. Infections introduced into the domestic cat, the white-tailed deer, the brocket deer, and the collared peccary resulted fatally. The chicken proved to be the only animal in the series refractory to infection.

---

* Experiments with certain antimalarial drugs at the Gorgas Memorial Laboratory antedated agreement on and publication of international non-proprietary names by the World Health Organization. For this reason, these antimalarial drugs are designated by the trade name in use at the time of their employment. The following table gives the trade name utilized and the WHO international non-proprietary name.

Antimalarial drugs

Trade name utilized	WHO international non-proprietary name
Aralen (SN-7618) and (W-7618)	Chloroquine
Atebrin	Mepacrine
Chloroquine (SN-7618-5)	Chloroquine
Daraprim	Pyrimethamine
Isopentaquine	Pentaquine
Paludrine	Proguanil
Plasmochin	Pamaquine
Primaquine	Primaquine
Pyrimethamine	Pyrimethamine

27

In a study by Dr. Oliver R. McCoy, *Microfilaria ozzardi* was found in the blood of 44.5 percent of 119 Indians examined in the Tuira River basin of Darien Province. The infection rate in native villages in the same region varied from 2 to 57 percent and averaged 9.9 percent in the 244 natives examined. No evidence was found that *Mansonella ozzardi* is pathogenic or of any public health importance.

With the cooperation of Dr. Thomas Barbour of the Museum of Comparative Zoology of Harvard University, a snake census was conducted in three river valleys. The high incidence of snake bites in Panama indicated the necessity of determining the prevalence of species of poisonous snakes in various parts of the country. Of a total of 1,170 snakes collected, 405, or 34.6 percent, belonging to seven species, were poisonous.

On May 6, 1932, the Gorgas Memorial Laboratory received a gift in the sum of $1,100 from the Gorgas Auxiliary No. 2 of Chagres Camp No. 1, United Spanish War Veterans to be used as a library memorial.

During 1932, the following visiting scientists spent varying periods of time at the Laboratory:

Dr. Oliver R. McCoy, University of Rochester.

Professor R. W. Hegner and Dr. Carl M. Johnson, The Johns Hopkins University.

Dr. Adolph Schultz, The Johns Hopkins University.

Dr. George B. Wislocki, Harvard Medical School.

Dr. Ray Carpenter, Yale University.

Dr. William H. Taliaferro and Dr. Lucy G. Taliaferro, University of Chicago.

The following Service people were assigned to the Laboratory during 1932:

Sanitary Engineer W. H. W. Komp, U. S. Public Health Service.

Lt. Col. H. S. Eakins, U. S. Army.

Lt. Commander Paul W. Wilson and Chief Pharmacist Mate Charles E. Martin, Medical Corps, U. S. Navy.

1933 Malaria studies were continued at the Santa Rosa Field Station. Results with atebrin treatment in Chagres River villages indicated that this drug was superior to quinine in terms of a shorter course of treatment and freedom from disagreeable reactions. However, relapses occurred with the same relative frequency as with quinine and the cost of the drug was considered prohibitive for routine use. The proportion of estivo-autumnal (*P. falciparum*) malaria increased slightly during the year and constituted 89.2 percent of all cases of infection.

Growth of aquatic plants around the borders of Gatun Lake provided excellent breeding conditions for anopheline mosquitoes, including *A. albimanus,* the local vector of malaria. In studies conducted by Mr. Komp and Dr. D. P. Curry, evidence was gathered that this vector is able to make flights by interrupted stages for distances of 12 or more miles.

Lt. Commander Paul W. Wilson conducted malaria surveys in the vicinity of the Darien Field Station. Of 1,885 persons examined, 505, or 26.7 percent, were positive for malaria and 109, or 5.7 percent, were infected with *Mansonella ozzardi*. *Plasmodium falciparum* was found in 78.2 percent of the malaria positives, *P. vivax* in 13.6 percent, and *P. malariae* in 8.1 percent. Nearly all of the quartan malaria and filarial infections were found in Indians.

Commander Wilson also conducted research on yaws at the Darien Field Station. Observations were made on 447 patients. Oral therapy was attempted without success with a number of drugs, including carbarsone, stovarsol and spirocid. Insect transmission could not be demonstrated. The Darien yaws lesions appeared to be more local in character than those in Haiti. The strain of *Treponema pertenue* found in Panama was much less virulent than the Haitian strain.

At the Miraflores Veterinary Station, research on equine trypanosomiasis was continued. A combination of Bayer 205 (Suramin) and Tartar emetic proved more effective than any other method of therapy tried up to that time. Control measures were successful in eliminating the disease from the Canal Zone during the year.

The snake census was continued in cooperation with the Museum of Comparative Zoology of Harvard University. A total of 2,133 specimens were collected, of which 582, or 27.2 percent, proved to be poisonous.

The same Service personnel on duty on December 31, 1932 continued work at the Laboratory during 1933.

The extent of research potential at the end of the year 1933 may be gauged in part by the number of persons on the staff. There were two full time professional members, one part time, and four Service people. Non-professional staff included 21 full time and one part time member.

1934 Malaria observations in the Chagres River villages indicated that the year witnessed naturally declining parasite rates, as evidenced by the results in the control village. The question arose concerning the value of the continued drug therapy and its effect on the occurrence of malaria in the five villages over a period of 4 years. It became more apparent that cyclical variations in the parasite rate may have influenced the evaluation of the results. For instance, in 1934, plasmochin-atebrin was administered on a voluntary basis with good results. However, the effect was difficult of assessment because of lower parasite rates occurring spontaneously in the control village. It was felt that the general health of the population of the villages had been improved, because of a reduction in chronic malaria infections and encouragement given them to seek medical aid for other conditions.

Dr. Curry conducted extensive investigations into the breeding of various species of anophelines in Gatun Lake which had developed an aquatic flora of several species of *Chara* and bladderwort (*Utricularia mixta*). *A. albimanus* is more domestic and more anthropophilous, and bred more profusely in the lake in exposed patches of *Chara*. *A. albitarsis* is not anthropophilous and preferred exposed *Utricularia* as a breeding place. During the dry season, the water in the lake receded thus providing a canopy of these plants, a situation extremely favorable for breeding. Sanitated areas in the Canal Zone were visited, before the onset of the rains, by flights of *A. albimanus* with a resulting sharp rise in the malaria rate. Because of the great size of Gatun Lake and the extensive breeding areas, control was not found feasible. However, it was considered that the construction of the Madden Dam would eventually result in maintaining a higher water level in the Lake during the dry season and thus obviate much of the anopheline breeding.

Mr. Dunn continued over the years to make notable contributions in his studies of insects affecting man and animals. He reported a natural infection of *Trypanosoma cruzi* in *Rhodnius pallescens,* as well as in *Eratyrus cuspidatus.* Attempts to transmit *T. cruzi* by the bites of the ticks, *Ornithodorus talaje* and *O. venezuelensis* were unsuccessful. However, it was found that the parasite persisted in the latter tick for a period of 6 months.

Lt. Commander Paul W. Wilson conducted a survey for the prevalence of yaws and syphilis in five small towns situated near the junction of the Chagres and Gatuncillo Rivers. Results were based on physical examinations, case histories, and Wassermann and Kahn reactions. The incidence of yaws in the villages was 16.4 percent and the probable incidence of syphilis was 5.3 percent. The author warned against accepting all positive serological reactions as of syphilitic origin, as many clearly defined yaws cases also showed such reactions.

At the Miraflores Veterinary Station, Lt. Col. H. S. Eakins isolated *T. hippicum* from 5 of 150 beef cattle from Coclé, Herrera and Los Santos Provinces. This was the highest infection rate yet encountered in cattle in Panama. The strain was subjected to virulence tests in horses which acquired the acute disease. Further observations were made on the effect of the parasite on calves. These young animals will retain the parasite for periods of 4 to 8 months without any evidence of disease. The complement fixation test was positive in four of the calves. Vampire bat feedings on such carriers indicated that only 1 in 3 can acquire the parasite from such lightly infected animals.

Dr. Oliver R. McCoy conducted a survey of filariid parasites of monkeys in three areas in Panama, viz: (1) Along the Río Boquerón in the upper Chagres Valley, Colon Province; (2) in the valley of the Río Chucunaque, Darien Province; and (3) along the Río La Vaca, Chiriqui Province. The yellow titi monkey, *Saimiri oerstedii,* was obtained only in Chiriqui Province. Black spider monkeys, *Ateles dariensis* (= *A. fusciceps*), and marmosets, *Leontocebus geoffroyi* (= *Saguinus geoffroyi*), were obtained only in Darien Province. Red spider monkeys, *Ateles geoffroyi,* were obtained both in the Chagres valley and Chiriqui Province, while white-faced monkeys, *Cebus capucinus,* were secured from all three localities. Five of the 6 black howler monkeys, *Alouatta palliata inconsonans* (= *A. villosa*), came from the Chagres valley while the other was obtained in Darien. Seven different species of filariid parasites were found in the monkeys, 87 percent of the 72 animals examined being infected with one or more species. *Acanthocheilonema gracile* was the parasite most frequently encountered; the adult worms were located in the serous cavities of the red and black spider monkeys and the white-faced monkey. Two new species belonging in the Genus *Tetrapetalonema* Faust were recovered and described. One of these, *T. atelensis,* was found beneath the fascia of the back muscles of the red and black spider monkeys; the other, *T. parvum,* was located in connective tissue between the back muscles of the white-faced and yellow titi monkeys. Two new species of microfilariae, *M. panamensis* and *M. obtusa,* were described from the two latter hosts, but the adult worms were not found.

During the year, the following visiting scientists worked at the Laboratory:

Dr. Oliver R. McCoy, University of Rochester.

Dr. Hamilton H. Anderson, University of California.

Dr. Murray Angevine, Cornell University Medical College.

Service personnel on duty during the year included Sanitary Engineer W. H. W. Komp, U. S. Public Health Service, Lt. Col. H. S. Eakins, U. S. Army and Lt. Commander E. G. Hakansson, Medical Corps, U. S. Navy together with two Navy Medical Corpsmen, J. F. Buckner and H. A. Down.

During the year, Lawrence H. Dunn, Assistant Director and Medical Entomologist, resigned.

The following new staff members entered on duty during the year:

Carl M. Johnson, Sc. D., Protozoologist.

A. O. Foster, Sc. D., Helminthologist.

L. E. Rozeboom, Sc. D., Medical Entomologist.

1935 Malaria studies were continued in the Chagres River villages. Since 1930, varying regimens of treatment had been given to the inhabitants of the five experimental villages, while quinine alone had been administered on a voluntary basis to people in the control village. During

1935, methods of treatment included atebrin and plasmochin, quinine and plasmochin and quinine alone. In spite of the consistent treatment with various drugs over a period of 4 years, beginning in January 1931, malaria reached epidemic proportions in the five villages and continued at a high level for 4 months. Subtertian parasite rates rose almost simultaneously in all the towns, to approximately the same levels, although four of the towns had received atebrin-plasmochin treatment, thoroughly supervised, for 2 years previous to the epidemic. During the 4 months, in spite of intensive treatment, the parasite rates continued high with many clinical cases and a great increase in heavy infections. On the contrary, in the control town, Chilibre, in which quinine was being given only on a voluntary basis, parasite rates were much lower and clinical attacks were less severe. The epidemic was considered to be a manifestation of the cyclical variation characteristic of malaria in Panama.

In the conclusion of the report of the 5-year study of the disease in the Chagres River villages, the following is stated:

"Our increased knowledge of the local conditions has caused us to abandon the method used in the past, the attempt to reduce malaria incidence by treatment directed against the reservoir of malaria in young children and adolescents. We fear that more harm than good has been done by the method, and believe that our objective, to increase labor efficiency, may be more easily obtained by treatment of clinical cases as they occur, using atebrin as the drug of choice."

In June 1935, Mr. Komp made a malaria and mosquito survey of the Caripito Division of the Standard Oil Company of New Jersey in eastern Venezuela. Mr. Komp discovered the presence in the area of *Anopheles darlingi,* one of the most efficient of malaria vectors. During the next 3 months, at the invitation of the Rockefeller Foundation, Mr. Komp conducted mosquito surveys in an endemic area of yellow fever around Restrepo, in the Intendencia of Meta, Colombia. The identity of the vector suspected on epidemiological grounds was established, and the life histories of other mosquito species were elucidated. Over 75 species were collected and identified.

Dr. Rozeboom was able to experimentally infect *Anopheles bachmanni* (= *A. triannulatus*) with *Plasmodium vivax.* The mosquito was found to breed in collections of *Pistia stratiotes* and females were observed to attack man in the jungle during daylight hours. A colony of *A. albimanus* was established in the Laboratory and details of the life cycle were elucidated.

Dr. Johnson reported the first case of a natural infection with *Trypanosoma hippicum* in the vampire bat, *Desmodus rotundus murinus.* The strain caused the usual type of the disease, which terminated fatally when inoculated into laboratory animals and a horse. Further studies on the mode of transmission indicated that the vampire bat is not a biological vector of *T. hippicum* and that transmission is merely mechanical. The trypanosomes reach the saliva of the bat through breaks in the oral mucosa, and possibly by migration through the intact mucosa.

Additional cases of Chagas' disease were diagnosed during the year bringing a total of 19 human cases with three deaths. The examination of 110 vampire bats disclosed a natural infection with *Trypanosoma cruzi* in five of the animals.

Lt. Commander E. G. Hakansson conducted examinations in mental patients for intestinal protozoa. Over 3,000 stools were examined and data obtained for additional studies on the epidemiology of amoebiasis. A study was conducted on morphological features of various intestinal protozoa. Aqueous smears were utilized and this method was useful in the differentiation of species. During the year, a case of *Dientamoeba fragilis* infection was found with frank clinical involvement.

Dr. Samuel F. Hildebrand, Senior Ichthyologist, U. S. Bureau of Fisheries, spent several months at the Laboratory. He studied conditions in Gatun Lake which were so favorable for anopheline breeding with the view of finding a species of fish which might feed on the plant life and aid in mosquito control. However, it was decided that conditions in the lake and the type of fish fauna precluded the introduction of new species which might be of value for the purposes mentioned. A census was also made of fish of all fresh and salt waters in and near the Isthmus.

The following research workers spent varying periods of time at the Laboratory during the year:

Dr. W. H. Taliaferro, Dr. Lucy G. Taliaferro and Mrs. Cessa Kluver, University of Chicago.

Dr. Samuel F. Hildebrand, U. S. Bureau of Fisheries, Washington, D. C.

The following Service personnel were on duty at the Laboratory during the year:

Sanitary Engineer W. H. W. Komp, U. S. Public Health Service.

Lt. Col. H. S. Eakins, U. S. Army.

Lt. Commander E. G. Hakansson, U. S. Navy with two technicians, J. F. Buckner and H. A. Down.

The Gorgas Memorial Laboratory
The Research Program 1928-1935
A Recapitulation

The year 1928 marked a turning point in the affairs of the Gorgas Memorial Institute. After many years of fruitless endeavor on the part of the Institute and its friends and supporters in Panama, the Laboratory came into being through the generosity of that Republic and the progressive policies of its Presidents Rodolfo Chiari and

Florencio Harmodio Arosemena. With the donation of a laboratory building by the Republic of Panama, the stage was set for the selection of a director, Dr. Herbert C. Clark, who assumed office on January 1, 1929.

The years 1928-1935 represented the developmental period in the history of the Laboratory, during which the research programs gradually emerged, took definite form and were pursued with increasing vigor. These were productive years, especially so when one considers that the professional staff represented a mere skeleton of essential personnel. But what it lacked in numbers, it made up by its imaginative approach to research on health problems of the area and its well designed and untiring efforts to provide solutions to these problems. Fortunately, the assignment of officers from the U. S. Army, Navy and Public Health Service, as originally visualized by the incorporators of the Institute, augmented the regular staff and contributed materially to the research program. In like manner, visitors from other institutions found opportunity and inspiration in carrying on investigations at the Laboratory.

In accordance with the expressed wishes of the founders, malaria became one of the first of the many problems receiving attention. Efforts were mainly concentrated in five Chagres River villages in a program designed to reduce parasite levels, clinical manifestations and relapses by means of various drug regimens. Initial voluntary treatment was followed soon by drug administration to all positive individuals. Quinine was followed by plasmochin and then atebrin, all administered alone or in various combinations. In a control village, quinine was the only drug employed and this only on a voluntary basis mainly in clinical cases. The first 4 years of the program witnessed a significant reduction in parasite rates, although with some fluctuation depending on anopheline breeding. The fifth year was marked by a severe epidemic of subtertian malaria in the villages with elevated parasite rates and severe clinical manifestations. This circumstance led to a reevaluation of the program and a change in objectives.

Other malaria activities during the period included a study of the infection in Panama monkeys, which showed a parasite resembling morphologically the human quartan species. Human volunteers were resistant to infection with the monkey parasite.

Monkeys injected with great numbers of *P. falciparum* from man failed to retain the infection beyond a period of 8 days.

Quartan malaria in monkeys caused by *P. brasilianum* was utilized for studies on immune mechanisms.

Anopheline breeding in Gatun Lake during the dry season was associated with aquatic flora consisting of several species of *Chara* and the bladderwort, *Utricularia mixta*. *A. albimanus* bred extensively in the above location and was found to have an interrupted flight range of 12 miles or more.

34

Fig. 5. Home of the first case of Chagas' disease diagnosed in Panama.

A colony of *A. albimanus* was established in the laboratory and details of the life cycle were elucidated. *A. bachmanni* (= *A. triannulatus*) was experimentally infected with *P. vivax*. This species was observed to be a jungle day biter.

The life cycle of the warble fly, *Dermatobia hominis*, was demonstrated by means of voluntary and involuntary human infection. Penetration and development of the larvae in the tissues were followed by a pricking sensation, intense pruritis, fever, lassitude and severe pain with disturbed sleep. The lesions exuded blood, serum and pus. The first larva emerged 46 days and 15 hours and the last 55 days after penetration. The emerged larvae were allowed to pupate and the adult flies emerged in 22 to 24 days. The experiment provided the first specific data on the life cycle of the fly.

Outbreaks of Murrina or equine trypanosomiasis due to *Trypanosoma hippicum* were studied. The disease was almost invariably fatal to horses and mules; cattle retained the parasite for long periods without clinical involvement, thus serving as reservoirs of infection. Transmission by the bites of the vampire bat, *Desmodus rotundus murinus*, was demonstrated and infected bats were found in nature. Transmission was shown to be of a mechanical and not of a biological nature. Various methods of treatment were tried; the most successful proved to be a combination of Bayer 205 (Suramin) and Tartar emetic.

Human cases of Chagas' disease were diagnosed for the first time in Panama and increasing numbers were recognized during the period in question. Spontaneous or natural infections with *Trypanosoma cruzi* were encountered in dogs, squirrels, armadillos, opossums and bats. The most common vectors appeared to be *Triatoma geniculata* (= *Panstrongylus geniculatus*) and *Rhodnius prolixus*.

Microfilaria ozzardi was found to be a frequent parasite among Darien Indians but no clinical manifestations were evident.

Eighty-seven percent of 72 Panama monkeys harbored seven different species of filariid parasites. *Acanthocheilonema gracile* was the parasite most frequently encountered. Two new species, *Tetrapetalonema atelensis* and *T. parvum*, were discovered.

Various surveys were conducted for intestinal parasites in different population groups. Significant data were obtained from a study of *Entamoeba histolytica* in Panama monkeys.

In cooperation with the Museum of Comparative Zoology of Harvard University, a snake census of Panama was begun on January 1, 1929. Up to September 30, 1935, a total of 4,306 snakes had been collected, of which 993, or 23.06 percent, were poisonous.

In a survey of five small towns near the junction of the Chagres and Gatuncillo Rivers, the incidence of yaws was 16.4 percent and the probable incidence of syphilis was 5.3 percent. Oral therapy of yaws was attempted with various drugs with negative results. Insect transmission of the disease could not be demonstrated. There was evidence that the strain of *Treponema pertenue* found in Panama was much less virulent than strains from Haiti.

Activities of the Gorgas Memorial Institute 1928-1935

1928

One of the acts of the Board of Directors in 1928 concerned the return of the Institute office to Washington from Chicago. The move was authorized on June 4, 1928 and the Washington office was established on August 5, 1928 by Miss Gladys R. Newman.

At the annual meeting in Boston, Massachusetts, on October 10, 1928, Rear Admiral Cary T. Grayson, MC, U. S. Navy was elected President, Dr. Gilbert Fitz-Patrick Vice President, and Dr. Franklin H. Martin Chairman of the Board of Directors.

Dr. Cary Travers Grayson was born at the family estate "Salubria," near Culpeper, Virginia, on October 11, 1878. Both his father and grandfather were physicians and it was only natural that Cary Grayson should follow in their footsteps. His father, Dr. John Cooke Grayson, served as Surgeon in the Confederate Army during the War Between the States, the aftermath of which left the family fortunes in a precarious state. Dr. Grayson's mother died when he was a small child and his father when he was 12. Largely on his own resources, Cary Grayson obtained his pre-medical education at the College of William and Mary between 1895 and 1898. In spite of the necessity for working his way, Grayson maintained a high academic standing and was elected to Phi Beta Kappa. He received his M.D. degree from the University of the South in 1902 and also an M.D. degree from the Medical College of Virginia in 1903, while serving an internship at the Columbia Hospital for Women in Washington, D.C.

Dr. Grayson was appointed Acting Assistant Surgeon in the Naval Medical Corps on July 14, 1903; Assistant Surgeon on June 28, 1904; Passed Assistant Surgeon on June 28, 1907; Surgeon in August 1916 and Rear Admiral on August 29, 1916.

Dr. Grayson graduated from the U. S. Naval Medical School in 1904 and was assigned to the Naval Dispensary in Washington where he served until 1905. As Surgeon on the U.S.S. Maryland he made the world cruise of the U. S. Navy between 1905 and 1907. He returned to duty in Washington after that cruise and became physician to Presidents Theodore Roosevelt and William Howard Taft. He continued as White House Physician during the Administration of President Wilson.

Admiral Grayson was a medical member of the Council on National Defense during World War I. He served also on the staffs of several Washington Hospitals. After his retirement from the Navy on December 30, 1928, he served as Director of the Warwick Memorial Clinic and Medical Director of the Washington Gas Light Company. During his later years, Admiral Grayson became a prominent thoroughbred breeder and headed the National Capital Horse Show.

Admiral Grayson held the office of President of the Gorgas Memorial Institute between 1928 and 1935. On the death of Dr. Martin, he relinquished the presidency and became Chairman of the Board of Directors, a position which he held until his death on February 15, 1938.

On March 1, 1935, he became Chairman of the Central Committee of the American Red Cross and served in that capacity until his death.

Many honors came to Admiral Grayson, including an honorary LL.D. degree from the College of William and Mary, the Navy Cross, Commander Legion of Honor of France, and Commander Order of Leopold of Belgium.

Following the death of Admiral Grayson, an editorial in the Washington Star paid an unusual tribute to him. The following interpretation of his personality is quoted from that editorial:

"It seems that he was born to the part he played in the pageant of his time. His inheritance of chivalrous manners opened to him the hearts of great personalities. A certain natural trustworthiness, similarly inbred, preserved for him the affection he so easily won among the high and humble. There were moments when by tactless talk he might have overturned his country. But sound judgement, instinctive sanity, kept him silent. Without formal recognition, he was a diplomat and statesman equal in talent to the best of his contemporaries."

Dr. Martin, the retiring President, in his report for the year 1928 summarized the activities of the Institute. As related to other than the Gorgas Memorial Laboratory, these activities embraced the Health Publicity Campaign, the Mosquito Control efforts, the Gorgas Essay Contest and miscellaneous matters.

The Health Campaign was apparently dear to Dr. Martin's heart, as he continued to promote it vigorously, by every means at his disposal. During 1928, 170,000 letters were dispatched to physicians, corporation directors and leading businessmen. A total of 3,054 drug stores displayed posters provided by the Institute. Newspaper publicity continued and the United Press was selected as the exclusive publicity agency.

During the year, a plan for caravan speeches was adopted through the cooperation of the Metropolitan Life Insurance Company which gave financial support to the program. Following the appearance of the speakers, effort was made to organize a community Gorgas Health Corps consisting of a physician as president, a dentist as secretary, a pharmacist as vice president with representative laymen. These units were designed to promote interest in periodic health examinations. Thirty-three of these corps were organized during 1928. Caravan speakers appeared before 200 audiences totalling 63,765 people in 12 states.

The Mosquito Control Program was enlarged during 1928. The department helped to direct abatement projects in eight states.

Gorgas desk health calendars were introduced and sold for $2.50 each. It appears that only a small amount of revenue was derived from this source but the publicity feature more than paid for the effort.

Following a luncheon given by Dr. Martin at the Willard Hotel in Washington on November 14, 1928 for Latin American diplomats, invitations were issued to 21 Latin American countries to participate in the maintenance of the Gorgas Memorial Laboratory. It was hoped that such financial assistance would reach a total of $87,500. However, this hope was not realized. In 1930, the Government of Ecuador contributed $760 and in 1931 Venezuela made a gift of $1,150.26. In April 1929, Peru issued a decree authorizing an annual appropriation of $1,755.60 to begin in 1930. However, no funds were ever received from the Peruvian Government. The above sums represent the total support received from Latin American countries other than Panama.

1929   The annual meeting was held in Chicago, Illinois, on October 16, 1929. Admiral Grayson was reelected President and Dr. Martin Chairman of the Board; Dr. C. Jeff Miller was elected Vice President. President Grayson reported progress during the year in the health campaign. Because of undisclosed reasons, the project was temporarily abandoned in April and not resumed until October. In spite of the interim of inactivity, the campaign reached 25 states; 457 health talks were given to a total audience of 148,346; 72 Gorgas Health Corps were organized; 32 newspapers were added to the Gorgas syndicate; 525 health posters were distributed; 55 showings of a health film were viewed by 29,243 persons; and radio talks were continued regularly over a score of stations under contract to the Institute. The field and press programs were made possible largely through the generosity of the Metropolitan Life Insurance Company.

Engineers in the Department of Mosquito Control under the direction of Major Edwin M. Skinner continued to make surveys of mosquito breeding areas and to offer recommendations for control. Fourteen communities in 10 states received attention during the year.

Through the support of Mr. Charles R. Walgreen of Chicago, the First Gorgas Essay Contest was held in the spring among junior and senior students in public high schools in 34 states. The subject was "William Crawford Gorgas, His Life and His Work." On May 23, 1929, President

Herbert Hoover, Honorary President of the Institute, awarded at the White House the first prize of $500 to the national winner, Miss Gertrude Carter Stockard of Mountainburg, Arkansas. The second place winner was Miss Margaret Hastings of Watertown, Mass. Each state winner received $20 and local high school winners were awarded a bronze Gorgas Medallion.

1930   The annual meeting was held in Philadelphia on October 15, 1930. Admiral Grayson was reelected President, Dr. Miller Vice President and Dr. Martin Chairman of the Board of Directors.

The Health Education Campaign was carried out on a limited budget because of the depression. However, 10 health talks were given and reached a total of 7,575 persons. A few radio addresses were made.

The Second Gorgas Essay Contest was on the subject: "The Gorgas Memorial Institute: Its Relation to Better Personal Health and the Periodic Health Examination." Over 5,000 high school seniors submitted essays. On May 12, 1930, President Hoover presented at the White House the first prize to the winner, Miss Pauline Lodge of Lakewood, Ohio.

Mosquito control activities were continued. Several thousand copies of a new manual on mosquito control were distributed. Surveys and control campaigns were sponsored in Massachusetts, New Hampshire, Maine and Arkansas.

1931   The annual meeting of the Gorgas Memorial Institute was held in the Waldorf-Astoria Hotel in New York City, on October 14, 1931. Admiral Grayson was continued as President, Dr. Miller as Vice President, and Dr. Martin as Chairman of the Board of Directors.

The year witnessed a continuing regression in the prior activities of the Gorgas Memorial Institute due to the economic depression and difficulties encountered in the solicitation of funds. The educational campaign was continued on a limited scale through the media of public lectures, the press and the radio. Special attention was devoted to providing health posters and other health educational material to rural schools, largely through contacts with public health nurses.

Mr. Charles R. Walgreen of Chicago provided support for the Third Gorgas Essay Contest. The subject was "Keeping Fit: The Gorgas Program of Personal Health." Schools in 43 States participated and approximately 12,000 papers were submitted. First prize of $500 was awarded to Miss Helen Dale of Point Loma High School, San Diego, California. The presentation was made on the Esplanade of the Pan American Union in Washington. The Pathe Film Company made a sound picture which was shown in RKO Theatres throughout the country and later Miss Dale read her essay over a nation-wide radio network.

1932 The annual meeting of the Gorgas Memorial Institute was held in Washington on November 21, 1932. Admiral Grayson was reelected President, Dr. Miller Vice President, and Dr. Martin Chairman of the Board of Directors. A resolution of sympathy was adopted on the death of Major Edwin M. Skinner, former Director of Mosquito Control of the Gorgas Memorial Institute.

The Fourth Gorgas Essay Contest was launched through the support of Mr. and Mrs. Henry L. Doherty of New York City. A total of 15,000 essays were submitted on the subject: "Mosquitoes, Their Danger as a Menace to Health and the Importance of Their Control."

The first prize of $500 was presented by President Hoover at the White House on June 9 to Miss Harriet Jones of St. Agnes School, Albany, New York. The second prize winner was Mr. H. Shepard Fuller, Central High School, Washington, D. C.

1933 The annual meeting of the Gorgas Memorial Institute was held in Chicago, Illinois, on October 11, 1933. Admiral Grayson was continued in the office of President, Dr. Miller as Vice President, and Dr. Martin as Chairman of the Board of Directors.

The Fifth Gorgas Essay Contest was supported by Mr. and Mrs. Henry L. Doherty. Approximately 18,000 manuscripts were submitted on the subject of "The Problem of the Mosquito and other Insect Life in Relation to Sanitation, Health and Industry."

First prize was awarded to Mr. Joseph S. Brendler of Messmer High School, Milwaukee, Wisconsin. The second prize went to Miss Margaret M. Harris of Roland Park Country School, Baltimore, Maryland.

1934 The annual meeting of the Corporation was held in Boston, Massachusetts, on October 17, 1934. Admiral Grayson, Dr. Miller and Dr. Martin were reelected to the posts previously held. The former reported that distribution of health posters to schools had been continued and that numerous requests for health educational literature had been received.

Mr. and Mrs. Henry L. Doherty continued as donors of the prizes for the Sixth Gorgas Essay Contest, the subject for which was: "Past Benefits and Future Importance to Man of the Control of Disease-Bearing Mosquitoes." Interest in the contest was widespread and 18,500 manuscripts were received from high schools in 46 States. The first prize winner, Mr. George A. Delhomme, Jr. of Houston, Texas, received his award from

President Roosevelt at the White House on October 23, 1934. The second prize went to Mr. John E. Dacey of Biloxi, Miss.

1935   A special meeting of the Board of Directors of the Gorgas Memorial Institute was convened at Washington on June 15, 1935, to consider necessary changes in the By-Laws and to fill certain vacancies. The vacancy in the Chairmanship of the Board of Directors occasioned by the death of Dr. Martin on March 7, 1935, was filled by the election of Admiral Grayson, who then resigned as President. Dr. Bowman C. Crowell was elected President to succeed Admiral Grayson. Resolutions of sympathy were adopted on the death of Dr. Martin, and Mrs. Martin was elected to serve on the Board of Directors.

Dr. Crowell's experience and qualifications were well adapted to the needs of the Gorgas Memorial Institute. Born in Yarmouth, Nova Scotia, on January 10, 1879, he attended McGill University, from which he received a Bachelor's Degree in 1900 and M.D. and C.M. degrees in 1904. He was resident pathologist and later an interne in the New York City Hospital from 1904 to 1907, and Instructor in Pathology at New York University and Bellevue Medical College from 1907 to 1911. During this period, he also served as pathologist to Bellevue Hospital. In 1911, Dr. Crowell was called to the Philippines to serve as pathologist to the Bureau of Science in Manila. From 1912 to 1914, he was Associate Professor of Pathology and Bacteriology, and from 1912 to 1918, Chief of the Department at the University of the Philippines. From 1916 to 1918 he was Director of the Graduate School of Tropical Medicine and Public Health of the University.

In 1918, Dr. Crowell became Chief of Service of the Department of Pathology of the Oswaldo Cruz Institute, Rio de Janeiro, Brazil, where he served until 1922. From 1922 to 1923, he was Professor of Pathology at the Medical College of the State of South Carolina. In 1923 he joined the faculty of Jefferson Medical College in Philadelphia, where he remained until 1926. At the same time, he was visiting pathologist at the Philadelphia General Hospital.

In 1926, Dr. Crowell became connected with the American College of Surgeons as Associate Director and Director of Clinical Research, where he remained until his retirement in 1949. He continued his teaching in pathology at Northwestern University Medical School. He was a member of many medical organizations, both in the United States and abroad. In October 1949 he received the first award of the American Cancer Society, in recognition of his contributions in that field. He died on April 26, 1951.

The annual meeting of the Corporation was held in Washington, on November 13, 1935. At this meeting, Dr. Crowell was reelected President,

41

Dr. Miller Vice President, and Admiral Grayson Chairman of the Board of Directors.

The Seventh Gorgas Essay Contest was announced and supported through the continued interest of Mr. and Mrs. Henry L. Doherty. On May 7, 1936, the President bestowed at the White House the first prize of $500 to Miss Helen Mae Collentine of Milwaukee, Wisconsin. The second prize winner was Miss Peggy Weber of New Orleans, La. The subject of the essay is not a matter of record.

Chapter 3.

The Pre-War and War Years
1936-1945

The Gorgas Memorial Laboratory; Research Programs; Problems Related to Military Medicine; Activities of the Gorgas Memorial Institute.

"Arts and sciences are not cast in a mould,
but are formed and perfected by degrees."
—MICHEL DE MONTAIGNE

1936 Research programs during the year represented largely a continuation of those initiated in previous years. As an exception there may be mentioned the expanded observations on equine parasites. Most of this work was done at the Miraflores Veterinary Station.

Malaria Studies: In spite of failure to prevent or control epidemic malaria experienced in 1935 in the Chagres River villages, the same program was continued in 1936. The reason for unaltered continuation concerned the relatively short observation period of 5 years. Observations through another cyclic period were deemed advisable.

About 350 inhabitants of four villages (Santa Rosa, Guayabalito, Gatuncillo and Las Guacas) were checked monthly and those positive for malaria parasites were treated with 0.1 gram atebrin 3 times a day for 5 days followed by plasmochin simplex 0.01 gram twice a day over a succeeding period of 5 days. A native girl in each village assisted the supervisor in the administration of the drugs.

New San Juan had about the same population as the above-mentioned villages. The treatment here consisted in 15 grains of quinine sulphate per day for 5 days followed by plasmochin simplex 0.01 gram twice a day for the next 5 days.

The control group consisted of three villages along the Madden Highway. Here the people were surveyed once a month and positive cases were offered quinine sulphate by a village officer.

Of 811 positives during the year, 74.8 percent had *P. falciparum,* 12.6 percent *P. vivax,* 0.6 percent *P. malariae* and 11.9 percent mixed infections. Compared to the initial surveys in 1931, the percent of *P. falciparum* and mixed infections had increased with corresponding reductions in *P. vivax* and *P. malariae* cases.

The average monthly malaria rate for the various treatment groups was, as follows:

Atebrin-plasmochin	9.1
Quinine-plasmochin	12.3
Quinine	18.5

Of those examined at every monthly survey, more than half showed parasites in the blood during the year; a comparable group in 1931 had a rate of 93.3 percent. The consistent therapy with various drugs over the period in question had the effect of materially lowering the overall parasite rate. However, the year was characterized by a low transmission cycle, which may have accounted in part for the lower rate.

Dr. Clark conducted surveys for malaria parasites in infants for 12 consecutive months after birth. Of 60 examined during the first 6 months, 11, or 18.3 percent, were positive. The rate for 12 months was 22.7 percent of 220 examined. No positives were detected during the first 2 months of life indicating the absence of congenital infections and the presence of a protective immunity derived from the mother. It was concluded that the acquisition of malaria during the first 12 months of life may serve to some extent as a measure of new infections in an endemic area.

Medical Entomology: Details of the life cycle of *Anopheles albimanus* were worked out in a laboratory colony. Ovarian development took place in approximately 7 days at a temperature of 80° to 86° F. and a relative humidity of around 80 percent. Six females deposited an average of 435 eggs; each female oviposited from 2 to 6 times; oviposition took place during the night. Eggs usually hatched after an incubation period of 40 to 48 hours in water at a temperature of 27° to 30° C. The larval stage usually consumed 8 to 13 days, the pupal stage usually 30 to 33 hours. Of 10,003 adults that survived emergence, 42.7 percent were males and 57.3 percent were females. Approximately 3 weeks was required for the development of one generation.

Other entomological studies were conducted during the year. Dr. Rozeboom observed differences in the blood feeding habits of Brazilian and Panamanian *Anopheles albitarsis,* and a marked dissimilarity in the morphology of the eggs of strains in the two countries. It was apparent that the species is divided into at least two separate races. The egg of *A. pseudopunctipennis* was also described and compared with that of the species in other countries.

Mr. Komp spent several months in British Guiana and Trinidad as well as in eastern Venezuela studying local anopheline species. During the year he published several papers, among them an important one on anopheline species of the subgenus *Kerteszia,* some of which are concerned in the transmission of malaria.

Chagas' Disease: Dr. Johnson and Lt. Col. Raymond A. Kelser of the Army Medical Research Board conducted complement fixation tests for Chagas' disease on 1,251 individuals in 12 communities in Panama. Thirty-seven were positive and 11 gave suspicious reactions, a combined rate of 3.83 percent. The infection rate was low in children under 15 years of age but rose sharply above this age. None of the positive cases presented any appreciable symptoms attributable to the infection. No cross reactions were obtained in *Trypanosoma equiperdum* and *T. hippicum* infections but bats infected with an unidentified trypanosome gave strongly positive reactions with *T. cruzi* antigen.

In conjunction with the surveys of the human population for *T. cruzi,* search was made for the trypanosome among various reservoir hosts. Of 50 armadillos examined, 8 were found infected. Thirty opossums proved to be negative, although previous studies had indicated this to be a good host.

The course of *T. cruzi* infection in the dog was found to simulate closely that in man. After an incubation period of approximately 6 weeks, the parasites appeared in the peripheral circulation. A steady increase in numbers followed with a peak in 10 to 15 days; in a similar period of time the numbers decreased and then the parasite could no longer be recovered from the blood. Infections in the dog were usually mild and assumed a chronicity which lasted during the lifetime of the animal. No evidence could be obtained of prenatal infection in the dog.

Trypanosomes similar in morphology to *T. cruzi* were recovered from the white-faced monkey and the vampire bat. The parasites could not be cultured on artificial media, thus differing in this respect from *T. cruzi.*

A fourth vector of Chagas' disease in Panama was discovered during the year. This was *Triatoma dimidiata,* which proved to be naturally infected with *T. cruzi.*

Studies on Equine Parasites: Studies conducted by Dr. Foster on 97 horses and mules revealed the presence of a variety of parasites. The most frequently occurring forms belonged to the Subfamily Strongylinae Railliet, 1893. Thirty-four species were recovered, of which 15 accounted for about 98 percent of the strongylid parasites. Percentage of infection with other parasites was, as follows:

Species	No. infected	Percent infected
Oxyuris equi	32	33
Probstmayria vivipara	57	66
Parascaris equorum	12	12
Habronema muscae	72	74
H. megastoma	8	8
(= Drascheia megastoma)		
H. microstoma	60	62
Setaria equina	18	19
Anoplocephala magna	1	1
A. perfoliata	1	1
Paranoplocephala mamillana	1	1

Strongylid parasites occurred in equines up to 30 years of age but animals from 9 to 25 years old were more than twice as heavily infected on the average. This age difference in the strongylid worm burden was interpreted as evidence of age resistance. However, no quantitative differences were noted in the age distribution of *Strongylus vulgaris*. There appeared also no evidence of age resistance against stomach worms.

In additional postmortem studies on over 200 equines, active verminous arteritis or aneurysm was found in about 80 percent. The lesions were encountered in animals of all ages. The typical lesions occurred in the anterior mesenteric artery and were characterized by tortuosity, sclerosis, thrombosis, and diminished caliber. These lesions are caused by the larvae of *Strongylus vulgaris* and constitute a serious condition which not uncommonly results in rupture of the aneurysm and death of the animal.

Miscellaneous Investigations: Lt. Commander E. G. Hakansson conducted observations on chromatoid bodies in the cysts of *Entamoeba histolytica*. The chromatoid matter in the cysts apparently occurs in two forms, manifest and latent. The transition to the latent stage appears to take place as the cysts grow older in fecal material and is apparently not related to nuclear development. It was doubted from the studies that the theory that chromatoid bodies constitute a food reserve is a valid one.

During his stay at the Gorgas Memorial Laboratory, Dr. Samuel F. Hildebrand conducted studies on tarpon in the Panama Canal. It was apparent that the fish had occurred in Gatun and Miraflores Lakes, from whence they could apparently descend to Panama Bay, probably through the Gatun Locks. The tarpon apparently was able to withstand the changes from salt to fresh water and *vice versa*.

Visiting Scientists: The following visiting scientists worked at the Gorgas Memorial Laboratory during 1936:

Dr. Puthenveetil Varghese George, Research Health Officer, Madras Health Department, India.

Dr. John Paul Gens, Yale University.

Sanitary Engineer W. H. W. Komp, U. S. Public Health Service, and Lt. Commander E. G. Hakansson, Medical Corps, U. S. Navy, continued their assignments.

1937 *Malaria Studies:* Malaria studies were continued with the same treatment regimens in the Chagres River villages as noted last year. The group in the Madden Highway villages was dropped from the project during the year. Because of changed conditions, the group was no longer serving as an effective control for the experiments. The monthly blood-parasite rates in groups treated with atebrin-plasmochin, quinine-plasmochin and quinine without supervision were. respectively, 7.4, 14.4 and 16.2 percent. These rates were slightly lower than those registered last year. The cumulative blood-parasite rate was 43.5 percent, the lowest of any to date. The percentage of infections with the various species of malaria parasites was not significantly different than that encountered in 1936. The infection rate in 355 *Anopheles albimanus* dissected during the year was 1.1 percent, a rate higher than that obtained in the first survey in 1932, when it was 0.48 percent.

Medical Entomology: Studies were conducted on the eggs of the *Nyssorhynchus* group of *Anopheles* in Panama. In most instances specific identification can be made on the basis of egg structure. However, the presence of three types of *A. strodei* (= *A. evansae*) eggs in Panama indicated that egg structure alone is not a dependable criterion for distinct races of species in this group.

In further studies, the Nearctic species of *A. quadrimaculatus* and *A. punctipennis* exhibited a high degree of susceptibility to infection by strains of *P. vivax* and *P. falciparum* derived from their own as well as from the Neotropical region. On the other hand representatives of the Neotropical species *A. albimanus* from Cuba and Panama showed high susceptibility to infection with these malaria parasites from their own region but were distinctly refractory to certain strains of the malaria species from the Nearctic region.

In experiments on the infectibility of Panamanian *Anopheles* fed on *P. falciparum* gametocyte carriers, 4.0 percent of *A. albitarsis* became lightly infected, as compared to 32.7 percent infection in *A. albimanus*. *A. bachmanni* (= *A. triannulatus*) could be infected with human malaria parasites but its preference for animal blood renders it of little significance as a vector in Panama. *A. punctimacula* feeds on both man and lower animals but rarely was encountered in the Chagres River villages and was therefore not a factor in transmission.

Chagas' Disease: In studies on Chagas' disease, it was noted that the cardiac lesions in acute fatal cases in dogs appeared to be the same as those in fatal human cases. A chronic stage of the disease was encountered in dogs, in which the lesions differed from those in acute cases only in relative intensity. The outer and innermost layers of the myocardium were mostly affected with the central portions less involved.

Further surveys for prevalence data on *T. cruzi* infection were carried out during the year. The total number of individuals tested by means of complement fixation reached 1,626, of whom 3.7 percent were positive.

Two hundred and seventy specimens of blood sera taken during the above survey were tested by the Rockefeller Institute for yellow fever by means of the mouse-protection technique. Seven sera from individuals in Darien Province proved positive, indicating that the disease had existed there within the past 12 or 13 years.

Studies on Equine Parasites: In the helminthological studies, observations were continued on verminous aneurysms due to *Strongylus vulgaris* in equines. Effort was made to determine why the larvae of this parasite attack only the anterior mesenteric artery and how penetration is effected. A species of stomach worm, *Trichostrongylus axei,* was recovered from equines in Panama for the first time. Observations were made on the occurrence of stomach worm larvae, *Habronema* sp. and *Drascheia* sp., in the vector, *Musca domestica.* Seven percent of 233 flies captured at Fort Clayton carried the parasites.

Miscellaneous Investigations: A new and economically important parasite was found in captive monkeys. This species was believed to be *Protospirura muricola,* normally parasitic in the stomach of rats. The cockroach, *Leucophaea maderae,* serves as the intermediate host. A considerable number of deaths in monkeys was attributed to this parasite, which occurred in the stomach and other portions of the digestive system. Lesions were particularly severe in the stomach and perforations of the wall resulted fatally.

Surveys for intestinal parasites in inhabitants of the Chagres River villages were conducted during the summer by Dr. Harry E. Wright. Of 478 individuals examined, 92.4 percent were found to harbor one or more parasites. A finding of special note was the occurrence of eggs of *Hepaticola hepatica* (= *Capillaria hepatica*) in 16 of 194 examinations in one village, New San Juan. It is probable that the eggs were present as a simple contamination and that the individuals were not actually infected.

During his tour of duty at the Gorgas Memorial Laboratory, Lt. Commander E. G. Hakansson conducted therapeutic trials of carbarsone in cases of amoebiasis and amoebic dysentery. The trials included two series of patients, one comprising 35 inmates in a mental institution and the other

10 members of laboratory personnel and their families. Varying dose rates were employed. Toxicity was noted in only one patient. Relatively small doses of the drug failed to eliminate *E. histolytica* in carrier cases. A relatively large dose of 0.025 gram per kilogram of body weight administered twice daily for 10 days resulted in a clinical cure in frank cases of dysentery and in some cases was effective in eradicating the infection.

The role of the food handler in the transmission of *Entamoeba histolytica* was investigated by Lt. James J. Sapero, Navy Medical Corps and Dr. Carl M. Johnson. The study comprised 14 groups with a total of 919 persons who had been served food and drink by carriers of the organism. No evidence was found to support the belief that infected food handlers were important agents in the transmission of amoebiasis.

Dr. Samuel F. Hildebrand investigated the possibility of the Panama Canal serving as a passageway for fish to cross to opposite oceans. It had been questioned whether fish could successfully negotiate the locks and whether any could endure the journey of about 40 miles through the fresh water between locks at the opposite ends of the canal. It was found that the tarpon had definitely completed the passage and that certain fresh water fishes had crossed the divide from the Pacific to the Atlantic side of the canal and *vice versa*.

During his stay at the Laboratory, Dr. George B. Wislocki of the Harvard Medical School conducted observations on twinning in marmosets. In 40 pregnancies or births in marmosets, twins occurred in 87.5 percent of the cases.

Visiting Scientists: The following visiting scientists worked at the Gorgas Memorial Laboratory during the year:

Dr. Samuel F. Hildebrand, U. S. Bureau of Fisheries, Washington, D. C.
Dr. Harry E. Wright, Baylor University, Dallas, Texas.
Dr. George B. Wislocki, Harvard Medical School.
Dr. Sydney W. Britton, University of Virginia.
Dr. Gerrit S. Miller, Jr., Smithsonian Institution, Washington D. C.
Dr. Raymond L. Ditmars, New York Zoological Park, New York, N. Y.
Dr. Alphonse Walti, Merck & Co., Rahway, N. J.

The following Service personnel were assigned to the Laboratory during the year:

Sanitary Engineer W. H. W. Komp, U. S. Public Health Service.

Lt. Commander E. G. Hakansson, Medical Corps, U. S. Navy, terminated his tour of duty on July 28, 1937.

Lt. James J. Sapero, U. S. Navy, began a tour of duty on July 6, 1937.

Pharmacist Mate H. A. Down, U. S. Navy, departed on May 3, 1937.

Pharmacist Mate L. E. Boston, U. S. Navy, continued on duty.

Regular staff change:

Dr. Lloyd E. Rozeboom, Medical Entomologist, resigned on September 30, 1937.

1938   *Malaria Studies:* Malaria studies were continued in the Chagres River villages, the inhabitants of which had been under observation and drug treatment since 1931. The regimens of treatment employed in 1937 were continued without alteration. The prevalence of various species of parasites was nearly the same as in the previous year, with a slight decrease in *P. falciparum* and a slight increase in *P. malariae.* As prophesied in last year's report, an epidemic occurred during the year in spite of previous continuous treatment with three potent drugs. There was little active malaria present prior to July. During the balance of the year parasite rates were twice to three times as high as in the preceding months. Along with this increase, there was a concomitant rise in the number of new infections and heavy infections. Clinical cases also appeared in considerable numbers. At the end of the year, the epidemic was still continuing. Stagnant river conditions led to an increase in aquatic vegetation and anopheline breeding in the Chagres River area during the spring months. The increase in mosquitoes was followed by an increase in malaria rates in the river villages. However, there appeared to be no increase in the mosquito population in the town of New San Juan, although this town also experienced epidemic malaria.

Dr. William H. Taliaferro and Mrs. Cessa Kluver studied the hematology of malaria due to *Plasmodium brasilianum* in Panamanian monkeys. The investigation added further evidence supporting the view that the lymphoid hyperplasia in malaria augments the mesenchymal reserve from which monocytes (which are partially differentiated in a phagocytic direction) and newly formed macrophages arise. The findings in the peripheral blood, however, only inadequately reflected the findings in the tissues.

Studies on Human Intestinal Parasites: Lt. Sapero carried out studies on the occurrence of *Entamoeba histolytica* and other intestinal parasites in Navy personnel who had been stationed in the Orient and in the American tropics. The examination of 1,021 individuals revealed 11.6 percent infections with *E. histolytica.* The major portion of the positives were incident to residence in the United States, prior to naval service, as indicated by an infection rate of 14.7 percent in recruits from the southeastern part of the country, and 7.8 percent in those from other parts of the United States. For men in the American tropics, the rate was 9.5 percent. On the other hand, 26.1 percent of men returned from the Orient were infected. There was no evidence of transmission of amoebiasis aboard naval vessels. Hookworm occurred in 14 percent of southern recruits and the prevalence of the parasite remained fairly high in other groups, which appeared to have acquired the parasite prior to naval service. *Ascaris* and other helminths were acquired during service in the Orient. The prevalence of 17.1 percent of *Dientamoeba fragilis* found in one group represented the highest rate reported from the United States.

In another study of Lt. Sapero, 216 cases of non-dysenteric amoebiasis were investigated, of which 100 were found to have symptoms. Of 106 apparently healthy men harboring *Entamoeba histolytica,* 46, or 43.4 percent, registered complaints. A control group of 108 cases negative for intestinal protozoa revealed but 8, or 7.4 percent, to have complaints. Of 236 individuals harboring other intestinal protozoa, the percentage with symptoms was similar to that found in the control group with the exception of individuals with *Dientamoeba fragilis,* in which 27.3 percent of 44 cases presented symptoms. All complaints in the amoebiasis cases were primarily referable to the gastrointestinal tract; chronicity, recurrence and mildness of symptoms were characteristic features.

Miscellaneous Investigations: In helminthological studies in animals, Dr. Foster described five apparently new species of worms from the woolly opossum. Numerous species were found in domestic animals, including the fowl, sheep, goat, cattle, swine, the dog and the cat.

In entomological studies, Dr. Fairchild published several papers dealing with tabanid flies.

E. R. Dunn and J. R. Bailey of Haverford College reported on 268 snakes from the uplands of eastern Panama collected from 1936 through 1938 by Dr. Clark. Work on the snake census continued during the year, by the end of which 8,520 specimens had been collected, of which 25.4 percent proved to be poisonous.

Staff Changes: Mr. Daniel M. Jobbins reported for duty on July 1, 1938, as a replacement for Dr. Rozeboom, who resigned last year.

Dr. Graham B. Fairchild reported for duty on October 1, 1938.

Visiting Scientists: The following visiting scientists carried on studies at the Laboratory during the year:

Dr. George R. Cowgill, Yale University.

Dr. S. W. Britton and Mr. R. Klein, University of Virginia.

Dr. Marion Hood, University of Illinois College of Medicine.

The following Service personnel were on duty at the Laboratory during the year:

Sanitary Engineer W. H. W. Komp, U. S. Public Health Service.

Lt. James J. Sapero, Medical Corps, U. S. Navy.

Mr. L. E. Boston, Chief Pharmacist Mate, U. S. Navy.

1939 *Malaria Studies:* The year marked the 10th anniversary of the establishment of the malaria studies in the Chagres River villages. During this time control was attempted by drug administration alone without any recourse to control of the mosquito vectors. Treatment has been confined to parasite-positive individuals and at no time has mass treatment of the entire population been attempted. Drug regimens employed during the year were unchanged.

During the 10 years, there was considerable fluctuation in the average monthly parasite rates. In the treated groups the rate in 1930-31 was 21.6 percent. It reached a low point of 6.6 percent in 1937-38 and was 8.0 percent in 1938-39. The control groups showed similar fluctuations, although comparisons are not wholly valid because the number of monthly surveys varied from 1 to 12. The highest rate was 27.5 percent in 1932-33 and the lowest 16.2 in 1936-37. In 1938-39, the rate was 20.8 percent. Parasite rates in children were consistently higher than in adults. The use of plasmochin in the treated villages did not reduce the gametocyte rate in *P. falciparum* infections to a point where malaria transmission was prevented.

One disadvantage of drug treatment referred to the consistently higher percentage of heavy infections in the treated villages as compared to the control villages. In 1939 for instance, heavy infections in the treated villages were over twice those in the control villages. It was visualized that continuous drug therapy results in a lowered immunity and therefore a predisposition to heavier parasite rates and more frequent clinical manifestations.

Medical Entomology: An Entomological Field Station was established last year at Juan Mina and has been renovated so that it is suitable for living and working quarters. The Station is now being used for field observations on anopheline breeding and malaria transmission patterns. A low water gradient in the Chagres River resulted in a buildup of *Cabomba* vegetation with enhanced opportunities for mosquito breeding in the early spring. Breeding of *A. albimanus* reached a peak in late April. Adult emergence occurred at a slightly lower rate for the next 3 months but sufficient to maintain quantities of mosquitoes in Santa Rosa and Guayabalito. In January, February and March the average number of mature anopheline females captured in houses in Santa Rosa was, respectively, 4.8, 5.4 and 4.6. In April the figure was 10.7 and in May the peak was reached with an average of 16.6.

Insect repellent studies were initiated during the year.

Numerous publications in medical entomology reported work conducted during 1939. Dr. Fairchild was responsible for a series of papers on Tabanidae and Simuliidae of Panama. Dr. William Trager studied the problem of acquired immunity to Argasid ticks. Mr. Komp and collaborators published on the mosquitoes of Costa Rica. Another paper by Mr. Komp reported the presence of *Anopheles darlingi* in British Honduras, Guatemala and Spanish Honduras. Dr. Mark F. Boyd and Mr. Daniel M. Jobbins found that *A. albimanus* from Panama exhibited a susceptibility to a coindigenous strain of *P. falciparum* similar to that observed in a Floridian strain of *A. quadrimaculatus* when infected with the same strain.

Miscellaneous Investigations: Dr. Johnson conducted studies on the pathology of *Entamoeba histolytica* infections in Panamanian monkeys with the view of obtaining data applicable to human infections. The gross appearance of the large bowel was normal. Microscopic examination of the tissues revealed minor damage which was usually limited to the superficial mucosa and appeared to have been produced by the mechanical activity of the trophozoites.

Studies by Lt. Sapero and collaborators demonstrated the existence of large and small races of *E. histolytica* with a racial constancy both as regards size and physiological characteristics.

The presence of eggs of *Capillaria hepatica* in the stools of human patients was explained by the finding of the parasite in three new animal hosts which are commonly a part of the human diet in rural Panama. When the livers of these animals are consumed by man the eggs of the parasite appear in the stools. Such appearance, therefore, is not an indication of human infection.

A survey of internal and ectoparasites was conducted in racing greyhounds, hunting dogs and mongrel animals from Chagres River villages. The heartworm, *Dirofilaria immitis,* was present in 45 percent of the greyhounds, 8 to 61 percent of three packs of hunting dogs and 22.5 percent of mongrels. There was a high prevalence of hookworms in all groups of animals.

As a result of his studies at the Gorgas Memorial Laboratory, Dr. S. W. Britton published on the habits and parasites of the sloth.

A change in the regular staff of the Laboratory occurred when Dr. A. O. Foster resigned as of May 31, 1939.

Visiting Scientists: Visiting scientists during the year included the following:

Dr. S. W. Britton, University of Virginia.

Miss Barbara Belzner, Camden Hospital, Camden, Ark.

Dr. William Trager, Rockefeller Institute, Princeton, N. J.

Dr. J. Elliston Farrell, Long Island Medical School.

Dr. Emmett R. Dunn, Haverford College.

The following Service personnel were on duty at the Laboratory during 1939:

Sanitary Engineer W. H. W. Komp, U. S. Public Health Service.

Lt. James J. Sapero, U. S. Navy until July 16, 1939.

Mr. M. H. Williams, Pharmacist Mate, U. S. Navy, until July 31, 1939.

1940 *Malaria Studies:* The malaria program inaugurated at the Santa Rosa Malaria Control Station in 1930 was discontinued in August 1940. The administration of various drugs and combination of drugs to the parasite-positive inhabitants of the Chagres River villages demonstrated that it was impossible to eradicate malaria parasites by such means, or to reduce them to the point where transmission is very greatly decreased. It was found also that drug-control methods cannot prevent an epidemic of malaria when unusually large numbers of anopheline vectors are present. The studies did show, however, that the method applied was successful in reducing almost to the vanishing point the cases of severe clinical malaria.

A malaria survey in the Tuira River valley in Darien Province revealed an infection rate in four towns of 10.8 percent. The rates ranged from 7.4 percent in tidewater El Real to 19.7 percent at Yape, an upland river town. *Anopheles albimanus* and *A. punctimacula* were the only vectors encountered; vector populations were sparse and few were found in houses.

Medical Entomology: At the Juan Mina Entomological Station studies were continued on the relation between malaria incidence and vector activity. Efforts to reduce house populations of *A. albimanus* by intensive collecting failed of the objective. The use of cloth strips impregnated with insect repellents was partially successful in reducing mosquito populations in houses. Breeding conditions in the Chagres River were studied extensively in relation to amount and type of vegetation and the occurrence of various algae. The life cycle of *A. albimanus* was studied for comparison with previous data for laboratory colonies.

Dr. Fairchild continued his studies on Tabanidae. *Simulium sanguineum,* a species formerly known from Colombia, was collected in Darien Province. A special study was made of the Simuliidae some of which are vectors of onchocerciasis in Mexico and Guatemala. To the two species formerly described from Panama, 10 were added, of which 3 appeared to be new. Two of the species responsible for the transmission of onchocerciasis in Guatemala were described from Panama.

Miscellaneous Investigations: Dr. Johnson continued his studies on amoebiasis in monkeys. Material from rhesus monkeys indicated that *E. histolytica* can and does penetrate the tissues of the host with minimum damage.

Trypanosoma vivax was found for the first time in cattle in the Republic of Panama. The trypanosome was well established in the local animals, since surveys of a number of herds revealed infection rates from 5 to over 50 percent. Presumably the parasite was introduced with cattle from countries to the south where it has long been known to occur. Symptoms exhibited by infected animals consisted of fever, anemia and emaciation. Some animals showed weakness of the posterior extremities, edema and loss of appetite. A number of different animals were inoculated with the parasite but infections were established only in calves, goats and horses.

Trypanosoma ingens, a non-pathogenic trypanosome of antelopes, which has been reported from the ox, was found in a dairy cow in Panama.

Because of lock expansion in the Panama Canal, it was necessary to vacate the Miraflores Veterinary Station on August 1, 1940. The station was moved to the Corozal Hospital Farm. In addition to providing facilities for veterinary research, the station was used for the breeding of all small animals needed for the Laboratory.

Visiting Scientists: The following visiting scientists worked at the Laboratory during 1940:

Professor H. H. Bartlett, University of Michigan.

Dr. Tobias Lasser, Caracas, Venezuela.

Dr. C. A. Mills, University of Cincinnati.

Dr. Edmond J. Farris, Wistar Institute, Philadelphia, Pa.

Dr. Emmett R. Dunn, Haverford College.

Mr. Robert B. Folsom, University of California, arrived on September 19, 1940 for a year's volunteer services in the Department of Entomology.

Sanitary Engineer W. H. W. Komp, U. S. Public Health Service, was the only Service representative on duty during the year.

1941 *Malaria Studies:* It was decided to continue the malaria investigations at the Santa Rosa Malaria Control Station although on a smaller scale. Drugs employed in the past were in continued use. Treated villages remained the same but a new control village, Río Pescado, was added. In this village, quinine was provided for those who requested it. During the year *P. falciparum* was reduced and *P. vivax* increased. No notable change over past years was obvious as regards parasite rates, relapses and percent of heavy infections.

Observations were continued on mosquito breeding in relation to types of vegetation in the Chagres and Pescado rivers. The response of *A. albimanus* to various types of repellents was studied. During the year, Mr. Jobbins carried out malaria and entomological surveys for the Haitian-American Agricultural Development Corporation in the Republic of Haiti. In the Bayeux region on the north coast, the malaria parasite rate was

32.6 percent and in the Grand Anse Valley on the southern peninsula, it was 19.8 percent. An analysis of the seasonal distribution of tabanid flies was being made for publication. Of 12,000 specimens, 13 species accounted for over 97.0 percent. A single species (*Neotabanus lineola* var. *carneno*) comprised over half of the total number of specimens.

Protozoal Diseases of Cattle: Additional surveys were made for the occurrence of *Trypanosoma vivax*. A new infected area was found near Pacora about 30 miles east of Panama on the Chepo Highway. There were many thousands of cattle in the region. In some of the herds, infection rates as high as 64.0 percent were found, with the average between 20.0 and 30.0 percent. Symptoms of the disease included loss of appetite with consequent weight reduction. Intermittent fever and anemia were evident. One animal was apparently completely blind but sight was restored after successful treatment.

The effect of promin on piroplasmosis of cattle was studied in a few cases. The drug appeared to be of value since administration was followed by clinical improvement, a reduction in temperature and improved appetite.

Effects of Tropical Climate: Dr. C. A. Mills studied the effects of tropical climate on growth and development. Growth and sexual development appeared to have progressed more rapidly in children who had only recently left temperate climates to enter the Panama Canal Zone. With prolongation of residence more and more of the advantages of the former temperate zone residence were lost. In another study with Robert W. Chapin, D. D. S., it was found that dental caries rates in children in the Canal Zone were exceptionally high, as compared with most areas in the United States. The rate was significantly higher in children born in the Canal Zone, as compared to those who had migrated from the United States. It was suggested that the high rates might be associated with low fluorine content of Gatun Lake water which supplies the Zone.

The studies of Dr. Mills led to certain cooperative laboratory experiments with Dr. Johnson on the effect of temperature on certain animals, which were maintained at a constant temperature of 68°F. A control group was kept at usual prevailing outside temperatures. Results were based on a comparison of antibody production, growth rates, reproduction and hemoglobin levels. It was found that the "cold room" animals, consumed more food, grew faster, were more active and had a higher birth rate with more rapid maturity of the young than the control animals. Hemoglobin values were considerably higher in the experimental group as compared to the control group.

Snake Census: Dr. Emmett R. Dunn published on new or noteworthy snakes from Panama. Dr. Clark summarized records of venomous snakes from certain Central American countries and recorded the incidence of snake-bite accidents. In a record of 104 snake bites, 54 occurred on the upper extremities and 50 on the lower extremities. Seven, or 6.73 percent, of the cases resulted fatally.

Visiting Scientists: The Laboratory provided facilities for the following visiting scientists during the year:

Professor H. H. Bartlett, University of Michigan.

Dr. C. A. Mills, University of Cincinnati.

Dr. L. T. Coggeshall, International Health Division, Rockefeller Foundation.

Dr. Henry W. Kumm, International Health Division, Rockefeller Foundation.

Sanitary Engineer W. H. W. Komp, U. S. Public Health Service, continued his tour of duty at the Laboratory.

1942 *Malaria Studies:* Examination and treatment periods for malaria in the Chagres River villages were reduced from monthly to bimonthly. Plasmochin was dropped from the therapeutic regimen because it had not seemed to lower the transmission rate. Beginning with 1942, the only drugs used were atebrin and quinine separately. There was little change in the distribution of malaria species. The average parasite rate for the atebrin treated towns was slightly higher than that of the quinine treated villages. Both rates were higher than those of the previous year. Of individuals positive for parasites, 19.6 showed heavy infections which were more numerous in the atebrin treated towns. The year's work confirmed previous conclusions that the transmission rate can be lowered to some extent by drug therapy but eradication and prevention of relapses cannot be accomplished by this means.

Medical Entomology: Mr. Jobbins conducted studies on insects of medical importance under contract with the Committee on Medical Research, Office of Scientific Research and Development. Field and laboratory tests under controlled conditions disclosed a number of new synthetic compounds far more effective as mosquito repellents than previously known substances.

Mr. Komp was on detached duty for 6 months during the year with the Office of the Coordinator for Inter-American Affairs, as a consultant on the malaria program. His monograph, "The Anopheline Mosquitoes of the Caribbean Region" was published during the year and constituted an authoritative reference work on the subject. It proved to be especially valuable to military forces stationed in the area.

Dr. Fairchild completed his studies on the horse flies of Panama, 89 species of which were known to occur in the country. A tick study showed the Panama fauna to include 29 species, of which at least 7 were of economic importance either as pests or disease vectors. A study of sandflies, *Phlebotomus* spp., was initiated during the year.

Miscellaneous Investigations: Dr. Johnson conducted studies under two grants from the Committee on Medical Research of the Office of Scientific Research and Development. One grant was for malaria investigations and concerned the employment of immunological tests in diagnosis. The other was for trypanosomiasis studies. Since the spleen appeared to constitute one mechanism of defense in protozoal infections, studies on proteolytic activity of that organ were initiated in rabbits infected with *Trypanosoma hippicum* and monkeys infected with *Plasmodium brasilianum*. In general, it was found that in the trypanosome infections in rabbits the proteolytic activity of the spleen increases in the earlier stages of the disease but in the terminal stages, when the animals are obviously losing ground, the activity decreases and continues to do so until the animal dies. It would appear that when the spleen reaches its limit of activity, the infection gains the upper hand and the animal succumbs. Experiments with malaria and splenic proteolytic activity gave less significant results.

Additional observations on *Trypanosoma vivax* infection in cattle added a new endemic area. The disease was known to cover the area of the Pacific slope which is bounded on the east by the Colombian border and on the west by the town of Santiago.

Equine Trypanosomiasis: The last case of equine trypanosomiasis in the Canal Zone was recorded in October 1931. During the present year, a case was diagnosed in an Army horse. A survey of all Army equines in the Zone disclosed two additional cases. Two foci were known to exist in Panama and presumably infection was acquired by animals used in maneuvers.

Visiting Scientists: The following scientists made use of Laboratory facilities during the year:
Professor H. H. Bartlett, University of Michigan.
Dr. C. A. Mills, University of Cincinnati.

1943　　*Malaria Studies:* Continuation of the malaria studies in the Chagres River villages was deemed advisable because of cyclical variations in transmission and the desirability to correlate malaria prevalence with the entomological studies at the Juan Mina Station.

Certain changes in aquatic vegetation control in the Chagres River by the Panama Canal could result in lowered malaria transmission, although it was believed that the chief vector breeding areas were in branches of the river not affected by the above changes.

Blood films and drug treatment were continued on a bimonthly basis. On alternate months, Dr. Clark visited all villages and treated all fever cases. A new treatment town, Camarón, was added to the treatment villages. Positive individuals in this town were given a course of atebrin 0.1 gram 3 times a day for 5 days plus three additional doses of 0.1 gram in intervening weeks; thus the total monthly dose rate consisted of 24 tablets of 0.1 gram each. In addition to Río Pescado, control groups from the villages of Mendoza and Los Azules were included. Quinine was available to these groups on a request basis.

Average monthly parasite rates were, as follows:

Treated groups:	*Percent positive*
Atebrin group	10.9
Quinine group	8.9
First year atebrin group	18.8
Control groups:	
Río Pescado	25.6
Mendoza	4.0
Los Azules	10.9

It is noteworthy that the actual numbers on whom blood films were obtained during the year is considerably less than the total population of each village. In fact, the greatest coverage in any village represented only one-third of the population. This unsatisfactory situation was occasioned by population movements both temporary and permanent, which rendered evaluation of results more difficult.

The percentage of clinical relapses during the year was 10.8 for the atebrin group, 24.6 for the quinine group, 42.7 for the new atebrin group in Camarón, 50.0 for Río Pescado, and 21.0 for Mendoza and Los Azules.

Medical Entomology: Much of the program in medical entomology planned for the year could not be carried out because of difficulties in arranging transportation on account of wartime conditions. Changes in personnel were several. Major Marshall Hertig arrived on June 15 to take charge of the program on study of repellents for the Office of Scientific Research and Development. Dr. Fairchild received an Army commission and was assigned to this program. Later, the group was joined by Lieut. W. C. McDuffie and Lieut. Roy Melvin. No reports of the project are available at this writing, as the material was restricted military information. Mr. Jobbins accepted a commission as a reserve officer in the U. S. Public Health Service and left the Laboratory.

Miscellaneous Protozoan Studies: Dr. Johnson continued studies on the immunological diagnosis of malaria and trypanosomiasis under contract with the Committee on Medical Research of the Office of Scientific Research and Development. The contract was renewed to cover the calendar year 1943. For malaria the complement fixation test was found superior to other standard reactions and when the problem of producing a suitable antigen is solved, the test should prove useful. *Trypanosoma cruzi* antigens produced by repeated freezing and thawing of cultures of the formalized parasites were found superior, both in quality and in sensitivity in the test, to those prepared by extraction of the parasites or by their preservation in glycerin solutions.

A species of *Toxoplasma* was reported for the first time from Panama, having been isolated from Army carrier pigeons. The organism was responsible for epizootic illness among pigeons, characterized by sudden onset, high fever, extreme weakness, inability to maintain balance and generalized convulsions. The disease resulted fatally in many instances. Microscopically, the parasites were found intracellularly in a variety of cells, associated or unassociated with lesions. A noteworthy finding concerned the invasion of nerve trunks and nerve cells by the organism. The parasite was transferred to guinea pigs. Intraperitoneal inoculation was followed by death in 6 to 10 days with widespread invasion of the lungs and the central nervous system, as well as marked peritonitis.

Observations were conducted on treatment of equine trypanosomiasis. On account of wartime conditions, the most effective drug for this purpose was no longer available. Tests were carried out with a new compound, P-carbamylamino-phenylarsonic acid, in horses naturally infected with *T. hippicum* and on two animals experimentally infected. Two apparent cures were obtained in the naturally infected animals.

A colony of vampire bats has been maintained ever since the species was found to transmit *T. hippicum*. One bat has lived for 9 years and two others for 8 years in the colony. One bat survived the infection, the only one known not to have succumbed to the disease.

Col. H. S. Eakins, Veterinary Corps, U. S. Army, returned to Panama in August 1942 as Chief of the United States Military Commission, and was provided with facilities at the Laboratory. During 1943, he was engaged on studies on equine and bovine trypanosomiasis. Of 2,061 blood films, 63 from horses revealed *T. hippicum* and 47 from cattle showed *T. vivax*. Piroplasma were recorded from 49 horses and eight cattle. Experiments were conducted on repellents and killing fluids for the control of *Dermatobia hominis* in cattle.

Snake Census: The snake census assumed new importance during the year because of increased military personnel in the Canal Zone and the operations of mobile units. A number of lectures were given on recognition of poisonous species and snake-bite prevention and treatment. Up to

September 30, 1943, a total of 13,061 specimens had been collected in Panama, of which 3,143, or 24.06 percent, proved to be poisonous. These represented 15 species.

1944 *Malaria Studies:* Malaria studies in the villages reported in 1943 were continued without change in method or direction. Again, the movement of population was a deterent factor in overall effectiveness of the program and its evaluation. Average monthly parasite rates were as follows:

Treated groups	Percent Positive
Atebrin group	9.0
Quinine group	5.5
2nd Year atebrin group (Camarón)	17.7
Control groups	
Río Pescado	16.5
Mendoza	2.9
Lirio (Substituted for Los Azules)	18.5

These rates were not statistically different than those from the year before when numbers involved are considered.

The percentage of relapses during the year was 20.9 in the atebrin group, 30.0 in the quinine group, 50.8 in the Camarón atebrin group, 38.3 in the Río Pescado control group and 18.7 in the Mendoza control group. Relapses in the atebrin group were about twice those of the year before. The second year's treatment with enhanced atebrin dosage failed to reduce relapses in the Camarón group.

Medical Entomology: Entomological studies during the year were conducted by the United States Army Sanitary Officers assigned to the Laboratory. Some of the work concerned tests of various types of insect repellents against *Anopheles albimanus, A. punctimacula* and several species of *Mansonia*. Of the eight substances or mixtures tested, all gave adequate protection for an average time of at least 160 minutes. The timing of the experiments was associated with the optimum mosquito activity; the tests began between 5.30 and 6.30 p.m. and continued until 9.30 to 10.30 p.m.

Interesting observations were made on the biting habits of mosquito species, the attractiveness of the human bait subjects, and the efficacy of the repellents in relation to different body surfaces. The repellent activity was of less duration against *Mansonia* as compared with other species. *Mansonia* tended to bite more frequently on the arms while the reverse was true in the case of *A. albimanus*. Repellent protection persisted longer in old subjects than those in the late teens and early twenties. *A. albimanus* bit more frequently in the young subjects. Repellent action was affected adversely in heavily perspiring subjects.

Studies on the control of sandflies were carried out in Peru. The three repellents tested gave 100 percent protection for at least 3 hours and 60 to 80 percent protection for an additional 2 hours. In a small number of tests, Army Freon-pyrethrum aerosol bombs and 2.5 percent DDT in kerosene rid houses of sandflies and rendered daytime resting places untenable for several days.

Good protection against mites was obtained by the impregnation of uniform cloth with certain chemicals. One compound was still lethal to mites after seven washings of the cloth. Subjects wearing treated clothing were protected against chiggers. Five washings and 6 weeks of wear were required to render the clothing ineffective.

Extensive tests were conducted with DDT in oil and various emulsions as an anopheline larvicide. Heavy dosages applied either as floatable dusts or in oil were effective for 2 to 6 weeks in heavy growths of *Jussiaea,* but only from 2 to 4 weeks in the more open *Naias.* Decreases in effectiveness of DDT in time were apparently not due to loss of toxicity of the chemical but to dispersion by wind, waves and current. Comparative tests of Paris green-talc and DDT-talc dusts indicated that DDT was 5 to 10 times as toxic to anopheline larvae.

A long term project was designed to evaluate the periodic spraying of houses with DDT. Houses will be sprayed inside and out and another area will be set aside in which individual houses are sprayed to secure data on the residual properties of the chemical against *A. albimanus* and *A. punctimacula.*

Sanitary Engineer W. H. W. Komp conducted malaria surveys during the year in Colombia, Venezuela and various parts of the Republic of Panama.

Miscellaneous Protozoan Studies: Dr. Johnson completed his malaria study contract with the Office of Scientific Research and Development. Evaluation of antigens was continued. Antigens prepared from blood cells of monkeys with heavy infections of *Plasmodium brasilianum* were sufficiently active to demonstrate malaria antibodies in sera of native individuals with a history of long-continued malaria infections. They were not of value for diagnosis of recently acquired infections. Antigens prepared from human malarial placentas gave much better results with the complement fixation test.

Isospora hominis, a human coccidial parasite, was found for the first time in Panama.

Studies on cutaneous leishmaniasis were inaugurated during the year. Heretofore, it was thought that this disease was of rather rare occurrence in Panama. However, a focus was discovered in the town of Arraiján with six proved cases and two suspected cases of infection.

Filariasis in Monkeys: Postmortem examinations of wild captive monkeys disclosed an undescribed type of filariasis. Three colony monkeys succumbed to pulmonary filariasis; adult worms were encountered in the muscle and facia as well as in the serous cavities. It was thought that this species might be the adult of one of the two microfilariae described by McCoy in 1934.

Chemotherapy of Amoebiasis: Dr. Johnson carried out therapeutic trials with oral emetine in amoebiasis in cooperation with Dr. Bliss C. Shrapnel and Dr. J. H. Sandground. Twenty cases were treated with emetine hydrochloride in tablets protected by a special ("Enseals") coating, which was designed to release the contents in 3 to 4 hours after ingestion. Total dose rates varied between 3 grains for the youngest to 22 grains for the oldest patient. Amoebae disappeared from the stools in 3 to 4 days. Fifteen of the patients were freed of amoebae as disclosed by rigorous follow-up techniques for 1 to 7 months. Four of those not cured from a parasitological standpoint, remained free of symptoms. No side effects were observed.

Laboratory Staffing: Staffing of the Laboratory during 1944:
Only two regular staff members were on duty, viz: Dr. Herbert C. Clark and Dr. Carl M. Johnson.
The following U. S. Army personnel were present during the year:
Major Marshall Hertig, who reported for duty on June 15, 1943 and who departed for overseas duty on July 17, 1944.
Captain Graham B. Fairchild, who was commissioned in the Army on April 28, 1943.
Captain W. C. McDuffie, who joined the Laboratory on April 28, 1943 and left for temporary duty overseas on June 11, 1944.
First Lieut. Roy Melvin who joined the Army Unit at the Laboratory on October 5, 1943 and was reassigned on September 10, 1944.
Lieut. Harold Trapido who reported for duty on July 4, 1944.

1945 *Malaria Studies:* The malaria work in the Chagres River villages was continued for the 15th consecutive year for the following stated reasons: (1) The regular blood-film surveys offered a measure for the entomological experiments in progress at the Juan Mina and Santa Rosa Field Stations; (2) it provided an opportunity to study cyclical variations in malaria incidence; and (3) it assisted in the protection of the Canal Zone and Army personnel in nearby locations. Mosquito control in the general area was practiced during the year through the killing of aquatic vegetation, the continued employment of paris green as a larvicide and the DDT experiments against adult anophelines. All of these factors may have influenced malaria rates to some extent.

There was no essential change in blood examinations and drug treatment regimens during the year. However, because of transient movement to and from the town of Camarón, all houses were sprayed with DDT, the first application having been made in August of 1945.

Average bimonthly or monthly parasite rates were as follows: Atebrin group 10.2, quinine group 13.0, Camarón atebrin 8.7, Río Pescado control 12.2, Mendoza control 3.0 and Lirio control 4.3. The difficulty of evaluating results of drug treatment as carried out under the conditions of these experiments was emphasized by comparative parasite rates in the control town of Lirio for the respective years, 1944 and 1945. In 1944 the average monthly rate was 18.5 and the cumulative rate was 23.6. In 1945, the average monthly rate was 4.3 and the cumulative rate 4.3. During the year DDT spraying was started in the Chagres River town of Gatuncillo, where the inhabitants had been receiving atebrin. Treatment was continued on the same basis during 1945. However, the houses were sprayed 3 times with DDT. The malaria rate in the town was reduced by 50 percent during the year, obviously mainly as a result of the DDT control and not from drug treatment, since no such marked reduction had taken place in prior years when drug treatment alone was employed.

Medical Entomology: In various studies dealing with medical entomology, Major Hertig and Capt. Fairchild made observations on the occurrence and distribution of sandflies, *Phlebotomus* spp., in Panama. Four species previously reported from Panama were collected. In addition, the collections included 30 other species which remained to be identified. Only five species were taken biting man. *P. suis* and *P. panamensis* were by far the most common ones attacking man and animals. The sandfly collections were made from various types of habitat, including houses, horse-baited traps, masonry ruins, tree buttresses and hollow trees.

Investigations in Peru in 1944 indicated that sandflies were probably especially susceptible to DDT. This observation led to the assignment of Major Hertig to Italy and Palestine during the latter part of that year. Extensive and well controlled observations on various species of *Phlebotomus* under varying conditions indicated that the spraying of buildings with DDT gave a high degree of protection against bites of the flies.

Because the Mediterranian observations indicated that area control might be possible, Major Hertig and Capt. Fairchild carried out further studies on this problem in Peru during June to August 1945. A number of project sites were sprayed with DDT. A high degree of area control was obtained with minimal treatment when only certain types of outdoor surfaces such as walls or structures of loose stone were sprayed.

Capt. Fairchild and P. A. Engineer E. A. Barreda, USPHS conducted studies on control of *Simulium* spp., vectors of *Onchocerca volvulus* in an endemic area in Guatemala. Using an emulsion containing 4 percent DDT prepared from a stock concentrate containing 20 percent DDT, 20 percent Triton X-100 and 60 percent xylene, complete eradication of *Simulium* larvae from streams for distances up to 10 kilometers was effected at concentrations of 1 part DDT to 10 million parts of water. Efforts to prolong larvicidal action by absorbing emulsions and solutions of DDT on porous substances were unsuccessful.

Lieut. Charles D. Michener extended his experiments on the impregnation of clothing with various acaricides, viz: Dimethyl phthalate (DMP), dibutyl phthalate (DBP), 2-phenyl cyclohexanol (ESNN) and benzyl benzoate (BEN). ESNN killed chigger mites more quickly but washed out more easily. Best results were obtained with DBP and BEN which retained some activity even after eight washings. When impregnated clothing was worn by test subjects, a 4 percent emulsion of benzyl benzoate (BEN) proved to be the most effective and retained some activity through four washings. Area control was achieved by application of DDT micronized in talc applied at the rate of 40 pounds of DDT per acre and 4 percent DDT in kerosene at the rate of 22 quarts of solution per acre. However, mites returned to the treated plots within 7 to 10 days. Larvae of *Eutrombicula batatas* [= *Trombicula* (*Eutrombicula*) *batatas*] and *E. goldii* [= *Trombicula* (*Eutrombicula*) *goeldii*] were used in all the tests.

Lieut. Michener also tested the above-mentioned repellents against larvae and nymphs of *Amblyomma cajennense,* one of the most common species of ticks found in Panama. Benzyl benzoate gave better results than did the other chemicals and clothing treated with it protected after 8 days of regular wear. However, thorough laundering greatly reduced or eliminated the protective qualities.

Lieut. Michener completed a number of papers on Acarina.

Experiments conducted by Lieut. Trapido indicated that protection against bites of *Culicoides* spp. can be afforded by painting the inside and outside of screens in a room with a 5 percent solution of DDT in kerosene. The biting rate in the experimental room was reduced to zero for 10 days following which it gradually rose to less than one bite per 15 minutes at the 50th day. Some protection was even afforded up to the 90th day, when the rate was only one-ninth of the pre-treatment level.

Lieut. Trapido conducted trials with 5 percent DDT in kerosene as a residual spray in houses in Gatuncillo, one of the Chagres River villages, reserving the other two, Guayabalito and Santa Rosa, as controls. Pretreatment and post-treatment observations by means of house catches and horse-baited traps were employed to measure the effectiveness of the method. Previous work had indicated that *A. albimanus* is not a house resting mosquito but after engorgement does remain in houses for a time. Entrance and exit were usually through the interstices between the canes constituting the walls of the houses. Consequently, the spray was applied to both the inside and outside of the houses, as well as to outhouses and domestic animal shelters. Applications were made at intervals of 4 months. Marked reductions occurred in anophelines in the treated village. After the third spraying in July 1945, the ratio of anophelines in the treated village was 0.004, or only 4 anophelines versus 1,000 in the control villages. Of the engorged vectors taken in the treated houses, very few survived for 24 hours. A comparison of cumulative malaria rates indicated a reduction of 50 percent in Gatuncillo compared to that in the control villages. There was some evidence that the spraying resulted in reduction of vectors outside the houses and even in the forest surrounding the sprayed village.

Mr. Komp continued to act as consultant to various governmental and other agencies in Central and South America. Countries visited during the year included Venezuela, Trinidad, British Guiana, French Guiana and Costa Rica, as well as various areas in Panama.

Personnel Changes and Staffing: Personnel changes and personnel on duty in 1945:

Dr. Carl M. Johnson resigned as of December 31, 1944 and entered the Medical School of Leland Stanford University on January 5, 1945.

Sanitary Engineer Director W. H. W. Komp, USPHS continued on duty.

The following officers of the Sanitary Corps, Army of the United States, were on duty at the Laboratory during all or part of the year:

Major Marshall Hertig, Captain G. B. Fairchild, First Lieut. Harold Trapido, First Lieut. Charles D. Michener, Captain W. C. McDuffie and First Lieut. Roy Melvin. Technical Sergeant Edson H. Fichter, Jr. was also assigned to the Laboratory.

The Gorgas Memorial Laboratory
The Research Program 1936-1945
A Summation

The 10-year period 1936-1945 was one of growth for the Gorgas Memorial Laboratory. The new staff members who arrived in 1934 were now adding materially to the research output and the varied talents represented resulted in a broader and more diversified program. Beginning in 1943, the assignment of a cadre of Army Sanitary Corps officers led to the establishment of a vigorously pursued and unusually productive series of investigations in medical entomology as related to military health needs. Because of this and other factors, projects in medical entomology represented a considerable proportion of the total research aggregate during the period. However, important findings were recorded in other fields as well. As in the previous period, Service personnel assigned to the Laboratory contributed materially to the program and conducted studies in many varied fields. Visiting scientists continued to find the facilities favorable for research. A brief summary of research accomplishments during the period is given by subject matter.

Malaria Studies: Principal efforts concerned the continuation of blood-film surveys and drug therapy in the Chagres River villages. The period witnessed various alterations in the program including control villages, control of anopheline breeding and the beginning in 1944 of DDT residual spraying in one of the treatment villages. On the whole, drug treatment was no more successful in reducing parasite rates and relapses than in the previous period. On the other hand the application to houses of four residual sprayings of 5 percent DDT in kerosene reduced the parasite rate in 7 months in the village of Gatuncillo by 50 percent. Drug treatment, however, had undoubtedly brought about a reduction in severe clinical cases of malaria and was therefore of value from that standpoint.

The complement fixation test was found superior to other serological tests for the diagnosis of malaria infections. Antigens prepared from blood cells of monkeys with heavy infections of *Plasmodium brasilianum* were sufficiently active to demonstrate malaria antibodies in sera of native individuals with a history of long continued malaria infections. However, such antigens were not of value for diagnosis of recently acquired infections. Antigens prepared from human malarial placentas gave much better results.

Other Protozoal Diseases: Trypanosomiasis. Of 1,626 individuals in 12 communities in Panama, 3.7 percent were positive on the complement fixation test for Chagas' disease. *T. cruzi* antigens produced by repeated freezing and thawing of cultures of formalized parasites were found superior to those prepared by extraction of the parasites or by their preservation in glycerin solutions. *T. cruzi* infection in the dog was found to simulate closely that in man. Cardiac lesions were encountered in fatal cases. *Triatoma dimidiata* was identified as the fourth vector in Panama.

In 1940 *Trypanosoma vivax* was found in Panama for the first time. A number of herds of cattle revealed average infection rates of between 20 and 30 percent. Sick animals exhibited fever, anemia, loss of appetite, edema, emaciation and weakness of the posterior extremities. The parasite could be passed to calves, goats and horses but not to other animals.

In *Trypanosoma hippicum* infection in rabbits, the proteolytic activity of the spleen increased in the earlier stages of the disease but in the terminal stage the activity was markedly diminished.

Intestinal Protozoal Infections: Relatively small doses of carbarsone failed to eliminate *Entamoeba histolytica* from carrier cases. A relatively large dose of 0.025 gram per kilogram of body weight twice daily for 10 days resulted in a clinical cure in frank cases of dysentery and in some cases was effective in eradicating the infection. In investigations involving 929 persons who had been served food and drink by carriers of *E. histolytica,* no evidence was found to support the belief that infected food handlers were important agents in the transmission of infection. In examination of 1,021 Navy personnel, the infection rate in the tropics was less than that encountered in the southeastern United States. However, a relatively high rate of 26.1 percent was noted in men returning from duty in the Orient. There was no evidence that transmission takes place on the Navy vessels studied. The existence of large and small races of *E. histolytica* was demonstrated with racial constancy both as regards size and physiological characteristics. The use of emetine hydrochloride in specially coated tablets given by mouth gave good results; 15 of 21 patients were freed of amoebae while four, which were not cured parasitologically, remained free of symptoms. A prevalence rate of 17.1 percent of *Dientamoeba fragilis* was found in one group of Navy personnel, the highest rate recorded from the United States up to that time. *Isospora hominis* was found for the first time in Panama.

Other Protozoal Infections: A species of *Toxoplasma* was reported for the first time from Panama. The parasite was responsible for epizootic disease among Army carrier pigeons.

Human and Animal Helminthology: The appearance of the eggs of *Capillaria hepatica* in human stools in Panama was explained by the finding of the parasite in the livers of a number of animals commonly eaten by certain natives in rural Panama.

Studies on 97 horses and mules revealed infection with 44 species of worm parasites. The most frequently occurring forms belonged to the Subfamily Strongylinae Railliet, 1893. Fifteen of the species accounted for about 98 percent of the strongylid parasites. Active verminous arteritis or aneurysm was found in about 80 percent of the animals. The lesions were due to the larvae of *Strongylus vulgaris* and were confined to the anterior mesenteric artery. *Trichostrongylus axei* was recovered from equines in Panama for the first time. Seven percent of house flies, *Musca domestica,* were found to carry the larvae of the equine stomach worms, *Habronema* sp. and *Drascheia* sp. A new parasite was found in captive monkeys and was responsible for a considerable number of deaths. The species was believed to be *Protospirura muricola* transmitted by the cockroach, *Leucophaea maderae.*

Medical Entomology: Details of the life cycle of *Anopheles albimanus* were worked out in a laboratory colony. Approximately 3 weeks were required for the development of one generation. *A. albitarsis* became infected to the extent of 4 percent when fed on *P. falciparum* gametocyte carriers compared to 32.7 percent of *A. albimanus. A. bachmanni* ($= A.$

triannulatus) could be infected but was not considered to be a significant vector because it feeds for the most part on animal blood. *A. punctimacula* feeds on both man and animals but is not an abundant species. *A. darlingi,* an efficient malaria vector, was found in British Honduras, Guatemala and Spanish Honduras.

Extensive studies were conducted in Panama and abroad in the prevention and control of insects of medical importance from a military standpoint by the cadre of Army Sanitary Corps officers stationed at the Gorgas Memorial Laboratory. These studies included repellents for mosquitoes, sandflies (*Phlebotomus* spp. and *Culicoides* spp.) and acarine mites and insecticides for the control of mosquito vectors of malaria, sandflies which transmit leishmaniasis, and the *Simulium* vectors of onchocerciasis.

In tests conducted in Peru and the Mediterranean area, DDT was discovered to be extremely effective in ridding houses of sandflies, *Phlebotomus* spp., and in area control by the spraying of rock fences and other structures of loose stone.

DDT was found to be 5 to 10 times more effective as a mosquito larvicide than Paris green.

Good protection against acarine mites was provided by clothing impregnated with various chemicals. A 4 percent solution of benzyl benzoate proved to be the most effective and retained some activity through four washings. This chemical also gave good protection against larvae and nymphs of the tick, *Amblyomma cajennense,* although efficacy was reduced by thorough laundering.

In tests in Guatemala, DDT in a concentration of 1 part to 10 million parts of water destroyed all larvae of the *Simulium* vectors of onchocerciasis for a distance of 10 kilometers down stream.

A 5 percent solution of DDT in kerosene painted on the inside and outside of screens gave almost complete protection against bites of *Culicoides* spp. for 50 days. Some protection was afforded even up to the 90th day.

In carefully controlled experiments in one of the Chagres River villages, residual sprays of 5 percent DDT in kerosene were applied to the inside and outside of houses at intervals of 4 months. After the third spraying, the ratio of anophelines in treated houses was 0.004 or only 4 anophelines against 1,000 in the control villages. In 7 months, the cumulative malaria parasite rate was reduced by 50 percent, a reduction far greater than that usually obtained by drug treatment.

The period witnessed the publication of numerous contributions to the taxonomy and distribution of insects of medical importance. One of the outstanding publications of the period was the monograph on "The Anopheline Mosquitoes of the Caribbean Region" by Sanitary Engineer Director W. H. W. Komp of the U. S. Public Health Service, who had been long assigned to the Gorgas Memorial Laboratory.

Activities of the Gorgas Memorial Institute 1936-1945

1936

Annual Meeting: The annual meeting of the Gorgas Memorial Institute was held in Washington on November 5, 1936. Dr. Bowman C. Crowell was continued as President and Admiral Cary T. Grayson as Chairman of the Board of Directors; Dr. George Crile was elected Vice President. Resolutions of sympathy were passed on the deaths of Dr. C. Jeff Miller, Sir Henry Wellcome and Dr. Ernst A. Sommer, former members of the Board of Directors.

Arrangements were underway for launching the Eighth Gorgas Essay Contest, the subject of which was "The Importance of Mosquito Control and the Gorgas Memorial." There is no information in the records concerning the winners of this contest.

1937

Annual Meeting: The annual meeting was convened in Washington on December 10, 1937. Dr. George Crile was elected President and Dr. Bowman C. Crowell Vice President; Admiral Cary T. Grayson was reelected Chairman of the Board of Directors.

Dr. Crile was born at Chili, Ohio, November 11, 1864. He received a B.S. degree from Ohio Northern University in 1885; A.M. in 1888; M.D. from Wooster University (now Western Reserve) in 1887; and A.M. in 1894. He was a student in Vienna in 1893, London in 1895, and Paris in 1897. His honorary degrees included Ph.D. from Hiram College in 1901; LL.D. from Wooster University in 1916; M.Ch. from University of Dublin in 1925; LL.D. from the University of Glasgow in 1928; Doctor honoris causa from the University of Guatemala in 1939.

Dr. Crile was Lecturer and Demonstrator in Histology, 1889-90, Professor of Physiology, 1890-93, and Professor of Principles and Practice of Surgery, 1893-1900 at Wooster University. He was Professor of Clinical Surgery 1900-1911, and Surgery 1911-1924 at Western Reserve University, Visiting Surgeon at Lakewood Hospital 1911-1924; and one of the founders of the Cleveland Clinic Foundation and Director of Research. Dr. Crile served as Brigade Surgeon Volunteers, and Major in Cuba and Puerto Rico, 1898; Major Medical Corps, O.R.C. and professional Director of U. S. Army Base Hospital No. 4, Lakeside Unit (B.E.F. No. 9) in service in France May 1917 to May 1918; Senior Consultant in Surgical Research May 1918 to January 1919; Lt. Colonel, June 1918; Colonel, November 1918; Brigadier General O.R.C., 1921; Brigadier General Auxiliary Reserve Corps 1929 to his death.

Dr. Crile received many honors during his career. He was awarded the D.S.M. (United States) 1919; Honorary Member Military Division, 3rd Class, Companion of Bath (British), 1919; Chevalier Legion of Honor

Fig. 6. The first five presidents of the Gorgas Memorial Institute of Tropical and Preventive Medicine.

Upper row left to right: William C. Braisted, Rear Admiral, MC, USN (Ret.), President 1921-1923. Franklin H. Martin, M.D., Chairman of the Board of Directors 1923-1925, President and Chairman of the Board of Directors 1925-1928, Chairman of the Board of Directors 1928-1935.
Center: Cary T. Grayson, Rear Admiral, MC, USN (Ret.), President 1928-1935, Chairman of the Board of Directors 1935-1938.
Lower row left to right: Bowman C. Crowell, M.D., President 1935-1937. George Crile, M.D., President 1937-1938, President and Chairman of the Board of Directors 1938-1940.

(French), 1922; Alvarenga Prize, College of Physicians, Philadelphia, 1901; Cartwright Prize, Columbia, 1897 and 1903; Senn Prize, A.M.A., 1898; American Medal for Service to Humanity, 1914; National Institute Social Sciences Medal, 1917; Trimble Lecture Medal, 1921; 3rd Laureate of Lannelongue Foundation (Lannelongue Nationale de Chirurgie de Paris), 1925; Cleveland Medal for Public Service, 1931; Distinguished Service Gold Key, American Congress of Physical Therapy, 1940.

Dr. Crile was a member of many medical societies both in the United States and abroad. He played a prominent role in many of these organizations and served as an officer at various times. He was author of numerous papers on surgery and allied fields, as well as 23 books.

Endowment Fund Deficit: An important item of business at the above meeting concerned a deficit of approximately $80,000 in the Endowment Fund of the Corporation. Apparently, the deficit originated because funds collected for an endowment fund were diverted to pay administrative costs and other expenses incurred in the fund raising campaigns. It had been anticipated that funds from such campaigns would be available to repay those diverted from the endowment fund. This was not realized. On the advice of counsel, the amount was charged off.

Ninth Gorgas Essay Contest: Announcement was made concerning the Ninth Gorgas Essay Contest. The contests were still being made possible through the generosity of Mr. and Mrs. Henry L. Doherty. The subject was to be "The Achievements of William Crawford Gorgas and Their Relation to our Health." A total of 18,074 essays were received from 720 public and parochial high schools in 48 states and the District of Columbia. The first prize winner was Miss Frances Babin of the South Side High School, Memphis, Tenn. The second prize went to Miss Genevieve Rourk of Messmer High School, Milwaukee, Wisconsin. President Franklin D. Roosevelt presented these prizes at the White House on May 16, 1938. This event regrettably marked the termination of the annual Gorgas Essay Contests.

These contests had inspired thousands of high school seniors to become knowledgeable of the great contributions of General Gorgas and the activities of the Gorgas Memorial Institute. One hopes also that they had been the means of instilling in these young people and those closely associated with them an added sense of patriotism and love of country and an awareness of the notable achievements of a past generation in conquering disease in the tropics, an accomplishment which permitted the completion of the most stupendous engineering feat of its time. In any event, the contests brought an incalculable amount of favorable publicity to the Gorgas Memorial Institute.

1938 At a special meeting of the Executive Committee on May 16, 1938, Dr. Clark, Director of the Gorgas Memorial Laboratory, was authorized to accept a part-time appointment as Consulting Director of the School of Animal Pathology at the University of Pennsylvania at an annual salary of $5,000, which amount was to be turned into the Gorgas Memorial Laboratory account.

Annual Meeting: The annual meeting of the Corporation was held in Washington on November 7, 1938. It was proposed that the position of Chairman of the Board of Directors, vacated by the death of Admiral Grayson, be combined with the office of the President. After favorable vote, suitable changes were made in the By-Laws.

At the meeting of the Board of Directors, resolutions were adopted on the death of Admiral Grayson. The Board approved the action of the Executive Committee in regard to Dr. Clark's part-time employment by the University of Pennsylvania. Dr. Crile was reelected President and Dr. Crowell Vice President.

Effort had been made without success to secure financial support for the Essay Contests after Mr. Doherty withdrew his sponsorship. Further consideration was to be given the matter.

1939 *Annual Meeting:* The annual meeting was held in Philadelphia, Pa. on October 20, 1939. Consideration was given to the advisability of inviting certain members of Congress to serve on the Board of Directors. The meeting was adjourned for further exploration of this move. It was reconvened in Washington on January 17, 1940, at which time Senator Lister Hill and Congressman William B. Bankhead, Speaker of the House of Representatives, were elected to the Board.

At the meeting on October 20, the By-Laws were changed to provide for a Board of Directors consisting of 45 individuals, of whom 34 would be elected members and 11 related directors. The related directors would be the heads of interested organizations.

At the annual meeting of the Board of Directors on October 20, 1939, a committee appointed to explore possibilities of obtaining support from Congress for continuing the Gorgas Essay Contests reported that it appeared impossible at the time to secure any such support.

Dr. George Crile was reelected President and Dr. Crowell Vice President. Dr. Crile reported on the successful public meeting held in Washington on April 15, 1938, and addressed by himself, Dr. Herbert C. Clark and Rear Admiral E. R. Stitt.

1940 *Annual Meeting:* The annual meeting of the Corporation was convened in Washington November 19, 1940. Dr. Crile requested the Vice President Dr. Bowman C. Crowell to take the chair, after which Dr. Crile announced that he did not feel he could continue to undertake the duties of President.

Certain changes were made in the By-Laws so that elected Directors would total 33 instead of 34.

At the annual meeting of the Board of Directors held on the above mentioned date, Dr. Hugh S. Cumming was elected President and Dr. Bowman C. Crowell reelected Vice President.

Dr. Cumming brought to the Presidency of the Gorgas Memorial Institute a wealth of experience in the field of tropical medicine.

Dr. Cumming was born in Hampton, Virginia, August 17, 1869. His education was obtained at Symmes Eaton Academy and Baltimore City College. He was graduated from the University of Virginia Department of Medicine, Charlottesville, in 1893 and from the University College of Medicine, Richmond, 1894, in which year he entered the U. S. Public Health Service as Assistant Surgeon. In 1899 he was promoted to Passed Assistant Surgeon and served as chief quarantine officer in the South Atlantic and San Francisco until 1906, when he became medical officer attached to the U. S. Consulate in Yokohama, Japan. While chief quarantine officer at Hampton Roads in 1911, he was promoted to Surgeon, in 1918 to Assistant Surgeon General and in February 1920 to Surgeon General. Subsequently he made a study of the pollution of navigable streams which was followed by an investigation of coastal waters along the Atlantic seaboard. During World War I he was detailed to the Navy as adviser in sanitation and later was sent to Europe in charge of public health service activities relating to sanitation, returning troops and the resumption of trade. He then served as president of the Inter-Allied Sanitary Commission to Poland, from where he was recalled to the United States to assume the position of Surgeon General of the Public Health Service in 1920. In 1945, on his 25th anniversary as director of the Pan American Sanitary Bureau, he received the Gold Medal from the Republic of Guatemala. He was president of the National Board of Medical Examiners from 1934 to 1936, president of the Southern Medical Association, 1930, American Public Health Association, 1931 and in 1924 the Association of Military Surgeons of the United States, from which in 1943 he received the Gorgas Medal. He was the recipient in 1936 of the Hartley Gold Medal of the National Academy of Sciences and in 1944 the William Freeman Snow Medal from the American Social Hygiene Association. He had represented the United States as head of the American delegation at the Pan American Sanitary Conferences at Lima, Peru; Havana, Cuba and Buenos Aires, Argentina; in 1919 he was a member of the Cannes Conferences and of the Advisory Committee of the League of Red Cross Societies; served as president of the fifth Pan American Conference of National Directors of Health and was a member of the American Delegation to the

Immigration Conference in Rome. He was head of the American delegation at the meeting of the Office International d'Hygiene Publique, which proposed the new International Sanitary Treaty, and a member of the international meeting which proposed the Pan American Sanitary Code. He was a member of the Permanent Committee of the Office International d'Hygiene Publique, and a member of the health committee, League of Nations, since its inception and vice president for many years. Dr. Cumming received the decoration of Commander of the Legion of Honor of France and the decoration Commander with Star, Polonia Restituta (Poland), and had been tendered the Order Al Mérito of Ecuador, the Order of Carlos Finlay of Cuba and El Sol of Peru. He also received decorations from Chile, Colombia, Dominican Republic, Haiti, and Mexico. Dr. Cumming's administration of the Public Health Service is credited with completion of the federal quarantine system, inauguration of pre-immigration examinations at American consulates, establishment of the national leprosarium at Carville, La., and national narcotic farms, the construction of eight marine hospitals and fostering scientific research.

The President nominated Dr. Cumming for a fourth term as Surgeon General, effective March 10, 1932. He retired from active duty on January 31, 1936, having served as an officer of the U. S. Public Health Service for 42 years, and as Surgeon General for 16 years. In addition to duties directly connected with the Public Health Service, Dr. Cumming was a member of the Board of Hospitalization formed by the President for the purpose of making recommendations concerning the expenditure of funds for the purchase and erection of hospitals used by the Veterans Bureau. He was a member of the board of visitors of St. Elizabeth's, Garfield Memorial and Columbia hospitals, chairman of the Section on Public Health Organizations of the White House Conference on Child Health Protection, honorary chairman of the Section on Public Health and Medicine, Eighth American Scientific Congress and an honorary fellow of the American College of Surgeons, American College of Physicians, Royal Society of Medicine, London, National Academy of Medicine, Peru, and the National Academy of Medicine, Mexico. He received the honorary degrees of Sc.D. from the University of Pennsylvania in 1930 and LL.D. from Yale University in 1933. Dr. Cumming was honorary professor at the University of Santo Domingo, honorary director of the National Public Health Service of Paraguay, member of the Medical Society of the Dominican Republic, member of the Sigma XI and other honor societies. He died on December 20, 1948.

1941   *Annual Meeting:* The annual meeting of the Gorgas Memorial Institute was held in Washington on November 24, 1941. Action was taken to terminate a trust agreement with the Chicago Title and

Trust Co. of Chicago for handling investments for the Corporation, because of the expense entailed by the relatively small sum involved.

The Board of Directors met after the adjournment of the Corporation meeting and elected Colonel Joseph F. Siler as President, and reelected Dr. Bowman C. Crowell as Vice President.

Colonel Siler was unusually well qualified to serve the Gorgas Memorial Institute. He had long been engaged in research in tropical medicine and had served with distinction in the Philippines and Panama. The following biographical sketch is taken from material he prepared at the time of his retirement from the Army, a document which is now in the National Library of Medicine's Historical Section.

Colonel Siler was born June 8, 1875 at Orion, Pike County, Alabama. He attended the Public Schools in Orion and Troy, Alabama, graduated from the State Normal College at Troy and completed his junior year at the Alabama Polytechnic Institute at Auburn (1892). He entered the Medical School of the University of Virginia in January 1896, graduating with the degree of M.D. in June 1898. He completed a 2-year rotating internship in the New York Post Graduate Hospital in New York City in August 1900 and immediately thereafter accepted a contract for active service in the Medical Corps of the Army as a Contract Surgeon. He was ordered immediately to the Philippine Islands, serving in northern Luzon from September 1900 to November 1901. On returning to the United States, he was assigned to duty at Ft. McPherson, Georgia. He was commissioned a First Lieutenant (Assistant Surgeon) in July 1903 and was ordered to the Army Medical School in November to take the Basic Course. After graduation the following April, he was assigned to duty at Ft. Logan, Colorado.

In 1905 Colonel Siler was again ordered to the Philippine Islands. He was on duty first at Ft. McKinley, Luzon and subsequently at Zamboanga, Mindanao, where he was Sanitary Inspector for the military station and the town of Zamboanga. He returned from the Philippines in November 1907, was assigned to duty at Ft. Des Moines, Iowa in June 1908, and was transferred to Ft. Slocum, New York. In a report to the Surgeon General of the Army (December 1908) of studies at Ft. Slocum, he showed that recruits from southern states had a high prevalence of hookworm disease whereas the disease was not encountered in individuals from northern states.

During the period March 1909 to November 1911, Colonel Siler was assigned to duty in New York City. During this period he gave lectures in tropical medicine and conducted a laboratory course in tropical diseases at the New York Post Graduate Medical School and Hospital, having served his 2-year internship in that hospital prior to service in the Army.

Between 1909 and 1911, he served on temporary duty for the following purposes: August-September 1909, Illinois State Hospital for the Insane at Peoria, investigating pellagra; January-March, and May 1910, London School of Tropical Medicine, as a student; April 1910, in Northern Italy investigating pellagra; August-October 1919, Illinois State Hospital for the Insane at Peoria, investigating pellagra; May-June 1911, West Point Military Academy as instructor in Military Hygiene.

Colonel Siler was on duty at Fort Sam Houston, Texas from November 1911 to April 1912. He was then ordered to New York to serve as Chairman of a Pellagra Commission organized by the Post Graduate Medical School for the purpose of investigating the epidemiology of the disease in the southern states. He served with this Commission from May 1912 to October 1915 with Field Headquarters at Spartanburg, S. C. During the period September-November 1913 Colonel Siler accompanied members of a British Pellagra Commission to Jamaica, Trinidad and Barbados.

From October 1915 to March 1916 Colonel Siler was a student at the Army Medical School taking the Advance Course in Tropical and Preventive Medicine. From April 1916 to Juiy 1917 he served as Director of the Department Laboratory, Southern Department, Ft. Sam Houston, Texas. In July 1917 he was ordered to New York to take command of Base Hospital No. 8 (New York Post Graduate Hospital) and sailed for France with that unit on August 7, 1917. In November 1917, he was relieved from duty as Commanding Officer, Base Hospital No. 8, and ordered to Neufchateau to organize and assume direction of the Division of Laboratories and Infectious Diseases, American Expeditionary Forces, and to develop a Central Medical Department.

Colonel Siler returned to the United States in June 1919 and during the period June 1919-August 1923 was on duty in the Office of the Surgeon General, first as Director of Laboratories and, subsequently, as Chief of the Division of Preventive Medicine and Laboratories.

He returned to the Philippine Islands in August 1923 and served until May 1925 as Chief of a Medical Department Research Board investigating the mosquito responsible for and the exact mechanism of transmission of the virus causing dengue fever.

Departing from the Philippine Islands in May 1925, Colonel Siler spent 2 months in China and Japan, and returned to the United States in July 1925. He was again assigned to duty in the Office of the Surgeon General as Director of the Division of Preventive Medicine and Laboratories, in which position he served until June 1929 when he was assigned to duty as Chief Health Officer, the Panama Canal, where he remained for 5 years. He returned to the United States in June 1934 and was Commandant of the Army Medical School, and Assistant Commandant of the Army Medical Department Professional Service School (beginning 1935), until June 1939 when he was retired on account of age.

In 1934 he and other members of the technical staff of the Army Medical School initiated an investigation of selected strains of the typhoid organism in the hope that it might be possible to find a strain that would give better protection than the strain in current use. Such a strain was found and has been used by the Army since 1939.

Colonel Siler was recalled to active duty in November 1941 and served as a member of a Retiring Board until February 1944 when he again reverted to a retired status.

Colonel Siler was member of many medical and professional organizations, among them: The American Society of Tropical Medicine, President, 1926, Honorary Member, 1948; the American College of Surgeons, Fellow; the American College of Physicians, Fellow; the American Academy of Tropical Medicine, President, 1938; the Washington Academy of Medicine, President 1942-43; the Medical Association of the Isthmian Canal Zone, President, 1931; Honorary Life Member, 1934; the Association for the Study of Pellagra, President, 1915. Many honors were conferred upon Colonel Siler; he received the Distinguished Service Medal, World War I Victory Medal, 1919; the Kober Award, 1939; and the Order of Vasco Núñez de Balboa, Comendador, Republic of Panama, 1946.

Colonel Siler died on February 7, 1960.

1942   *Annual Meeting:* The annual meeting of the Corporation was held in Washington on November 23, 1942. At the meeting of the Board of Directors, Colonel J. F. Siler was reelected President and Dr. Bowman C. Crowell, Vice President. At this meeting there was considerable discussion of a proposal to establish a graduate training program at the Gorgas Memorial Laboratory for health officials and technical personnel with the support of the Office of Inter-American Affairs. It was finally decided to hold the project in abeyance pending the successful completion of World War II.

Early in the year contracts were executed with the Office of Scientific Research and Development covering two national defense projects to be undertaken at the Gorgas Memorial Laboratory. One contract was for the testing of mosquito repellents by Senior Entomologist D. M. Jobbins. The second project was for the development of sero-diagnostic tests for malaria by Senior Protozoologist Carl M. Johnson.

Trust Agreement: The Trust Agreement with the Chicago Title and Trust Company of Chicago was formally terminated on February 2, 1942. The total Institute funds so invested amounted to $8,000. The net receipts from the investment were $5,784.63 in cash with the balance represented by certificates of beneficial interest in two liquidating trusts. Any additional returns would depend on successful liquidation of the trusts. A net loss of $1,000 was anticipated in addition to the loss of interest during past years. At the same time, pledges secured in past years, were written off as uncollectable.

Dr. Clark's contract as Director of the Gorgas Memorial Laboratory was renewed at a reduction in salary of $1,400 at his request, in order that salary increases could be granted to Dr. Johnson, Dr. Fairchild and Mr. Jobbins.

Capital Investments: The market value of the capital investments of the Gorgas Memorial Institute was reported to be approximately $32,500. The Executive Committee expressed the view that the Riggs National Bank should be authorized to supervise investments with the approval of the Committee. Negotiations to this end were authorized.

Accounting Procedures: It was pointed out by President Siler that the accounting system was extremely complex and involved maintaining two bookkeeping systems, one in Washington and one in Panama. Consolidation seemed desirable and was to be effected if approval of Institute auditors and the General Accounting Office could be obtained. The Executive Committee was also authorized to review the By-Laws with the view of eliminating archaic provisions and revising pertinent portions in keeping with the current objectives of the Institute.

1943   *Annual Meeting:* The annual meeting was convened in Washington on November 22, 1943. At the meeting of the Board of Directors, Colonel Siler was continued as President and Dr. Crowell as Vice President.

In the report of the President, it was stated that no further developments had occurred in the establishment of the Inter-American University in Panama, in which it had been proposed that the Gorgas Memorial Laboratory have a part.

Losses in personnel at the Gorgas Memorial Laboratory due to war-time conditions were alleviated through negotiations with the Surgeon General of the Army. Lieut. Graham B. Fairchild was assigned to the Laboratory and other Army personnel were supplied to conduct research of military importance.

It was found impossible to change then current accounting procedures because of the phraseology of Acts of Congress. The matter was referred to Counsel Maurice H. Thatcher and Mr. William B. Oliver of the Executive Committee for further study and recommendations.

Canal Zone Fund: It was brought out at the meeting that in 1926 residents of the Panama Canal Zone had raised a fund of $2,116.46 for medical research in Panama. This sum was given to the Gorgas Memorial Laboratory with the provision that it be employed for this purpose. The fund had been kept intact but involved bookkeeping inconveniences. With the permission of those members of the Donor Committee who could be reached and by resolution of the Board of Directors the money was transferred to the investment account of the Institute.

1944 *Annual Meeting:* The annual meeting of the Corporation was held in Washington on November 27, 1944. At a concurrent meeting of the Board of Directors, Colonel Siler and Dr. Crowell were reelected to the positions of President and Vice President, respectively.

The matter of the two sets of accounts, mentioned at the previous meeting, was again discussed. It developed that the Committee appointed to investigate the situation found that a change could not be instituted because of basic laws. It was felt that the matter was not of sufficient importance to justify a request to Congress at that time.

A School of Tropical Medicine: A lengthy discussion was held concerning the pros and cons of establishing a School of Tropical Medicine at the Gorgas Memorial Laboratory. The return of military personnel from overseas with various tropical diseases already was regarded as a possible hazard. Many physicians in the United States were unfamiliar with most of these diseases, a fact which might be responsible for incorrect diagnoses and spread of these infections. The cessation of hostilities and the end of the war would add substantially to the influx.

The desirability of establishing a School of Tropical Medicine was recognized but it was pointed out that the number of tropical diseases in Panama was actually limited and that clinical material for some important conditions was not and would not be available there. Importation of diseased persons for clinical instruction would not be feasible because of quarantine regulations of the Panama Canal and the inherent danger of spread of infection within the country itself.

After extended remarks, a resolution was adopted authorizing the President to appoint a committee to give further study to the proposal.

1945 *Annual Meeting:* The annual meeting was held in Washington on November 26, 1945. At the meeting of the Board of Directors, Colonel Siler was reelected President and Dr. Crowell Vice President.

The Proposed School of Tropical Medicine: The Committee appointed by President Siler to consider the establishment of a School of Tropical Medicine in connection with the Gorgas Memorial Laboratory met on several occasions.

Senator Lister Hill, Chairman of the Committee, had appointed a Sub-Committee to study the matter further. Dr. R. E. Dyer was named as Chairman of the Sub-Committee which held two meetings and reported its conclusions to the full Committee. The recommendations stated that it would be impractical to maintain such a school in Panama because of the lack of variety and volume of tropical diseases. However, it was concluded that the Isthmian area would lend itself well as a location for a School of Public Health and Hygiene.

The establishment of such a school would entail an estimated expenditure of $750,000 to $1,000,000 for buildings and operational costs of $250,000 to $400,000 per year. It appeared that support could not be granted from funds from the Medical Corps of the Army and Navy and the Public Health Service. Likewise, it was problematic that financial support would be forthcoming from Latin American countries. It was not thought that Congress would be sympathetic toward providing the necessary funds. The full Committee concurred in the conclusions of the Sub-Committee.

Expansion of Gorgas Memorial Laboratory: It was agreed that any expansion of the Gorgas Memorial Laboratory should be confined to research activities. It was suggested that efforts be made to encourage the Army, Navy and Public Health Service to assign personnel to the Laboratory. Mr. Thatcher was named as Chairman of a Sub-Committee to contact the Surgeons General of the above-mentioned organizations who in reply expressed sympathy toward the proposal.

Mr. Thatcher's Sub-Committee recommended also that the Executive Committee appoint a special Committee to "make such further entailed study, as may seem necessary or desirable, and to prepare and submit to the proper committees of Congress such measure or measures expanding the Laboratory activities and providing funds therefor, as may seem to the special Committee desirable; and to take all action that may seem appropriate to bring about enactment of the desired legislation."

This report was approved.

Chapter 4.

The Intermediate or Post-War Years
1946-1955

The Gorgas Memorial Laboratory; Research Programs; Changing Directions; New Objectives; New Approaches to Malaria Control; Virus Diseases; Yellow Fever Appears; Activities of the Gorgas Memorial Institute

"All the wide world is little else, in nature
But parasites or sub-parasites."
—BEN JONSON, VOLPONE, ACT III.

1946 The year 1946 marked the virtual end of the wartime studies on the control of insect vectors of diseases of military importance, which had been conducted by a cadre of Army Sanitary Corps officers. Major Hertig continued on duty. Capt. Charles D. Michener departed on January 25, 1946. Capt. G. B. Fairchild was discharged on July 31, 1946 and later returned to his civilian position at the Laboratory. First Lieut. Harold Trapido was separated from Army service on August 21, 1946 and at the close of his terminal leave joined the staff as a biologist. First Lieut. Dale W. Jenkins, who reported for duty at the Laboratory on December 30, 1945, departed on April 11, 1946. Sanitary Engineer Director W. H. W. Komp, U. S. Public Health Service continued on duty.

Malaria Studies: The malaria treatment project in certain Chagres River villages was continued for the 16th year for the following stated reasons: (1) The regular blood-film surveys offered a measure for the entomological experiments in progress at the Juan Mina and Santa Rosa Field Stations and also provided local health officers with statistics on rural malaria; (2) it provided an opportunity for studies on cyclical variations in malaria incidence; and (3) it assisted in the protection of Canal Zone, Army and Republic of Panama personnel in nearby locations.

The village of Agua Clara was removed from the atebrin treatment group, which then consisted of Santa Rosa, Guayabalito, Madronal and Las Guacas. In addition, the village of Camarón continued to receive enhanced atebrin dosage. This village was sprayed twice during the year with DDT.

Gatuncillo continued to receive atebrin but houses were sprayed with DDT. The village of New San Juan continued on a quinine regimen. The control villages consisted of Río Pescado and Mendoza. There was no change in the treatment regimens during the year.

The following presents information regarding parasite rates in the various villages during 1945 and 1946:

Village	Monthly parasite Rates		Cumulative parasite Rates	
	1945	1946	1945	1946
Chagres River, four villages (atebrin)	10.3	13.7	27.6	33.3
New San Juan (quinine)	13.0	12.2	27.0	27.6
Mendoza (control)	3.0	4.8	7.0	11.2
Camarón (enhanced atebrin)	8.7	4.7	29.1	17.8
Río Pescado (control)	12.2	13.7	26.5	44.6

The data appeared to indicate a rise in the malaria rate in the control villages together with a slight increase in the rates in the four Chagres River villages receiving atebrin treatment. On the other hand, there was a marked decrease in the rates in Camarón, in which DDT was applied to houses twice during the year. Separate rates for Gatuncillo were not available for the year 1945; hence the effect of DDT usage in this village during the year cannot be determined.

Comparative relapse rates for 1945 and 1946 are given below:

Village	Relapse Rate	
	1945	1946
Atebrin group (four towns)	29.2	39.5
Quinine group	33.8	33.7
Gatuncillo (atebrin and DDT)	21.7	11.7
Camarón (atebrin and DDT)	34.9	34.1
Río Pescado (control)	16.6	40.0
Mendoza (control)	29.4	13.7

There was an increase in the relapses in the four Chagres River villages but no increase in New San Juan, the quinine treated village. Gatuncillo in which DDT was first employed in 1945 showed a marked drop in the relapse rate which on the other hand was not noted in Camarón in which DDT was also used. Comparisons on a 2-year basis are probably not significant.

Medical Entomology: During November and December 1945, while on temporary duty in Washington, Major Hertig compiled for the Office of the Surgeon General of the Army a history of the *Phlebotomus*-borne diseases in American troops during World War II. Major Hertig also acted as technical consultant in the production of an Army film on *Phlebotomus*-borne diseases. Capt. Fairchild completed a paper on Panamanian Tabanidae, including a description of a number of new species and adding several others to the list of species known from the Republic.

Capt. Michener continued his studies on acarine mites. *Eutrombicula batatas* [= *Trombicula (Eutrombicula) batatas*] was found to be the most common species of chigger mite in open grassy areas in Panama. The larvae feed on a wide variety of birds and mammals. Larvae of *Eutrombicula vanommereni* [= *Trombicula (Eutrombicula) alfreddugèsi*] and *E. helleri* [= *Trombicula (Eutrombicula) goeldii*] were found on reptiles, birds and mammals. *Trombicula panamensis* [= *Trombicula (Leptotrombidium) panamensis*] was found on rats. *Trombicula (Megatrombicula) alleei* [= *Blankaartia alleei*] and *T. (M.) velascoi* [= *Blankaartia velascoi*] were recovered mainly from birds. Difficulty was encountered in rearing *T. (E.) batatas* and *T. (E.) alfreddugèsi*, although Lieut. Jenkins had greater success in rearing *T. (E.) batatas* and *B. alleei*.

Lieut. Trapido continued his experiments with residual house spraying with DDT in Gatuncillo. The quantity required was approximately 1 to 1.5 gallons of 5 percent solution of the chemical in kerosene per 1,000 square feet. Anophelines visiting sprayed houses were affected in three ways, as follows: (1) A large reduction in the numbers of mosquitoes; (2) a marked reduction in the percent of anophelines which engorged; (3) the 24-hour survival rate in engorged mosquitoes was low for 3 months following spraying. Under the conditions of the experiment, the cost per house was calculated at $1.31. A DDT-xylene-triton emulsion used inside houses was found to be extremely irritating because of the xylene content.

Trials with DDT were inaugurated in the town of Natá, where the houses were made of quincha with roofs of native tile, thatch or galvanized iron. The clay surfaces of the quincha walls apparently absorbed the oil solution with a consequent crystallization of the DDT so that the material was less toxic to mosquitoes than similar solutions applied to the cane walls of the Chagres River villages. The problem was to find some other mixture of DDT which would obviate the objections of the kerosene solution.

Sanitary Engineer Director W. H. W. Komp continued to serve as consultant to a number of organizations interested in malaria control. In behalf of the Institute of Inter-American Affairs, he visited field parties in Bolivia and Brazil to advise on methods of making malarial surveys and conducting mosquito control.

Miscellaneous Activities: Col. H. S. Eakins, Veterinary Corps, U. S. Army, Chief of the U. S. Military Mission to Panama, continued to use the facilities of the Laboratory until his retirement on July 4, 1946. Seven cases of equine encephalitis due to an undetermined cause were observed in a herd of horses. A third case of trypanosomiasis due to *Trypanosoma hippicum* was found in a dog.

The snake census was continued by Dr. Clark. Up to September 1945, a total of 13,442 specimens had been collected, of which 3,201, or 23.8 percent, represented poisonous species. In all, 15 species of poisonous snakes were represented in the collection.

Professor A. S. Romer, Department of Comparative Anatomy, Harvard University, used the facilities of the Juan Mina Station during the year.

1947   The year 1947 was marked by increasing activity. The malaria control program was considerably altered for the purpose of taking advantage of new antimalarial drugs and the additional testing of residual insecticides.

Malaria Studies: During the year, the program comprised six villages plus three new ones employed for the first time. The program was then constituted, as follows:

1. Santa Rosa received atebrin only at a dose rate of 0.1 gram 3 times a day for 5 days to parasite positives. No DDT was employed and there was no larval control.

2. New San Juan received quinine 15 grains a day for 5 days to positives with no DDT and no larval control.

3. Gatuncillo, Guayabalito, Las Guacas and Madronal comprised the group in which all houses were sprayed with DDT 3 times during the year. In addition, all malaria positives found on bimonthly surveys received chloroquine 0.3 gram of base 1 day each week for a month. Acutely ill persons received additional treatment. Children received a suitable dose of aralen.

4. Camarón was continued on atebrin 0.1 gram 3 times a day for 5 days. In addition, on 1 day each week between the blood-film surveys, the group found positive was each given three atebrin tablets of 0.1 gram. Each treated person, therefore, received 24 atebrin tablets during the month. All houses were sprayed with DDT.

5. Río Pescado continued as a control village with quinine or atebrin available on request.

6. Mendoza, another control village, was in the same status as Río Pescado.

7. Three new Gatun Lake villages, Ciricito, Lagarterita and Cuipo, were added to the program during the year. The first two towns were placed on mass chloroquine treatment on February 6, 1947 at the rate of 0.3 gram of base per week. Children were given aralen in a dose of 0.25 gram or 0.15 gram of base. The third village, Cuipo, was started on mass treatment with paludrine 0.1 gram per week on May 15, 1947. After the first month's experience, it was necessary to double the dose.

In the long established program, the following were the average bi-monthly or monthly and cumulative parasite rates:

Group	Average bimonthly or monthly rates	Annual cumulative rate
Atebrin (Santa Rosa)	12.3	40.4
Quinine (New San Juan)	7.4	20.0
Chloroquine and DDT (Gatuncillo, Guayabalito, Las Guacas, and Madronal)	7.9	22.3
Río Pescado (control)	16.7	26.8
Mendoza (control)	4.6	10.3
Camarón (enhanced atebrin and DDT)	5.7	22.8

In Ciricito, results were available after 30 weeks of chloroquine treatment. At the beginning of the therapy, 92, or 26.2 percent, of 351 inhabitants had malaria parasites. At the end of 30 weeks, the rate was 2 percent.

In Lagarterita, the malaria rate on October 4, 1946 was 43.5 percent. On that date, 1,000 tablets (0.1 gram) of atebrin were left in the school in Ciricito and Lagarterita. In Lagarterita at the end of 30 weeks of chloroquine treatment, the malaria parasites were present in 10, or 5 percent, of 200 persons.

In Cuipo, where paludrine was given, the initial blood-film survey of 271 persons revealed malaria parasites in 109, or 40.2 percent. At the end of 3 months of paludrine treatment, the rate was 8.9 percent.

Both chloroquine and paludrine proved to be valuable but the former appeared to give somewhat better results.

The studies on the effectiveness of residual DDT house sprays for malaria control, initiated in 1944, were continued by Dr. Trapido, although on a somewhat more restricted scale. While entomological studies of the DDT treated village, Gatuncillo, in the Chagres River group indicated that malaria transmission was at a very low level, this was not wholly substantiated by the results of the malaria surveys. The discrepancies were probably due to the great amount of transient movement into and out of the village. Effort was made to reduce the impact of transient movement by using malaria rates which were based on individuals examined at least 5 or 6 times. The following is a summary of the residual DDT spray program together with the status of drug therapy in the sprayed villages.

Gatuncillo—Sprayed in November 1944, March and July 1945, January, May, and December 1946, and May 1947.

Guayabalito—Used as a control until 1947 when it was sprayed in January and May.

Santa Rosa—Unsprayed control village until September 1947.

The following is a summary of drug treatments given to the inhabitants of these villages:

Gatuncillo—On atebrin until September 1946 after which it was on chloroquine.

Guayabalito—On atebrin until September 1946 after which it was on chloroquine.

Santa Rosa—On atebrin.

The following table gives a comparison of malaria rates in the three Chagres River villages, based on the cumulative rate in individuals examined either 5 or 6 times during the year.

Village	Total number of individuals	Number examined 5 or 6 times	Percent positive of those examined 5 or 6 times
Santa Rosa			
1945-46	116	58	43.1
1946-47	126	61	55.7
Guayabalito			
1945-46	71	28	57.1
1946-47	46	26	19.2
Gatuncillo			
1945-46	67	32	34.4
1946-47	65	34	20.6

The rate in the unsprayed village of Santa Rosa remained high. There was a marked reduction in the rate in Guayabalito following application of DDT to houses in January and May 1947. In Gatuncillo, in spite of chloroquine treatment and house spraying, the results were disappointing. While there was a reduction from 34.4 to 20.6 percent, the rate was higher than the low rate of 14.3 percent after the initial spraying in 1944. It was believed that the increased rate reflected the acquisition of malaria while inhabitants were away from their native village.

Medical Entomology: Laboratory experiments were conducted on the effectiveness of DDT wettable powders on quincha surfaces. Such powders proved to be of distinct advantage over DDT in kerosene. However, formulations of various manufacturers varied considerably as regards the rate of settling in water. Further inquiry was being made to find a formulation which would not clog filters and nozzles of hand-pumped knapsack sprayers.

Dr. Trapido spent the month of June in Puerto Rico as a consultant on the malaria control program. He also served as consultant on the Republic of Panama control campaign under Mr. Pedro Galindo.

Studies were conducted on mosquito distribution in the Chagres River area as affected by DDT residual spraying. By characterization of the eggs, it was found that the two *Anopheles* of the *Nyssorhynchus* group could be distinguished. Behavior patterns could then be followed. During the latter part of the wet season *A. triannulatus* was the abundant species while *A. albimanus* was dominant during the dry season. A study was initiated on the crepuscular activities of *A. albimanus* in the field. Light value, temperature, humidity and air movement will be recorded. Precipitin tests indicated that more than 80 percent of engorged *A. albimanus* in the Chagres River area had fed on man.

Major Hertig returned to Peru on March 11 to check on the DDT experiments on the control of *Phlebotomus* carried out over a year and a half before. Nineteen months after the application of the insecticide, sandflies in the rural houses were extremely scarce. In two area control experiments, few flies could be found and new cases of cutaneous leishmaniasis were negligible; there had been no new cases of bartonellosis since the spray program.

Virus and Rickettsial Diseases: A laboratory was established during the year for the study of virus and rickettsial diseases in cooperation with the Panama Health Department. Dr. Enid C. de Rodaniche was placed in charge. A second case of Q fever was diagnosed and a strain of *Rickettsia prowazeki* ($=$ *R. typhi*) was isolated from a sporadic case of endemic typhus fever. The occurrence of many cases of nervous disease of unknown etiology was thought to be associated with equine encephalomyelitis; however, protection tests in mice against the eastern strain of this virus proved negative, as did attempts to isolate a neurotropic virus from spinal fluid and autopsy material.

Sanitary Engineer Director W. H. W. Komp, U. S. Public Health Service was transferred to the National Institutes of Health, Bethesda, Md. on August 7, 1947 having been on duty at the Gorgas Memorial Laboratory for 16 years and 4 months. During this time, he published some 25 papers on malaria control and the taxonomy of Central and South American disease-carrying mosquitoes.

1948   The personnel of the Laboratory at the end of the year numbered 32. The scientific staff was increased to seven. Dr. Marshall Hertig at the completion of his service in the Army of the United States joined the staff of the Laboratory and continued his studies on *Phlebotomus*. Mr. Pedro Galindo, chief of the antimalaria/campaign of the Department of Public Health of the Republic of Panama, continued on the laboratory staff as liaison member on malaria control. Señora Teresina P. de Pinzón was assigned duties in connection with the projected tuberculosis survey of certain rural towns in Panama to be followed by a 5-year study on the results of the BCG vaccination of tuberculin negative individuals.

Malaria Studies: The year marked the 18th in which studies had been carried on with drug treatment in the Chagres River villages. Chloroquine treatment was continued in adults with children receiving aralen. All treatment villages were sprayed 3 times during the year with 5 per cent DDT in kerosene. The control villages, Río Pescado and Mendoza, were not sprayed and drugs were available only on request. The seacoast town of Camarón received the same drug treatment as above but was sprayed only once with DDT.

Average parasite rates during the year based on bimonthly blood films were, as follows: Six Chagres River villages 3.6; Camarón 3.0; Río Pescado 10.4 and Mendoza 4.7. The annual cumulative rates were, as follows: Six Chagres River villages 14.5; Camarón 12.0; Río Pescado 17.4; and Mendoza 9.4.

Studies were continued on the use of chloroquine and aralen in the Gatun Lake villages of Ciricito and Lagarterita and paludrine in the village of Cuipo. The initial malaria rate in the first two villages of 26.5 per cent had been reduced at the end of one year's mass treatment to 0.7 per cent. In Cuipo, the initial rate of 34.8 per cent had fallen at the end of that time to 1.5 per cent.

Virus and Rickettsial Diseases: Dr. Rodaniche experimentally infected *Amblyomma cajennense* with *Rickettsia burneti* (= *Coxiella burnetii*) during the larval stage. Infection was transmitted to guinea pigs by feeding during the nymphal and adult stages but transovarian passage was not obtained. In a study of 26 cases of atypical pneumonia and fever of undetermined origin, two were identified as due to *R. burneti* (= *Coxiella burnetii*). The organism was isolated from one case. *Taxoplasma* was isolated from Panamanian guinea pigs, the first time the organism was recognized other than in imported animals.

Dr. Carlos Calero, research associate of the Laboratory, reported an epidemic of 13 cases of murine typhus in Panama City between January 15 and February 5, 1947. The same author reported in 1948 the first case of cutaneous myiasis due to *Sarcophaga haemorrhoidalis* and *Cochliomyia hominivorax*.

Tuberculosis Survey: In cooperation with the Division of Tuberculosis, Health Department of the Republic, a survey of tuberculosis was instituted in the Gatun Lake villages in which malaria studies were being conducted. Señora Teresina P. de Pinzón undertook the studies with the view of determining tuberculosis rates in rural Panama, preparatory to a BCG vaccination campaign.

Medical Entomology: From June to October 1948 Dr. Hertig carried out sandfly studies in Greece and Crete, as well as in Italy, under the sponsorship of the World Health Organization. An evaluation was made in terms of *Phlebotomus* control accomplished by the extensive DDT-malaria control campaign which had been in progress in Greece since 1946. In unsprayed places the sandfly population was normal in abundance and distribution of species when compared with reports of previous observations. Sprayed buildings were uniformly negative for *Phlebotomus* of any species. Night observations out-of-doors showed sandflies to be at a very low level within sprayed areas. The reduced sandfly abundance in the cities of Athens and Canea, Crete, which had not been sprayed *in toto,* may have been due in part to the peripheral effect of the many treated buildings scattered through the urban areas, and in part to the use of household sprays.

A very marked decline in kala azar had occurred prior to the use of DDT and was associated with the destruction of infected dogs. However, a sharp drop in oriental sore with the development of relatively few cases in the last 2 years coincided with the introduction of DDT in 1946.

Dr. Hertig visited a recently initiated project for the control of oriental sore in the Abruzzi, Italy and made observations on the supposed vector, *P. perfiliewi.* The use of residual DDT had resulted in a marked reduction in the sandfly population. In Sardinia, where every man-made structure had been treated with DDT, houses were negative 8 to 9 months later and sandfly occurrence was at an extremely low level. It was concluded, as the result of the observations, that treatment of interiors with residual DDT gives immediate and virtually complete protection from sandflies indoors and reduces the *Phlebotomus* population within the sprayed areas to near the vanishing point.

Dr. Fairchild continued studies on *Phlebotomus* in Panama. Thirty-three species had been identified, of which 17 appeared to be new. Distribution and habits of the 16 known species were summarized. In addition, species collected in various countries by staff members and others were studied.

The national malaria control campaign was continued under the supervision of Mr. Pedro Galindo with the cooperation of Dr. Harold Trapido. The latter modified the Lofstrand sprayer so that it was suitable for use with DDT water suspensions as well as with kerosene solutions. DDT in both formulations proved very effective in rapidly decreasing malaria transmission. However, it was evident that residual insecticides alone would not solve the malaria problem in Panama because of the fact that the rural population was not grouped in well defined communities but was scattered over widely spaced areas. Twenty percent of the total population was widely dispersed. It was decided to supplement the residual spraying with drug treatment following methods which Dr. Clark found to be successful in the Gatun Lake villages.

Dr. Trapido conducted studies on the normal feeding habits of *A. albimanus* because of his observations on the modified behavior of this species in DDT sprayed houses. In erect test subjects, it was found that 96.3 percent of the alightings of this mosquito were on the lower extremities which represented only 40 percent of the body surface. In supine subjects, the alightings on the lower extremities represented only 5.2 percent of the total. In subjects in both positions at 1 and 2 meters above the ground, there was a decline in the number of alightings but not a complete cessation as was expected. It was concluded that changes in the circulation brought about by the varied positions of the body probably influenced the number and position of the alightings.

Experiments were also conducted by Dr. Trapido with new herbicides on aquatic vegetation which favored breeding of malaria vectors. The herbicide 2,4-D gave variable results with different plant species. It was most effective against the water hyacinth, *Eichornia crassipes*. However, recovery ensued within 3 months.

Dr. Trapido visited Colombia and Venezuela as a consultant on problems of yellow fever and malaria.

1949   Research objectives of the Laboratory were materially altered by the recognition in January 1949 of yellow fever as the cause of death of five patients in Santo Tomás Hospital in November and December of 1948. These cases came from an area above Pacora, 10 to 15 miles east of Panama City, and occurred in farmers in contact with the jungle. The diagnosis of yellow fever led the Pan American Sanitary Bureau to organize a Yellow Fever Service under Dr. K. O. Courtney, Assistant to the Chief Health Officer of the Panama Canal. Cooperating in this Service were the Department of Public Health, Republic of Panama, the Panama Canal, the United States Army, the United States Navy, and the Gorgas Memorial Laboratory.

The appearance of yellow fever at this time brought to mind and emphasized the significance of the finding of yellow fever immunes in Darien Province in 1937.

The role of the Gorgas Memorial Laboratory concerned cooperation in the antimalarial campaign which was extended to include an *Aedes aegypti* eradication campaign, an investigation of animal reservoirs of jungle yellow fever, studies on forest canopy mosquitoes as regards speciation and distribution and attempts to isolate yellow fever virus from such mosquitoes.

The DDT campaign was intensified between May 1 and August 31, 1949 when 25,000 houses in 200 communities had been sprayed. It was estimated that by the end of the year, a total of 50,000 houses would have been treated. *Aedes aegypti* was practically eliminated from Panama and malaria rates in the Republic and the Canal Zone were the lowest ever recorded.

Yellow Fever Investigations: The appearance of three new fatal human cases of yellow fever along the transisthmian highway in the Buena

90

Vista area, between Madden Dam and Colón, during the month of August 1949, led to an intensification of the studies on forest mosquitoes as transmitters of the infection and a search for animal reservoirs. In January 1949 a cooperative program for the study of vectors had been established under the supervision of Mr. Pedro Galindo representing the Department of Public Health of Panama, Lt. Col. Stanley J. Carpenter, M.S.C. of the Office of the Surgeon, Caribbean Command, United States Army, and Dr. Harold Trapido representing the Gorgas Memorial Laboratory. A series of seven stations were selected in diverse types of forest habitats. It was hoped to secure a sample of the forest mosquito population fluctuations from sea level to ridge tops in the area of known jungle yellow fever occurrence east of Panama City, from the central part of the Isthmus and the Atlantic side, where there was a large increase in rainfall over that experienced on the Pacific side. The operation of the stations was begun in February 1949, and was to be continued for 1 year.

Only tentative results appear in the Laboratory report for 1949. However, certain of the forest mosquitoes thought to be vectors of jungle yellow fever in South America had already been collected in Panama. *Haemagogus spegazzinii falco* Kumm et al. (= *Haemagogus capricornii falco*) was found in some numbers and *Aedes leucocelaenus* Dyar and Shannon proved to be an abundant species. The most common species encountered were *Haemagogus lucifer* Howard, Dyar and Knab and *Haemagogus equinus* Theobald.

On March 15, 1949, the Coordinator of the Yellow Fever Service requested the Gorgas Memorial Laboratory to undertake a survey of aboreal forest mammals in order to determine the wild animal reservoirs of yellow fever virus. Dr. Clark directed a team of hunters. Between March and September 1949 nine expeditions were made in that part of the Republic of Panama which lies east of the Canal Zone; later the remainder of the Republic was to be covered. Seventeen species of aboreal mammals were represented in the collections. Preliminary laboratory data indicated that 41 of the first 116 animals collected were positive on the mouse-protection test for yellow fever. The positives included black howler, marmoset, cebus, red spider and night monkeys and the kinkajou. Negative findings were obtained in the case of the 3-toed sloth, the anteater, a squirrel, porcupine, ocelot and collared peccary.

Rickettsial disease studies by Dr. Enid de Rodaniche were continued in the early part of the year. Two new strains of *Rickettsia mooseri* (= *R. typhi*) were isolated from human blood. Experimental transmission of Q fever by *Amblyomma cajennense* was completed. Most of the year was occupied by studies on yellow fever virus. Protection tests were performed on the blood sera of 14 patients in local hospitals, of whom 7 were found positive. A project was initiated for attempted isolation of yellow fever virus from wild-caught aboreal mosquitoes. A total of 1,063 attempted isolations were made from five species of mosquitoes. Tests were conducted on the immune status of animals purchased for yellow fever studies. Of 44 monkeys, 5 were positive; 23 other animals representing eight species were all negative.

BCG Vaccination Program: Activities were continued under the direction of Señora Teresina P. de Pinzón with headquarters at the Gorgas Memorial Laboratory, in cooperation with the Servicio de Vacunación BCG of the Government of Panama. From February to August 31, 1949, a total of 5,194 persons attended the vaccination clinic in Panama City and 147 the clinic in Colón.

The tuberculosis survey was continued in the Gatun Lake villages of Ciricito, Cuipo and Lagarterita, in cooperation with the Antituberculosis Campaign Section of the Department of Health of the Republic of Panama. A total of 1,048 persons in the three villages were tuberculin tested, of whom 621, or 59.3 percent, were positive. No previous accurate data were available on the prevalence of tuberculosis in rural Panama.

BCG vaccination was carried out on 128 persons in Ciricito, 122 in Cuipo and 129 in Lagarterita with material prepared by the BCG Laboratories of the Consejo Nacional de Tuberculosis in Havana, Cuba. Varying results were obtained with different lots of vaccine. The diminution in the efficacy of the vaccine, as measured by its capacity to convert non-reactors to reactors to tuberculin, was thought to have been caused by maintaining the vaccine at room temperature for prolonged periods of time. Delays were also encountered in transmission by air mail from Havana.

Medical Entomology: Dr. Trapido returned to Puerto Rico in May 1949 for further consultation on the project involving the bionomics of *Anopheles albimanus*. Collections of *Phlebotomus* spp. indicated widespread distribution in Puerto Rico; members of the genus were also collected in St. Thomas, Virgin Islands. Dr. Trapido and Dr. Fairchild were called to active Army duty for 30 days in May and June to conduct *Phlebotomus* surveys in the West Indies. The sandflies were found in 13 localities in Jamaica, eight in Cuba, two in Haiti and 10 in the Dominican Republic. Until recently, *Phlebotomus* was thought to be absent from the West Indies; the present limited observations would indicate that members of the genus are well distributed.

Studies on the taxonomy of *Phlebotomus* were continued by Dr. Hertig and Dr. Fairchild. A new taxonomic character for the genus was discovered. The sclerotized plates (sternites) on the ventral side of the abdomen, and particularly those of the second segment, exhibit a distinctive pattern. This observation would seem to provide an additional character of importance in the identification of species in this genus.

Dr. Fairchild departed on September 8, 1949, on leave of absence, to give a graduate course in medical entomology at the University of Minnesota during the academic year.

Malaria Studies: Malaria observations were continued in the Chagres River villages for the 19th consecutive year. All villages were sprayed with DDT and positive inhabitants were treated with aralen. There were no noteworthy changes in malaria incidence.

Malaria treatment was continued in the Gatun Lake villages of Ciricito, Lagarterita and Cuipo. The supply of chloroquine was exhausted and aralen was substituted in the first two places. Cuipo was continued on paludrine. Blood films were taken every two months. Treatment was in the hands of local persons hired for that purpose. Between March and September 1949, of 294 persons examined 4 times in Ciricito and Lagarterita, 1.7 percent were positive for malaria parasites. The rate in Cuipo was 3.1 percent in 130 individuals.

Visiting Scientists: Dr. Lloyd E. Rozeboom, The Johns Hopkins University, spent 4 weeks in July and early August studying *Anopheles oswaldoi.*

1950   The year's activities substantially followed the course of the 1949 research program, with increasing emphasis on yellow fever studies, on potential vectors among forest mosquitoes and search for wild animal reservoirs of the virus.

Yellow Fever Investigations: The survey of aboreal forest animals for reservoirs of jungle yellow fever was continued. Main areas studied were in western Panama between the Panama Canal and the border of Costa Rica, although the survey of eastern Panama from the Panama Canal to the boundary of Colombia instituted last year was completed. Blood specimens taken from animals at the site of the kills were forwarded to the Carlos Finlay Institute in Bogotá, Colombia, for the mouse-protection test. Live wild animals caught or purchased were tested at the Gorgas Memorial Laboratory.

In the eastern region of Panama, 201 animals were collected of which 104, or 51.7 percent, were positive for yellow fever antibodies. Fifteen different species were represented. As before, positive tests for immunity were found mainly in various monkey species, although one 3-toed sloth, one ocelot and one conejo pintado were positive. Of 224 animals taken in the western zone, 68, or 30.3 percent, were positive. Positive tests were encountered mainly in various monkeys, although 1 of 2 opossums was positive. In order to secure more definitive information on active foci of the disease, a separate record was kept concerning the mouse-protection tests in infant and juvenile animals. In both regions of Panama, 57 young animals were taken, of which 14, or 24.6 percent, were positive.

The attempted isolation of yellow fever virus from wild-caught mosquitoes was continued by Dr. Rodaniche. A total of 4,395 mosquitoes of 5 different species were tested by the method of intracerebral inoculation of young Swiss mice with suspensions of macerated mosquitoes. From the end of September 1949 to the beginning of January 1950, 2,723 mosquitoes representing 20 separate catches were received from the collecting station at Pacora, and 1,672 mosquitoes representing 25 separate catches from the station at Buena Vista. Both of these stations were in areas from which yellow fever patients had come. In addition, 7 monkeys negative for neutralizing antibodies for yellow fever were exposed to *Haemagogus spegazzinii falco* (= *Haemagogus capricornii falco*) from the Pacora station and 4 negative monkeys to the same mosquito from the Buena Vista station. There was no evidence of infection in any of these animals. One native red spider monkey was exposed to natural infection at the Pacora station from December 5, 1949 to January 6, 1950. This monkey showed no evidence of yellow fever infection and was subsequently negative on the mouse-protection test. Mosquito catches were too small to offer definite conclusions with the exception of *Haemagogus lucifer*. The data would seem to indicate that this species was not a vector in Panama or that yellow fever was not active in the areas studied between October 1949 and January 1950.

Field studies on forest mosquitoes were continued by Mr. Galindo, Dr. Trapido and Lt. Col. Stanley J. Carpenter. *Haemagogus equinus* and *H. lucifer* proved to be not only the most abundant representatives of the genus in the areas studied but also greatest numbers of these species were taken at the stations nearest the places of exposure of the fatal human cases. Both were sufficiently aboreal to satisfy the requirements of a jungle yellow fever transmitter. On the other hand the peak of abundance of these species occurred during the first part of the rainy season when the human cases did not occur, although *H. lucifer* did demonstrate a second lesser peak later in the rainy season when the human cases did appear. *H. lucifer* was at higher levels during the months of August, September, November and December when all but one of the fatal human cases occurred than was *H. spegazzinii falco* (= *H. capricornii falco*), the proved South American vector. While low in numbers, the latter species was present throughout the rainy season. The fact that the number of recognized yellow fever cases in the area was relatively small may have influenced the negative virus findings.

Aedes leucocelaenus appeared to be as abundant as *H. spegazzinii falco* (= *H. capricornii falco*) and from an ecological standpoint would seem to fit the requirements of a vector. Other mosquitoes would not appear to be involved with the single exception of *Sabethes chloropterus.* The ecology of the latter would seem to favor it as a possible vector, although there was at the time no laboratory evidence of its capability to transmit the virus.

Plans were made to continue the study with the establishment of collecting platforms in certain localities in western Panama and adjacent Costa Rica.

Chagas' Disease: At the request of the Pan American Sanitary Bureau, a survey for the presence of Chagas' disease in western Panama was instituted by Dr. Johnson and Mr. Galindo. As part of the survey, triatomid bugs were collected from five localities. *Rhodnius pallescens* and *Triatoma dimidiata* were the species represented. Forty percent of the *Rhodnius* captured in houses were found infected with a herpetomonad flagellate similar to the intermediate stages of *Trypanosoma cruzi,* and three guinea pigs were successfully infected with this strain.

Medical Entomology: Field collections of *Phlebotomus* were extended to parts of Panama not previously covered. The introduction of the Shannon light trap proved to be of distinct advantage over other apparatus. The number of species known from Panama were 53, of which only four were on record prior to the institution of the present studies. Ten Panamanian species are known to bite man.

During the period February to May 1950, Dr. Hertig conducted a survey for leishmaniasis and vectors in Paraguay under the auspices of the International Health Division, U. S. Public Health Service. He was assisted by Mr. C. H. Wharton, an American mammalogist and two Paraguayans, Dr. Alejandro Arce Q. and Dr. Jorge Ottaviano. Field studies were carried out in the two areas of the heavily forested region where mucocutaneous leishmaniasis was endemic. Between 4,000 and 5,000 *Phlebotomus* were collected; the list of three previously known species was extended to 15. Data were collected on the ecology of *P. whitmani,* which was very abundant and bites man freely. In a search for animal reservoirs of leishmaniasis, almost 270 mammals were trapped and autopsied. Of the material examined thus far, no lesions of leishmaniasis were encountered. A considerable number of agouties were obtained with lesions reported in Brazil to be due to leishmaniasis. However, *Leishmania* could not be demonstrated in the lesions.

Dr. Harold Trapido was assigned to the International Health Division of the Rockefeller Foundation for the period April 20 to September 28, 1950, for the purpose of advising on the program for the eradication of *Anopheles l. labranchiae* from Sardinia.

BCG Vaccination Program: Señora Teresina P. de Pinzón continued the studies with headquarters at the Gorgas Memorial Laboratory. The vaccination program was continued in Panama City and Colón and two new areas were added, one in the town of Chorrera and one in Bocas del Toro Province in cooperation with the Medical Department of the United Fruit Company. Up to August 1950 tuberculin tests were carried out on 14,266 individuals, of whom 5,667 were positive and 8,599 negative. BCG vaccinations were given to 5,473 new-born infants and 8,297 persons who had been tuberculin tested. Post-vaccinal allergy was tested in 5,689 persons, of whom 5,571 were positive and 118 negative. Revaccinations were done in 98 individuals. Of a total of 379 individuals vaccinated between December 1948 and July 1949, 274 were tuberculin tested. The number of positives considerably exceeded the number of negatives, although it appeared from the latter that the vaccinations were not as effective as might have been anticipated.

The program of tuberculin testing and BCG vaccination was continued in the Gatun Lake villages of Ciricito, Cuipo and Lagarterita. School children in another village, Cerro Cama, were added to the program.

Malaria Studies: Malaria control in the Chagres River villages was continued for the 20th year. The seacoast town of Camarón was dropped from the program. In the other villages, the same drug treatment was continued and houses were sprayed 3 times during the year with 5 percent DDT in kerosene. Control villages received aralen on request but were not sprayed. Results were not especially noteworthy compared to past findings. Low residual malaria rates continued in all villages.

The Gatun Lake villages were continued under observation with aralen being employed on a voluntary basis in Ciricito and Lagarterita and paludrine in Cuipo. At the end of the 2-year period in which the drugs were administered under supervision, the rate for towns in which chloroquine and aralen had been used was 0.7 percent, while the rate for the paludrine town was 1.5 percent. Under this year's voluntary use of the drugs, the rates were 2.2 and 4.4 percent, respectively.

Snake Census: Dr. Clark continued the snake census of Panama. From 1929 through 1950, a total of 13,611 snakes had been collected, of which 3,234, or 23.8 percent, were poisonous varieties.

1951 Research projects were continued without notable change from the previous year.

Yellow Fever Investigations: At the request of the Pan American Sanitary Bureau, a team headed by Dr. Clark conducted investigations in southern Mexico to determine whether yellow fever had occurred in monkeys in the area in recent years. Collections were made in the general vicinity of Palenque and Cintalapa in the State of Chiapas. Because of the absence of refrigeration and the remoteness of the areas, some of the blood specimens proved unsatisfactory for mouse-protection tests. Of 40 monkeys taken near Palenque, two were positive and 14 definitely negative. Tests in others were inconclusive. Of 37 monkeys collected near Cintalapa, one was positive and 24 negative. Blood sera from 74 of 77 monkeys were tested also by the National Yellow Fever Service, Rio de Janeiro, Brazil. The same three sera found positive at the Gorgas Memorial Laboratory were also reported positive by that Service. In addition, nine other specimens were positive.

A report of the death of monkeys near the village of Chorcha in Chiriqui Province of Panama led to an investigation which collected nine howler monkeys all of which proved to be negative on mouse-protection tests for yellow fever.

Dr. Rodaniche continued search for yellow fever antibodies in live forest animals. A total of 91 animals were examined, including 75 monkeys and 16 others. Of the total number, three were positive. One of these was a red spider monkey which had been captured near Gatuncillo; another a black spider monkey from the Bayano River area; and the third a 2-toed anteater taken in Curundu in the Canal Zone. Yellow fever virus was isolated for the first time during the current outbreak in Panama from a 25-year old male from the Province of Bocas del Toro near the Costa Rican border.

Studies on forest canopy mosquitoes were continued by Dr. Trapido and Mr. Galindo and extended into western Panama and adjacent Costa Rica. In all, some 72,000 mosquitoes were collected attacking man, and were identified. A total of 41,000 of these were from the forest floor and 31,000 from the forest canopy. The proved yellow fever vectors, *Haemagogus spegazzinii falco* (= *Haemagogus capricornii falco*) and *Aedes leucocelaenus,* were found to be distributed in the area indicating that there was no natural barrier to limit the westward spread of yellow fever through western Panama and southern Costa Rica. Human yellow fever fatalities occurred in the latter country from April to July 1951, thus confirming epidemiological findings of the mosquito survey. Because of the occurrence of additional cases of the disease in the Almirante area of Panama in April 1951, collecting stations were established for further studies of mosquito ecology.

Other Virus and Rickettsial Diseases: Dr. Rodaniche was able to isolate three strains of poliomyelitis virus during an epidemic of the disease, the first to be recorded in Panama. The disease was transmitted to local howler monkeys, *Alouatta palliata aequatorialis* (= *A. villosa*). *Rickettsia rickettsii* was isolated from a fatal case of Rocky Mountain spotted fever.

Chagas' Disease: The investigations were continued by Mr. Galindo and Dr. Johnson. Serological surveys were conducted in 10 localities in five Provinces of the Republic. Results on over 2,000 blood specimens indicated a very spotty distribution of the infection. Domiciliary collections of triatomid bugs were carried out in many of the above localities. The collections consisted mainly of *Rhodnius pallescens* with fewer specimens of *Triatoma dimidiata* and *Panstrongylus geniculatus*. An aboreal species, *Triatoma dispar,* was taken in some areas during the mosquito surveys. A large percentage of *R. pallescens* proved to be infected with *Trypanosoma cruzi.*

Medical Entomology: The work on the collection and classification of *Phlebotomus* sandflies, together with field observations, was continued. Some 10,250 specimens were processed during the year, of which about 5,000 were collected during Dr. Hertig's leishmaniasis investigations in Paraguay last year. Ten new species were identified from Panama, making a total of 60 recognized from that country. The *Phlebotomus* studies have provided something of a pattern concerning distribution and habits which may be of importance in the epidemiology of leishmaniasis. Of the eighty-odd Central American species, 12 are known to bite man, and five of these are rather common in forested areas. Three of the five bite man readily during day and night. These three species extend from the northern to the southern limits of endemic areas of leishmaniasis in the Western Hemisphere.

BCG Vaccination Program: This was continued under the direction of Señora Teresina P. de Pinzón. The Chitre District, Herrera Province, was added to the program. Pre-vaccinal tuberculin tests were conducted on 13,744 individuals, of whom 5,961 were positive and 7,783 negative. A total of 13,508 persons received BCG vaccinations and post-vaccinal tuberculin tests were carried out on 7,099 persons, of whom 6,923 were positive and 176 negative.

Malaria Studies: Dr. Clark's malaria investigations were continued for the 21st year. The same procedures were employed as in the 3 previous years.

It seems well to review at this time the history of these investigations. The initial thick blood-film survey in 1929 of five Chagres River villages revealed 45.6 percent positive for malaria. From 1930 to 1934, inclusive, all positives found on regular blood surveys were treated with quinine; plasmochin was added beginning in 1932; at the close of this period the positive rate was 21.6 percent. From 1935 to and including 1947, all positives were treated with atebrin and plasmochin. Following this regimen, the positive rate dropped to 10.1 percent. Three features, independent of drug application, assisted in the control of malaria. These included application of chemicals to destroy vegetation in contiguous streams; the Panama Canal continued to employ Paris green or DDT over a large part of the Chagres River near the experimental villages; and experimental use of DDT was initiated. Beginning in 1948, houses in the Chagres River villages were sprayed regularly with DDT 3 times a year and in 1947 the treatment of positive cases was changed to chloroquine or aralen. The average monthly rate for malaria dropped to 3.6 in 1948, 2.2 in 1949, 1.06 in 1950, and less than 1.0 percent in 1951.

Visiting Scientists: The following utilized the facilities of the Laboratory for varying periods of time during the year:

Dr. Clay G. Huff, Naval Medical Research Institute, National Naval Medical Center, Bethesda, Maryland.

Prof. Frank A. Hartman, Ohio State University, Columbus, Ohio.

Dr. Paul Allen, Research Department, United Fruit Company.

1952   The BCG vaccination program inaugurated in January 1949 under the direction of Señora Teresina P. de Pinzón was transferred to the Servicio Cooperativo Interamericano de Salud Pública. Señora Pinzón resigned as director on December 31, 1951 but continued on duty until April 1952 in order to train field vaccinating teams.

At the request of the Division of Medicine and Public Health of the Rockefeller Foundation, Dr. Harold Trapido returned to Sardinia for several months as consultant in the compaign designed to eradicate *Anopheles l. labranchiae* from that island.

From April 21 to July 17, Dr. Marshall Hertig was in Korea as a member of a research team from the Armed Forces Epidemiological Board to study epidemic hemorrhagic fever.

Virus and Rickettsial Diseases: Dr. Rodaniche completed the survey of live forest animals for yellow fever antibodies, a survey which was begun in 1949. Blood from a total of 267 animals was examined; these included 209 primates and 58 other species of mammals. A total of 12, or 5.7 percent, of the primates were positive, including 5 of 85 squirrel marmosets, 6 of 45 spider monkeys, and 1 of 35 night monkeys. Five of the 6 spider monkeys were juveniles probably 8 to 18 months of age, thus indicating recent transmission of yellow fever virus in the areas concerned. One of the immune monkeys came from Darien Province, where human immunes were found in 1937.

The 58 non-primate animals examined represented 15 different species. A strongly positive reaction was obtained in one pigmy anteater, *Cyclopes didactylus,* from the Canal Zone and a tentative positive in two agouties, *Dasyprocta punctata.* In the latter two cases, conclusions could not be drawn because of the apparent non-specificity of the protection test in non-primates.

An outbreak of poliomyelitis of unprecedented proportions between August 1950 and April 1951 provided opportunity for a study of strains. During this period, 142 cases were reported in the Republic, a rate of 51 per 100,000. Twenty-nine cases were non-paralytic and 104 paralytic. Nine deaths occurred, all from the bulbospinal type. Three strains of virus were isolated in the monkey, *Macaca mulatta,* one from the spinal cord, and two from the feces. It was possible to infect two species of native monkeys, *Alouatta palliata* (= *A. villosa*) and *Cebus capucinus,* with rhesus passage cord.

By means of animal pathogenicity cultivation in chick embryo and cross-immunity studies, Herpes simplex virus was identified from a rapidly fatal case of encephalitis in the Canal Zone.

Isolation of *Rickettsia rickettsii* was made from a fatal case of Rocky Mountain spotted fever from Ollas Arriba, north of Capira, Republic of Panama. This was the third case from this locality. Dr. Fairchild and Mr. Galindo collected three species of ticks from the area, *Amblyomma cajennense, A. oblongoguttatum* and *Otocentor nitens* (= *Anocenter nitens*). Dr. Rodaniche recovered a highly virulent strain of *R. rickettsii* from a group of 11 adult *A. cajennense* from a horse brought to Ollas Arriba from the hills beyond Caimito.

Yellow Fever Investigations: Mr. Galindo and Dr. Trapido continued their observations on forest canopy mosquitoes with collecting stations at Cerro La Victoria, Arraiján and near Almirante in the Province of Bocas del Toro. In the month of May 1952 a 1-year study was completed at four tree collecting stations near Almirante. A total of 21,186 mosquitoes were captured. Of these, 13,627 were taken at the forest floor; only 22 were *Haemagogus* and 21 *Aedes leucocelaenus.* The *Haemagogus* mosquitoes consisted of 15 *H. equinus,* five *H. lucifer* and two *H. spegazzinii falco* (= *H. capricornii falco*). Of a total of 7,559 mosquitoes collected in the forest canopy, 552 were *H. equinus,* 571 *H. lucifer,* 792 *H. spegazzinii falco* (= *H. capricornii falco*), and 295 *Aedes leucocelaenus.*

Medical Entomology: The work on the collection and classification of *Phlebotomus* sandflies was continued throughout the year. An interesting observation was the collection of an aboreal species at the stations in the Almirante area. This species was abundant and bit man readily. One of the tree-top collectors contracted cutaneous leishmaniasis.

A total of 6,317 Tabanidae were collected mostly at the yellow fever collecting stations near Almirante. Eight new species were identified making the total number of species known from Panama to be 118.

Fig. 7. Tree platform at Cerro La Victoria, Republic of Panama, for the collection of aboreal mosquitoes in the studies on the epidemiology of yellow fever.

Malaria Studies: Observations were conducted by Dr. Trapido on the behavior of *Anopheles albimanus* in the Chagres River villages after the employment of DDT residual sprays for 8 years. It was found that gross numbers of the mosquito in dwellings were no longer drastically reduced and the selective killing of engorged females was no longer evident. Evidence indicated that if these changes were due to resistance to DDT, such resistance was of a very low order and not detectable by customary tests. There was the suggestion that a strain had evolved which was hyper-irritable to DDT and possessed an enhanced positive phototropism. The mosquitoes no longer rested on walls of houses long enough to obtain a lethal dose of DDT but tended to accumulate around kerosene lamps. Relatively few females were successful in obtaining a blood meal. Laboratory experiments were to be devised for further studies.

Drug therapy was continued in the Chagres River and Gatun Lake villages as in the previous year. There were no notable changes in malaria rates during the year.

1953   During the year, Dr. Marshall Hertig was on leave of absence as field director of the Commission on Hemorrhagic Fever in Korea.

Yellow Fever Investigations: The extension of yellow fever northward in Central America led to additional studies on forest canopy mosquitoes. At the request of the Pan American Sanitary Bureau, collecting stations were established in the following places:

Nicaragua: East of Villa Somoza and a point 20 kilometers southwest of Managua.

Honduras: The Lancetilla Valley inland from the port of Tela.

Guatemala: Three fincas near Iztapa and at a point near Palín.

Mexico: Teapa, Tabasco State.

Preliminary observations at Villa Somoza, Nicaragua, indicated the presence of *Haemagogus spegazzinii falco* (= *Haemagogus capricornii falco*) but the absence of *Aedes leucocelaenus.* Since yellow fever was present in this area in 1952, the occurrence of the latter species is apparently not necessary for transmission. *Haemagogus* of the *mesodentatus* series, morphologically related to *H. spegazzinii falco* (= *H. capricornii falco*) were found in the deciduous tropical forest and open mesquite as far north as Tapachula, Mexico. This finding seemed to open a new vista in the epidemiology of the disease.

During the year, Dr. Rodaniche studied the immune status of 34 monkeys from the Chepo-Pacora section to determine whether yellow fever virus was still active in the locality of the outbreak in 1948. All monkeys were negative with the exception of one in which the test was inconclusive.

Malaria Studies: In further studies on behavioral alterations in *Anopheles albimanus* in DDT sprayed Chagres River villages, Dr. Trapido found that the MLD of DDT to these mosquitoes was not significantly different from that of the stock laboratory colony, which had no prior contact with DDT.

Dr. Clark continued his malaria studies in the Chagres River villages for the 23rd year. There were no changes in drug regimens or DDT spraying. Malaria rates rose during the year. While the cumulative annual rate during the previous 3 years had ranged from 2.3 to 3.3 percent, in 1953 the rate was 8.0 percent. In adults the rate for 3 previous years averaged 2.5 percent, whereas in 1953 it was 9.9 percent. The figures for children were 2.7 and 6.2 percent, respectively. It remained to be seen whether changes in behavioral patterns in *A. albimanus* could account for the difference.

Dr. Clark instituted new drug studies in the isolated village of Río Indio on the Atlantic coast of Panama about 20 miles west of the Canal Zone. A new formulation (Win-1258) containing 30 mg. of primaquine and 300 mg. of plaquenil was employed. Dosage varied with the body weight, the above being the average adult dose. Treatment was administered weekly to 42 adults and 51 children for from 20 to 26 weeks. After the first 3 weeks, only six were found positive for malaria parasites. The initial rate was 52.2 percent. Treatment ended on March 5, 1953. Sixteen weeks later the rate in 42 adults was 14.3 percent and that in 53 children was 24.5 percent. No toxic effects were observed.

Medical Entomology: Dr. Fairchild continued studies on *Phlebotomus* and Tabanidae. A total of 31,759 specimens of the former were received from yellow fever stations near Almirante. A number of papers were published.

Visiting Scientists: The following individuals utilized facilities of the Laboratory during the year:

Dr. Libero Ajello, Communicable Disease Center, Atlanta, Georgia.

Prof. Donald Griffin, Harvard University.

Mr. Prentice Bloedel, Harvard University.

Dr. Frank A. Hartman, Ohio State University.

Dr. Leslie W. Scattergood, Food and Agriculture Organization, United Nations.

1954 June 30, 1954 marked the retirement of Herbert C. Clark, M.D., Director of the Gorgas Memorial Laboratory for 25 years and 6 months. Dr. Clark was succeeded by Carl M. Johnson, Sc.D., M.D.

It seems fitting to review at this juncture the achievements of Dr. Clark during this period. As the first director, he was responsible for transforming a concept and an idea into a practical reality.

When he came on duty on January 1, 1929, Dr. Clark's first task was to supervise alterations in the building in Panama City, the gift of the Republic of Panama, in order to make it suitable for laboratory purposes. In spite of the time required for this project, he conducted a considerable amount of research. In 1929, field surveys for malaria and blood-sucking arthropods were carried out in 45 locations in Panama and the Canal Zone.

The relatively modest funds provided by Congress for the operation of the Laboratory did not allow for the employment of a large professional staff. To offset this deficiency in part, Dr. Clark adopted a plan of encouraging the use of the Laboratory by visiting scientists from various universities and medical schools. As a result, during the first 5 years, a total of 18 investigators from eight different institutions spent varying periods of time at the Laboratory. Research subjects covered many fields including malaria, intestinal helminths and protozoa, trichinosis, filariasis, medical bacteriology, medical entomology, herpetology, fisheries, anthropology and animal behavior.

In keeping with the original concept of the incorporators of the Gorgas Memorial Institute, the Uniformed Services of the U.S.A. assigned to the Laboratory during this period a total of five officers for extended tours of duty. In addition, seven members of the scientific staff of the Panama Canal rendered assistance at various times.

The visiting scientists provided valuable contacts and helped to augment the research output of the Laboratory. However, some of the investigations were not correlated with the Gorgas program and nearly all were of short duration. Research conducted by officers from the Uniformed Services probably represented more substantial adscititious contributions. Such projects were more closely allied to Laboratory programs and time was available for extended observations. There were of course exceptions in both cases.

In spite of the fact that Dr. Clark had spent so much of his professional life at the laboratory bench, he seemed from the very beginning of his days with the Gorgas Memorial Laboratory to show a distinct propensity to take to the field. The primeval jungle, its streams, its fauna and its people seemed to have a peculiar fascination for him. Certainly, it was here that he made his greatest contributions to tropical medicine. Previously a pathologist, now he became largely an epidemiologist.

Dr. Clark possessed an amazing ability to work with native peoples. He thoroughly enjoyed contacts with them and he dearly loved his monthly and bimonthly trips to the Chagres River villages where he conducted malaria control studies for almost 25 years. Any field trip was a highlight to him.

Even while with the Board of Health Laboratory and the United Fruit Company, he had been interested in field work. Perhaps the inclination was intensified because of a realization that so little was known concerning the epidemiology of diseases endemic in Panama. Thus, he visualized that this was a field which would provide quick and handsome returns, a visualization which proved to be correct.

During the war years, research in military preventive medicine received his fullest support. From his long time field observations he had an acute awareness of the importance of such problems. The appearance of yellow fever in Panama in 1948 renewed his interest in this disease. His background and experience contributed incalculably to the studies on its epidemiology in Panama and Central America. The role of the Gorgas Memorial Laboratory in this research probably represented one of its outstanding achievements.

Like many other pathologists, Dr. Clark's interests were catholic. He made notable contributions to such diverse subjects as malaria, Chagas' disease, equine trypanosomiasis, equine verminous aneurysm, equine periodic ophthalmia, tuberculosis, amoebiasis, relapsing fever, herpetology and medical practice and climatology in the tropics. Furthermore, he actively supported research in the Gorgas Memorial Laboratory in these and many other equally diverse fields. Dr. Clark served as a continual inspiration to his staff. Under his aegis, the record of achievement was impressive.

His place in the hearts of the people of Panama is best exemplified by the honors bestowed upon him on the occasion of his retirement. Both the Municipal Council of the City and the National Assembly of the Republic of Panama passed resolutions of appreciation for Dr. Clark's contributions to the welfare of the people of the city and the nation.

Following his retirement, Dr. Clark moved to Allentown, Pa. to be near his son, Dr. John W. Clark. He died on November 8, 1960.

In his eighty-second year, Dr. Clark was signally honored by the American Foundation for Tropical Medicine. At the annual dinner of the American Society of Tropical Medicine and Hygiene in Indianapolis, Indiana, on October 30, 1959, Dr. Clark received the Foundation's Richard Pearson Strong Medal. The citation accompanying the Medal read as follows:

"PIONEER IN MEDICINE for more than half a century: TIRELESS INVESTIGATOR of diseases of man and beast in the tropics; STALWART GUARDIAN of malaria ridden villages of the Chagres River, bringing health to its humble victims; STIMULATOR OF RESEARCH at the bedside, in the laboratory and at the diseases' lair in the bush; RELENTLESS PURSUER of the yellow fever virus, harassing it throughout the jungles of Middle America; INQUISITIVE PATHOLOGIST who makes lesions, microscopic and gross, divulge their morbid secrets; BELOVED TEACHER of his juniors, colleagues and seniors at the autopsy table, international rostrum and hotel lobby, whose kindly wit helps to firmly fix biologic principles."

Dr. Carl M. Johnson, who succeeded Dr. Clark as Director, had his first tour of duty at the Gorgas Memorial Laboratory in 1931 while a teaching fellow at the Johns Hopkins University School of Hygiene and Public Health. He joined the staff in 1934 and continued on duty through 1944 when he resigned to attend the Medical School at Leland Stanford University.

Dr. Johnson's early association with the Gorgas Memorial Laboratory, his subsequent long tour of duty as a staff member, his knowledge of the traditions and workings of the institution and his familiarity with the Panama scene rendered him unusually adapted for the directorship. Also he had served as Assistant Director from 1935 through 1944.

Dr. Johnson was born in York, Pa. on August 13, 1905. He took his baccalaureate degree at Mt. Union College in 1929, an Sc.D. at Johns Hopkins in 1931 and an M.D. degree at Leland Stanford in 1949. He interned at the Stanford Hospital and returned to Panama as a resident in pathology at the Gorgas Hospital, a position he held until 1951 when he became pathologist at the same institution. From 1951 to 1953, he served as Chief Health Officer of the Canal Zone Government, Panama.

Dr. Johnson was held and still holds many consulting positions. His consultantships include the Gorgas Hospital, United Fruit Co., Middle America Research Unit of the National Institutes of Health, and Santo Tomás Hospital. He has served as a member of the Advisory Committee on Tropical Medicine of the National Academy of Sciences-National Research Council. In 1962, he was Clinical Professor of Tropical Medicine at the Louisiana State University Medical School. Since 1956 he has been Profesor Extraordinario ad honorem at the University of Panama School of Medicine.

Dr. Johnson is a member of many scientific and medical societies and a diplomate of the American Board of Preventive Medicine. He was the recipient of the Robbins Award in 1962 and has been decorated by the Republic of Panama with the Order Vasco Núñez de Balboa.

There was little change in the research activities of the Gorgas Memorial Laboratory during 1954. Dr. Marshall Hertig was still in Korea on leave of absence as Director of the Commission on Hemorrhagic Fever of the Armed Forces Epidemiological Board. Dr. Fairchild spent 11 weeks in museums in London and Paris studying Tabanidae.

Yellow Fever Investigations: Collections of forest canopy mosquitoes were continued at the previously described stations in Nicaragua, Honduras, Guatemala and Mexico. On the basis of collections for 1953, it was thought that the northern distribution limits of *Aedes leucocelaenus* were in the basin of the Río San Juan, between Costa Rica and Nicaragua. In 1954, the species was identified in northern Nicaragua and from the north coast of Honduras. Although not of common occurrence, *Haemagogus spegazzinii falco* (= *Haemagogus capricornii falco*) was found at Lancetilla in Honduras.

Haemagogus mesodentatus from Costa Rica and El Salvador was found to represent three forms, whose relationship had not yet been clearly defined. *H. anastasionis,* another member of the *H. spegazzinii* (= *H. capricornii*) group, was common in collections on the Pacific Coast of Nicaragua during the course of an epizootic in monkeys thought to be due to yellow fever. The only other species of *Haemagogus* present was *H. equinus.*

In July and August, Mr. Galindo and Dr. Trapido investigated cases of mortality in monkeys in the vicinity of La Masica on the northern coast of Honduras. Deaths were found to be due to yellow fever, the first time in a quarter of a century that the disease had been known to occur in Honduras. The only species of *Haemagogus* taken from the area was *H. equinus;* other aboreal mosquitoes included *Trichoprosopon magnum, Sabethes chloropterus* and small numbers of other sabethine species.

Laboratory results indicated that there was a greater dry season activity of *Haemagogus* and *Aedes* populations, as measured by egg deposition, than could be judged by the number of mosquitoes biting man.

H. equinus was cultivated in the laboratory and material was available for attempts to establish colonies of *Sabethes chloropterus, H. spegazzinii falco* (= *H. capricornii falco*), *H. mesodentatus,* and *Aedes leucocelaenus.* It was hoped to evaluate the role of these species as vectors of yellow fever in Panama, Central America and Mexico.

Studies on Poliomyelitis and Rickettsial Diseases: With the cooperation of Dr. C. W. Jungeblut of Columbia University, Dr. Rodaniche extended previous studies on various strains of poliomyelitis virus. Spider monkeys were found to be susceptible to Col SK virus and all three of the Type I strains tested. However, the monkeys were completely refractory to Type II and Type III strains.

Two species of Panama monkeys, the marmoset, *Saguinus geoffroyi* and the night monkey, *Aotus trivirgatus,* were found to be extremely susceptible to *Toxoplasma* infection. Thirty-one marmosets and 15 night monkeys developed a uniformly fatal illness with death in 3 to 11 days after exposure by various inoculation routes. The marmoset proved highly susceptible also to inoculation by dropping the organisms on the conjunctiva.

Malaria Studies: Studies in the Chagres River villages were continued for the 24th consecutive year. There were no changes in drug treatment and DDT was continued as in the past. It will be recalled that last year, there had been an increase in the malaria rate in the villages, which was thought possibly to be associated with changes in behavioral patterns in *Anopheles albimanus.* This year there was no further increase in the rate but for the first time in 5 years an infant was found positive.

Dr. Clark conducted an evaluation of pyrimethamine (daraprim) in the village of Nuevo Vigía situated on Madden Lake 2 miles from the transisthmian highway. Suppressive treatment was started on January 20, 1954 and continued until May 19, 1954. The drug was given in a weekly dose of 25 mg. for adults and children over 2 years of age. Younger children were given one-half of this dose. The malaria rate prior to treatment was 35.1 percent in 134 individuals. Blood films from 35 of the 47 malaria-positives examined regularly became negative after 3 weeks of treatment. The remainder became negative after periods up to 6 weeks.

Visiting Scientists: The following individuals visited and worked at the Laboratory during the year:

Dr. A. Novick, Harvard University.

Prof. Alfred M. Elliott, University of Michigan.

Dr. Neal A. Weber, Swarthmore College.

Prof. Patrick A. Buxton, London School of Hygiene and Tropical Medicine.

On March 8, 1954, Dr. Leon Rosen, Laboratory of Tropical Diseases, National Institutes of Health, Bethesda, Maryland, began an assignment of 1 year for investigations on dengue and related viruses.

1955   The new Director, Dr. Johnson, instituted certain needed changes in the physical facilities of the Laboratory. Alterations were made in the main building and air conditioning was provided. The make-shift insectary was wholly inadequate and a new modern structure was built.

Dr. Hertig returned to duty in July, after the completion of his service with the Commission on Hemorrhagic Fever in Korea.

Yellow Fever Investigations: The survey of forest canopy mosquitoes was continued as a result of the epizootic of yellow fever on the north coast of Honduras in July and August 1954. A human fatality from the disease occurred at San Pedro Sula, Honduras, in September 1954. A prolonged dry season in Guatemala and Honduras during the first 6 months of the year was thought to have had a deterrent effect on the epidemiology of the disease, since there were no further recorded cases in these countries.

Eggs from suspected vectors of yellow fever were obtained from mosquitoes collected in vials. The eggs were transported to the Laboratory to obtain stocks of various species. The mosquitoes were fed on monkeys. In none of these animals was a Trinidad strain of yellow fever virus transmitted by bite, although virus was demonstrated by mouse inoculation in all species except *Haemagogus lucifer*.

Testing for antibodies was continued on recently captured monkeys. Positive results were obtained in marmosets from the Bayano River area, Darien Province and the Tocumen and Pacora areas, where human cases of yellow fever appeared in 1948.

Attempts were made to isolate yellow fever virus from mosquitoes captured in Honduras in the area in which the disease occurred in 1954. Intracerebral inoculation of white mice and subcutaneous injection of rhesus monkeys with pools of a total of 10,309 mosquitoes gave completely negative results.

Preliminary studies by Dr. Trapido and Mr. Galindo indicated that *Haemagogus equinus* was rather short-lived in laboratory colonies, shorter in fact than *H. spegazzinii falco* (= *H. capricornii falco*) and *H. mesodentatus* related forms. The life span of *H. equinus* would seem to approximate closely the extrinsic incubation of yellow fever virus. This gives support to epidemiological findings that yellow fever has not appeared in areas where *H. equinus* alone is the common species.

After intensive trials, a colony of *Sabethes chloropterus* has been maintained in the Laboratory for four generations. Difficulties were encountered in evaluating the species as a vector because of the reluctance of the females to bite, although the species is a voracious feeder in nature. Further studies were in progress.

Hemorrhagic Fever in Korea: Dr. Hertig's assignment as Field Director of the Armed Forces research group was terminated. Few clues were obtained as to the epidemiology of this condition although it would appear to be arthropod-borne. In spite of frustrations, many data were secured which it was believed will be of future value.

Malaria Studies: Dr. Johnson continued studies in the Chagres River villages. The procedures in vogue during the past 4 years were continued. Former control villages, Río Pescado and Mendoza, had lost their value in this respect because of DDT sprayings, and Nuevo Vigía was substituted. There was no increase in the cumulative malaria rate over that of the previous year.

Dengue Fever: Experiments were conducted by Dr. Leon Rosen on assignment from the Laboratory of Tropical Diseases, National Institutes of Health. In a serological survey of the human population some 1,400 serum specimens were collected.

Various serological tests indicated that the epidemic of "dengue-like" disease which occurred in Panama in 1941-42 was in all probability due to dengue Type II virus. Some evidence was obtained that dengue Type I virus had not been endemic in Panama since 1942.

A total of 30 monkeys were inoculated with strains of Type I and Type II dengue virus which had never been passaged in laboratory animals. Although none of the monkeys showed overt signs of illness, almost all developed hemagglutination (HI) or neutralizing antibodies. Viremia was demonstrated in four species of monkeys of three different genera 4 to 6 days after inoculation. This experiment provided the first data on the susceptibility of New World monkeys to this virus.

Visiting Scientists:
Dr. Alexander Wetmore, Smithsonian Institution.
Dr. Neal A. Weber, Swarthmore College.
Dr. George Bevier, Pan American Sanitary Bureau.

The Gorgas Memorial Laboratory
The Research Program
1946-1955
A Recapitulation

Many changes took place during the decade not only in the research program but in personnel as well. The appearance of yellow fever in Panama in November and December 1948 was followed by the organization of the Yellow Fever Service, in which the Gorgas Memorial Laboratory was destined to play an important role. Malaria studies were augmented by observations on the behavior of *Anopheles albimanus* following continuous exposure to DDT and the employment of new drugs as suppressive treatments. Studies were initiated on virus and rickettsial diseases. The Laboratory was the headquarters for a BCG vaccination program. In the latter part of the period, research was inaugurated on dengue and related fevers. The decade witnessed a marked expansion of activities, an excursion into new fields of endeavor, increased cooperation with international agencies, and an unusual record of accomplishment in comparison with past years.

The period also marked the retirement on June 30, 1954 of Dr. Herbert C. Clark as Director, after a period of service of 25 years and 6 months, and the appointment of Dr. Carl M. Johnson to succeed him. The beginning of the period witnessed the departure of the cadre of Army officers and the termination of the wartime studies on insecticides and repellents of military importance. Dr. Graham B. Fairchild received his discharge from the Army on July 31, 1946 and returned to his civilian position at the Laboratory. Dr. Harold Trapido joined the staff following his discharge from the Army on August 21, 1946. Mr. Pedro Galindo became associated with the Laboratory in 1947 as a liaison member on malaria control. Dr. Enid C. de Rodaniche became a virologist on the staff in February 1947. Señora

Teresina P. de Pinzón joined the staff in 1948 in connection with tuberculosis studies. Major Marshall Hertig was discharged from the Army and became a regular staff member in 1948. Sanitary Engineer Director W. H. W. Komp, U. S. Public Health Service, was transferred to the National Institutes of Health, Bethesda, Maryland on August 7, 1947 after having been on duty at the Gorgas Memorial Laboratory for 16 years and 4 months. On March 8, 1954, Dr. Leon Rosen, Laboratory of Tropical Diseases, National Institutes of Health, was assigned to the Laboratory for a period of 1 year for studies on dengue and related fevers.

Malaria Studies: Drug treatment was continued in the Chagres River villages without any marked reduction in parasite rates until the inauguration in 1948 of DDT residual spraying, following which the rates were markedly decreased.

Additional drug studies were inaugurated in 1947 in the Gatun Lake villages of Ciricito and Lagarterita, the inhabitants of which received chloroquine and aralen, and Cuipo, where paludrine was administered. After 30 weeks, malaria rates were markedly reduced; chloroquine gave better results than paludrine. After 2-years' treatment, malaria rates were negligible. In 1953, a remedy consisting of 30 mg. of primaquine and 300 mg. of plaquenil was employed in the village of Río Indio about 20 miles west of the Canal Zone. Marked reduction was observed in the malaria rate but 16 weeks after the end of the therapy, the rate had increased to almost half of the initial rate. Pyrimethamine was administered to inhabitants of Nuevo Vigía on Madden Lake in 1954 for a period of 4 months. The pretreatment rate in 134 persons was 35.1 percent. All positives became negative after 6 weeks of treatment.

After the employment of DDT in the Chagres River villages for 8 years, changes were noted in the behavioral pattern of *Anopheles albimanus.* Gross numbers of the mosquito in dwellings were no longer drastically reduced and the selective killing of engorged females was no longer evident. If such changes were due to resistance to DDT, it was of a very low order and not detectable by customary tests. There was the suggestion that a strain had evolved which was hyper-irritable to DDT and possessed an enhanced positive phototropism, since the mosquitoes no longer rested on the walls of the houses but at night congregated around kerosene lamps. Studies on the feeding habits of this species indicated that changes in the circulation brought about by varied positions of the body probably influenced the number and position of the alightings.

Yellow Fever Investigations: These studies were divided into efforts to determine vectors or potential vectors of yellow fever, and surveys to evaluate aboreal mammals as reservoir hosts of the virus. The first named investigations were conducted by Dr. Trapido, Mr. Galindo and Lt. Col.

Stanley J. Carpenter of the Army. Dr. Clark was responsible for the studies on aboreal mammals and Dr. Rodaniche conducted mouse-protection tests on live-caught animals, as well as attempting to isolate yellow fever virus from wild-caught mosquitoes.

Tree-top collections in Panama, Central America and Mexico indicated that vectors and potential vectors of jungle yellow fever were prevalent in many areas. *Haemagogus spegazzinii falco* (= *Haemagogus capricornii falco*) a tropical rain-forest mosquito, ranged through Panama and as far north as the northern coast of Honduras. *H. equinus* was found throughout Middle America. *H. lucifer* was recovered from the forests of Panama at elevations below 3500 feet. It was replaced near the Costa Rican border by the closely related species, *H. iridicolor,* (first thought to be *H. lucifer*) which extended into northern Nicaragua. The *H. mesodentatus* complex was found in deciduous tropical forests as far north as Tapachula, Mexico. *H. anastasionis* was common on the Pacific coast of Nicaragua.

Aedes leucocelaenus was recovered in the forests of Panama but became uncommon in Costa Rica and rare in Nicaragua and Honduras. *Sabethes chloropterus* was common throughout the entire region covered by the investigation and appeared epidemiologically to be involved in transmission in certain areas, although its ability in this respect had not been demonstrated at the time. *Trichosprosopon magnum* was common on the north coast of Honduras.

In spite of the fact that epidemiological evidence pointed strongly to the involvement of many of the above-mentioned species as vectors of yellow fever, attempts to infect susceptible animals by injection of mosquito pools were uniformly unsuccessful. Effort was being made to colonize these species in order that transmission experiments might be conducted.

Search for yellow fever antibodies in Panama aboreal mammals killed in the jungle revealed positives in 172, or 39.6 percent, of 434. Of 77 animals taken in Mexico, 12 or 15.6 percent were positive; these may have been false reactions. In surveys of animals captured alive, 12 of 301, or 4.0 percent, were positive. The majority of positives in both categories were in the primate group but a few non-primate mammals also showed antibodies.

Rickettsial Diseases and Virus Diseases Other Than Yellow Fever: Dr. Rodaniche experimentally infected *Amblyomma cajennense* with *Rickettsia burneti* (= *Coxiella burnetii*) and transmitted the infection to guinea pigs during the nymphal and larval stages of the tick. The organism was identified from two of 26 cases of fever of undetermined origin. Two new strains of *R. mooseri* (= *R. typhi*) were isolated from human cases. *R. rickettsii* was isolated from a fatal case of Rocky Mountain spotted fever.

An outbreak of poliomyelitis of unprecedented proportions occurred in Panama between August 1950 and April 1951. Three strains of virus were isolated. Spider monkeys were susceptible to Col SK virus and to all three of Type I strains tested. However, the monkeys were completely refractory to Type II and Type III strains.

Two species of Panama monkeys, the marmoset, *Saguinus geoffroyi,* and the night monkey, *Aotus trivirgatus,* were found to be extremely susceptible to *Toxoplasma* infection which resulted fatally in 3 to 11 days.

BCG Vaccination Program: Señora Teresina P. de Pinzón conducted tuberculosis surveys in three Gatun Lake villages. Of 1,048 persons tuberculin tested, 621, or 59.3 percent, were positive. This was the first intimation of the prevalence of the infection in rural Panama. BCG vaccinations were carried out in those villages and clinics in Panama City and Colón. In 1952, the program was transferred to the Servicio Cooperativo Interamericano de Salud Pública.

Chagas' Disease: At the request of the Pan American Sanitary Bureau, a program on Chagas' disease was instituted in 1950. The requirements for yellow fever studies, however, limited the time which could be devoted to the project. *Rhodnius pallescens* and *Triatoma dimidiata* were the predominant species of triatomes collected. Some 40 percent of the former were infected with *Trypanosoma cruzi.* Serological surveys in 10 localities in five provinces indicated a very spotty distribution of the disease.

Medical Entomology: The decade was marked by the increased cooperation of the staff with national and international organizations. Dr. Marshall Hertig returned to Peru in 1947 for further observations on the effect of DDT on *Phlebotomus.* At the request of the World Health Organization, he spent some time in Greece and Italy in 1948 observing the effect of DDT residual spraying on the occurrence of sandflies and the prevalence of leishmaniasis. In 1950, he conducted a survey of leishmaniasis and vectors in Paraguay. In 1952, Dr. Hertig was assigned to the Armed Forces Epidemiological Board and served as Field Director of its Commission on Hemorrhagic Fever in Korea. He returned to duty at Gorgas in 1955.

In 1948, Dr. Trapido visited Colombia and Venezuela as a consultant on problems of yellow fever and malaria. In 1949, he served as a consultant for the malaria eradication program in Puerto Rico. In 1949, he and Dr. Fairchild investigated the occurrence of *Phlebotomus* in certain Caribbean Islands, while on active duty with the U. S. Army. At the request of the Rockefeller Foundation, Dr. Trapido served in Sardinia in 1950 and again in 1952 as a consultant on the campaign for the eradication of *Anopheles l. labranchiae* from that island.

Dr. Fairchild was on leave of absence from September 8, 1949 to give a graduate course in medical entomology at the University of Minnesota during the academic year. In 1954, he spent 11 weeks in London and Paris studying Tabanidae material in various museums.

Taxonomic studies on *Phlebotomus* were continued and 60 species had been identified from Panama, of which only four had been known prior to the Gorgas Memorial Laboratory investigations. The distribution and habits of species in Panama and Central America had provided a pattern of importance in the epidemiology of leishmaniasis. Of the eighty-odd Central American species, 12 were known to bite man and five of these are rather common in forested areas. Three species extend from the northern to the southern limits of the endemic areas of leishmaniasis in the Western Hemisphere.

Dr. Fairchild continued his work on the Tabanidae, of which 118 species had been identified from Panama.

Activities of the Gorgas Memorial Institute 1946-1955

1946

The Presidency of Colonel Siler: The entire period 1946-1955 was marked by the presidency of Col. J. F. Siler, who was particularly active in promoting the affairs of the Institute. The first activity occurred on February 23, 1946 when the Executive Committee appointed a special committee to explore the possibility of securing increased appropriations from Congress for the Gorgas Memorial Laboratory. It was pointed out that the Laboratory had lost competent professional personnel because of the low salary scale. This deficiency in staffing had been offset during the war by the assignment of a number of Army officers to the Laboratory. Earlier contracts with the Office of Scientific Research and Development had also helped to ameliorate stresses due to the limited budget. Because of inadequate quarters, a new building was urgently needed requiring an appropriation of $200,000. Needed additions to the staff and provision for salaries of personnel comparable to those in other institutions would necessitate an annual operating budget of $100,000.

Commissary Privileges for Laboratory Staff: At this same meeting, the matter of securing commissary privileges for staff members in the Canal Zone was discussed. This was taken up with the Government of Panama but it was found that treaty obligations precluded such an arrangement at the time. During these negotiations the Ambassador of Panama indicated his willingness to request his government to provide an annual appropriation for the Gorgas Memorial Laboratory.

Need for New Laboratory Facilities and a Retirement Plan: The Executive Committee met again on June 6, 1946. The possibility of securing aid from the Government of Panama in providing a new building was discussed and President Siler was authorized to communicate with the American Ambassador in Panama concerning the matter. The need for retirement provisions for the Laboratory staff was also brought up.

Annual Meeting and President's Report: The annual meeting of the Gorgas Memorial Institute was held in Washington on November 25, 1946. At the ensuing meeting of the Board of Directors, Colonel Siler was re-elected President, and Dr. Bowman C. Crowell Vice President.

The President indicated that the Veterinary Station in the Canal Zone had been used for breeding laboratory animals for the Health Department of the Canal Zone and the Army. The operation had been an expensive one. The station had been turned over to the Canal Zone Health Department and in the future laboratory animals would be purchased.

Governor Thatcher, Chairman of the Special Committee to develop plans for the expansion of the Gorgas Memorial Laboratory, reported that Congress would probably hesitate to provide funds for a new building since the site of the Laboratory and the building was held by the Institute under a restricted title. The possibility of building in the Canal Zone had been considered. The Committee was continued.

1947   The Executive Committee convened on July 24, 1947. Routine business was conducted.

Annual Meeting: The annual meeting of the Corporation was held in Washington on November 24, 1947. A resolution of sympathy was adopted on the death of Dr. Leo S. Rowe, one of the incorporators of the Institute.

The meeting of the Board of Directors followed. Colonel Siler was re-elected President and Dr. Bowman C. Crowell Vice President.

The President reported that the Government of Panama could not under its Constitution give an unrestricted title to the Gorgas Memorial Laboratory property. Further inquiries had been made regarding construction of additional facilities in the Canal Zone. A site had been set aside by the Governor of the Zone but estimates for the construction of necessary buildings amounted to $2,460,000, a sum thought to be impossible to obtain. It appeared that it might be possible to secure as surplus property a building or buildings in the Zone for laboratory use.

1948   The Executive Committee met on March 4, 1948, to discuss the problem of additional funds for the Gorgas Memorial Laboratory. Governor Thatcher pointed out that it was too late to secure additional appropriations for the fiscal year 1949. Since Dr. Clark had estimated that $25,000 at least would be needed, it was decided to apply for research grants from the U. S. Public Health Service.

Annual Meeting: The annual meeting of the Corporation was held in Washington on November 22, 1948. The Board of Directors at its concurrent meeting reelected Colonel J. F. Siler as President and elected Governor Maurice H. Thatcher as Vice President.

President's Report: The President reported that three applications for research grants had been made to the U. S. Public Health Service and that one of these had been approved in the sum of $8,800. However, it was found unnecessary to accept the funds as the 80th Congress during its closing days had increased the appropriation for the Gorgas Memorial Laboratory. Public Law 867—80th Congress, Chapter 787—2nd session (S. 2342) amended the act of May 7, 1928 (45 stat. 491) by raising the limit of yearly support from $50,000 to not to exceed $150,000. Thanks were expressed by the President in behalf of the Board of Directors to Senator Lister Hill and Governor Maurice H. Thatcher for their efforts in making this increase possible.

Resolutions were passed to mark the death of Rear Admiral Edward R. Stitt, one of the incorporators of the Gorgas Memorial Institute and that of the Honorable William Bacon Oliver, who had long served the Institute in various capacities.

1949   *Annual Meeting:* The annual meeting of the Gorgas Memorial Institute was held in Washington on November 28, 1949. A resolution was adopted memorializing the death of former President Hugh S. Cumming. At the ensuing meeting of the Board of Directors Colonel J. F. Siler and Governor Maurice H. Thatcher were reelected President and Vice President, respectively.

Accounting Procedures: Certain action was taken concerning accounting procedures. Because the Certificate of Incorporation permitted the Institute to engage in activities other than medical research and in fact the Institute had previously engaged in such activities, it had been necessary to maintain two accounting systems. Advice from the General Accounting Office indicated that this procedure could be dispensed with by suitable resolution of the Board of Directors. Because the Institute was now only concerned with research problems, the necessary resolution was adopted so that accounts could henceforth be combined.

The amendment to the Act of Congress authorizing the annual appropriation for the Laboratory called for the submission of a budget. On advice of the General Accounting Office, the Board of Directors formally approved the budget of $114,000 for the fiscal year 1951.

1950 The Executive Committee met on November 1, 1950 and approved the suggestion of the General Accounting Office that the two accounts mentioned above be combined at the beginning of the current fiscal year, an action which had apparently been taken. A resolution was adopted to change the date of the annual meeting to conform with the date of the annual meeting of the American Society of Tropical Medicine.

Latin American Countries—Lack of Support: The Office of the Comptroller General called attention to the fact that the Institute was not complying with the letter of the law by not inviting contributions from Latin American countries. On June 14, 1950, President Siler had discussed this problem at a meeting with representatives of the Department of State, the Office of the Comptroller General, the U. S. Public Health Service and the Pan American Sanitary Bureau. It was the consensus of this meeting that before any steps were taken to renew such invitations consideration should be given to having the Laboratory bill amended to delete this provision. Governor Thatcher was asked to draft such an amendment for consideration of the Board of Directors at its meeting on November 27, 1950.

Personnel Matters: The matter of retirement benefits for United States employees of the Gorgas Memorial Laboratory was discussed. Governor Thatcher was asked to investigate the possibility of having these employees blanketed in under the U. S. Civil Service Retirement program.

Under Law 8 of the Republic of Panama an employee was entitled to a month's pay for each year of service after 10 continuous years of employment. This law was repealed when the Panama Social Security Law was enacted in 1941. However, certain Panamanian employees of the Laboratory still believed that they were entitled to this emolument. The matter was discussed but tabled for future consideration.

The Committee recommended that 15 days leave with pay be granted to Reserve Officers of the Armed Forces on the Laboratory staff when called to active duty for such a period.

The President was authorized to purchase shares in an investment trust with certain endowment monies and the proceeds of a bequest by the late Dr. Earl Mayne.

Annual Meeting: The annual meeting of the Corporation was held in Washington on November 27, 1950. The By-Laws were amended to hold the annual meeting on the second Wednesday in October. Certain changes were made in the By-Laws to include the Surgeon General of the Air Force as a member of the Board of Directors.

At the meeting of the Board of Directors on the same day, Colonel J. F. Siler was reelected President and Governor Maurice H. Thatcher Vice

President. The budget in the sum of $152,000 was approved for the fiscal year 1952. The matter of retirement for United States employees of the Gorgas Memorial Laboratory was brought up by the President. Apparently, a special Act of Congress would be needed for inclusion of personnel in the U. S. Civil Service Retirement system.

Latin American Countries—Support Situation: President Siler reviewed the entire situation concerning support from Latin American countries and cited the history of efforts to secure such support. In accordance with the conclusions of the Executive Committee at its meeting on November 1, 1950, a resolution was introduced and passed authorizing the General Counsel of the Institute to investigate possibilities of action and also to make further inquiry into methods of providing retirement for Gorgas staff members.

The Board passed a resolution expressing gratification at the election of General Gorgas to the Hall of Fame of New York University.

1951 *Annual Meeting:* The annual meeting was convened in Washington on October 10, 1951. A resolution on the death of Dr. Bowman C. Crowell was adopted. Dr. Crowell had served the Institute for many years, first as Chairman of the Scientific Board from 1923 to 1935, as President from 1935 to 1937 and as Vice President from 1938 to 1948.

The annual meeting of the Board of Directors followed. Governor Maurice H. Thatcher, the General Counsel, presented a draft of an amended bill to replace the Act of May 7, 1928, to omit the provisions requiring the Institute to solicit contributions from Latin American Governments.

A budget for $140,800 was approved for the fiscal year 1953.

Dr. Clark was granted a power of attorney giving him certain additional authority in negotiations with the Government of Panama with regard to the tax status of the Laboratory and the exemption of United States staff members from import duties and Panamanian taxes.

Colonel J. F. Siler was reelected President and Governor Maurice H. Thatcher Vice President.

1952 *Budget Reductions for 1953:* A meeting of the Executive Committee was held on February 28, 1952. The main topic of business concerned a Bureau of the Budget reduction in the 1953 budget from $140,000 to $50,000. The appeal from the Department of State had been disregarded. Through the intervention of many prominent persons, an amount was restored to bring the budget to $117,600, the same as the 1952 budget. It was deemed inadvisable to make further protestations.

Personnel Matters: When the Panama Social Security Law was enacted legal counsel sought by Dr. Clark advised that United States members of the staff of the Laboratory were exempt. However, in 1948 the Laboratory was billed for back taxes in the amount of $8,700. Through a verbal agreement, demand for payment was not pressed. It was agreed that the matter should be settled for once and for all and Governor Thatcher was asked to confer with State Department officials concerning the matter.

The matter of granting leave with pay to Laboratory staff members during attendance at scientific meetings was discussed. It was agreed that such attendance was beneficial to the Laboratory. However, it was thought inadvisable because of shortage of funds to formulate a definite policy at that time.

Financing of Gorgas Memorial Laboratory: The Executive Committee met again on July 30, 1952, mainly to discuss financing of the Gorgas Memorial Laboratory program. In view of the reduction in the 1953 budget, efforts had been made without avail to secure outside support. It was thought that acceptance of research grant funds from the U. S. Public Health Service might alienate relations with agencies concerned with the regular budget and with Congress. It was decided that the budget request for 1954 should be in the amount required, regardless of the Bureau of the Budget reductions in the 1953 budget. The question of the low salaries of staff members was discussed. Dr. Clark was authorized to grant any increases possible under the 1953 budget. Increases were to be provided for in the 1954 budget. A committee was appointed to review personnel policies and salaries.

Exemption from Panama Taxes and Other Benefits: The President announced that Contract No. 46 of May 24, 1952 between the Republic of Panama and the Gorgas Memorial Institute of Tropical and Preventive Medicine had been approved by the Government of Panama by passage in the National Assembly of Law No. 5 of February 5, 1953. The Contract contained multiple provisions.

Under the Contract, the Grantee was obligated to conduct research for the following purposes:

(a) To discover fundamental facts relating to tropical diseases and their vectors and other problems of public health.

(b) To organize and experiment on new methods and systems of control, prevention and cure of tropical diseases.

(c) To act as consultant of, and to cooperate with, those Government officials and bureaus which are engaged in the prevention, control and solution of the sanitary problems of the Republic of Panama.

In recognition of the benefits to be derived from the above-mentioned activities, the Republic of Panama agreed to the following obligations:

(a) To exempt the Grantee from all types of national taxes.

(b) To exempt the Grantee and the scientists of foreign nationalities which serve on its staff from the obligation to pay the Social Security taxes which cover the latter.

(c) To exempt the scientists of foreign nationalities which serve on its staff from payment of income and import taxes, as well as from consular duties and taxes, visas, entry, sailing and re-entry permit duties, and from immigration deposits.

In addition the Gorgas Memorial Institute was relieved of payment of any Social Security taxes owing to the Government of Panama.

Annual Meeting: The annual meeting of the Corporation and the Board of Directors was held in Washington on October 29, 1952. Resolutions were passed on the death on July 5, 1952 of General Merritt W. Ireland, one of the incorporators of the Institute and Rear Admiral Harold W. Smith, long a member of the Board of Directors, who died on February 4, 1952.

Dr. L. L. Williams, Jr. reported for the Committee on Personnel. Several recommendations were included for procedural mechanisms for a retirement plan. It was moved that the Executive Committee be empowered to carry out the recommendations.

Governor Thatcher reported on steps which might be taken to obviate the obligation of the Institute to invite contributions from Latin American nations for support of the Gorgas Memorial Laboratory. A resolution was adopted to take the necessary action to have the Act of 1928 so amended as to strike out this provision.

The Board of Directors adopted a budget for fiscal year 1954 of $151,182 of which $143,550 would be requested from Congress.

Colonel J. F. Siler was reelected President and Governor Maurice H. Thatcher Vice President.

1953 *Personnel Actions:* The Executive Committee held a meeting on June 20, 1953. Dr. Bloedorn was appointed Chairman of a Committee to seek replacement for Dr. Clark, who had expressed a desire for retirement.

Dr. L. L. Williams, Jr. reported for the Personnel Committee on salary adjustments. It was recommended and adopted that salaries of GML scientists and those of the Washington Office staff conform to U. S. Civil Service standards. However, the 1954 budget would not permit immediate increases of such magnitude. It was necessary to place a limit of 10 percent on immediate raises.

Further consideration was given to adoption of a retirement plan but it was deemed advisable to consult with the Comptroller General before proceeding further.

Proposed Change in Budget Sponsorship: Another meeting of the Executive Committee was held on July 17, 1953. President Siler pointed out that hearings on the 1954 appropriation had raised the question of State Department sponsorship of the Gorgas budget and the intimation that such should be in the Public Health Service. This suggestion was regarded unfavorably by the Executive Committee and it was decided to take action necessary to have the State Department retain the authority.

The Executive Committee met again on October 21, 1953 to select a successor to Dr. Clark. It was agreed that it was "quite likely absolutely necessary" that the director be a medical man. Five candidates were considered, none of whom evinced any interest in the position. It was decided to offer the position to Dr. Carl M. Johnson.

Annual Meeting: The annual meeting was held in Washington on October 30, 1953. The usual business was completed following which the Board of Directors met. Colonel J. F. Siler was reelected President and Governor Maurice H. Thatcher Vice President.

The President reported that the retirement plan based on individual annuity contracts by the Teachers Insurance and Annuity Association of New York (TIAA) had not been put into effect at the beginning of the fiscal year (July 1, 1953) because the Comptroller General had not yet passed on the legality of using government funds for this purpose.

The recommendation of the Executive Committee that Dr. Carl M. Johnson be offered the position as Director was approved.

Governor Thatcher reported that an amendment relieving the Institute of inviting contributions from Latin American countries had been introduced in the form of a bill in the Senate (S. 1456) and had been passed. Action was awaited in the House of Representatives.

A budget for fiscal year 1955 was approved in the sum of $152,213.

1954 *Budget Bureau Action Regarding Gorgas Budget:* The Executive Committee met on January 4, 1954. A motion was adopted to place Dr. Clark on an emeritus status following his retirement with a stipend of $5,000 per annum. The President referred to the action of the Bureau of the Budget in transferring on October 9, 1953, responsibility for the Gorgas budget from the Department of State to the Department of Health, Education and Welfare. However, up to the date of the meeting, official notice of this change had not been received.

The letter of October 9, 1953 from the Bureau of the Budget also raised the question as to whether or not there should be continued appropriations for the Gorgas Memorial Laboratory. The Secretary of the Department of Health, Education and Welfare was requested to make an evaluation of the need for further support by the United States.

On December 8, 1953, the Secretary of the Department of Health, Education and Welfare advised the Bureau of the Budget that the 1955 budget estimates for the Gorgas Memorial Laboratory had been included in the Department's budget. The letter also stated that the Public Health Service would in the near future undertake a study to determine the need for future support.

The President also introduced a letter which he had written to the Secretary, Department of Health, Education and Welfare regarding the matter. It was thought desirable to leave the responsibility in the Department of State and effort would be made accordingly.

Dr. Johnson's Employment as Director: The Executive Committee met again on January 14, 1954 to consider a contract to be offered to Dr. Johnson for his employment as Director of the Gorgas Memorial Laboratory. Dr. Johnson had addressed a letter to the President to the effect that the salary offered was unsatisfactory. A new contract was drawn up.

The retirement plan was reconsidered, the Comptroller General having indicated that the law did not give him authority to approve or disapprove the proposal. The TIAA plan was discussed in detail and it was adopted to be made effective on January 1, 1954.

Another meeting of the Executive Committee was held on February 10, 1954, to reconsider the contract with Dr. Johnson. Dr. Johnson refused the new contract on March 28, 1954. Further negotiations were conducted and the Executive Committee on May 5, 1954, appointed Dr. Johnson as Director following his acceptance of the contract under date of May 3, 1954.

Annual Meeting: The annual meeting was held in Washington on October 29, 1954. The meeting of the Board of Directors occurred after adjournment of the meeting of the Corporation. Colonel J. F. Siler and Governor Maurice H. Thatcher were continued in the offices of President and Vice President, respectively. The Assistant Treasurer, Mr. Donald A. McCormack, reported that investments in the Endowment Fund had a market value of $48,449 as of June 30, 1954.

It was voted to approve the action of the Executive Committee in recommending the adoption of a Provident Fund Plan to cover employees deprived because of age of the benefits of the Retirement Plan. Subsequently, on November 19, 1954, the Executive Committee met and adopted the Plan.

A motion was adopted expressing appreciation to Dr. Clark for his long service as Director of the Gorgas Memorial Laboratory and regret over his retirement.

Public Law 339—83rd Congress: Counsel Thatcher reported that the bill to amend the Act of May 7, 1928, to obviate the obligation of soliciting funds from Latin American countries had passed the House and been signed by the President on April 19, 1954. This bill (S. 1456) became Public Law 339-83rd Congress, Chapter 160—2nd Session.

The President reported that his request to the Secretary of the Department of Health, Education and Welfare for need for future support of the work at the Gorgas Memorial Laboratory had been referred to the Surgeon General, Public Health Service. The latter had appointed a committee which reported on May 3, 1954 and recommended continued support for the Laboratory.

Similar recommendations had previously been made by the Department of State and the Department of Defense.

A budget of $147,000 was approved for the fiscal year 1956.

1955   *Salary Increases:* The Executive Committee met on July 21, 1955. It was pointed out that Public Law 94 of the 84th Congress had provided a salary increase of 7.5 percent for U. S. Civil Service employees as of March 1, 1955. The Personnel Committee recommended that a similar increase be provided for Gorgas Memorial Laboratory scientists and Washington Office staff. The Executive Committee approved this recommendation and made the new pay scale retroactive to March 1, 1955.

Annual Meeting: The annual meeting was held in Washington on October 27, 1955. A resolution was adopted on the death of Dr. Carlos Dávila, Secretary General of the Organization of American States and ex-officio member of the Gorgas Board of Directors.

At a meeting of the Board of Directors which followed Colonel J. F. Siler was reelected President and Governor Maurice H. Thatcher Vice President.

The President reported that the sum of $18,000 had been approved by the Army Medical Research and Development Command for new insectary facilities which were badly needed for the yellow fever studies.

The budget for fiscal year 1957 was approved in the sum of $156,386.

Chapter 5.

Years of Increasing Momentum
1956-1962

The Gorgas Memorial Laboratory; Research Programs; Old Problems—Yellow Fever Reappears; New Objectives; Increased Emphasis on Arboviruses; A Broadened Program on Leishmaniasis; Activities of the Gorgas Memorial Institute.

"The man who makes the experiment deservedly claims the honor and the reward."
—HORACE

The period 1956-1962 witnessed greater support for the Gorgas Memorial Laboratory, improved physical facilities, some additions to the staff, broader and better defined objectives, the adoption of new research programs and extension and revitalization of old programs.

Fortunately yellow fever surveillance was maintained on a vigorous scale for the disease reappeared in the Cerro Azul area in 1956 and in the Buena Vista area in 1957. Other arboviruses received increased attention and interest in this program was no doubt enhanced by the occurrence during the period of Venezuelan equine encephalomyelitis in horses and the human population in certain areas. The studies on leishmaniasis were extended to include detailed observations on epidemiology, ecology and colonization of sandflies, reservoir hosts, and experimental therapy.

A new malaria treatment project was instituted. Research on American trypanosomiasis included observations on the ecology of vectors, attempts at tissue cultivation of certain hemoflagellates, new methods of treatment and the possible role of Chagas' disease in the production of megacolon and megaesophagus.

1956   *Yellow Fever Investigations:* A new series of studies was inaugurated with the following objectives:

(a) To determine the vector ability of species of *Haemagogus* which replace in Middle America the known vectors in South America.

(b) To secure detailed information on the taxonomy, ecology, and zoogeography of the Middle American species of *Haemagogus*.

(c) To attempt to demonstrate the continued presence of jungle yellow fever in eastern Panama by recovery of the virus from natural vectors.

(d) To determine the vector ability of *Sabethes chloropterus,* a species suspected to transmit the disease during the dry season.

This program was to be carried out by Medical Entomologist Pedro Galindo and Dr. Trapido with assistance of Dr. Rodaniche, who was to continue studies on other virus diseases and the rickettsioses.

In efforts to determine the geographical limits of the species of *Haemagogus* responsible for yellow fever transmission in Middle America and Mexico, *H. equinus* was found as far north as Brownsville, Texas. The northernmost record of the genus on the Pacific side was a single female of *H. mesodentatus gorgasi* taken near the southern border of the State of Sinaloa, Mexico. *H. equinus* was collected near San Blas in the State of Nayarit, Mexico, on the Pacific side. On the Caribbean side, *H. mesodentatus mesodentatus* was taken near Ciudad Santos, north of Tamazunchale, Mexico.

Early in 1956, monkeys began dying from yellow fever in the Motagua River Valley of Guatemala, an area in which South American vectors, *Haemagogus spegazzinii falco* (= *Haemagogus capricornii falco*) and *Aedes leucocelaenus,* did not occur. In cooperation with the Pan American Sanitary Bureau, forest canopy mosquitoes were collected and transmitted to the Gorgas Memorial Laboratory. Mouse inoculation with pools of these mosquitoes demonstrated yellow fever virus in *Haemagogus m. mesodentatus, H. equinus* and *Sabethes chloropterus.* This was the first recorded virus isolation from the latter species. The virus was also isolated from the liver of a monkey shot in the area.

Transmission of infection from monkey to monkey was accomplished by the bites of *Haemagogus m. mesodentatus, H. mesodentatus gorgasi* and *H. equinus* but not by the bite of *Sabethes chloropterus.*

Examination of captured Panamanian arboreal mammals for yellow fever antibodies revealed four positives in 78 animals tested. Most of these came from the Bayano River Valley of eastern Panama. Two of the positive monkeys were young animals, thus confirming the current existence of the virus in the Bayano River Valley. This interpretation was confirmed by the occurrence of a fatal human case of yellow fever in August 1956 in the Cerro Azul portion of this area.

Arboviruses Other Than Yellow Fever: A virus previously isolated in mice from a group of 50 mosquitoes of the genus *Psorophora* proved to be that of Ilhéus encephalitis. This represented the first isolation of this virus in Central America. Other arboviruses were isolated from the mosquitoes collected during the studies in Guatemala.

Fig. 8. Dr. Carl M. Johnson at the malaria clinic at Guayabalito, Republic of Panama.

Leishmaniasis Studies: Dr. Hertig, Dr. Fairchild and Dr. Johnson were engaged in these studies. In recent years there had been an increase, or at least an increased recognition, of cutaneous leishmaniasis in certain areas, especially near Almirante, at Camp Piña, a U. S. Army installation at the mouth of the Chagres River and at Buena Vista on the transisthmian highway where 95 active cases were diagnosed. Since these areas are within easy access to the Laboratory, they were selected for intensive studies on the epidemiology of the disease. Colonization studies were initiated and limited success was attained in rearing a few species of *Phlebotomus* in the laboratory. Animal trapping in the above-mentioned areas resulted in catches composed principally of marsupials and a variety of rodents. The blood of captured animals was examined with the hope of finding *Leishmania*. The first success was attained early in the year when a strain was recovered from a culture of the blood of a spiny rat, *Proechimys semispinosus*. This strain was subsequently inoculated into a human volunteer with the production of a typical lesion of cutaneous leishmaniasis, from which *Leishmania* were demonstrated in smears, sections and cultures. Following this, three additional isolations have been made from the spiny rat.

American Trypanosomiasis: This program was under the supervision of Dr. Johnson. Investigations were continued on a limited scale. Complement fixation reactions were obtained in four individuals from whose blood trypanosomes were first demonstrated in 1936. The parasites could no longer be found in the blood. Further tests were made on 500 sera from one of the blood banks in Panama; these tests revealed only three positives. Experimental studies on animals by other workers indicated that isopentaquine was of value for the treatment of trypanosomiasis. When tried on chronic cases in man it apparently was without value. Trials were yet to be made in early acute infections.

Malaria Studies: The administration of antimalarial drugs to positive individuals in the Chagres River villages was continued by Dr. Johnson. Villages continued to be sprayed with DDT. The results paralleled those of previous years.

Cooperation with Other Organizations: This continued on the same basis as in the past and the Laboratory facilities were made available to visiting scientists, 32 of whom spent varying periods of time during the year.

Staff Changes: Dr. Harold Trapido, who joined the staff in 1946, resigned as of June 30, 1956 to accept a position with the Rockefeller Foundation. He had contributed significantly to the investigations on malaria and yellow fever.

1957 *Yellow Fever Investigations:* Studies in Central America were discontinued in order that more emphasis might be placed on unsolved problems on the epidemiology of the disease in Panama. These problems concerned the question as to whether the disease was truly endemic in eastern Panama, the role of mammals other than monkeys as reservoir hosts of the virus and the means by which the virus is maintained during the dry season when *Haemagogus* mosquitoes are absent. In connection with the latter problem, the role of *Sabethes chloropterus* as a dry season vector was to be investigated more thoroughly.

A new collecting station was established at Mandinga on the Atlantic watershed in the San Blas territory. From a total of 8,123 mosquitoes collected at this station, yellow fever virus was isolated once from a pool of 137 *Haemagogus lucifer* collected between September 1 and 6, 1956.

At the Cerro Azul field station, mosquito collections were made at the exact spot at which a fatal case of yellow fever had been contracted previously. Yellow fever virus was isolated from mosquitoes collected between September 13 and October 9, 1956 but not after January 1957. Isolations were made from pools of *Haemagogus lucifer, H. spegazzinii falco* (= *H. capricornii falco*), *Sabethes chloropterus* and once from *Anopheles neivai*. The fact that no isolations were made after January 1957 would seem to indicate that yellow fever virus was not present in the area after that time.

The failure to transmit yellow fever to monkeys by the bite of *Sabethes chloropterus,* as mentioned in last year's summary, led to a reevaluation of the conditions of the experiment and further studies on the life cycle of this species. It was found that females of the species do not begin to suck blood before the sixth day after emergence and in fact most females do not take a blood meal until 10 to 15 days after emergence. The mean life span after the first blood meal is over 30 days. Females were kept alive in the laboratory colony for as long as 5 months. With these new facts, experimental procedures were altered and yellow fever was successfully transmitted to a clean monkey 37 days after the infective blood meal. Furthermore, the virus was repeatedly isolated by inoculating mice with mosquitoes employed in this experiment.

The studies on virus isolation from Guatemala mosquitoes were completed. A total of 10,263 mosquitoes were received from March to the middle of November 1956. In the final analysis of results, yellow fever virus was isolated 21 times, 3 from pools of *Haemagogus equinus,* 14 from *H. mesodentatus* and 4 from *Sabethes chloropterus*. No isolations were made from mosquitoes captured after July 1956. Three other arboviruses were recovered during this study. One was identical with a Honduran strain of Ilhéus virus. The others remained to be identified.

The project concerning yellow fever antibodies in Panama mammals was discontinued. By the end of 1956, a total of 604 monkeys had been tested over an 8-year period. Of these 33 were positive. In 1956, there was a marked rise in positives from the Bayano River Valley and contiguous areas. In August of that year, it is of note that one fatal human case and two serologically positive recovered cases of yellow fever occurred in the general area.

Leishmaniasis Studies: The receipt of a grant-in-aid from the National Institutes of Health for this project on September 1, 1956 allowed for the hiring of additional temporary personnel. As of September 1, 1957, supplementary funds became available from this grant to hire additional professional personnel. With increased financial support, the studies were considerably expanded.

A weekly clinic was established at the local school at Buena Vista, and as a result about 100 cases of the disease were found.

Additional search was made for animal reservoirs. The number of spiny rats, *Proechimys semispinosus,* from which *Leishmania* had been cultivated now reached 21, or 10.5 percent, of 200 of this species trapped in six endemic foci. It was still found impossible to demonstrate the organisms *in situ* in any tissue; furthermore, infection could not be produced by inoculation by various routes in spiny rats born in the laboratory or by inoculation of hamsters.

The collection of sandflies was enhanced by the discovery that horses are particularly attractive to the insects. The principal species collected, all of which bite man, were *Phlebotomus trapidoi, sanguinarius, panamensis, gomezi, paraensis* and *ylephiletor,* in that order of abundance.

Difficulties encountered in the rearing of the man-biting species were finally overcome. The number of species now reared successfully totals 15. Further difficulty was encountered, however, in getting sandflies to feed in the attempted infection experiments. Some success was had in using human peritoneum as the membrane through which feeding could take place. Transmission of *Leishmania* was attempted through the inoculation of wild-caught sandflies into experimental animals. With over 2,000 sandflies so injected, no infections have resulted.

Very few specimens of young stages of *Phlebotomus* have ever been found in nature. Search for these forms was initiated in various types of potential breeding places. Success was achieved by the recovery of 57 larvae and one pupa from the top 4 inches of soil taken from buttresses of forest trees. Surviving forms were transferred to breeding pots, which yielded seven adults of three species.

Malaria Studies: Drug treatment was continued in the Chagres River villages for the 27th consecutive year. For 13 years the villages have been sprayed with DDT. The malaria rates for adults remained the same as for 1956 but increased for children from 2.1 percent to 7.2 percent.

Visiting Scientists:

Dr. Charles O. Handley, Jr., U. S. National Museum.

Dr. Neal A. Weber, Swarthmore College.

Mr. Bernard Ludes, Columbia University.

Additions to the Staff:

Dr. Phyllis T. Johnson, Division of Insects, U. S. Department of Agriculture, came on duty for a period of 6 months to assist in *Phlebotomus* rearing. In November 1957, she was relieved by Miss Mary Lou Morrow.

Mr. Wilford J. Hanson of the University of Kansas reported for duty in September 1957, in connection with the field ecology of *Phlebotomus.*

Dr. Ellicott McConnell of the University of Minnesota came on duty on December 1, 1957, on the leishmaniasis program.

1958   *Yellow Fever Investigations:* A number of new stations for the collection of forest canopy mosquitoes were established during the year. These were at Orchid Island in Gatun Lake, Pintupo in the Bayano River Valley, Piña on the north shore of Gatun Lake and on the Paya River in Darien Province. It was anticipated that the additional stations would provide a broader coverage and a more accurate determination of the direction which jungle yellow fever was taking. A total of 26,891 mosquitoes belonging to at least 51 different species were taken at these and previously established stations. No virus isolations were obtained from the Orchid Island mosquitoes. In the first week of July 1957, two suspected cases of yellow fever originated in the Buena Vista area near the place where a fatal infection had been contracted in 1949. A collecting team was dispatched to the area and collections started on July 9. One of the local collectors hired for the occasion contracted the disease 5 days later. Of 1,501 mosquitoes taken at this station, yellow fever virus was isolated 2 times from pools of *Haemagogus spegazzinii falco* (= *H. capricornii falco*) and twice from pools of *H. lucifer.* The Pintupo station yielded few mosquitoes and was abandoned. A total of 3,487 mosquitoes were collected at the Piña station but no virus isolations were obtained, apparently indicating that the disease had not crossed the Panama Canal and gained entrance into the tropical rain forests of northwestern Panama. At the Paya River station, a total of 5,387 mosquitoes were taken. No yellow virus was recovered but three other unidentified viruses were isolated. At the previously established Cerro Azul station, mosquito catches totalled 11,416 specimens, but no yellow fever virus was recovered. However, two unidentified viruses were isolated.

In efforts to obtain some clue concerning the reasons for the persistence of yellow fever virus during the dry season, an analysis was made of potential vectors collected at the Cerro Azul station during 1956, when virus was shown to have been present in the vicinity. The most efficient vectors were rare or absent during the dry season and only *Haemagogus lucifer* was encountered to any degree and then in only small numbers. On the other hand, *Sabethes chloropterus* was much more numerous and appeared in collections during all of the 19 weeks of the dry season.

Additional transmission experiments were undertaken with *S. chloropterus*. Two *Macaca mulatta* monkeys were exposed to bites of infected mosquitoes and both developed yellow fever. Infected mosquitoes found dead or dying in the course of the experiment were injected intracerebrally into mice, some of which succumbed. The titer of the virus was variable. The conclusion was reached that *S. chloropterus* is capable of transmitting yellow fever, although a high titer of the virus in the infective meal, a prolonged incubation period and a highly susceptible host are required. Transmission experiments with *Ateles* monkeys were all negative.

The project on protection tests for yellow fever in the sera of wild mammals was resumed during the year. Tests were conducted on 316 animals, including 154 primates and 162 non-primates. Eight, or 5.2 percent, of the 154 primates were positive. Eight opossums had a high enough protection ratio to be considered positive; all came from Piña. One rice rat, *Oryzomys* sp., and one grison, *Galictis allamandi,* gave doubtful positives.

Arboviruses Other Than Yellow Fever: A number of viruses other than yellow fever were recovered from mosquitoes collected at the various stations. One isolated from *Sabethes chloropterus* as well as from the blood of a mosquito collector was identical with St. Louis or more closely related to it than to other Group B viruses. Four other encephalitogenic viral agents were recovered but remained to be identified.

Leishmaniasis Studies: In continued search for potential reservoir hosts, blood cultures were made from about 600 wild-caught animals representing 35 species. Of these about 130 were spiny rats, *Proechimys semispinosus,* which in previous studies had yielded cultures of *Leishmania.* All cultures from this species this year were negative. However, one of about 60 spiny rats, *Hoplomys gymnurus,* from La Zumbadora was positive. Attempts to establish infections in a variety of experimental animals were unsuccessful.

Some progress was made in efforts to infect sandflies with *Leishmania.* Feeding by pipette, although a delicate operation, resulted in the infection of two species, *Phlebotomus sanguinarius* and *P. panamensis;* the mortality from the manipulations was high.

Last year initial success was attained in discovering the breeding places of certain species of *Phlebotomus* in the soil around tree buttresses. Search was continued and resulted in larger takes of larvae, many of which were reared to adults. However, almost none of the man-biting species were recovered in this type of location. Through a fortunate circumstance, larvae of these species were detected on the forest floor in moist, rotting leaves covered by thick vegetation. An apparatus was being constructed for bulk washing of large quantities of such material.

Malaria Studies: Malaria treatment in the Chagres River villages was continued for the 28th year. The last spraying with DDT was done in July 1957. This year there was a substantial increase in malaria rates; for the first time *P. falciparum* exceeded *P. vivax;* and infection occurred in infants under 12 months of age.

Visiting Scientists:
Dr. Charles O. Handley, Jr., U. S. National Museum.
Dr. Alexander Wetmore, Smithsonian Institution.
Mr. George Kunkel, University of Pennsylvania.
Dr. Félix Pifano and Dr. Ignacio Ortiz, Instituto de Medicina Tropical, Universidad Central de Venezuela.
Dr. W. A. A. Brown and Dr. J. P. Duret, World Health Organization.
Dr. O. P. Forattini and Dr. J. Lane, University of São Paulo, São Paulo, Brazil.

1959 *Yellow Fever Investigations:* Collection of forest canopy mosquitoes was continued at various stations. At the Cerro Azul station, 7,040 mosquitoes were taken but no yellow fever virus was isolated. However, three other unidentified viruses were recovered from pools of these mosquitoes. At the Paya River station, 10,888 mosquitoes were captured alive. Yellow fever virus was not recovered but four other virus isolations were made; two of these were identified as strains of St. Louis encephalitis virus. During the year a collecting station was established on the slope of Mount Tacarcuna in Darien Province at an elevation above 1,500 feet. A total of 4,530 mosquitoes were taken at this station, none of which yielded yellow fever virus, although a single isolate of St. Louis encephalitis virus was obtained. During the year a second camp was established on the banks of the Tacarcuna River for a survey of the mammalian fauna of the region. Some 90 species of mammals were collected.

In the survey of the captured forest animals for antibodies against yellow fever, some 261 primates and other mammals were collected. Tests were completed on 119, of which two were positive. Both animals were from the Chepo area; the positives probably represented only residual immunity from the last known outbreak of yellow fever in that area in 1956.

The Ecology of Arboviruses Other Than Yellow Fever: Additional findings of St. Louis encephalitis virus were of special interest because they added to previous isolations in 1957 and 1958, which represented the first recovery of the virus from Panama. Identification was confirmed by several other laboratories. In transmission experiments with this virus, a number of mosquito species were utilized. Infection was obtained in two chickens through bites of *Culex pipiens quinquefasciatus*. Trials with *Sabethes chloropterus* were unsatisfactory because of death of all but one of the mosquitoes during the incubation period. However, the injection of the dead mosquito material into mice transmitted the virus.

An outbreak of equine encephalitis in horses in 1958 near Pacora led to a cooperative project with the Middle America Research Unit (MARU) of the National Institutes of Health to determine mosquito vectors of the virus. A total of 23,089 mosquitoes were collected but attempts to isolate the virus were unsuccessful. However, another unidentified virus was isolated.

Leishmaniasis Studies: A number of areas were surveyed for cases of cutaneous leishmaniasis. At Quebrada Bonita, 28 families consisting of 144 persons were examined; these families resided along the highway. In houses removed from the highway and accessible by trail, 29 families with 124 persons were surveyed. A history of leishmaniasis was obtained in 43 cases, of which 39 had been in areas removed from the highway. La Zumbadora in the Cerro Azul area continued to be an active focus of the disease; four members of the field force of the laboratory contracted the disease in this area, three of them within the past year. Of 82 persons who had lived in the area for more than 4 months, 47 contracted the disease. During March 1959 another focus of the disease was discovered in and near the village of Carriazo on the Pacora River about 30 miles east of Panama City. Twenty-five cases were observed. Another focus was found at Santa Clara in Chiriqui Province.

Negative results were obtained in attempts to isolate *Leishmania* from 612 wild-caught animals during the year. Even spiny rats from the active focus at La Zumbadora proved negative.

Inoculations were made in a number of experimental animals without establishing any infections. A series of 16 spiny rats were inoculated intracardially with rich cultures of *Leishmania*. Positive cultures from the liver were obtained at 6½ hours but not after 24 hours. One of many sandflies fed on the rats became infected. Infection followed skin inoculation of suckling mice but the infections did not persist; apparently immune mechanisms began to operate within a period of 15 to 16 days thus stifling the growth of the organisms.

Inability to keep sandflies alive in culture beyond 4 or 5 days following the first oviposition had materially retarded efforts to experimentally transmit *Leishmania* infections. Persistent attempts have been made to overcome this difficulty. Success has now been achieved in maintaining *Phle-*

botomus sanguinarius and *P. gomezi* through the fifth and seventh laboratory generations, respectively. *P. trapidoi* and *P. ylephilector* have been maintained through the second and third generations, respectively.

Continued studies were made on infecting sandflies by feeding with a pipette. A total of 223 *P. sanguinarius* were fed, of which 36 out of 50 dissected showed flagellates in the mid-intestine. Other species also became infected by this method. Continued practice led to success in about 85 percent of the trials.

Further studies were made on breeding areas of sandflies and evidence indicated again that the man-biting species do not breed in the soil surrounding tree buttresses. Search has been made for diurnal resting places of the man-biting species. Collections were obtained in small numbers by disturbing leaves and vegetation on the forest floor. Adults were found also in considerable numbers on the trunks of certain trees.

American Trypanosomiasis: Continued search for *Trypanosoma cruzi* in Panama mammals has been made by the blood culture technique. The parasite is widely disseminated and has been recovered from 13 genera representing five separate orders of mammals. *Trypanosoma rangeli* has been encountered in a wide variety of rodents.

The absence of one of the vectors, *Rhodnius pallescens,* in houses was formerly thought to be due to the widespread use of residual insecticides. However, more recent observations indicated that the insect is attracted by light and enters houses during the evening hours. A very high percentage of this species was found infected with *T. cruzi.*

Malaria Studies: Drug treatment was continued in the Chagres River villages, which were sprayed once during the year with Dieldrin. There was a marked reduction in the average bimonthly and cumulative parasite rates; no infections were encountered during the year in infants under 12 months of age; in comparison with last year only *Plasmodium vivax* infections were noted.

Visiting Scientists:

Dr. C. O. Handley, Jr. and Mr. B. R. Feinstein, U. S. National Museum.

Major Herbert C. Barnett and Mr. William Suyemoto, Walter Reed Army Institute of Research.

Dr. Saul Adler, Hebrew University, Jerusalem, Israel.

Several members of the post-graduate medical fellowship program of the Louisiana State University School of Medicine visited the Laboratory, as in past years.

Additions to the Staff:
Phyllis T. Johnson, Ph.D. rejoined the staff as a biologist on the leishmaniasis project.

Eustorgio Méndez, M.S., came on duty as a vertebrate zoologist.

1960   ***Yellow Fever Investigations:*** These studies were continued by Medical Entomologist Pedro Galindo and Dr. Rodaniche, the Virologist.

The Cerro Azul project was maintained with partial support from a grant from the National Institutes of Health. Mosquito collecting stations have been maintained in this area without interruption since 1949. The area is east of Panama City and is heavily forested. Yellow fever virus was active in the area in 1948 and again in 1956. Mosquito collections during the year were restricted to daytime; a total of 8,992 mosquitoes were taken. Mosquito pools were inoculated intracerebrally into mice for virus isolation. Yellow fever virus was not isolated. Four other viral agents were detected; one was identified as that of St. Louis encephalitis from *Wyeomyia* spp. This virus had been recovered in three sections of Panama, from Cerro Azul in 1959, from Paya in Darien Province in 1958 and from Buena Vista in 1957. The three other virus isolations were from *Haemagogus spegazzinii falco* (= *Haemagogus capricornii falco*), *H. equinus* and *Sabethes* spp.

The survey of Panama animals for antibodies against yellow fever was continued for the 10th successive year. With the exception of 44 howler monkeys from Bocas del Toro Province, most of the primates tested were obtained from sections of Panama east of the Panama Canal. Of 131 monkeys tested, one was positive. This animal came from Darien Province. Seven positive reactions were encountered in 308 other animals and birds. These reactions may have been non-specific.

The Ecology of Arboviruses Other Than Yellow Fever: A 3-year project, supported in part by a grant from the National Institutes of Health, was initiated in the Almirante area in cooperation with the Middle America Research Unit of the National Institutes of Health and the United Fruit Co. The investigations embraced previous objectives in attempting to isolate viruses from wild-caught arthropods, and to search for antibodies in the blood of man and wild and domestic animals. In addition, special attention was to be given to the role of birds as reservoirs of viruses. At the same time, search was made for Plasmodia occurring in different species of birds.

A total of 138,064 mosquitoes and *Phlebotomus* sandflies were captured during the year. Isolation studies were conducted both at the Gorgas Memorial Laboratory and the Middle America Research Unit. A total of 622 pools of 68,899 diptera were tested. In all, 25 viral agents were isolated but remained to be identified. Of the 25 viral agents obtained, nine were from mosquitoes of the subgenus *Janthinosoma* of *Psorophora,* while *Phlebotomus* yielded an equal number.

Blood samples were obtained from a total of 1,306 mammals, 650 birds and 35 reptiles. Ilhéus virus was isolated from the blood of a little blue heron, *Florida caerulea,* and from a keel-billed toucan, *Ramphastos sulfuratus.* In addition, antibodies against this virus were found in the blood of 5 of 62 birds tested.

In the survey for avian Plasmodia, the following organisms were encountered: *Plasmodium,* five species; *Haemoproteus* spp., *Leucocytozoon* sp. and *Trypanosoma* spp.

An outbreak of eastern equine encephalitis in horses in the Tocumen area led to the establishment of a mosquito collecting station in the area. In August 1959 over 32,000 mosquitoes were captured; two viral agents were isolated but neither proved to be that of eastern equine encephalitis.

Early in 1959, blood specimens were taken from 195 inhabitants along the Tuira, Pucro and Paya Rivers in Darien Province. In addition, 248 blood specimens were obtained from mammals and birds in the region. During the present year, the sera were tested against three group B viruses. Of the human bloods, 8.4 percent neutralized two or more logs of St. Louis virus; 43.7 percent neutralized two or more logs of Ilhéus virus; and 42 percent neutralized two or more logs of yellow fever virus. The yellow fever positives may have been due to immunization by vaccination. Eleven, or 10.3 percent, of the avian bloods were positive for St. Louis virus.

Leishmaniasis Studies: Therapeutic trials were made with pyrimethamine alone and in combination with sulfadimethoxine. Results were of considerable promise, particularly in children in whom the lesions healed promptly and completely. The addition of sulfadimethoxine was of advantage in cases with pronounced secondary infection of ulcers.

Epidemiological studies were continued. Blood isolations of *Leishmania* were attempted from 590 animals; all were negative. Intradermal implantation of *Leishmania* in suckling mice was continued with the same results as before; the parasites disappeared in about 21 days. A Peruvian highland strain was used for intradermal injection in the face of hamsters. Some 12 or 15 hamsters have been infected; the lesions were slight and there appeared to be considerable variation in the infectivity of strains. Following the successful infection of hamsters by Garnham and Lewis with a strain of *Leishmania* in British Honduras, efforts were made to secure strains from Guatemala, which are apparently closely related to that from the former country. Lesions produced in hamsters were somewhat more pronounced than those with strains from Panama.

Sandflies continued to be infected by the pipette route. However, feeding of infected sandflies on spiny rats and other animals did not result in infection. In one case, a human volunteer remained negative.

In search for breeding places of sandflies, larvae of *Phlebotomus trapidoi* and *P. ylephilector* were recovered under decaying leaves and other debris on the forest floor.

Arthropod Taxonomy: The work on *Phlebotomus* and other biting arthropods was continued. Dr. Fairchild spent two months in Brazil revising the collection of Tabanidae formed by the late Dr. Adolpho Lutz at the Instituto Oswaldo Cruz. In addition to assisting in the leishmaniasis project, Dr. Phyllis Johnson continued her studies on sucking lice, *Anoplura*. Mr. E. Méndez, in cooperation with Capt. V. J. Tipton, continued his study of the fleas of Panama.

Malaria Studies: Malaria treatment was continued in the Chagres River villages for the 29th year. There was little change in infection rates over last year, although it was evident that transmission was still taking place.

Cultivation of Hemoflagellates: The U. S. Naval Medical Science Unit at the Gorgas Memorial Laboratory was reestablished in September 1959 with the assignment of Lt. Commander Alan C. Pipkin and HMC William C. Coles. The unit has been engaged in studies of the development of the tissue phase of several hemoflagellates of man. In certain types of culture cells, *T. cruzi* developed to some extent. Some success was achieved also in preliminary experiments with *L. donovani*. Explants prepared from newborn Syrian hamster spleen and liver grown on coverglass substrate in Leighton tubes at 37°C for 8 to 10 days were seeded with conventional diphasic blood agar cultures of *L. braziliensis*, producing fair numbers of intracellular leishmaniform organisms in both types of cells. The parasite penetrated macrophages from peritoneal exudate from cotton rats.

Visiting Scientists:

Dr. John Strangways-Dixon and Dr. Ralph Lainson, London School of Hygiene and Tropical Medicine.

Dr. C. O. Handley, Jr., U. S. National Museum.

Twenty-two fellows in the tropical medicine program of the Louisiana State University School of Medicine spent 7 to 10 days at the Laboratory.

1961 *The Ecology of Arboviruses Other than Yellow Fever:*
        This project represented a continuation of that established last year in the Almirante area and other areas previously employed. The work included attempted virus isolations from human patients, arthropod vectors, sentinel mice and wild vertebrates. Various techniques were employed in the collection of arthropods. A total of 249,528 were captured alive. One-

half of each pool was tested at the Gorgas Memorial Laboratory and the other half at the Middle America Research Unit. Twenty-nine viral agents were isolated at Gorgas and 18 at the latter laboratory. Isolations were made from *Phlebotomus* spp., and species of *Culex, Psorophora, Mansonia* and *Aedes* mosquitoes. The host preference of mosquitoes and sandflies was studied with man, the horse, chickens and laboratory mice as attractants. *Culex vomerifer* appeared to be the species with the widest host range; *Mansonia venezuelensis* (=*Coquillettidia venezuelensis*) also exhibited a wide range of hosts; *Phlebotomus* spp. fed on man, the horse and mice but not on chickens.

Exposure of sentinel mice was initiated in the month of January. Exposure was for 24 hours at pre-determined locations. From January 15 to April 25, a total of 64 litters consisting of 422 mice were exposed with negative results. From May 2 to August 15, 52 litters of 369 were exposed; 55 viral agents were obtained from mice of 19 different litters.

Sera from 160 birds belonging to 45 species were inoculated into suckling mice for virus isolation. Two agents were obtained from the scarlet-rumped tanager, *Ramphocelus passerinii,* and one from the clay-colored robin, *Turdus grayi.*

Sera from 184 mammals representing eight species were inoculated into suckling mice for virus isolation. Thirteen viral agents were obtained from the cotton rat, *Sigmodon hispidus,* and five from the spiny rat, *Proechimys semispinosus.* No viruses were obtained from the 12 blood specimens from *Iguana iguana.*

In the month of June, 30 cases of febrile illness of unknown origin were admitted to the Almirante Hospital. Of 720 persons inhabiting part of the town of Almirante, 52 suffered a febrile illness of more than 2 and less than 6 days duration in the month of June. Venezuelan equine encephalomyelitis virus was isolated from human patients, sentinel mice, mosquitoes and wild rodents. Previous epidemiological studies indicated that the virus was absent from the area from September 1959 to April 1961. The first isolation was obtained from a pool of 157 *Culex vomerifer* collected 2 miles outside of Almirante between April 27 and May 2. The following week the virus was recovered from a spiny rat. Other rodent isolations were secured in May and June. First virus recovery from man was made in June. A virus resembling VEE in its pathogenicity for mice was isolated from the following species of mosquitoes: *Culex vomerifer, Culex taeniopus* and *Culex pipiens quinquefasciatus.* The mosquitoes were captured in the vicinity of the outbreak, some outside and some inside of the houses of ill persons. VEE virus was isolated from 18 sentinel mice and nine wild rats, four of which were trapped near the residence of one of the human cases from which VEE virus was recovered. The cotton rat, *Sigmodon hispidus,* would appear to be a reservoir host of importance.

In April of 1961 a boy from the town of Cañito on Gatun Lake died in Hospital del Niño in Panama City; VEE virus was isolated from autopsy material by the Middle America Research Unit. In cooperation with that Unit, epidemiological studies were carried out in the vicinity. Sera were collected from all the inhabitants as well as from domestic animals and were to be processed at MARU. A total of 20,519 mosquitoes, *Phlebotomus,* and *Culicoides* were collected during the month of May. At Gorgas, 10,292 insects were inoculated into suckling mice. Five viral agents were isolated; two from *Culex* spp., two from *Psorophora ferox* and one from *Anopheles* spp. Positive identification of the agents was awaited but one of the isolates elicited a response in mice similar to VEE virus.

Hemoparasites of Birds: Dr. Octavio Sousa came on duty in January to pursue these studies. They were designed to determine the frequency of such parasites, the time of life in which high incidence occurred, and the mosquito vectors, as well as to investigate groups of birds serving as reservoir hosts for arthropod-borne viruses. Examinations were made of 1,152 slides from 102 species of birds. The overall infection rate was 22.8 percent. A number of species showed a high prevalence of infection. Intensive studies were conducted with two common species, *Ramphocelus passerinii* and *Sporophila aurita corvina.* The first 54 specimens of the former species showed an infection rate with hemoparasites of 90.0 percent. Parasites encountered were *Plasmodium spp., Haemoproteus* spp., microfilariae and trypanosomes.

Leishmaniasis Studies: Endemic areas in which these studies were conducted included Quebrada Bonita on the transisthmian highway, La Zumbadora in the Cerro Azul region, the rain forest on the Caribbean side in Bocas del Toro Province near Almirante and at Santa Rita on the Pacific side about 25 miles west of the Canal Zone.

Natural infections of wild-caught Panamanian *Phlebotomus* sandflies with leptomonad flagellates, consistent morphologically with *Leishmania,* were first found in January of 1961. Dissections in previous years had not disclosed such infections. Following this discovery, an infection rate of 6.4 percent was found in 3,112 females representing six species of *Phlebotomus.* Five of the species were the commonest man-biting forest sandflies.

The source of infection in the sandflies had not been determined. There was a suggestion that sandfly collections in the forest canopy may indicate the possibility of an arboreal infection source. Unlike the classical type of infection in kala azar and oriental sore of the Old World, where the organisms occur mainly in the anterior part of the midgut and extend into the pharynx, the majority of infections encountered in local sandflies were in the hindgut. However, most infections were extremely light. In the man-

137

biting species there was suspicion that cultured leptomonads might represent two different species. In regard to the hindgut infections, the same growth pattern of leptomonad flagellates attached and multiplying in a limited section of the hindgut just posterior to the Malpighian tubules, had also been noted in the large series of sandflies fed artificially on cultures of human strains, together with growth in the anterior part of the midgut.

Efforts were continued to infect hamsters with human strains of *Leishmania*. Infections could be established at will by the use of heavy inoculum from recent isolates. Older strains in culture for several years provided less predictable results. The strain obtained from Guatemala was producing extensive lesions in hamsters.

Cultivation of Hemoflagellates: The U. S. Naval Medical Science Unit continued work on this project. Emphasis was placed on the development of techniques for intracellular growth of the parasites in tissue culture. Effort was being made to demonstrate immunologic differences between strains of *Leishmania* with the view of clarifying the relationship of strains. Thus far animals infected with *L. tropica* strains from the Middle East had proved resistant to infection with a Guatemalan strain of *L. braziliensis*.

American Trypanosomiasis: Studies were instituted during the year on megaesophagus and myocardial pathology in persons with positive complement fixation tests for Chagas' disease. Recent reports from South America have indicated a direct association between *Trypanosoma cruzi* infection and delayed esophageal transit time and megaesophagus. A study by Dr. Carl M. Johnson in cooperation with Dr. Rafael Sabonge of Santo Tomás Hospital and Dr. César Pinilla, a resident in tropical medicine at the Gorgas Memorial Laboratory, was carried out on 98 individuals of both sexes and varying ages who came from rural areas and Panama City. Approximately one-half had positive complement fixation reactions for Chagas' disease. The negatives constituted the control group. The number showing delayed esophageal transit time was found to be exactly the same for both groups. Since the results were at variance with those from South America, further investigations were contemplated.

Malaria Studies: Therapy was continued in the Chagres River villages for the 30th year. Administration of antimalarial drugs was begun in Río Hato, in cooperation with the U. S. Armed Forces, in an area in which a training center was located.

A combination of pyrimethamine and primaquine was employed in the treatment of the inhabitants of the villages of La Represa and Mendoza on the west side of Gatun Lake about 30 miles northwest of Panama City. Therapy was on a voluntary basis with the drug being available in schools in the two areas. The drugs were supposed to be taken at weekly intervals at a dose rate of 50 mg. of pyrimethamine and 40 mg. of primaquine for a person 100 lbs. of weight and over. Graduated smaller doses were used for individuals of lesser weights.

In La Represa, four surveys between March and June 1960 revealed combined malaria rates for adults and children between 14.6 and 20.3 percent. In Mendoza, three surveys between April and June 1960 showed rates of 5.4 to 6.7 percent. Inquiry revealed that 65 percent of the people took the drugs once a week as instructed and an additional 25 percent on an average of every 2 weeks. The remaining 10 percent was made up of individuals who moved out of the area after the beginning of the program or those who visited the area during the year. Monthly surveys indicated that after August 1960 no malaria occurred in the study area.

Visiting Scientists:
Dr. Alexander Wetmore, Smithsonian Institution.
Dr. John Legler, University of Utah.
Dr. Saul Adler, Hebrew University, Jerusalem, Israel.
Dr. D. J. Lewis, British Museum, London, England.
A total of 17 Fellows in four groups spent about a week each in the Laboratory in connection with the post-graduate tropical medicine fellowship program of the Louisiana State University School of Medicine.

Dr. Sarah B. Pipkin was engaged on studies on the genetics of *Drosophila.*

Staff Changes:
Dr. Enid de Rodaniche resigned in May to accept an appointment in the Medical School of the University of Panama. However, she continued to work part time on the identification of viruses isolated during the arbovirus program.

Dr. Margaret A. Grayson joined the staff as a virologist in June.

Dr. Octavio Sousa was appointed parasitologist on the staff in January.

Mr. W. J. Hanson, a temporary appointee for studies on the ecology of *Phlebotomus,* returned to the University of Kansas.

César Pinilla, M.D. joined the staff as a medical resident.

1962 Construction was well along on the new laboratory building provided by the 86th Congress (P.L. 86-617 of July 12, 1960) with an appropriation of $500,000 and dedication ceremonies were being planned for early 1963. Plans were being made for a new modern insectary to be constructed from private funds.

Research in clinical tropical medicine was enhanced through the co-operation of the Government of Panama, which agreed to provide beds as needed in the Hospital del Niño for research in children's diseases. Similar arrangements and facilities have been made available for a number of beds in nearby Santo Tomás Hospital.

The Ecology of Arboviruses: The work represented a continuation of the Almirante and Cerro Azul projects and further surveillance for yellow fever in eastern Panama. Identification of viral agents was considerably curtailed because of construction of the new building and the remodeling of facilities in the old building.

Reisolations were made from sera collected in the Almirante area last year. Two isolations were tentatively identified as VEE virus. Antigen and antisera from the blood of three mosquito collectors were sent to the Belem Virus Laboratory, Belem, Brazil, which reported that of the group C isolates, the "Ossa" isolate was closely related to or identical with Apeu virus. This represented the first isolation of a Group C virus from Middle America.

In initial isolations from 1962 collections, 38 human sera from febrile patients were inoculated into suckling mice. Three viral agents were isolated.

Mosquito collections were curtailed because of the remodeling. However, more than 23,500 blood-sucking Diptera were gathered, of which 4,195 specimens composing 159 pools were inoculated into suckling mice. Two viral isolations were made from mosquitoes.

Work during the previous 2 years had demonstrated the importance of birds in the ecology of Ilhéus encephalitis virus in Almirante. This agent was isolated from the blood of three species of birds and serological tests had indicated a high rate of infection in these species and in other avian hosts as well. There was initiated on March 1, 1962 a year's cycle of studies to determine the importance of nestlings in transmission of Ilhéus and other viruses. Detailed information was recorded concerning each bird's nest found, the nature of the environment, the number of eggs, and the number of nestlings or fledglings. Finally, the parent birds were bled, the fledglings were captured and the nests collected for recovery and identification of ectoparasites. During a period of 4 months, 1,158 nests belonging to 54 different species were found and tagged. Of these, 335 nests contained fully fledged birds from which 612 nestlings were collected. From 169 tissues removed from nestlings and inoculated intracerebrally into suckling mice, nine viruses were obtained from five species of birds, as follows: Two specimens of *Ramphocelus passerinii,* one *Myiozetetes similis,* two *Myiozetetes granadensis,* one *Crotophaga sulcirostris,* and one *Icterus prosthemelas.*

During the year 128 mammalian and six avian sera were inoculated into suckling mice with the isolation of six viral agents. Studies with sentinel mice were continued. During a period of 9 months, 1,352 mice in 198

140

liters were exposed, from which nine viral agents were isolated, all in the month of October.

In cooperation with the Middle America Research Unit, virus studies were continued in the Almirante area. Of 371 human sera, 108, or 29.1 percent, were positive for VEE virus on both complement fixation (CF) and hemagglutination (HI) tests. Of 32 other sera from humans, seven were positive for VEE virus. The sera of 69 equines, two calves and two dogs collected in August 1961 were tested for CF and HI antibodies to VEE, EEE and Una viruses. Twenty-six of 60 equine sera contained CF antibodies to VEE. Two sera negative for VEE were positive for EEE. The sera of the two dogs contained VEE antibodies. These results indicated the widespread distribution of VEE virus in and near Almirante during the outbreak of last year.

Surveillance for jungle yellow fever in eastern Panama during the year failed to disclose the presence of the virus.

Leishmaniasis Studies: Leptomonad infections in wild-caught sandflies were first found in January of last year. Following this discovery intensive search was made for infected flies, and for all of 1961, they were found in 416 of 4,885 females of six of the seven common man-biting species. The infected sandflies represented catches in seven different areas, five of which were known to be endemic foci of cutaneous leishmaniasis. During the current year, out of 685 females dissected, 10 percent were infected. Cultures have been made of leptomonads recovered from the sandflies and two strains have produced lesions at the tip of the nose in hamsters. The lesions were indistinguishable from those produced by local human strains of *Leishmania*.

It had still not been possible to find reservoir hosts in lower animals. Xeno-diagnosis was tried in a number of opossums trapped in an area where human cases have occurred. A flagellate found in the hind gut of one of the sandflies fed on the animals was probably the crithidiform stage of a trypanosome. A Peruvian strain of *L. braziliensis* from a case of espundia produced nasal lesions in a hamster with destruction of surrounding tissues.

Treatment of cutaneous leishmaniasis has been continued with pyrimethamine on an experimental basis. During the past year the drug has been given orally with notable success in patients ranging in age from 2 months to over 50 years. The drug is apparently more effective in children than adults for reasons yet unknown. Toxic reactions have been minimal and apparently were associated with the antifolic acid property of the drug.

American Trypanosomiasis: The U. S. Naval Medical Science Unit conducted field studies on the triatomid vectors of *Trypanosoma cruzi* mainly in the Chorrera district of Panama Province. A total of 1,640 triatomid bugs have been taken from human and animal habitations, most of the specimens being caught at night. Infectivity rates with *T. cruzi* averaged 32.6 percent. With the exception of six specimens, all of the bugs collected were *Rhodnius pallescens*. In spite of its close association with man, evidence indicated that this species was not an efficient vector.

Malaria Studies: The communities of La Represa and Mendoza, in which voluntary treatment with pyrimethamine and primaquine was initiated in 1960 were free of malaria. With the view of a later withdrawal of the drug from the two villages, treatment was started in an extensive peripheral zone.

Arthropod Taxonomy: Work on the taxonomy and host relationship of the ticks of Panama has been continued on a collaborative basis with Major V. J. Tipton, U.S. Army and Dr. Glen M. Kohls, Rocky Mountain Laboratory. Over 1,000 lots of adult ticks and some 200 lots of nymphs and larvae have been tabulated as to host and locality. Also in collaboration with Major Tipton, a project on the fleas of Panama was in progress. To date, 37 species and subspecies belonging to 22 genera have been studied, of which six were new to science and seven new to the fauna of Panama. Dr. Fairchild continued his studies on Tabanidae; four additional new records brought the known species for Panama to 136.

Staff Additions:
Vernon E. Thatcher, Ph.D., Insect Ecologist, Leishmaniasis Project, and Manuel A. Vásquez, M.D., Medical Resident, joined the staff during the year.

The Gorgas Memorial Laboratory
The Research Program
1956-1962
A Summation

Yellow Fever Surveillance: Yellow fever surveillance was continued throughout most of the period. Early in 1956, the disease appeared in the Motagua River Valley in Guatemala and the virus was isolated from captured *Haemagogus mesodentatus mesodentatus, H. equinus* and *Sabethes chloropterus* mosquitoes. In August 1956 a fatal case of the disease was contracted in the Cerro Azul area of Panama Province. The virus was obtained from 4 of 78 aboreal mammals from the general vicinity. Virus isolations were made from captured mosquitoes but not after January 1957. In the first week of July 1957 two suspected cases of the disease occurred in the Buena Vista area and a member of a mosquito collecting team contracted the disease. The virus was isolated from pools of *Haemagogus spegazzinii falco* (= *Haemagogus capricornii falco*) and *H. lucifer* captured in the area. In a survey of aboreal mammals in 1958, two from the Chepo area were positive on protection tests. These probably represented residual immunity from the last known outbreak of yellow fever in the area in 1956. In 1960, one animal from Darien Province was positive. Surveillance in eastern Panama in 1962 failed to disclose the presence of the virus.

Yellow Fever Investigations: Previous failures to transmit yellow fever by the bites of *Sabethes chloropterus* led to a study of the life cycle and biology of this species. As a result of these observations, experimental procedures were modified and successful transmission of the disease to monkeys (*Macaca mulatta*) was accomplished. The capability of this species of mosquito to transmit the disease during the dry season in Middle America was thus demonstrated. It appeared, however, that a high titer of virus in the infective meal, a prolonged incubation period and a highly susceptible host are required.

The Ecology of Arboviruses Other Than Yellow Fever: Increasing emphasis was placed on studies with other arthropod-borne viruses; much of the work was in collaboration with the Middle America Research Unit of the National Institutes of Health. In this work a number of devices were employed; these included search for viruses in wild and domestic mammals, wild birds, captured mosquitoes, sentinel mice and human sera. A considerable number of viruses were isolated, some of which remained to be identified at the end of the period. First isolations in Middle America were made of Ilhéus and a Group C virus. The recovery of St. Louis encephalitis virus was the first from Panama.

Outbreaks of equine encephalomyelitis occurred in horses at Pacora in 1958 and Tocumen in 1959. Human cases appeared at Cañito Island on Gatun Lake in April 1961 and Almirante in June 1961. The latter outbreak involved a considerable number of individuals. Venezuelan equine encephalomyelitis virus was isolated from human patients, sentinel mice, mosquitoes and wild rodents. The first mosquito isolation was made from *Culex vomerifer;* subsequently other species were found to be involved. The cotton rat, *Sigmodon hispidus,* appeared to be an important reservoir host.

Birds collected for the arbovirus studies were examined for blood parasites. Those encountered were *Plasmodium* spp., *Haemoproteus* spp., microfilariae and trypanosomes.

Leishmaniasis Studies: Leishmaniasis studies were considerably augmented. Several important foci of human infection were discovered. In initial efforts to determine lower animal reservoirs, in 1956 and 1957 *Leishmania braziliensis* was cultured from the blood of several spiny rats, *Proechimys semispinosus* and *Hoplomys gymnurus.* Consistent failures were encountered in subsequent isolation attempts from these animals as well as from others. The parasite from a spiny rat produced a typical lesion of cutaneous leishmaniasis in a human volunteer.

Difficulties in initial attempts at rearing man-biting species of *Phlebotomus* were finally overcome, so that a number of species could be maintained through several generations and in two cases through continuous laboratory generations.

In transmission experiments, sandflies refused to feed on lesions and had to be infected by pipette. Hamsters could be infected by injection of the organism into the tip of the nose. Lesions were usually limited in extent, although a Peruvian strain from an espundia case produced extensive involvement. Transmission was not accomplished by bites of infected sandflies.

Clues were obtained concerning the breeding and resting places of sandflies. Larvae of certain species were found in the soil around tree buttresses in the forest but most of these represented species which did not bite man. Larvae of some of the man-biting species were recovered from under leaves and debris on the forest floor. Adults of some species were observed resting on tree trunks. In 1961 for the first time, sandflies infected with *L. braziliensis* were discovered in nature.

Considerable success was achieved in the treatment of cutaneous leishmaniasis with pyrimethamine administered orally. For unknown reasons, the drug was more effective in children than in adults. Toxic reactions were minimal.

American Trypanosomiasis: *Trypanosoma cruzi* was found to be widely disseminated in wild mammals and was recovered from 13 genera representing five different orders. *Rhodnius pallescens* appeared to be mainly responsible for transmission of infection to man. On the basis of reports from South America that *T. cruzi* infection was associated with delayed esophageal transit time and megaesophagus, studies were conducted on 98 individuals about one-half of whom were infected. The negative group served as controls. The number showing delayed esophageal transit time was approximately the same in both groups.

Malaria Studies: Malaria treatment in the Chagres River villages was continued without notable change in results. Voluntary treatment was instituted in 1960 in two villages on the west side of Gatun Lake. A combination of pyrimethamine and primaquine was provided for use once a week. Monthly surveys indicated that no malaria had occurred in the villages after August 1960.

Other Activities: The U. S. Naval Medical Science Unit was reestablished in September 1959. The Unit was engaged in cultivation of hemoflagellates and studies on the epidemiology of Chagas' disease.

Alterations were made in the physical plant during the period. At its close, construction was well along on a new laboratory building. Plans were being made for a new modern insectary to be built with funds provided by a private foundation.

A number of staff changes occurred during the period with a considerable number of additions to the professional staff.

Activities of the Gorgas Memorial Institute 1956-1962

1956

Annual Meeting: The annual meeting of the Corporation was convened in Washington on November 7, 1956. President Siler explained that the date of the meeting had been changed from the second Wednesday in October, as provided by the By-Laws, in order that certain members of the Gorgas Memorial Laboratory staff could be in the country to attend the meetings of the American Society of Tropical Medicine and Hygiene from November 1 to 3.

After the usual business, the meeting of the Board of Directors followed. President Siler reported that Army contracts governing the hemorrhagic fever and yellow fever studies had been extended for fiscal year 1957 without authorization for additional funds. It was reported also that a grant-in-aid for leishmaniasis research had been approved by the National Institutes of Health in the sum of $25,200 for the period September 1956 —September 1957 and in the sum of $14,800 for 2 additional years.

The budget for 1958 in the sum of $147,000 was approved with recommendation that the Executive Committee consider increasing the appropriation to be requested from Congress to $150,000, the limit of the ceiling.

Colonel J. F. Siler was reelected President and Governor Maurice H. Thatcher, Vice President.

Executive Committee Meeting: The Executive Committee met on November 9, 1956 and voted a budget increase to $150,000 for fiscal year 1958. It was suggested that efforts be made to secure from Congress an increase in the annual appropriation. A figure of $200,000 to $250,000 was discussed but no conclusions were reached. Dr. Johnson who attended the meeting reported dissatisfaction among non-professional Panama employees over the provisions of the TIAA annuity plan. A request had been made by them to participate in the Provident Fund Plan as this would provide a lump sum payment upon retirement in lieu of annuities which would be too small. Dr. Johnson was requested to investigate the matter further.

1957 *Annual Meeting:* The annual meeting was held in Washington on October 24, 1957. Resolutions were adopted on the deaths of former directors Dr. Augusto S. Boyd and Captain Colón Eloy Alfaro. Following the election of directors, the meeting adjourned and was followed by that of the Board of Directors. The budget for fiscal year 1959 in the sum of $150,000 was approved. It was pointed out, however, by President Siler that the total funds available would be about $235,034 due to Army contracts and U. S. Public Health Service grants-in-aid.

The election of officers for 1957-58 followed. Colonel Siler felt that he could not accept the presidency again and requested that he not be placed in nomination.

Accordingly, Dr. Walter A. Bloedorn was elected President and Governor Maurice H. Thatcher reelected Vice President. Colonel Siler was designated as President Emeritus. Suitable resolutions were adopted thanking Colonel Siler for his long service as President, a service which began in 1941, and for his continued efforts to promote the interests of the Gorgas Memorial Institute and the Gorgas Memorial Laboratory.

Dr. Walter A. Bloedorn was the third of a group of distinguished retired Naval Medical officers to serve the Gorgas Memorial Institute in the capacity of president.

Walter Andrew Bloedorn was born in Platte Center, Nebraska, November 22, 1886. Educated in his native Nebraska, he received his M.D. degree from Creighton University in 1909. Following graduation, he became Acting Assistant Surgeon at the Navy Medical School and Hospital in Washington, D.C., and was Executive Officer from 1925-28. He did graduate study at the New York Postgraduate Medical School and, later, served abroad at hospitals in London and Vienna.

Dr. Bloedorn has had a long and distinguished medical career at The George Washington University. He earned his M.A. degree from GW in 1915, and in 1948 GW presented him with the honorary degree of Doctor of Science. In 1926, he joined the faculty as Professor of Tropical Medicine and upon his retirement in 1928, as Commander, U. S. Navy Medical Corps, Dr. Bloedorn began serving the University in increasingly responsible positions. He was named Professor of Medicine (1930), Director of Clinics (1931), Assistant Dean (1930), and Dean (1939) of the School of Medicine. He also served as Medical Director of the University Hospital from 1932 until his retirement in 1957. During his 18 years' deanship, there was noticeable improvement in the size of the student body, expansion of the full time teaching staff, a marked increase in research activities, and construction and staffing of a modern University Hospital and Outpatient facility. In 1965, the medical alumni honored him with a citation in recognition of his distinguished service and outstanding contributions to the University and its School of Medicine from 1928 to 1957.

Dr. Bloedorn performed long service as a member of the Executive Committee and, later, as president of the National Board of Medical Examiners. A former president of the Association of American Medical Colleges and member of its executive council and various committees, Dr. Bloedorn has had a nationwide interest in the advancement of medical education. He was chairman of the Audiovisual Education Committee from 1946-57, and rendered valuable service on the Committee for Financing Medical Education.

Dr. Bloedorn's service to medical education continued in both governmental and international affairs. During World War II, he helped establish Army Special Training and Navy V12 programs. In 1959, the Government of Panama decorated Dr. Bloedorn with the Order of Vasco Núñez de Balboa for his service with the Gorgas Memorial Institute and his contribution to the health of the people of Panama.

Dr. Bloedorn served as a consultant for the U. S. Government in military and public health medicine and medical education. He held membership on the Medical and Advisory Board of the Kellogg Foundation, the National Commission of the United Nations Educational, Scientific and Cultural Organization, and served in international activities with the World Health Organization.

Executive Committee Meeting: A meeting of the Executive Committee took place on December 13, 1957. Miss Helen A. King of the Washington Office had been scheduled for retirement on June 30, 1956. By telephone vote her period of service was extended until June 30, 1957 and again to June 30, 1958. Through an oversight the Executive Committee had not formally approved these changes which were now made official.

Retirement Plan for Panama Employees: Because of dissatisfaction of the Panama employees of the Gorgas Memorial Laboratory with the retirement plan, a resolution was passed modifying its original provisions. It was thought more equitable if the requirement for an attained age of 30 was eliminated and also provision was made for voluntary retirement prior to the age of 65.

Staff Regulations: In 1955, the Executive Committee had adopted leave regulations for professional employees of the Gorgas Memorial Laboratory providing among other things that not more than 15 days of annual leave may be accumulated in any one calendar year. United States professional employees much preferred to accumulate their leave for 2 years so as to be able to spend a full 60 days in the United States every second year. After a discussion, the leave regulations were so altered.

A discussion was held concerning staff regulations for the Gorgas Memorial Laboratory, which had been found wanting in certain respects when actually put into operation. The Personnel Committee was asked to review the situation and make recommendations for needed changes.

Personnel Actions: A proposal of Dr. Johnson to increase the salary of Dr. G. B. Fairchild and to designate him as assistant director was approved.

At the request of Dr. Johnson, the service of Dr. Marshall Hertig was extended beyond the normal retirement age of 65 to June 30, 1959.

President's Contemplated Visit to Panama: Dr. Bloedorn stated that since accepting the presidency, he had endeavored to obtain a clearer understanding of activities of the Gorgas Memorial Laboratory, both past and present. He had found this difficult because there had never been a compilation of its activities and accomplishments. This constituted a handicap in efforts to gain additional support for the institution. It was agreed that the President should visit the Laboratory in order to gain first hand information concerning its research program and methods of operation.

1958 *Annual Meeting:* The annual meeting of the Corporation was held in Washington on October 22, 1958. The Board of Directors met after the adjournment of the Corporation meeting. Colonel J. F. Siler was reelected President Emeritus, Dr. Walter A. Bloedorn President and Governor Maurice H. Thatcher Vice President.

President's Report: The President stated that a salary increase of 10 percent for professional employees had been made effective as of January 1, 1958, to correspond with an increase granted U. S. Civil Service employees. On July 1, 1958, a similar increase was granted to other employees.

The President gave an account of his trip to Panama and his visit at the Gorgas Memorial Laboratory. He stated that as a result of the visit he had a greater appreciation of the research accomplishments and a better comprehension of the operational problems.

The President reported that the Executive Committee had discussed at length various possibilities for securing additional financial support for the Gorgas Memorial Laboratory. Public Health Service grants had been received for $43,840 per year for 5 years for the continuation of the leishmaniasis project, and a grant for $25,000 per year for 2 additional years for the yellow fever studies. A third grant in the sum of $35,000 per year for field studies on arthropod-borne viruses had been requested to begin September 1, 1959. While these grants had eased budgetary demands, it was felt that continual dependence should not be placed on this form of research support.

Conferences were held with Senator Lister Hill following which the Senator introduced a bill on April 16, 1958 to amend the Act of May 7, 1928, to increase the authorization to not to exceed $500,000 for "maintenance, operation, expansion, remodeling and alteration." The Bureau of the Budget failed to act on the bill prior to the adjournment of Congress. It was stated that Senator Hill was prepared to reintroduce the bill in the next session of Congress.

The budget for the fiscal year 1960 was adopted in the sum of $278,649, of which $150,000 was requested as a direct appropriation from Congress.

Retirement Plan Changes: The Executive Committee held a meeting on November 28, 1958. Approval was given for employees recruited from positions where they had been included in a TIAA retirement plan to participate in the Institute's plan without any waiting period. The waiting period for other employees was reduced from 3 years to 1 year. Participation in the plan was placed on a voluntary rather than a compulsory basis.

Need for an Executive Officer at GML: Discussion was had on the need for an Executive Officer at the Gorgas Memorial Laboratory. Mr. Frederick R. De Roever, recommended by Dr. L. L. Williams, Jr., was engaged to begin his duties on July 1, 1959.

1959 *Annual Meeting:* The annual meeting of the Gorgas Memorial Institute was held in Washington on November 3, 1959, following which the Board of Directors held its annual meeting. Dr. Walter A. Bloedorn and Governor Maurice H. Thatcher were reelected President and Vice President, respectively.

The President said that it was a pleasure to report the passage of S. 2219 (P.L. 86-296 of September 21, 1959) raising the ceiling on the annual appropriation for the Gorgas Memorial Laboratory from $150,000 to $250,000 and providing an additional $250,000 for the expansion of the physical plant, remodeling of buildings and site improvements. The President stated that this had been accomplished through the aid of numerous individuals and that he was particularly grateful to Senator Hill for his support.

A budget of $393,000 was adopted for the fiscal year 1961, of which $250,000 represented the amount to be requested from Congress and the remainder unobligated funds from the prior year, Public Health Service research grants, and other income.

1960 *Annual Meeting:* The annual meeting of the Gorgas Memorial Institute was held in Washington on November 17, 1960. After the election of directors, adjournment was followed by the meeting of the Board of Directors. Dr. Walter A. Bloedorn was reelected President and Governor Maurice H. Thatcher Vice President. Resolutions were adopted on the deaths of Col. J. F. Siler on February 7, 1960 and Dr. Herbert C. Clark on November 8, 1960.

President's Report: The President reported that legislation (S. 3179) had been enacted to increase the appropriation for plant improvement from $250,000 to $500,000 (P.L. 86-617 of July 12, 1960). Following such passage, the Executive Committee had engaged Mr. Clarence W. May, retired Superintendent of Buildings and Grounds at the National Institutes of Health, as a consultant on the building program. A contract was entered into with the architectural firm of Schay & Holzer of Panama for preparation of plans for the new laboratory building and for the renovation of the animal house.

The President reported that the Executive Committee had approved pay increases for the GML professionals and Washington Office staff to conform with increases for Civil Service G.S. grades. The Executive Committee also authorized appointment of a parasitologist to the Gorgas Memorial Laboratory staff as a successor for Dr. Rodaniche, the virologist, who had resigned, and a successor for the Executive Officer, Mr. De Roever, who had resigned.

Certificate Award to Senator Hill: Governor Thatcher suggested that a "certificate of merit" be authorized and presented to Senator Lister Hill in appreciation of his invaluable assistance for initiating and supporting the legislation which provided for increases in the operating budget and the amount approved for expansion of the physical plant. Favorable action was taken on this suggestion and the suitably inscribed certificate was presented to Senator Hill on June 2, 1961.

The budget for 1962 in the sum of $344,837 was approved. This amount included the sum of $92,146 from Public Health Service grants-in-aid.

1961   *Annual Meeting:* The annual meeting of the Corporation was convened in Washington on October 30, 1961. The annual meeting of the Board of Directors followed. It was stated that Dr. Walter A. Bloedorn did not feel that he could continue to serve any longer as President. Out of deference to his wishes, Major General Paul H. Streit, Medical Corps, U. S. Army, (Ret.) was nominated and elected to the Presidency. Governor Maurice H. Thatcher was reelected Vice President.

General Streit brought to the presidency of the Gorgas Memorial Institute an unusual organizational ability and a rare experience in the administration of large medical research programs.

General Streit was born in Seguin, Texas on March 18, 1891, the son of a Methodist minister. His pre-medical education was obtained at the

Blinn Memorial College and the University of Texas. He enrolled in the Medical Branch of the University of Texas in Galveston in 1912 and received his M.D. degree in 1916. To augment the support which his parents were able to give him, he worked as an assistant in the pathological laboratory of the Medical School and sold to other students mimeographed notes which he compiled of various lectures.

In January 1917 he took the examinations for a commission in the Regular U. S. Army Medical Corps. He completed his interneship at John Sealy Hospital in Galveston in June of 1917 and was commissioned as a First Lieutenant in the Army Medical Corps on July 18, 1917. In 1918, he was a battalion surgeon with the 87th Division in the American Expeditionary Forces in France. Following the Armistice, he was ordered to the University of Bordeaux for an 8-months' course in otolaryngology. This was followed by an unusual assignment as commanding officer of the American War Brides camp at Brest, France.

In November 1919, General Streit volunteered to join the American Typhus Relief Expedition to Poland where he remained on duty for 1 year. His next assignment was at a station hospital at Coblentz, Germany with the American Army of Occupation. He returned from Germany in 1921 and subsequently graduated from the Army Medical Field Service School in Washington, D.C. in 1923. In 1925, he was ordered to New York for an additional year of post-graduate training in otolaryngology at the New York Postgraduate Hospital and the New York Eye and Ear Infirmary. Following this, in 1926 he was assigned to the U. S. Army Dispensary in Washington, D.C. as Chief of the Otolaryngology Section. During this period, he qualified as a Diplomate of the American Board of Otolaryngology, the first Army medical officer to be so certified by a specialty board. In 1929, he attended a special course in Broncoscopy by Dr. Chevalier Jackson, thus further qualifying in his specialty.

From 1929 to 1931, as a Major, he was in charge of the Eye, Ear, Nose and Throat Service at Sternberg General Hospital in Manila. From 1931 to 1935, he held the same position at Fort Leavenworth Station Hospital and as Lieutenant Colonel at the Army-Navy General Hospital, Hot Springs, Arkansas, 1935 to 1938, and at the Letterman General Hospital, Presidio, San Francisco, 1938 to 1941.

In December 1941 following the Japanese attack on Pearl Harbor, Colonel Streit was given command of the 147th General Hospital in Honolulu, which became an institution of increasing importance with the expansion of the American war effort in the Pacific. In 1943, he was given the post of Surgeon in Chief, Central Pacific Base Command. He returned to the United States in the fall of 1945 and commanded Dibble General Hospital at Menlo Park, California; following this assignment he was in command of Brooke General Hospital at Fort Sam Houston, Texas.

In January 1949, General Streit was placed in command of Walter Reed General Hospital and Walter Reed Army Medical Center in Washington, D.C. Under his aegis the research program was materially expanded and up-graded. General Streit was vitally interested in the graduate education training program instituted in the Army following World War II and with considerable opposition contributed materially in bringing that program up to its present excellent state. General Streit reached the permanent rank of Major General in March 1951 and retired in 1953. Since his retirement he has served as Clinical Consultant, Welfare and Retirement Fund, United Mine Workers of America.

General Streit was a member of the House of Delegates, American Medical Association 1950-1952. He is a member of the Washington Academy of Medicine, Honorary Life Member, Association of Military Surgeons of the United States of America, Fellow, American College of Surgeons, Member, American Medical Association, Honorary Member, Academia Brasileira de Medicina Militar, and Charter Member and First President of the Society of Military Otolaryngologists. His decorations include the Legion of Merit with Oak Leaf Cluster, the Commemorative Cross of Poland, the Medalla Militar, Republic of Chile and the Order of Vasco Núñez de Balboa, Republic of Panama.

Building Program: President Bloedorn reviewed the building program. Initially it had been thought best to enter into separate contracts for the new building and renovation of the animal quarters. As work progressed, however, it appeared more advantageous to include both projects under one contract. Bids were opened on August 25, 1961 and on September 25 a contract was signed with the construction firm of Díaz & Guardia. The cost figures for the new building were as follows:

Architect's fee for preparation of plans and specifications	$ 25,300
Construction contract	337,179
Architect's contract for supervisory services	9,000
Estimated cost of fixed equipment to be purchased by the Institute but installed by the contractor	50,000
TOTAL	$421,479

The construction costs were less than estimated and almost $80,000 remained for purchase of laboratory equipment and for unforeseen contingencies.

The cost of remodeling the animal quarters came to $68,692, a sum in excess of original estimates but well within the $90,000 budgeted.

Appointment of "Task Force": It was reported that the Executive Committee had appointed a "task force" to visit the Gorgas Memorial Laboratory and make recommendations concerning future research and other activities. The committee consisted of Dr. Frederick J. Brady, Assistant Director, Office of Public Health, International Cooperation Administration, Dr. William W. Frye, Dean, School of Medicine, Louisiana State University and Dr. Bernard V. Travis, Professor of Medical Entomology and Parasitology, New York State College of Agriculture at Cornell University.

Miss Calvo Comes on Duty: The President announced that Miss Gloriela Calvo had come on duty in the Washington Office on August 28, 1961, as an assistant and understudy to Miss Helen A. King.

Miss Calvo brought to the position a wealth of experience which was of special value to the Gorgas Memorial Institute. She is a graduate of The George Washington University and Certified Medical Technician from the University of Wisconsin. Her technical positions included service at the Santo Tomás Hospital in Panama and the Gorgas Hospital in the Canal Zone. Miss Calvo served as Attaché for Scientific and Cultural Affairs of the Embassy of Panama in Washington from 1953 to 1961. For many years she was a delegate of Panama to the Inter-American Commission of Women, one of the specialized agencies of the Organization of American States. Her bilingual capability, scientific background and political observations have proved to be of unusual benefit to the Gorgas Memorial Institute.

Budget for 1963: Budget estimates for 1963 in the sum of $403,705 were approved with a recommendation that the Executive Committee be granted authority to make necessary revisions. Of the estimated amount, $250,000 was anticipated as an appropriation from Congress, $5,000 was from endowment fund income, and $148,705 represented Public Health Service grants-in-aid.

Tribute to Dr. Bloedorn: Dr. Howard T. Karsner paid a tribute to Dr. Bloedorn in appreciation for his services as President and particularly for the unusual accomplishments which had resulted in a recent expansion of the research program and the provision for additions to the physical plant of the Gorgas Memorial Laboratory.

Executive Committee Meeting: The Executive Committee met on December 8, 1961 to hear reports from Mr. May on building progress at the Gorgas Memorial Laboratory.

Dr. Johnson was present and offered his views concerning future research expansion. Experimental pathology, comparative zoology and epidemiology were fields which he thought would provide additional opportunities for research. These and other research activities would require additional personnel.

The Committee approved an extension of Dr. Hertig's retirement to June 30, 1963. Certain grade increases were recommended for four staff members.

1962 *Executive Committee Meeting:* The Executive Committee met on April 24, 1962. President Streit reported on his visit to Panama in February of 1962 and on the progress achieved in the building and remodeling programs. Completion of the new building was scheduled for October 1962.

Review of Staff Regulations: During President Streit's visit, a number of matters arose concerning needed revisions in staff regulations. Among these items were the following:

(a) There were no regulations pertaining to freight, weight and volume limits on household property of United States employees hired for duty at the Gorgas Memorial Laboratory. The Committee decided that PAHO regulations should apply.

(b) It was decided to include transportation of a car as part of the total weight allowance for personal belongings.

(c) Travel allowances were changed to allow payment only for tourist class of travel.

(d) It was voted that non-professional personnel maintain the amount of annual leave prescribed by the Panamanian Labor Code.

(e) No change was to be allowed in home leave travel to "place of residence in the United States."

Appointment of Dr. Vernon E. Thatcher to fill a vacancy of field ecologist was approved effective March 15, 1963.

Dr. Parks was asked to act as chairman of a committee to draw up plans for the dedication ceremonies for the new building.

The Darien Gap Project: The Executive Committee met again on September 24, 1962. Dr. Ernestine B. Thurman, Executive Secretary of the Tropical Medicine and Parasitology Study Section, National Institutes of Health, reported on her recent visit to Panama and especially on the Darien Gap Project.

This project was to be financed by a grant-in-aid from the National Institutes of Health. It involved surveys for infectious diseases of man and lower animals in the area and determination of vectors and reservoir hosts of such diseases. The project would offer an opportunity for basic studies of disease among primitive peoples little exposed to outside influences and provide necessary data for the preventive medicine aspects of the proposed Pan American Highway through the region. A total budget of $216,042 was visualized for the first year of operations. A project-site visit was made in April 1963 by a committee from the Tropical Medicine and Parasitology

Study Section. The President expressed optimism that support would be forthcoming as a result of this visit.

Receipt of Gifts: President Streit announced the receipt of a gift of $32,387 (U.S.) from the International Research Foundation, Fort Erie, Ontario, Canada; also a gift of $100,000 from Mr. James H. Rand, through the Colonial Research Institute, to be used for the construction of a modern insectary. Mr. Clarence W. May, consulting engineer, was directed to prepare plans for the building.

Personnel Actions: Dr. Hertig's retirement date was extended to November 30, 1964. The appointment of Dr. Sunthorn Srihongse as a virologist was approved.

The staff regulations for the Gorgas Memorial Laboratory as rewritten and amended by the Personnel Committee were approved.

Annual Meeting: The annual meeting of the Gorgas Memorial Institute was held in Washington on November 7, 1962. After the election of directors the meeting was adjourned to be followed by that of the Board of Directors. Major General Paul H. Streit, MC, USA, (Ret.) was re-elected President and Governor Maurice H. Thatcher Vice President.

President's Report: President Streit reported on the progress of the building program. The new laboratory building was nearing completion and dedication ceremonies were set for January 23, 1963. Dr. John Parks had previously accepted chairmanship of the Dedication Committee. The final cost of the new building was stated to be $406,687 and the total cost of the renovation of the old building and modernization of the animal quarters was $80,036.

The Darien Gap Project: The Darien Gap Project for studies on the epidemiology of infectious diseases along the route of the Pan American Highway was discussed. Pending approval of a Public Health Service grant-in-aid, the President stated that he had authorized other funds for the inauguration of the work.

The New Insectary: Plans for the construction of the new insectary were well advanced. During the course of the meeting, President Streit received an overseas telephone call from Mr. James H. Rand of Freeport, Grand Bahama Island, to the effect that he had set aside an additional $500,000 as a reserve fund for the Gorgas Memorial Institute for special projects and emergencies. This amount was in addition to the $100,000 which he had contributed to the construction of the new insectary and $100,000 to cover a Gorgas budget deficit. Mr. Rand was former President and Chairman of the Board of Remington Rand Corporation.

Support from Mr. Rand: The President reviewed the circumstances which had led to the generous support of Mr. Rand. The interest of the latter in the Gorgas Memorial Laboratory and the Gorgas Memorial Institute apparently resulted from a casual visit to the Laboratory on April 9, 1962. He was escorted through the Laboratory by Dr. Johnson and was entertained at the country home of Dr. and Mrs. Fairchild. Later in May 1962, two representatives of Mr. Rand visited the Laboratory to review the research program.

The sustained interest of Mr. Rand was indicated by his telephoned invitation on June 12, 1962 to Dr. Johnson, Dr. Fairchild and their wives to visit him at Freeport, Grand Bahama Island. Due to other commitments, the invitation could not be accepted.

On June 20, 1962, Dr. Johnson visited Washington and informed President Streit of the above-mentioned events, whereupon President Streit called Mr. Rand on the telephone at his home at Freeport to express his appreciation for the interest of the latter in the work of the Laboratory. In response, Mr. Rand spoke of his favorable impression of the program and accomplishments of the Gorgas Memorial Laboratory and his high regard for the sincerity, dedication and ability of the professional staff. During the conversation, President Streit informed Mr. Rand that the new laboratory building financed by Congress had just been completed but that funds were sorely needed for construction of a modern insectary. Mr. Rand promptly offered to contribute the sum of $100,000 for this purpose. Following this telephone conversation, Mr. Rand voluntarily contacted several other foundations as a result of which $32,387 (U.S.) was received from the International Research Foundation of Fort Erie, Ontario, Canada. Thus a chance visit resulted fortuitously in bringing wholly unanticipated support for the Gorgas programs.

A resolution of appreciation was adopted thanking Mr. Rand for his sustained interest and for his generous donations.

Treasurer's Report: Mr. Donald A. McCormack, Assistant Treasurer, gave his report. The amount of net assets as of June 30, 1962 was $1,157,-607, of which $449,922 was in cash or short-term Treasury bonds and notes. Endowment Fund assets were $56,866.

Budget for 1964: Budget estimates for fiscal year 1964 were approved. Total funds available were estimated as $447,665. Total estimated obligations were $554,200, leaving a prospective deficit of $106,535. Mr. Rand's gift of $100,000 almost covered this deficit.

Personnel Actions: The service of Miss Helen A. King was extended for another year.

Dr. Marshall Hertig was presented with a certificate of merit in appreciation of his long and faithful service at the Gorgas Memorial Laboratory.

Chapter 6.

Years of Fruition
1963-1968

The Gorgas Memorial Laboratory; New Facilities; Additional Personnel; Expanded Research Programs; New Fields of Endeavor; Activities of the Gorgas Memorial Institute.

"The beginning of health is to know the disease."
—MIGUEL DE CERVANTES.

The period 1963-1968 was marked by numerous improvements and additions to the physical plant of the Laboratory. A new laboratory building was occupied in 1963 and in the same year renovation of the original building and the animal quarters was completed. In March of 1965, the new Rand Insectary was dedicated. The additional research facilities permitted the recruitment of new personnel. Departments of Serology, Bacteriology, Parasitology and Vertebrate Zoology were established. In addition to the usual laboratory and field research, extensive studies of disease agents, vectors and reservoir hosts were inaugurated in 1967 along the proposed Canal Routes 17 and 25 in Panama and Colombia.

1963   *Yellow Fever Surveillance:* These investigations were carried out by Medical Entomologist Pedro Galindo and Virologist Dr. Sunthorn Srihongse. Neutralization tests were continued to determine the presence or absence of yellow fever virus in Panama. Sera from animals from the Bayano and Pacora Basins showed negative reactions. These areas represent lowland, swampy forests where, even during times of intense yellow fever activity, animals have been little affected by the virus. Of sera collected in the Tuira Basin, three were definitely positive by neutralization tests and one showed an equivocal reaction. All positive reactions were encountered in young adult monkeys from 5 to 7 years of age, which could have acquired the infection during the last outbreak of jungle yellow fever in 1957. All juveniles and infants born since 1957 were negative. It was concluded that there was no evidence of recent yellow fever activity in eastern Panama up to July 1963.

Ecology of Arboviruses Other Than Yellow Fever: The following were concerned in these studies during the period 1963-1968: Medical Entomologist Pedro Galindo, Virologists Dr. Sunthorn Srihongse and Dr. Margaret A. Grayson, and Dr. Carl M. Johnson.

HI tests conducted on animals in the above-mentioned yellow fever surveillance studies, revealed information concerning the ecology of two Group A viruses. Five of 9 sera from monkeys inhabiting the swampy forests of the Bayano and Pacora Basins, were positive for VEE but were negative for Una virus. On the other hand, tests on 47 sera from monkeys captured in the well-drained forests of the Tuira Basin revealed 11 positives for Una virus and none for VEE, thus indicating a marked difference in the ecology of these two Group A viruses.

Serological tests were continued on material collected during the outbreak of VEE in the Almirante area in 1961 and 1962. Since this project got underway in September 1959, the following viral agents have been identified from the area. The identifications were made in part by the Gorgas Memorial Laboratory and in part by the Middle America Research Unit, the University of Panama Virus Laboratory and the Belem Virus Laboratory:

Venezuelan equine encephalitis: Source: Man, rodents, birds and mosquitoes.

Una: Source: Mosquitoes.

Ilhéus: Source: Birds and mosquitoes.

Bussuquara: Source: Mosquitoes.

Ossa: Source: Human serum.

Madrid: Source: Human serum.

Wyeomyia-complex (untyped): Source: Mosquitoes.

Guaroa: Source: Mosquitoes.

Guamá-group (untyped): Source: Mosquitoes.

Vesicular stomatitis (Indiana type): Source: *Phlebotomus* sandflies.

Ungrouped (Changuinola): Source: *Phlebotomus* sandflies.

During the year, new isolates were obtained from various sources. A total of 114 serum specimens from febrile patients were inoculated into suckling mice. A total of 10 viral agents, all resembling VEE virus in their pathogenicity for mice, were obtained; in two instances, the viruses were related to VEE by CF tests. Positive sera came from patients from Almirante, eastern Panama and from employees of the Gorgas Memorial Laboratory.

Unidentified isolates were secured from arthropods collected near Almirante and mosquitoes captured in the highlands of Bocas del Toro Province as well as from sentinel mice exposed in the field.

As mentioned previously, the scarlet-rumped tanager, *Ramphocelus passerinii,* is one of the commonest birds in the Almirante area; its importance as a host for arboviruses is demonstrated by the fact that VEE and Ilhéus viruses have been isolated from its blood and tissues. Long term studies have been planned in the ecology of this species, including age determination, banding of nestlings and adults and population determinations. Continued attention will be paid to isolation of viruses from the species.

Studies were instituted on the role of migratory birds in the dissemination of arboviruses. Observations had indicated that many such birds frequented the Almirante area. In the fall of 1962, a total of 1,665 thrushes in this area were banded. Of a total of 84 plasma samples from thrushes obtained in the spring of 1963, none was found positive on inoculation into suckling mice.

Observations on the host preference of mosquitoes and *Phlebotomus* sandflies were continued. *Aedes (Ochlerotatus)* species, *Psorophora (Janthinosoma)* species and *Culex nigripalpus* were commonly taken on large mammals and birds but seldom attacked rodents. On the other hand, some species like *Culex vomerifer, C. taeniopus* and other *Culex (Melanoconion)* species showed a preference for the blood of rodents but were also taken in appreciable numbers on man, birds and even reptiles.

Studies in Parasitology: Continued studies were conducted on avian blood parasites. Of 520 birds examined, 180 harbored one or more blood parasites, including 33 with *Plasmodium* spp., 138 with *Haemoproteus,* 10 with *Leucocytozoon,* seven with *Trypanosoma,* 33 with microfilariae and 29 with mixed infections.

In an examination of blood samples from 360 reptiles from the Almirante area, 83 were positive. *Plasmodium* was found in 54 and Hemogregarines in 43. *Haemoproteus* was encountered in one animal and mixed infections in 15.

Leishmaniasis Studies: During the 6-year period, these studies were conducted by Dr. Marshall Hertig, Dr. Aristides Herrer, Dr. G. B. Fairchild, Dr. Carl M. Johnson, Dr. Vernon E. Thatcher, and in part by Dr. Curt R. Schneider and Dr. Sam R. Telford, Jr.

The occurrence of natural infections of leptomonad flagellates in wild-caught sandflies has been followed ever since the discovery of these infections in January 1961. Up to the current year, 6,000 wild-caught sandflies have been dissected. From this total, 5,526 females of six or seven man-biting species were examined, of which 480, or 8.7 percent, were positive. An additional 1,250 females have since been dissected, of which 131, or 10.5 percent, were found infected. As previously, *Phlebotomus trapidoi* and *P. ylephiletor* had the highest infection rates, ranging from 10.5 to 23.2 percent; *P. panamensis* as usual had the lowest infection rate.

Eleven additional pure cultures of wild-caught sandfly leptomonads were obtained in 24 attempts, making to date a total of 101 pure cultures. Four infections were secured in hamsters inoculated with these leptomonad strains and these strains have been shown to be *Leishmania*. Identification, however, remained a problem, which was being approached in a number of ways.

Geographic strains of *Leishmania braziliensis sensu lato* were under continued study. There is considerable integration in the characteristics of such strains. Light visceral infections in hamsters have been encountered with Guatemalan and Panamanian strains. The former strain produces greatly swollen feet in hamsters with lesions rich in L-D bodies. Some Panamanian strains have been responsible for moderate foot lesions.

Various animal-baited traps have been devised for the collection of sandflies. During a period of 4 months beginning in February 1963, about 500 females were collected in such traps. The fed females all belonged to the man-biting species. From present results, it would appear that these species favor the larger aboreal animals as hosts. The kinkajou *(Potos flavus),* the three-toed sloth *(Bradypus infuscatus)* and the common opossum *(Didelphis marsupialis)* were all attractive to man-biting species. Certain other aboreal animals have not proved as attractive. Negative results were obtained when small rodents were employed as attractants.

An ecological study plat, with various types of natural and artificial sandfly habitats and daytime shelters, has been established in the Madden Forest Preserve in the Canal Zone.

In the chemotherapy of leishmaniasis, 101 cases were treated with pyrimethamine; of these 43 could be followed adequately. In these cases, the lesions healed completely and did not recur. Pyrimethamine is now the routine treatment and is considered the drug of choice in children.

American Trypanosomiasis: Most of these studies were conducted by the U.S. Naval Medical Science Unit under the direction of Commander Alan C. Pipkin.

Collections of triatomid bugs were made in villages bordering the backwaters of Gatun Lake just outside the Canal Zone. All specimens taken in the houses proved to be *Rhodnius pallescens*. About 40 percent of bugs in night collections in native houses were found to harbor trypanosomes.

In efforts to determine reservoir hosts of *Trypanosoma cruzi,* wild animals were taken in areas in which infected reduviid bugs had been collected. Results were based on examinations of heart blood and culture in artificial media. Of a total of 209 animals, 48, or 23 percent, were positive. Positive species included the opossum, the anteater, the coati, the marmoset *(Saguinus geoffroyi)* and the three-toed sloth *(Bradypus infuscatus).*

Studies on the feeding and defecation habits of *Rhodnius pallescens* indicated an average feeding time for adults of 7.5 minutes and for nymphs of 10 minutes. The mean defecation time after feeding was 47.5 minutes. Apparently this species is not as efficient a vector as other triatomids which are known to defecate immediately after the blood meal.

Toxoplasmosis Studies: These studies were inaugurated by the U. S. Army Medical Research Unit under the direction of Major Bryce C. Walton. Preliminary results indicated that chorioretinitis of toxoplasma etiology constitutes a hitherto unrecognized human disease problem of appreciable importance in Panama.

Malaria Studies: Observations on the effect of mass administration of antimalarial drugs for the control and eradication of malaria were continued for the third year in the communities of La Represa and Mendoza under the direction of Dr. Carl M. Johnson. It will be recalled that following therapy from July 1960, through June 1962, the malaria rate had been reduced to zero and there was no evidence of transmission. From September 1961 to June 1962, a buffer zone was established around these two communities. In July 1962, treatment was discontinued in the two communities but maintained in the buffer zone to minimize the re-introduction of infection. Monthly blood surveys in the test area during the period July 1962, through June 1963, turned up 11 cases of malaria in La Represa and 12 cases in Mendoza. These cases were re-treated with the combination of pyrimethamine and primaquine which had been employed throughout the studies. Ten of the new cases in La Represa were the result of the inadequacy of the buffer zone; the others were immigrants to the area or individuals who had been out of the study area.

Studies on Neotropical Drosophilidae: These studies were initiated in 1959 by Visiting Scientist Dr. Sarah B. Pipkin. Between September 1959 and March 1962, an ecological and taxonomic survey of members of this family was carried out in several areas. The ground feeding forms, caught chiefly by net sweeping, were divided into three groups according to the relative juiciness of fruits over which they were collected and also on the basis of their willingness to enter baited traps.

Group A species, of which 60 percent were members of the *Drosophila tripunctata* species complex, were collected by sweeping over falled fruits and blossoms. They either refused traps or came to them reluctantly. Group B, largely members of the *Sophophora willistoni* species group, were collected over the more juicy native fruits and over baited traps. Group C, consisting of about 15 species, were collected uncommonly over falled juicy native fruits but were consistently attracted to traps baited with cultivated fruits. Seasonal fluctuations were shown to take place for most species.

Eleven pairs of sibling species of the family Drosophilidae, 10 of them belonging to the genus *Drosophila,* have been identified. The high number of sibling species on the Isthmus of Panama was thought to be due to the movement of formerly isolated populations together in the Panama Land Bridge formed after the Tertiary water separation of the North and South America continents.

Cooperation with Other Organizations: In June 1963, laboratory facilities were supplied to the U. S. Army Research and Development Office, Panama, for research on fungal contamination on modular electronic components stored in a tropical environment and for tests of new types of tropical clothing and equipment.

The Laboratory continued to participate in the tropical medicine training program of the Louisiana State University. During the year, three groups of fellows spent from 7 to 10 days with the staff.

Some 160 scientists from various parts of the world visited the Laboratory during the year. Dr. Alexander Wetmore of the Smithsonian Institution and Dr. Charles Handley, Jr. of the U. S. National Museum spent several months during the year in continuing studies on the birds and mammals of Panama.

1964   Dr. Martin D. Young assumed the directorship of the Gorgas Memorial Laboratory on July 1, 1964. Dr. Young brought to this position an extensive background and unusual experience in both research and administration in the field of tropical diseases.

Dr. Young was born at Moreland, Georgia, July 4, 1909, the son of Joe Hugh and Jennie Sue (Martin) Young. His early education was obtained in Georgia schools and at Emory University from which he received a Bachelor of Science degree in 1931. This was followed by an M.S. degree at Emory in 1932 and a Doctor of Science degree from the Johns Hopkins University School of Hygiene and Public Health in 1937. Additional studies included courses at the Marine Biological Laboratory, Woods Hole, Mass., in 1933; Oak Ridge Institute of Nuclear Studies, Oak Ridge, Tenn., in 1951, and the Conference for Federal Executives, Brookings Institution, 1962.

Dr. Young served as Professor of Biology and Head of the Department at the Junior College of Augusta, Ga., 1932-34, and Visiting Professor of Biology, Tennessee East State Teachers College, Johnson City, Tenn., 1939. He entered the National Institutes of Health, U. S. Public Health Service in 1937. He was a staff member of the Malaria Research Laboratory, Columbia, S. C., from 1937 to 1941 and Director of that Laboratory from 1941 to 1950. From 1950 to 1961 he served as Head of the Section on Epidemiology of the Laboratory of Tropical Diseases and as Assistant Chief, Laboratory of Parasite Chemotherapy 1961-1962. From 1962 to

Fig. 9. The three directors of the Gorgas Memorial Laboratory. Top to bottom: Herbert C. Clark, M.D. 1928-1954; Carl M. Johnson, Sc.D., M.D. 1954-1964; Martin D. Young, Sc.D. 1964-

1964, he was Associate Director for Extramural Programs, National Institute of Allergy and Infectious Diseases.

Dr. Young has had extensive field experience in various countries. In 1943 he headed a malaria survey of Liberia; in 1957 he was a member of a 3-member panel to evaluate the malaria program in India; and in 1961 was consultant on malaria in Rumania. He has served as a consultant to the World Health Organization and has been a member of the Expert Committee on Malaria Chemotherapy. He has served on the Commission on Malaria and the Commission on Parasitic Diseases of the Armed Forces Epidemiological Board.

The new director has been identified with many professional and scientific societies and organizations in most of which he has held important offices. These include President-Elect of the National Malaria Society, 1952; President of the American Society of Tropical Medicine and Hygiene in 1952; and President of the American Society of Parasitologists, 1965. He is a Diplomate of the American Academy of Microbiology.

Dr. Young has been an important contributor to the literature of malaria and other parasitic diseases with over 100 papers in these subjects. In addition, he was responsible for the chapters on malaria in the third and fourth editions of the "Manual of Tropical Medicine" and has contributed to the Encyclopedia Britannica.

Many honors have come to Dr. Young. In 1953, he was one of the first recipients of the Rockefeller Public Service Award. He received the Jefferson Award of the South Carolina Academy of Science in 1946, 1952 and again in 1960. In 1963, he was awarded the Darling Medal and Prize of the World Health Organization. Also in that year, Emory University conferred upon him the honorary degree of Doctor of Science.

Ecology of Arboviruses Other Than Yellow Fever: Identification was attempted on 82 virus strains isolated in past years at Almirante. The hemagglutination inhibition (HI), complement fixation (CF) and mouse neutralization (NT) tests were employed. The following viruses were tentatively or definitely identified together with the source:

Venezuelan equine encephalitis: Human serum, various species of mosquitoes, seven species of birds, the cotton rat and sentinel mice.

Una: Two species of mosquitoes.

Mayaro: The mosquito, *Psorophora ferox.*

Ilhéus: The scarlet-rumped tanager.

Bussuquara: Two species of mosquitoes and sentinel mice.

Caraparú: Sentinel mice.

Madrid: Sentinel mice.

Nepuyo: The spiny rat.

Patois: The cotton rat and sentinel mice.

Zegla: The cotton rat and sentinel mice.

Guamá-group viruses (untyped): Two species of mosquitoes and sentinel mice.

The banding of migrant thrushes and catbirds was continued in connection with inquiries into the role of such birds in the transmission of viruses. A total of 4,440 birds were banded between September 1963 and May 1964. Large numbers of birds were bled for virus determinations. Of 136 plasma specimens inoculated into suckling mice, none produced infection. HI tests were carried out with 597 specimens against A and B Group antigens. Of 372 Swainson's Thrush specimens, 1.3 percent were positive for Group A and 2.6 percent for Group B. Of 99 catbirds, 4.0 percent reacted against Group A antigen and 6.1 percent against Group B. One of 78 gray-cheeked thrushes was positive for Group A antibodies. A single Veery of 17 tested reacted against Group B antigen.

Fifty tissues collected in 1962 from the scarlet-rumped tanager were inoculated into suckling mice with one isolation of Ilhéus virus. Sixty-two plasma specimens from this bird were tested by HI against 10 antigens. Six, or 9.7 percent, reacted positively against Group A antigens and three, or 4.8 percent, were positive against Group B antigens. Of 281 plasma samples collected during 1963 and 1964 and tested by HI against 11 antigens of Groups A, B, and C, all were negative.

Search was continued for arboviruses in various species of mosquitoes. A total of 10,872 mosquitoes in 280 pools were inoculated into suckling mice. Seven virus isolates were obtained as follows: Three from *Aedes (Ochlerotatus)* spp., two from *Psorophora ferox,* one from *Culex vomerifer,* and one from *C. taeniopus.*

In further extension of the arbovirus project, a surveying expedition was made into the forests of Tacarcuna between May and August 1963. Three campsites were selected for collection of vertebrates, insects of medical importance and blood and tissue specimens from various feral vertebrates.

Additional surveys were undertaken during the year among human and wild animal populations in several different regions of Panama. Preliminary HI tests have been run with 361 human sera from Almirante, 140 from Lídice, 145 from Cerro Azul, 157 from Pesé, 66 from Carriazo, 41 from members of the Peace Corps and 72 from domestic animals. The following antigens were employed in the tests: VEE, EEE, WEE, Mayaro, Una, Pixuna, Aura, SLE, YF, Ilhéus, Bussuquara, Dengue II, Caraparú, Oriboca, Murutucu, Nepuyo, Maguari and Turlock. High titers were obtained for VEE, Una, and Ilhéus in a number of instances. Of 228 sera tested against Group C antigens, 7.5 percent reacted positively.

During the year, tests for arboviruses were conducted on individuals with fevers of undetermined origin. One virus strain ("Saltarin") was isolated from a worker on the Pan American Highway. This virus was identical with a local strain of Wyeomyia virus isolated several times from mosquitoes in 1959 and 1960. Convalescent sera showed a rise in CF titers against both strains and some other members of the Bunyamwera group. The recovery of this virus from human serum represents the first isolation of Wyeomyia subgroup of arboviruses from man. Small numbers of sera collected among the native population of Darien were tested against the "Saltarin" strain by mouse neutralization test: Out of 25 sera, 5 gave positive protection.

The "Saltarin" strain isolated from man and a local strain of Wyeomyia virus (BT-219) isolated from the mosquito were studied in tissue culture. Both strains produced cytopathogenic effect (CPE) in HKTC and CETC.

Leishmaniasis Studies: Search was continued for a suitable experimental animal. Negative results were previously obtained after inoculation of the kinkajou, *Potos flavus,* certain opossums and the tree rat, *Tylomys panamensis,* with human strains of *Leishmania braziliensis sensu lato.* More recently a strain isolated from an adult Panamanian patient in April 1964, was inoculated into hamsters, cotton rats, tree rats, a kinkajou and a spiny rat. After an incubation period of 12 to 19 days, lesions appeared at the site of inoculation in all animals. The infection in the spiny rat was the first after numerous previous attempts.

Search of natural infections in wild-trapped animals has been continued with negative results. Animals trapped and brought to the laboratory for examination included 101 rodents of seven genera, 67 marsupials of five genera and 11 specimens of four other mammalian orders.

Studies on the chemotherapy of leishmaniasis were still in progress. Between June 1960 and June 1964, 169 patients were treated with pyrimethamine, 81 of whom completed treatment; of these 74, or 91.4 percent, were healed completely. In many patients it was found necessary to administer supplemental antibiotic therapy to control the secondary bacterial infection. The duration of treatment was governed by the time required to clear the lesions. As a rule, healing occurred in 3 to 6 weeks. Severe toxic reactions were encountered in only one instance.

In an effort to clarify taxonomic relations among various strains of *Leishmania,* miniaturized Ouchterlony agar-gel diffusion tests were performed with a Peruvian and a Guatemalan strain, three human Panamanian strains and a Panamanian strain isolated from a *Phlebotomus* sandfly. From the results of the tests, it seemed certain that in Panama at least there are two distinct strains of *Leishmania* which are capable of causing disease in man.

American Trypanosomiasis: Dr. Carl M. Johnson was in charge of these studies. Three new human cases of *Trypanosoma rangeli* infection were discovered. The trypanosome developed well in *Rhodnius pallescens* with massive infection of the salivary glands. Apparently this constituted the first report of *T. rangeli* of human origin developing to the salivary gland stage in *R. pallescens*. On the other hand, development failed to take place in *Rhodnius prolixus*.

Continued surveillance of Chagas' disease was carried out. In CF tests of a total of 6,444 blood donors, 1.2 percent were positive. Of 374 blood specimens collected during the malaria studies, 9 percent were positive. A total of 381 blood specimens were received from various medical institutions; of these specimens, 84, or 22 percent, were positive.

A trypanosome isolated from the anteater, *Tamandua tetradactyla*, was studied in culture and infection with culture forms was produced in mice and the pigmy anteater, *Cyclopes didactylus*. However, intraperitoneal injection of infected blood from the donor host failed to establish infection in a number of species of animals. The parasite developed in *Rhodnius pallescens* indicating that all natural infections of *R. pallescens* with *rangeli*-like organisms may not represent infections with *T. rangeli*.

The U. S. Naval Medical Science Unit continued investigations on the triatomid vectors of *Trypanosoma cruzi* until Commander Alan C. Pipkin was transferred to Bethesda, Maryland, in May 1964.

Previous observations had indicated that *Rhodnius pallescens,* one of the vectors of Chagas' disease, was frequently encountered in native houses during the night but was only present in small numbers during the day. This suggested an extradomicillary habitat for the bugs. Ecological studies indicated that the species occurs frequently in hen houses, pig pens and opossum nests; other extradomicillary niches examined produced fewer bugs than did these locations.

Malaria Studies: Chemotherapeutic studies in the La Represa and Mendoza areas have been referred to in accounts of previous years' work. Observations in the areas have been made through June 1964. The overall results of the trials have warranted the following conclusions:

The combination of pyrimethamine-primaquine was an effective drug in curing malaria. In the experimental areas only 7 of 138 positive individuals were found positive a second time after taking the drug in the prescribed manner. Similar results were being obtained in a much larger buffer zone of communities.

Malaria was effectively controlled with a reasonable amount of supervision when the drugs were given weekly on a mass basis. In the experimental areas this was accomplished over a 2-year period. One hundred percent participation of the population at risk was not necessary.

Pyrimethamine-primaquine combined into one tablet was given safely once a week over long periods of time, 2 years or more, without causing any untoward reactions or evidence of toxicity.

No evidence of development of resistance on the part of the parasite to the drug was noted in the study.

Dr. Carl M. Johnson conducted these studies.

With the increasing difficulties being encountered in malaria eradication programs based on the use of residual insecticides, the role of drugs is becoming more and more important. The current study indicated that the proper use of combinations of drugs properly administered on a mass basis may play an important role in eradicating malaria.

Studies on Other Parasitic Infections: During the period 1964-1968, the following staff members contributed to these studies: Dr. Octavio E. Sousa, Dr. Vernon E. Thatcher, and Dr. Curt R. Schneider.

In connection with the project on diarrheal diseases, examinations for intestinal parasites were conducted in 338 persons of different ages in three rural communities. Over 95 percent carried one or more species of parasites. Over 80 percent had hookworm infections; *Ascaris lumbricoides* was found in 65.4, 48.2 and 27.5 percent, respectively. Rates for *Trichuris trichiura* were 23.1, 60.6 and 34.5 percent. *Giardia lambia* occurred in over 40 percent of the children under 6 years of age. *Entamoeba histolytica* was encountered in 30.8, 22.9 and 15.5 percent, respectively.

A new parasite, *Besnoitia,* was found in lizards *(Basiliscus basiliscus)* from the area of Río Lagarto. Cysts of the parasite were morphologically indistinguishable from those of *Besnoitia jellisoni* Frenkel, 1963. Subsequently, three lizards, *Ameiva ameiva,* have been found infected. The parasite was passed to mice, which died after 6 to 7 days. However, the strain died out after the fourth passage in mice. Experimental intraperitoneal inoculation of heavily infected mouse peritoneal exudate failed to produce clinical disease in a number of other animals, including the rat, hamster, guinea pig, rabbit, rhesus monkey, the white-faced monkey *(Cebus capucinus)* and pigeons.

Studies on Diarrheal Diseases: The studies were initiated to determine the incidence and prevalence of enteric pathogens and associated epidemiological factors. Investigations were being conducted in the Children's Hospital in Panama City and in the rural communities of La Represa and Mendoza. Of 75 pathogens isolated from several hundred diarrheic children 2 years of age or less in Children's Hospital, 80 percent were enteropathogenic *Escherichia coli,* 11 percent *Shigella* and 9 percent *Salmonella.* There was an increase in enterobacterial pathogens associated with diarrheal cases during the onset of the rainy season in May and June. Investigations at La Represa and Mendoza had not uncovered any substantial findings to date. Dr. Miguel Kourany was in charge of the studies and was assisted by Dr. Manuel A. Vásquez.

Toxoplasmosis Studies: These studies were continued by the U. S. Army Medical Research Unit under the direction of Lt. Col. Bryce C. Walton.

The effect of altitude on toxoplasma infection was investigated by the indirect fluorescent antibody test (IFAT) on the sera of 350 school children living in communities at altitudes varying between 700 feet and 6,200 feet. The number of positive reactors in children at the 700 foot level was over twice that in those at levels of 4,200 to 6,200 feet.

Studies of Peace Corps volunteers were designed to detect acute acquired toxoplasmosis in susceptible individuals. Two individuals developed antibodies as determined by the IFAT after a prolonged febrile illness with lymphadenopathy.

Investigations were carried out to determine the possible effect of internal parasites in breeching the blood-brain barrier in concomitant infections with neuropathogenic viral agents administered extraneurally. *Trichinella spiralis* was the nematode parasite employed; the viral agents were EEE, Ilhéus and Japanese B encephalitis (JBE). Intraperitoneal dosages of EEE approaching the LD_{50} level produced 33 percent mortality in the virus control group and 97 percent mortality in the dual infection group. When the dosage of virus was decreased to approximately the MLD level, a corresponding reduction in mortality did not occur in the dual infection group which had a mortality of 80 percent. When the virus dosages were further reduced, no appreciable mortality occurred among the dual infection mice. The mechanism of the synergistic effect appears to be due to the early introduction of virus into susceptible neural tissue by the migrating larvae of the nematode, as indicated by the temporal distribution of deaths in the dual control group as compared with the virus group. It would appear that an ordinarily benign infection with a viral agent could result in an almost invariably fatal outcome if it should happen to coincide with the presence of wandering nematode larvae.

Studies on Drosophila Genetics: These studies were a continuation of those initiated in 1959 by Visiting Scientist Dr. Sarah B. Pipkin.

Observations were made on polymorphism in *Drosophila l. lebanonensis.* The study concerned the development of overdominance (euheterosis) at the *S, s* locus in cage populations begun as hybrids *(Ss)* between a homozygous pale strain of *Drosophila l. lebanonensis (SS)* and a homozygous dark strain *(ss)* of *D. l. casteeli.* The advantage of studying these hybrid populations was that phenotypic scoring of *SS, Ss,* and *ss* individuals is accurate, so that the gene frequencies of the *S* and *s* alleles, respectively, may be quickly ascertained in each generation. A total of 866 breeding tests of individual males taken from generations 2 to 17 and from generations 39 and 40 of all experimental populations proved that the males had been accurately scored according to inspection of their phenotypes.

The hybrid populations were begun with the ratio of the dark allele, s, to the light allele, S, equal to 1. In all four cage populations and the two half-gallon bottle populations, this ratio remained high for the first 3 to 5 generations, indicating a strain heterosis which later deteriorated. Following generation 5, the $s{:}S$ ratio declined steadily to the 11th generation in one cage population, to the 14th generation in two cage populations, and to the 19th generation in a fourth cage population. This decline is believed to be due to the breaking up of coadapted gene complexes because of random assortment of non-homologous chromosomes and recombination (crossing over) between homologous chromosomes. After the $s{:}S$ ratio reached a low point in each of the experimental cage populations, this ratio began to rise, accompanied by obvious fluctuations. An overall steady improvement in heterozygote superiority as expressed by a rise in the $s{:}S$ ratio occurred through the 42d generation of the four cage populations. At this time the $s{:}S$ ratio had increased to approximately its magnitude in generations 3 to 7. The rise in the $s{:}S$ ratio is believed to depend on the reintegration of the genotype due to cage selection, resulting in a development of overdominance at the s, S locus. Whether this overdominance (euheterosis) depends on the selection of a large number of modifiers on all chromosomes or of a second major fitness allele closely linked with the S, s locus, is not known. In any case this mesonotal polymorphism dependent on heterozygote (Ss) superiority is not due to intrinsic overdominance at the S, s locus, as demonstrated by the initial decline of the $s{:}S$ ratio, but rather to associative overdominance (i.e. a large number of modifiers or linkage with a second major fitness locus).

The development of overdominance by cage selection of the genetic background in populations begun as hybrids between *D. l. lebanonensis* and *D. l. casteeli* is of especial interest because no gene rearrangements occurred in these hybrids, according to studies of giant chromosomes of the salivary glands of F_1 hybrid larvae. Although a partial lack of pairing in the medium-sized chromosome arms was observed in about half the F_1 hybrid single larvae preparations, pairing was complete in F_2 larvae and also in larvae taken from later cage generations. Hence the partial lack of pairing in F_1 hybrids is apparently due to a maternal effect which is lost in later generations of the cage populations.

Therefore, the modification of the mesonotal polymorphism resulting in heterozygote superiority at the S, s locus was due entirely to genetic recombination and cage selection, unhampered by gene rearrangements which would have reduced recombination.

A temperature of 28°C. acted as a strong selective agent against the heterozygote *Ss* genotype in the replicates from generations 11 to 15 but not in those of 35 to 37.

In studies on the mating drive in hybrids between *D. l. lebanonensis* and *D. l. casteeli,* no differences were observed among *SS, Ss* or *ss* genotypes of the cage population utilized.

Cooperation with Other Organizations: The U. S. Army Tropic Test Center continued to occupy space in the Gorgas Memorial Laboratory. The limited initial research program defined in the 1963 report was expanded to include many other activities.

The long term cooperative studies of birds and mammals of Panama was continued under Dr. Alexander Wetmore of the Smithsonian Institution and Dr. Charles Handley, Jr. of the U. S. National Museum.

During the year 51 individuals from seven countries visited the Laboratory.

1965   ***The Ecology of Arboviruses Other Than Yellow Fever:***
Additional studies were made on sera obtained from various sources in the vicinity of Almirante in 1960, 1961 and 1962 during and following the outbreak of Venezuelan equine encephalitis.

Of 1,343 human sera tested by HI, antibodies were obtained to two Group A viruses; viz: VEE and Una. No antibodies to EEE were detected. The percentage of sera reacting positively for VEE in various years was as follows:

Year	No. Tested	Percent Positive
1960	451	42.6
1961	648	31.0
1962	244	37.3

These results indicate that VEE virus was widespread in the human population of the Almirante area between 1960 and 1962.

Examinations by the HI test for VEE antibodies in sera from domestic animals from the area, as well as sera from rodents, marsupials, reptiles and birds provided interesting results, as follows:

	No. examined	Percent Positive
Domestic Animals	82	69.5
Rodents	269	67.5
Marsupials	140	29.3
Reptiles	101	2.0
Birds	803	2.4

Further attempts were made to define the role of nestlings and migrating birds as reservoirs of arboviruses. No viruses were obtained from 197 nestlings, 56 parent birds and 57 nestlings and parents. A total of 3,353 birds were banded and released. Results of serological tests were not yet available.

In further studies on the status of arbovirus rodent-insect cycles in the Almirante area during 1965, 176 litters of sentinel mice were exposed. Four viruses were identified and eight other isolates remained to be studied.

A total of 724 rodents were captured and bled for virus isolation; a total of 17 arbovirus strains were isolated.

Virus isolations were attempted from 33,157 blood-sucking insects. VEE virus was isolated twice from *Culex vomerifer* and once from *Culex crybda* (= *Culex epanastasis*); a group A virus from *Culex taeniopus;* a Group C virus from *Culex vomerifer;* and other viruses yet to be studied.

Current studies on virus activity in the human population of the Almirante area embraced serological tests with Group A, B and C arbovirus antigens. Preliminary data indicated that of 347 sera about 27 percent were positive for Group A viruses, 25 percent for Group B and 5 percent for Group C. There appeared to be a relationship between rainfall and the monthly rate of virus isolations during the year with the greatest virus activity during the rainy season. The ecological studies indicated that the cotton rat and the spiny rat were important sources of VEE and Group C arboviruses in the Almirante area. It would appear that *Culex taeniopus* and perhaps other *Melanoconion* mosquitoes were important vectors of VEE.

During 1965, the ecology of arboviruses was studied in areas of Panama other than Almirante. In eastern Panama, yellow fever surveillance was continued without evidence of the presence of the virus. Many thousands of mosquitoes were collected in localities in this part of Panama. St. Louis encephalitis virus (SLE) was isolated for the first time from *Deinocerites* mosquitoes.

Tests on human sera from individuals in many other parts of Panama indicated a high percentage of reactions to Group A and Group B arbovirus antigens. Antibodies to Group C arboviruses were encountered less frequently. Chagres virus was detected in two humans. This virus was first isolated from man at the Middle America Research Unit in 1960 and was later designated a new virus belonging in the Phlebotomus fever group. The two newly isolated strains represented the second and third recorded cases of human infection with the virus.

Studies were continued on the behavior of arboviruses in various tissue culture systems. This technique gave promise of providing an additional means of isolating and categorizing these viruses.

Leishmaniasis Studies: In further studies on reservoir hosts, 259 animals representing 18 mammalian genera were trapped and brought to the Laboratory. One of 8 kinkajous showed a moderate number of L-D bodies in a small papule on one ear. Material from the papule produced typical lesions in hamsters and cultures from these hamsters infected others. This was the first time that a cutaneous leishmanial infection with a grossly demonstrable lesion, contracted in nature, was found in a non-human host in Panama. It was also the first report of *Leishmania* in a kinkajou or in this family of carnivores.

Search was made for L-D bodies in skin scrappings from a number of animals not showing lesions of leishmaniasis. Positive results were obtained from skin scrappings from a porcupine, *Coendou rothschildi*. This animal died from accidental causes and abundant growth of a leptomonad flagellate was obtained from the skin, spleen and liver. Subsequently, skin cultures from three other porcupines were positive, as well as cultures from the skin of 1 out of 5 opossums, *Didelphis marsupialis*. After about 1 month, this culture began to show certain crithidial forms, which with time replaced the leptomonads.

Immunological studies on strains of *Leishmania braziliensis* were continued and conclusions were confirmed that there are probably two strains of the organism in Panama capable of producing disease.

A strain of *Leishmania* from a sandfly which failed to infect hamsters was noted to have an unusual morphology and distribution in the sandfly gut. Further studies indicated that the strain showed a marked preference for the posterior half of the hindgut. This strain may be comparable to other leptomonad parasites of blood-sucking insects which have no relation to the vertebrate host of the insect. If so, it was believed that the observation was the first report of this occurrence in *Phlebotomus*.

Dr. Aristides Herrer became head of the Leishmaniasis Department on December 1, 1965.

American Trypanosomiasis: Surveillance was continued by the complement fixation test on blood sera from various sources. Of a total of 2,912 sera, 4.4 percent were positive.

Treatment of cases was continued with a new 8-aminoquinoline compound designated as C-349-C-59 (Burroughs-Wellcome, London), administered in a dose of 15 mg. daily for as long as the complement fixation test is positive. The chronic form of the disease is considered to be resistant to therapy but six cases became negative for the CF test indicating that treatment with this drug was successful in eradicating the parasites.

During the year 1,262 persons were sampled by culture methods for infection with *Trypanosoma rangeli;* of the determinations which had been made, 3.7 percent were found to have trypanosomes in the blood. Of these, *T. cruzi* was isolated in 4 percent of the samples and *T. rangeli* in 6 percent.

Dissection of triatomid bugs (nearly all *Rhodnius pallescens*) collected in or around houses in the district of La Chorrera revealed 77 percent to be infected with trypanosomes. Infections consisted both of *T. cruzi* and *T. rangeli*.

The more recent studies indicated the following conclusions:

Human infections with *T. rangeli* are more frequent than previously thought.

Both *T. rangeli* and *T. cruzi* occur in endemic areas of Chagas' disease. *R. pallescens* is a good natural host for both species.

The development of the parasite in the natural insect host *(R. pallescens)* presents some characteristics that are not known to occur in *R. prolixus.* The crowding and intensive multiplication of crithidia in both the outer and inner wall of the salivary glands is a striking characteristic offered by the Panamanian strains of *T. rangeli* not produced by a Venezuelan strain developing either in *R. prolixus* or *R. pallescens.*

T. rangeli can be transmitted to CFW mice by the bites of infected *R. pallescens.*

A high percentage of wild *R. pallescens* are naturally infected with *T. cruzi* and *rangeli*-like organisms.

The anteater, *Tamundua tetradactyla,* is susceptible to a *T. rangeli* strain of human origin. This animal may harbor mixed infections of *T. rangeli* and *T. legeri.*

Studies on Other Parasitic Infections: The species of *Besnoitia* isolated from a lizard has been designated *B. panamensis.* An opossum, *Didelphis marsupialis,* has been found infected. As measured by the LD_{50}, the virulence of *B. panamensis* gradually increased in mice over a period of 4½ months. Two strains of the parasite were less sensitive to sulfadiazine in mice than was *B. jellisoni.* There appeared to be some cross immunity produced by the Panama strains and *B. jellisoni* in mice immunized by drug therapy and by killed organisms but only partial protection was obtained against heterologous challenge.

In an effort to detect a pattern to the host specificity of *Besnoitia,* a number of animals were challenged with proliferative forms from mice. The marmoset, *Saguinus geoffroyi,* and squirrels, *Sciurus* sp., were highly susceptible to all three strains of the parasite. Some other animals were found to be susceptible also, although a number of others proved to be either innately or naturally resistant to one or more strains.

Four species of lizards and the common opossum have been found naturally infected with *Besnoitia.* There was some evidence to indicate that infection in lizards may be only a blind alley in the chain of transmission and the true life cycle still needs elucidation. In attempts to solve this life cycle, a tick and certain fleas were not found to be involved in transmission. Ingestion would seem to be the more likely route of transmission.

A total of 632 inhabitants of four rural communities were examined for intestinal parasites. Results were generally in accordance with those obtained previously; hookworm was the most common parasite.

Biopsy material from a patient in a Panama hospital revealed a hydatid infection of the liver; the hemagglutination and flocculation tests were positive. Following the death of the patient, a very large hydatid cyst was found in the liver. Subsequently, adult *Echinococcus* parasites were obtained from a puma, *Felis concolor.*

Studies on Diarrheal Diseases: Dr. Miguel Kourany conducted studies in Children's Hospital during 5 months of last year and 7 months of the current year, in which enterobacterial agents were obtained from 8.2 percent of 1,819 diarrheal cases examined. In general, the data indicated that the highest infection rates occurred during the rainy months of the year. During the first 2 years of life, *Shigella* and *Salmonella* apparently are less frequently associated with the infectious diarrheas than are the enterpathogenic *E. coli.* Of the 148 bacterial strains isolated from diarrheic children, 64.9 percent were enteropathogenic *E. coli,* 20.9 percent *Shigella* and 14.2 percent *Salmonella.* Nine of the 11 most common *E. coli* serotypes associated with infant diarrhea were isolated during the study. A total of 31 different *Shigella* isolates represented 2 of the 4 serologic groups. Twenty-one different *Salmonella* strains, representing six serologic groups, were isolated.

In studies in four rural communities involving material from a total of 591 individuals, the average incidence of intestinal bacterial pathogens was 8.5 percent.

Examinations of intestinal contents from 132 lizards revealed seven different *Salmonella* belonging to sero-groups B, D, G, and I.

Medical Entomology: Dr. Fairchild continued his studies on Tabanidae. Several months were spent in various cities in Europe studying specimens and types of over 250 neotropical species and others which had not been observed before.

Cooperation with Other Organizations: Dr. Pablo Barreto Reyes of the Universidad del Valle, Colombia, spent several weeks at the Laboratory in connection with taxonomic problems of mosquitoes and sandflies.

Dr. Alexander Wetmore of the Smithsonian Institution utilized the Laboratory again in connection with his field studies of the birds of Panama.

The largest group of visitors during the year comprised 150 members of the Organization on Medical Education for National Defense. In addition, there were 90 other visitors from 13 countries.

Cooperative arrangements with numerous other institutions were maintained as in the past.

1966   **Yellow Fever Surveillance:** Continued watch was maintained for the reappearance of yellow fever in eastern Panama. During the year the howler monkey population in Cerro Cana in the Pirre

Mountain range in Darien Province was greatly reduced. These monkeys readily succumb to yellow fever. Only one howler monkey of some 33 examined had positive serology; the age of this animal was 2 years or less.

No howler monkeys were observed in the Río Mono area of the Upper Tuira River basin in southern Darien Province near the Colombian border and fairly close to the Cerro Cana area. HI tests for yellow fever disclosed positive reactions in 14, or 24 percent, of 58 black spider monkeys and 1 of 19 white-faced monkeys. Two of the positive monkeys were juveniles less than 2 years old.

A third area surveyed was in the Chucunaque River basin in northern Darien Province, about 100 miles northwest of the two above-mentioned areas. The howler monkey population seemed to be of usual size. Only 2 of 73 spider monkeys were positive to yellow fever antibodies on the HI test; these were old monkeys with probably a residual immunity from the 1957 outbreak.

A fourth survey area was Cerro Azul, 16 miles east of Panama City, where yellow fever cases in man occurred in 1948 and again in 1956. There were many howler monkeys in the area. A total of 21 howler monkeys and two night monkeys were negative on HI tests. One of 16 white-faced and 2 of 15 red spider monkeys gave positive reactions. The positive animals were more than 6 years old.

Sentinel monkeys placed at two stations above Madden Lake and north of Cerro Azul remained healthy and no viruses were recovered from their sera or tissues. A total of 12,910 insects inoculated into mice in 436 different pools gave negative results.

The above findings indicated that yellow fever virus was probably widespread among monkeys in southern Darien Province between June 1963 and July 1966. This was the first evidence of yellow fever being present in Panama since the 1957 epidemic. Virus activity had not spread into northern Darien Province or central Panama Province as late as June 1966.

The Ecology of Arboviruses Other Than Yellow Fever: During the second year of the rodent-insect arbovirus study, 10 arbovirus strains were isolated from 461 pools of mosquitoes and 17 additional isolates were obtained from 378 wild rodents. Patois and Zegla viruses were recovered for the first time from rice rats, *Oryzomys.* Of 192 litters of suckling mice exposed in the field, 13 virus isolates were obtained. The golden hamster was utilized as a sentinel animal for the first time in the study area and proved advantageous for virus detection during the low transmission period when other methods have proved ineffective.

Early in the year there were an increased number of Group C isolations with a preponderance of Ossa virus which seemed to be accompanied by a reduction in the usual intensity of VEE virus. There was an accompanying increase of *Culex vomerifer* mosquitoes and a reduction in those of the *taeniopus-opisthopus* complex.

Because of the great amount of work involved in inoculating mice with pools of mosquitoes for virus isolation, a method was adopted of feeding captured mosquitoes on laboratory animals. The method appeared to be many times more sensitive than the former time-consuming one.

Preliminary experiments were conducted to determine susceptibility of certain Panama animals to inoculated VEE virus. The tree rat, *Tylomys panamensis,* had a viremia but tolerated the infection well. The green heron, *Butorides virescens,* also showed a viremia within 4 days after inoculation.

Surveys for viruses in eastern Panama were continued. Hemagglutination (HI) tests were conducted on 210 sera representing 18 species of aboreal and terrestrial animals from 18 different localities. Antibodies to VEE virus were found in three additional species of aboreal mammals and one rodent.

In central Panama serum samples were collected from 1,450 persons and tested by HI. Of the total, 34.5 percent were positive for one or more viruses. Group A antibodies were found in 11.1 percent, Group B in 25 percent, Group C in less than 1 percent and Bunyamwera Group in 2.9 percent.

Studies were initiated on pathology caused by various viruses in the animal host. Infection with Madrid, Ossa and other Group C viruses was associated with lesions in the liver, spleen and lymph nodes; VEE caused demonstrable lesions only in the lymphoid tissues. No central nervous lesions were encountered.

In further studies on fevers of undetermined origin, 96 human cases were observed and VEE virus was isolated from two, Ossa from three and Oriboca from one. The latter may have been acquired in the laboratory as this virus is not known to occur in Panama. In addition to the above, other viruses isolated from humans in Panama have been St. Louis encephalitis, Yellow Fever, Madrid, Wyeomyia, Chagres and Changuinola.

Leishmaniasis Studies: In continued search for reservoir hosts, cultures were made of skin scrappings from 217 animals with positive results in 6 porcupines *(Coendou rothschildi)* and a marmoset *(Saguinus geoffroyi).* Repeated heart blood cultures from the positive porcupines were negative and no lesions could be demonstrated. Positive cultures were secured from the spleen, liver, lymph nodes and bone marrow. The porcupine *Leishmania* produced no lesions after intradermal inoculation in hamsters.

Behavior of the porcupine and marmoset strains was observed in *Phlebotomus sanguinarius.* Only 2 out of 106 sandflies became infected after feeding on an infected porcupine. However, the strain did not develop in the sandflies. Observations were made on sandflies fed by the Hertig pipette technique. Ten of 36 *P. sanguinarius* were positive and 2 of 15 *P. gomezi* after feeding with cultures of the porcupine strain. The strain did not become established in these two species. On the other hand, the strain from the marmoset developed normally with the typical heavy growth in the cardia and the hindgut which characterizes the human strain. Interesting results were obtained by the micro-Ouchterlony technique which showed that the porcupine *Leishmania* was unrelated immunologically to common human strains from Panama but appeared to be identical with a strain isolated from *Phlebotomus trapidoi.*

Further investigations were conducted on the ecology of sandflies by the use of animal-baited 2-pan castor oil traps. Between March 1 and June 30, 2,083 sandflies were taken. Nearly all belonged to the commoner man-biting species. Two species made up the bulk of the captures and there was almost complete vertical separation of these species. *P. trapidoi* were nearly all taken in the forest canopy and *P. panamensis* at ground level. The canopy habitat of the former species suggested aboreal breeding places and search revealed a few larvae in dead leaves and litter from branches and tree holes 20 to 50 feet above ground.

Trials were initiated on the value of dihydrotriazine pamoate (Camolar®) in the treatment of leishmaniasis. Fourteen patients have received the drug. Those followed long enough for evaluation were cured.

American Trypanosomiasis: Complement fixation tests on the blood serum from 1,122 persons from 22 localities in Panama were positive in 8.8 percent. Of 3,306 sera tested from blood bank donors, 1.2 percent were positive on the CF test. The majority of the individuals were from urban centers. Seven cases of Chagas' disease were seen in local hospital wards. Three of the cases were fatal and pathological examination indicated severe acute myocarditis and scattered small focal lesions in the brain. None had any involvement of the esophagus.

In Brazil and other countries of South America, abnormalities in the functioning of the esophagus, manifested by prolonged transit time and dilation (megaesophagus) have been found in a high percentage of individuals infected with *Trypanosoma cruzi*. In 1961, initial clinical observations were conducted on a group showing positive CF tests for the organism. At that time, no esophageal dysfunction was observed in these individuals. In the current year, these studies were reinaugurated and 32 patients were studied. There was no evidence of esophageal pathology; the transit time was normal; and no megaesophagus was present.

Previously it had been shown that the common anteater, *Tamandua tetradactyla,* is naturally infected with *Trypanosoma rangeli* and that this infection could be transmitted to the pigmy anteater, *Cyclopes didactylus.* The inoculation of the latter species with human strains of *T. rangeli* produced an infection but of lower grade than the strain from *T. tetradactyla*. Further studies will be made on the possibility of the pigmy anteater being a reservoir host of human strains of *T. rangeli*.

Eleven strains of trypanosomes from monkeys were studied. Four from the marmoset, *Saguinus geoffroyi*, were *T. rangeli*. The other seven from four species of monkeys appeared to be *T. minasense*. Other strains of trypanosomes were secured from sloths, cotton rats and anteaters. A total of 13 new strains from wild animals were added to the reference collection.

Malaria Studies: A project was begun to determine whether human malarias could be established in Panamanian primates and whether a suitable laboratory model could be developed. Dr. Martin D. Young and Dr. James A. Porter were involved in these studies. Dr. David C. Baerg joined the project in 1967.

Two of 6 species of primates inoculated with *Plasmodium vivax* of human origin were found susceptible. Three of 14 marmosets, *Saguinus geoffroyi*, developed infections. Attempts to transfer the infection to other marmosets by subinoculation failed.

The night monkey, *Aotus trivirgatus*, was a much better host, as 14 out of 18 animals receiving human malarious blood became infected. The patent periods of the parasitemias ranged up to 54 days, often with high counts. Some monkeys died of the infection. *Anopheles albimanus* mosquitoes, the principal malaria vector in Panama, were infected by feeding on the monkeys and transmitted the infection by bites to human volunteers, who developed typical *vivax* attacks. The strain was transferred back into monkeys by the injection of infected human blood. *P. vivax* strains from four different human sources have proved infective to the night monkey. All of these strains have been passed from monkey to monkey by blood inoculation and one has been through six consecutive passages.

Attempts to transmit *P. falciparum* to three species of primates were successful only in the marmoset, *Saguinus geoffroyi*. Four of 8 marmosets became infected. The longest patent period was 15 days with only a moderate parasitemia. All subinoculations failed.

Except for the chimpanzee, these are the only other animals which have been shown to be susceptible to human *vivax* malaria. The results show promise of providing a useful primate host for studies of human malaria, a thing which has been previously lacking and which has hampered malaria investigations.

Primate malaria has been studied in the Laboratory off and on for many years. A survey of past records indicated that of 1,994 primates examined since 1931, the only species found was *Plasmodium brasilianum*, which infected 4 of the 7 species of Panamanian primates. The highest rate, 30 percent, was observed in the red spider monkey, *Ateles geoffroyi*. The

Fig. 10. The night monkey, Aotus trivirgatus, the first of several Panamanian monkeys demonstrated to be good hosts for human malaria at
the Gorgas Memorial Laboratory.

primates shown to be susceptible to human malarias, *A. trivirgatus* and *S. geoffroyi*, have never been found to have natural infections with any malaria parasite.

Studies on Other Parasitic Infections: The first autochthonous human case of hydatid disease in Panama was reported last year and led to a search for the adult parasite in lower animals. To date, two pumas and one jaguarundi have been found infected; one of the pumas had an estimated 100,000 adult worms in the gut and the parasite was determined to be *Echinococcus oligarthrus,* a relatively rare species, which had never been reported from Panama. It is believed that this species was the one responsible for the fatal case of hydatid disease in man and thus was the first human infection ever reported for this species.

The work with *Besnoitia panamensis* was continued and the parasite was transmitted to marmoset monkeys by feeding mouse peritoneal infected exudate. Of strains from the lizard and opossum, those from the latter proved more virulent. Depending on the size of the inoculum, blood parasites appeared 5 to 26 days later and the monkeys died during the following 24 hours. Sublethal oral inocula were capable of immunizing the animal against an intraperitoneal challenge with the homologous strain.

As the *Besnoitia* infections in lizards appeared to occur more often in areas where farm animals were present, the hemagglutination test was employed on sera from 527 cattle from various herds. Of these, 31 percent were positive. The specificity of the test needed to be established and further work was indicated. *Besnoitia* parasites are known to cause serious cattle disease in South Africa and the parasite has been reported from cattle in Venezuela.

Studies on Diarrheal Diseases: Long range studies continued in four rural communities. Of the 591 people involved, there were reports of 205 diarrheal episodes, giving an annual rate of 34.7 per 100 persons at risk. In the population studied, 12.5 percent were found with enteropathogenic bacteria as follows: *Salmonella,* 9.1 percent; *Shigella,* 2.4 percent; enteropathogenic *E. coli,* 0.5 percent; and *Arizona,* 0.5 percent. These rates are expressed as apparent and inapparent infections.

The role of various animals as reservoirs for enteropathogenic bacteria causing diarrhea in man was investigated further. Of 560 animals examined, Salmonellae were isolated from 47 percent of 72 lizards, *Ameiva ameiva.* Of 5 other species of lizards, 2 also harbored Salmonellae. A total of 228 monkeys of eight species were examined and pathogenic bacteria were found in 14 percent of black howler monkeys; 6 percent of marmosets; 5 percent of night monkeys; and 3 percent of spider monkeys. Other animals were negative.

Medical Entomology: Because of the important role of *Culex* mosquitoes of *Melanoconion* and allied subgenera, studies were being made on the taxonomy, biology and ecology of the group, which are very poorly known. Search was being made for preferred breeding places and larvae and pupae were being collected for taxonomic study and for attempted establishment of laboratory colonies for investigation of life cycles.

During his trip to several European museums last year, Dr. Fairchild was able to study many of the type specimens of Tabanidae described by various authors. Inadequate early descriptions and paucity of striking structural characters in this group have made correct determinations impossible without such study. On the basis of his European studies, he will attempt to prepare a more rational and accurate key to the genera with a check list of the species.

U. S. Naval Medical Science Unit: This unit was reactivated in July 1965 with the assignment of Lt. Commander Ralph D. Comer and HM-1 Paul Campbell. Studies were initiated on the use of the fluorescent antibody (FA) technique for the detection of malaria antibodies in man and experimental animals.

Studies on Herpetology: These studies were conducted during the year by two groups of visiting scientists.

Studies were done by Mr. Charles Myers and Dr. William Duellman, University of Kansas, to determine the kinds and distribution of amphibians and reptiles in Panama, to analyze the ecological relationships, to prepare guides and keys which will be useful for their identification in the future, and to study the influence of these animals upon human welfare.

An extraordinary complex of frogs was discovered whose skin secretions are very poisonous. These venoms are used on arrows by the Indians for hunting. Joint studies with Dr. John Daly, National Institute of Arthritis and Metabolic Diseases, resulted in the isolation of a new venom that shows promise of being useful in steroid precursor studies.

Lizards were shown to be reservoir hosts for bacteria causing diarrhea in man, and for parasites which may be infective to cattle. It has been suggested that they can act as hosts for eastern equine encephalitis virus in Panama.

As the importance of these animals to health problems becomes more apparent, the necessity of having information leading to their proper identification becomes increasingly necessary, as well as knowing more about their ecology.

Another research team, composed of Dr. John M. Legler and Mr. Edward O. Moll of the University of Utah investigated the life history and ecology of a neotropical slider turtle. The primary goal was to record and analyze the major events in the life cycle of this turtle in the Atlantic Isthmian region. The manner in which a tropical environment influences this aquatic vertebrate which also occurs in north and south temperate zone regions will be studied as well as whether differences noted in these various regions are genetic or adaptive. Special emphasis was placed upon growth, reproduction and other cyclic phenomena.

Preliminary data indicated that the populations tended to be divided into three age groups with distinct habitat preferences. The adults showed homing behavior. Other studies concerned the reproductive cycle.

As turtles constitute a potential important source of food, the information which was obtained may prove to be of much practical value.

Visiting Scientists: Dr. Alexander Wetmore of the Smithsonian Institution again used the Laboratory as a base for his studies on the birds of Panama.

Dr. Jon Straumfjord, Alabama Medical Center, visited the laboratory in connection with a cooperative project on the relation of isoenzymes to Chagas' disease and other parasitic diseases.

Two assistants of Dr. John N. Belkin, University of California at Los Angeles, spent several months working in the Rand Insectary on rearing field-caught mosquitoes in connection with a cooperative project on the Culicidae of Middle America.

Dr. Thomas Frothingham of Harvard University spent 2 weeks in the Laboratory in connection with a leishmaniasis project.

Dr. A. J. Walker of the Pan American Health Organization visited the Laboratory for 1 month for work on malaria.

Short term visits were made by graduate fellows and medical students sponsored by the Louisiana State University, as well as fellows from the University of Cincinnati, University of South Florida, and the U. S. Public Health Service Hospital, Baltimore, Md. Certain medical students remained at the Laboratory for a period of 2 months; these individuals were from Louisiana State University, University of Colorado, University of Michigan, University of Chicago, Leland Stanford University and the University of Rochester.

1967   *The Ecology of Arboviruses Other Than Yellow Fever:*
Long range investigations in the Almirante area were carried out for the third year. The hamster continued to be a sensitive indicator of virus activity. Of a total of 44 hamster tissues, 24 were positive for viruses, including Ossa, Madrid and VEE. The Ossa virus was extremely prevalent in the area. Most hamsters succumbed to the infection rapidly with the result that other virus activity was masked. Some hamsters were immunized against Ossa virus before being exposed in the field. Four of 6 such sentinels acquired other viruses.

Spiny rats continued to show high rates of infection with viruses of Groups A, B and C. Cotton rats had lower rates.

A total of 24 virus isolations were obtained from 1,006 pools representing 25,315 mosquitoes taken in the area. Three of the isolates, all from *Culex vomerifer,* were identified as VEE virus. This virus was also isolated from acute febrile human cases.

In order to determine further the chief vectors of arboviruses, 126 hamsters were exposed in the insectary to bites of 35,590 wild-caught mosquitoes. Eleven viruses were isolated from processed hamster tissues; most bites were by *Culex vomerifer.* Isolates were identified as Ossa and Madrid. Serological tests of surviving hamsters indicated the presence of Guamá virus.

Preliminary studies were conducted in an upland forest in the Almirante area to determine differences in viral activity between that type of environment compared to that in the low land swamp forests. Two Group C viruses were obtained from sentinel hamsters. Further observations were being made.

The occurrence of viral activity in the human population in various areas of Panama was studied by means of the HI test with 29 different arbovirus antigens. Most of the serum samples came from blood bank donors. A total of 495 samples came from four areas, viz: Panama City, Panama Province, central and peninsular areas and Chiriquí. Of these sera, 32 were positive for VEE and other Group A antibodies; 176 for Group B, some of which may have been due to yellow fever vaccination; and 18 for Group C. Low percentages of antibodies were found for Bunyamwera, Phlebotomus and Turlock groups. Neutralization tests with Group B—HI positive samples showed that 6 percent of them were positive for Ilhéus virus and 13 percent for Bussuquara virus. The results emphasized the wide distribution and extensive activity of various arboviruses in Panama.

A survey of the role of bats as reservoirs of arboviruses was instituted in cooperation with the Middle America Research Unit. A total of 286 bat tissue pools were processed; 124 were inoculated into suckling mice and 60 into monkey kidney (Vero) cell cultures. No virus isolates were obtained. A total of 127 bat sera were tested by HI using 16 arboviral antigens. Nine samples were positive, all for Group B viruses with the exception of one EEE positive.

Studies were carried out to determine the animal species serving as reservoir hosts for VEE virus and to select suitable experimental models. Preliminary results confirmed the fact that the tree rat, *Tylomys panamensis,* is susceptible to the virus. The striated heron, *Butorides striatus,* and the opossum, *Didelphis marsupialis,* also proved susceptible. Presumably these animals could serve as reservoirs for mosquito acquisition and transmission of the virus.

The mosquito, *Deinocerites pseudes,* was previously found in nature to be infected with St. Louis encephalitis (SLE) virus. Its ability to transmit VEE virus was tested in the laboratory. A large percentage of mosquitoes of this species became infected when fed on infected guinea pigs and in turn transmitted the virus to other guinea pigs and to hamsters.

Leishmaniasis Studies: Previously it was reported that *Leishmania* infections were found in two arboreal animals, the kinkajou and the marmoset monkey. During the year, infection was detected in a third animal, the olingo *(Bassaricyon gabbii).*

The porcupine continued to show high infection rates. Of 18 porcupines taken from four widely separated areas, 17 were infected. By contrast, only 2 of 7 from another area showed infections. The epidemiological significance of the difference is being studied. Of epidemiological importance was the fact that the infection was maintained for at least 15 months in porcupines kept in the laboratory.

A finding of note was the presence of scars in the ears of the kinkajou; in one case the septum of the nose had been destroyed. No leishmania were found in this animal during the year.

Further studies on the treatment of leishmaniasis were conducted by Dr. Carl M. Johnson with dihydrotriazine pamoate (Camolar®). Dosage ranged from 350 mg. for patients 11 years and older down to 140 mg. for those 6 months to 4 years of age. The drug was administered intramuscularly in a single dose. Patients studied were those in which a parasitological diagnosis of leishmaniasis had been made without evidence of chronic illness. Sixteen patients were reported on last year. A total of 34 have now been treated, although nine failed to return for completion of the study. Of the 25 remaining, 18 were considered cured and 7 were judged to be failures. A single case of mucocutaneous leishmaniasis was one of the failures. Healing was usually completed within 100 days; however, one case healed in 44 days and one required 128 days.

American Trypanosomiasis: Surveys for prevalence of infection in man were conducted by means of the complement fixation test, direct examination of blood smears, blood culture and xeno-diagnosis. Blood samples were derived from various sources. Of a total of 11,600 specimens, infection rates varied between 0.2 and 12.5 percent. Some areas showed many chronic infections. The results indicated a higher prevalence in areas near the Canal Zone in the Provinces of Panama and Colon. Infection was less prevalent in the populated areas of the Pacific slope west of the Province of Panama.

Of patients admitted to Santo Tomás Hospital with a positive serology for Chagas' disease, 101 were carefully studied. Forty-eight of these showed cardiac abnormalities with one or more of the following types:

Arrhythmias, right bundle branch block, left bundle branch block, ventricular enlargement, atrial enlargement, myocardial lesions and A/V block. There were four deaths, two with acute and two with chronic Chagas' disease. One of the fatal cases was 46 years of age; this was the first known death from this disease in Panama in anyone over 30 years of age. In South America acute fatal Chagas' disease deaths are said to occur only in children.

Ventricular aneurysms were found in the heart in two fatal cases, lesions which have not been reported previously in Chagas' disease patients in Panama. Contrary to previous concepts, it would appear that apical lesions may be commonly associated with the chronic disease in Panama.

In a study of 45 cases of Chagas' disease with positive complement fixation tests, xeno-diagnosis was found of little value in chronic cases. It may be of value in acute cases and in distinguishing *T. cruzi* from *T. rangeli* infection.

In further studies on the trypanosomes of wild animals, *T. cruzi* was found in the anteater, *Tamandua tetradactyla,* and the agouti, *Dasyprocta punctata. T. legeri* from the anteater has been maintained in culture through 50 passages. The agouti was found to be a host for another trypanosome, *T. coutinhoi.* Thirty-three new isolates were added to the trypanosome bank at the Laboratory.

Rhodnius prolixus is an important vector of *T. rangeli* in parts of South America but a poor vector in Panama. Different lots of this bug were subjected to gamma irradiation from a cobalt-60 source to determine if the protective response of the bugs could be altered. Irradiation dosages of 2.5 by 10^3, 5 by 10^3, 10^4, 2 by 10^4, and 4 by 10^4 roentgens did not alter the susceptibility of the bugs to this parasite. When culture forms of the parasite were inoculated into the haemocoele of the treated bugs, the parasites were destroyed within 48 hours.

Malaria Studies: Last year it was reported for the first time that *Plasmodium vivax* of human origin could be grown easily in a common small Panamanian primate, the night or owl monkey, *Aotus trivirgatus,* and to a lesser extent in the Panamanian marmoset, *Saguinus geoffroyi.* During the past year several different strains of *P. vivax* have been established in the night monkey, thus confirming the ability of this animal to serve as a suitable host. The Achiote strain of the parasite was maintained through 25 monkey passages and another strain, Santa Rosa, had been through 17 transfers. Although the infection was produced both in splenectomized and in intact monkeys, parasitemias were higher in the former. Of 67 monkeys inoculated, 58 became infected. The parasitemias reached high levels and a few persisted for over 90 days.

P. vivax appeared to become better adapted to the marmoset, *S. geoffroyi,* with passage.

A new host for *P. vivax* was found in spider monkeys *(Ateles).* Ten of 15 monkeys were infected but the parasitemias were lower and of shorter duration than in the night monkey.

Some 50,000 *Anopheles albimanus* mosquitoes were fed on monkeys infected with *P. vivax.* Many became infected but transmission of the infection to other monkeys by infected mosquitoes was not accomplished.

It was reported last year that *P. falciparum* from man would grow in the marmoset, *S. geoffroyi.* Additional attempts to infect this monkey with this human species of malaria have provided only partial success. A transient infection was established in one night monkey out of 14 attempts. Apparently the strain of *P. falciparum* is of some significance in transmission attempts, since other laboratories have established other strains of the parasite in the night monkey following the initial experiments in the Gorgas Memorial Laboratory.

Attempts to transmit *P. falciparum* from man to monkey through the bites of infected mosquitoes met with failure, as did also experiments to transmit *P. ovale* trophozoites of human origin to the night monkey.

The U. S. Naval Medical Science Unit under the direction of Lt. Commander Ralph D. Comer was engaged in a cooperative program with the Pan American Health Organization and the Ministry of Health of Panama to evaluate drug therapy in the control of malaria. Pyrimethamine and primaquine tablets were given every 2 weeks to the inhabitants of the Sambu River Valley. Participation of the 2,300 inhabitants averaged about 70 percent. The prevalence rate of malaria at the start of the experiments in May 1966 was 17.4 percent; after 1 year it was 0.6 percent and clinical malaria had virtually disappeared.

Studies on Other Parasitic Infections: The first natural hydatid infection by *Echinococcus oligarthrus* in wild animals in Panama was found in the agouti, *Dasyprocta punctata.* The jaguar, *Felis onca,* was recorded for the first time as a definitive host of the parasite.

Experiments indicated that infection is readily obtained by feeding eggs or proglottids of the tapeworm to local rodents, *Proechimys semispinosus, Tylomys panamensis* and *Dasyprocta punctata.* Presumably these rodents could serve as intermediate hosts of the parasite. Complete development of the adult tapeworm was demonstrated in the house cat, *Felis cattus.*

A survey of parasitic infections among Peace Corps volunteers was carried out upon entering and leaving the country. A total of 362 samples were examined, of which 119 were positive for at least one intestinal parasite. The most common finding was *Ascaris lumbricoides* in 6.0 percent of the cases; hookworm occurred in 2.6 percent.

A 2-year program of a study of parasitism in four rural villages was completed in December 1966 and the results assembled. In over 1,000 persons the overall infection rate was 98 percent. The prevalence rates in percent for various parasites were as follows: *Ascaris lumbricoides* 47, *Trichuris trichiura* 53, hookworm 84, *Entamoeba histolytica* 44 and *Giardia lamblia* 47. The findings were being evaluated for their possible relationship to the presence of enterobacterial pathogens.

In studies on immune reactions in *Besnoitia* infections, mice immune to *B. darlingi* and *B. panamensis* were susceptible to infection with *B. jellisoni*. On the other hand, *B. jellisoni* immune mice were immune to the two other species. There was cross immunity between the Panamanian species, *B. darlingi* and *B. panamensis*. On this basis *B. panamensis* becomes a synonym of *B. darlingi*.

Dr. William A. Summers of the Indiana University Medical School conducted research at the Gorgas Memorial Laboratory from July 23, 1966 to January 12, 1967. He studied the infectivity, morphology and growth rates of *Toxoplasma* and *Besnoitia* in tissue culture.

Toxoplasma gondii and three species of *Besnoitia* all infected and grew in both human monocyte and monkey kidney cell lines. Serial dilutions of inoculated parasites did not always establish infections in cell lines. The rapidity with which host cell invasion occurred and the morphological changes during growth were generally similar in the four species. All were infective for mice following at least one tissue passage. *Toxoplasma* reproduced faster than any of the *Besnoitia* species. Cytopathogenesis and the rapidity of host cell destruction was directly proportional to the rate of parasite growth. *Toxoplasma* infected cells underwent cytolysis most rapidly while *B. jellisoni* infected cells survived the longest period of time.

In experiments to determine the effect of homologous and heterologous antibody on infectivity, serum with a fluorescent antibody titer of 1:8000 obtained 1 month after recovery from acute toxoplasmosis markedly inhibited the ability of *T. gondii* to infect monkey kidney cells. This antiserum had no effect on the infectivity of *Besnoitia darlingi* or *B. jellisoni*. *B. darlingi* antiserum produced in rabbits having a hemagglutinin titer of 1:100,000 markedly inhibited the infectivity of *T. gondii* but had no effect on *B. darlingi* or *B. jellisoni*. A similar *B. jellisoni* antiserum did not adversely effect the growth of any of the species in tissue culture. An antitoxoplasmic serum obtained 4 years after recovery (FA titer 1:4000) had no effect upon parasite infectivity in tissue culture. The results suggested the possibility that growth inhibiting properties of the antiserum may reside in different forms of the antibody globulin. The studies pointed out the similarities of the organisms studied but indicated that further investigations on the immune relationships of the organisms might well offer information of value for the final determination of the taxonomic status of the different species.

Studies on Diarrheal Diseases: The long range study of diarrheal diseases continued in four villages involving 614 people. There were 196 attacks of diarrhea giving a rate of 32 per 100 persons. In one community the rate was 3 times that of last year but the rate in the other three communities decreased.

Opportunity was afforded to study an outbreak of acute diarrheal disease among Indians living in Ailigandí, one of the islands of the San Blas Archipelago. There was only 1 month in the year in which no acute diarrhea was observed in children 3 years of age and younger. *Shigella sonnei* was the most prevalent pathogen; it was present in the non-diarrheic controls at about one-third the rate of that in the diarrheic cases.

The prevalence of enteropathogens was studied in 1,178 children involved in a nutrition survey conducted in Panama by the Institute of Nutrition of Central America and Panama (INCAP). Preliminary findings indicated that 4.2 percent of the children all under 10 years of age harbored pathogenic enterobacteria.

Surveys for enterobacterial pathogens were continued in lower animals. A total of 322 animals were studied. A relatively high prevalence of *Salmonella* was found in certain lizards and toads. The three species involved are of common occurrence in and around human habitations; whether enterobacterial infections are associated with occurrence of these organisms in man needs to be determined.

Medical Entomology: Mr. Méndez continued his cooperation with Lt. Col. V. J. Tipton on studies on the fleas of Panama and other areas. An extensive paper was produced as a result of a collection of material from the State of Nuevo León, Mexico.

The isolation of St. Louis encephalitis virus from a pool of *Deinocerites* mosquitoes 2 years ago led to efforts to establish colonies of members of this genus for biological and virus transmission studies. Success has now been achieved in the colonization of two species, *D. pseudes* and *D. epitedeus.*

Interoceanic Canal Studies: In connection with feasibility studies of two proposed sites of a sea-level canal in Panama and Colombia, the U. S. Army organized a medico-ecological program to collect and deliver to the Gorgas Memorial Laboratory specimens of animals, vectors and other pertinent materials concerned with disease potentials. In addition, the U. S. Army and the Gorgas Memorial Laboratory are cooperating in a disease surveillance program whereby all persons going into the area to work are examined before entering the respective areas, while there, upon leaving and during periods of illness to detect disease agents and the character of infection. The operations on Route 17 through Panama started in November 1966 and those on Route 25 through Colombia in April 1967.

During the first year of the study, a total of over 36,000 vertebrates and insects of medical importance have been collected, representing 328 different species. The common Panama fauna was well represented but some new insect species were recovered.

Virus studies of collected material indicated the presence of antibodies to at least seven virus groups in serum samples. Only one virus was isolated from blood sera from 658 wild animals. Numerous pools of mosquitoes yielded no viruses.

Active malaria transmission was occurring along both proposed canal routes as indicated by contraction of the disease by workers. An investigation was made of a disease outbreak among the Morti Indians on Route 17. Three species of human malaria were involved; 38.5 percent of the people had parasitemia.

Evidence was obtained to indicate the presence of a chloroquine resistant *Plasmodium falciparum* strain among inhabitants of native villages near Curiche, the base camp at the Pacific end of Route 25 in Colombia. Several non-immune U. S. citizens came down with malaria due to this species without responding to the usual chloroquine regimen. The parasitemia rate in the villages was 41 percent and some treated individuals were resistant to chloroquine. Further studies were to be made.

Studies on Herpetology: A 3-year program of field studies on the reptiles and amphibians of Panama was concluded on June 30, 1967, by Mr. Charles Myers and Dr. William Duellman of the University of Kansas.

Approximately 10,000 specimens were accumulated. A nearly complete bibliography of the Panamanian herpetofauna has been compiled. It is anticipated that a monograph will be produced covering species encountered, geographical distribution, relative abundance, variational trends, relationships and taxonomic status.

Toxic extracts of arrow poison from frogs obtained during the study were being chemically analyzed by Dr. John Daly at the National Institute of Arthritis and Metabolic Diseases. Some of the toxins have strong pharmacological effects and hence are of potential medical interest.

An interesting discovery was made when visiting the type locality of a frog *(Atelopus)* that was described 41 years ago; the population had undergone a nearly complete change in basic coloration, thus providing a rare demonstration of rapid evolution within a natural population.

Cooperation with Other Organizations: As in the past, such cooperation has been in effect with many other research and professional organizations. During the year, cooperative studies were inaugurated with Dr.

Harold Trapido, Rockefeller Foundation, on new species of mosquitoes from Central America and Colombia; with Drs. William C. Reeves and C. H. Tempelis, University of California at Berkeley on determination of the blood meal in *Deinocerites* mosquitoes; with Dr. John N. Belkin, University of California at Los Angeles on the Culicidae of Middle America; with Dr. C. V. Vago of France on insect pathogens; and with Dr. William F. Scherer of Cornell University on virus transmission by mosquitoes.

The Laboratory continued to provide programs for medical students from various universities.

The following individuals conducted studies at the Laboratory during the year:

Dr. Ethel Joan Blanchette, The George Washington University School of Medicine.

Dr. William A. Summers, Indiana University Medical School.

Dr. John Thomas, Meharry Medical School.

1968   *The Ecology of Arboviruses Other Than Yellow Fever:*
Many aspects of the problem received attention during the year; investigations were divided into the following categories: Ecology of various viruses in the Almirante area; surveillance in various areas in Panama; the behavior of Venezuelan equine encephalitis virus in wild animal hosts; the role of *Deinocerites* mosquitoes in transmission; transmission experiments with VEE and SLE viruses; the susceptibility of the golden hamster to various arboviruses; and studies on vesicular stomatitis virus.

The long range investigation in the Almirante area was continued for the fourth year. A total of 55 virus isolations were made from 188 litters of exposed mice. Isolations included Venezuelan equine encephalitis (VEE), Ossa and Guamá viruses. Over half the isolations were from litters exposed during the months of June, July and August. Of 459 sera collected from rodents in previous years, and tested by the complement fixation test, 50 proved positive for Guamá virus, 13 for Wyeomyia and 13 for Melao. It was possible to recapture 23 rodents released after the first bleeding; five were shown to have contracted additional viruses over varying periods, including three with Guamá and one each with Wyeomyia and Melao. Attempts were made to isolate virus from 2,809 pools representing over 65,000 mosquitoes. Only *Culex vomerifer* and *Psorophora cingulata* yielded viruses, as did some *Phlebotomus* species. The bulk of the isolations were from *C. vomerifer* and included Guamá (12), Ossa (2), Nepuyo (1), VEE (1) and 9 unidentified strains.

Surveillance for virus activity was undertaken in a statistically selected random sampling of individuals in two urban communities, Patoistown and Zegla. HI tests were conducted on serum samples with 14 viral antigens. After 6 to 8 months, the same persons were again bled to determine any antibody conversions during that period. The first bleeding gave 36 positives of 109 in Patoistown and 54 of 190 in Zegla. The second bleeding of 98 persons in Patoistown showed that eight had converted to a positive status; in Zegla, 147 second samples were tested, of which seven had converted.

Observations on arbovirus activity in other areas of Panama were continued by various means. No virus strains were isolated from sentinel animals, although serological testing of blood from man and wild vertebrates in the Juan Mina-Guayabalito area of the Chagres River showed that VEE and Group B viruses were prevalent. Of 25 individuals with acute fever, one strain of VEE virus was isolated from an 18-year resident of Colon.

In studies on the behavior of VEE virus in a variety of wild animal hosts, 27 animals belonging to nine species, five orders and three classes were utilized. Virus titers reached the highest values in the blood of squirrels and sloths and lasted by far the longest in sloths. Since all species of positive animals were inoculated with relatively small doses of virus subcutaneously and all showed concentrations of virus presumably high enough to infect blood-sucking arthropods, all are likely possibilities as reservoir hosts. In this regard the sloths are especially good candidates as reservoirs in the forest canopy. Only a cayman *(Crocodilia)* failed to circulate virus or exhibit antibodies.

Intensive studies were carried out to evaluate the role of *Deinocerites* mosquitoes as arbovirus vectors. Formerly thought to seldom attack man or to take any vertebrate blood, the previous isolation of VEE and SLE viruses from members of the genus pointed strongly to their importance in this regard. Taxonomic studies, largely being carried out at the University of California at Los Angeles, indicated the presence of at least seven species in Panama, with two of them seemingly new to science. *D. pseudes* and *D. epitedeus* colonized last year continued to produce large numbers of adults. *D. melanophyllum* was colonized with comparative ease but *D. dyari* proved refractory. Field studies of *D. pseudes* at Nueva Gorgona on the Pacific Coast indicated that the species is active throughout the year with peaks of abundance in February and March at the height of the dry season. Through a cooperative arrangement with Drs. W. C. Reeves and C. H. Tempelis, University of California at Berkeley, antisera for precipitin tests have been prepared for a considerable range of Panamanian mammals, birds and reptiles. Of 3,053 wild-caught blood engorged specimens of five species of *Deinocerites* tested, most showed a wide range of hosts. Most of the species preferred certain animals but *D. epitedeus* showed a wider preference. *D. cancer* preferred heron blood and thus would be able to transmit malaria parasites and VEE virus, which have been shown to occur in the green heron in Panama.

D. pseudes proved to be a good transmitter of VEE virus in laboratory experiments with guinea pigs. However, the virus was not isolated from over 600 pools of *D. epitedeus* and *D. cancer* collected around Almirante. *D. pseudes* failed to transmit SLE virus to hamsters thus indicating again that the fact that mosquitoes are found to carry virus in nature or can be infected in the laboratory is no criterion of their ability to actually transmit infection.

In cooperation with the Middle America Research Unit, experiments were conducted to test the susceptibility of the golden hamster (*Mesocricetus auratus*) to New World viruses. Venezuelan, Eastern and Western equine encephalitis viruses (VEE, EEE and WEE), and several Group C viruses proved pathogenic with illness and death occurring in 1 to 3 days after inoculation. The following viruses produced no signs of illness: Mayaro, Una, SLE, yellow fever, Ilhéus, Wyeomyia, Guamá, Catu, Bimiti, Melao and Changuinola. Vesicular stomatitis (Indiana), Cocal, California encephalitis and Chagres produced illness or death when given intracerebrally but failed to kill all hamsters by the subcutaneous route. Only Patois and all Group C viruses produced HI antigen in the serum of injected adult hamsters.

A number of recently isolated viruses were shown, in cooperation with Dr. Robert S. Shope of the Rockefeller Foundation, to be sufficiently distinct to be placed in a group of their own within the Bunyamwera super group. This new virus group, designated Patois, included Patois and Zegla from Panama, and Shark River and Pahayokee from Florida.

Analysis of several thousand blood tests indicated that antibodies to vesicular stomatitis virus were far more prevalent in aboreal than terrestrial mammals. Most of the positives occurred in various species of monkeys, especially in *Ateles fusciceps*. However, none of apparently non-immune monkeys of this species showed any viremia after subcutaneous inoculation of the virus. Apparently this virus has an unusual epidemiological pattern.

Leishmaniasis Studies: Intensive studies on the epidemiology of leishmaniasis in four localities indicated that in three (Achiote, Las Tablitas and Gaspar Sabanas) the infection resulted from a movement of the population into an originally forested region. Most of the cases in the Achiote community represented old infections characterized by scars and there appeared to be little transmission at present. In the other two communities, there is active contact with the forest and new cases are occurring in all age groups. In another area, El Aguacate, which has been settled for 60 to 70 years, small patches of forest remain with animal populations. The disease is still being maintained in the community.

Search for *Leishmania* infections in forest animals was continued with emphasis on the Achiote and Gaspar Sabanas areas. A total of 433 wild mammals were collected from these areas, as well as 549 lizards. All of these animals were negative with the exception of sloths. Cultures from nine sloths, eight two-toed *Choloepus hoffmanni* and one three-toed *Bradypus infuscatus,* have yielded cultures of forms which are indistinguishable from *Leishmania braziliensis* when inoculated into hamsters. Other hemoflagellates were also isolated from the sloths. Sentinel animals exposed near various foci of human leishmaniasis remained negative. Efforts to isolate *Leishmania* from *Phlebotomus* sandflies captured in the vicinity of Gaspar Sabanas were also negative. Strains of *Leishmania* from other wild-caught sandflies were tested in hamsters to determine their longevity at the site of inoculation and their ability to invade the viscera. None of the strains survived at the inoculation site (the nose of hamsters) for as long as 7 days and none could be recovered from the viscera.

American Trypanosomiasis: The studies concerned a number of problems including the prevalence of Chagas' disease in man, diagnostic methods, trypanosomes in domestic and peridomestic animals, the use of guinea pigs as sentinel animals, infection rates in wild-caught triatomid bugs, biological characteristics of trypansome isolates and observations on trypanosomes of wild animals. Dr. John H. Edgcomb joined the project on January 1, 1968.

Blood culture techniques were utilized in prevalence surveys. None of 1,303 persons tested in the Almirante area showed trypanosomes. In contrast, of 1,860 individuals tested in the Panama-Colon area, 40 were infected, of whom 33 had *Trypanosoma rangeli,* 2 had *T. cruzi,* 4 represented a mixed infection, and 1 an infection with an organism as yet unidentified. Seventy percent of the positives occurred in the age group 15 years or under.

In a group of 110 individuals positive for Chagas' disease on the complement fixation test, xeno-diagnosis, blood culture and blood chemistry methods were applied to compare techniques with a negative group of 38 persons. Previous results with xeno-diagnosis confirmed the fact that the test reveals the presence of trypanosomes only in acute cases. This test gave negative results sooner than did blood culture. Abnormally high levels of Serum Glutamic Oxalacetic Transaminase and Serum Glutamic Pyruvate Transaminase were found in acute cases but not in chronic cases. About 28 percent of the latter showed abnormally high urea nitrogen in the blood.

Efforts were made to refine the serological tests employed for the diagnosis of human trypanosomiasis. Antigens prepared from three different strains of *T. cruzi* gave variable results. Cross reactions between *T. cruzi* and *T. rangeli* are not uncommon on the CF test. Preliminary trials with a hemagglutination test showed promise and effort was being made to purify the antigen.

Fig. 11. Lesions on the nose of a golden hamster inoculated with a strain of Leishmania isolated from a sloth at the Gorgas Memorial Laboratory.

Blood cultures were made from a total of 280 animals to assess their role in the epidemiology of Chagas' disease. Seventy pigs, 16 horses and four mules were negative. However, 19 of 82 dogs were positive, as were 22 of 108 rats *(Rattus rattus)*. Of the 19 positive dogs, 6 had *T. rangeli*, 4 *T. cruzi* and 9 mixed infections. Among the 22 positive rats, 11 had *T. cruzi*, 3 *T. rangeli* and 1 a mixed infection. In seven rats, identifications had not yet been made.

Guinea pigs have been employed as sentinel animals to detect trypanosome infections in peridomestic surroundings. The first month's observations were negative but it is anticipated that this method will prove of value in assessing opportunities for acquiring infection.

In studies on infection rates in wild-caught triatomid bugs, *Rhodnius pallescens* proved to be most commonly infected; 41 of 119 specimens carried either *T. cruzi* or *T. rangeli*. *T. cruzi* alone occurred only in *Triatoma dimidiata* and *Panstrongylus rufotuberculatus*.

In studies on the biological characteristics of trypanosomes, *T. rangeli* was found to give rise to rapidly developing, low level but long lasting parasitemias in mice without discernible tissue involvement. *T. cruzi* strains generally took longer to reach peaks of parasitemia but these may be of much higher level and may be fatal to mice. Although most strains of *T. cruzi* gave only a low level of parasitemia, nearly all showed good tissue phase development. There seemed to be no correlation between the virulence in mice and the source of the strain; a strain isolated from a fatal human case manifested only low parasitemia levels in mice.

T. rangeli and *T. cruzi* differ basically in their behavior in triatomid bugs. The former invades the body cavity and the salivary glands of suitable vector bugs and is apparently transmitted to vertebrates by the bite of the infected bugs. The latter develops wholly within the intestinal tract of the bug and vertebrates are infected in a manner other than by the bite of the vector. Tests of strains of trypanosomes isolated from man indicated that all species of bugs exposed can become infected with local strains of *T. cruzi* but that *R. pallescens* is the most susceptible.

During the year trypanosomes were found in the blood of about 400 animals, mostly mammals; 81 represented new isolates which were added to the trypanosome bank. In addition to strains of *T. cruzi* and *T. rangeli*, the isolates included at least five other species; six of the host species represented animals from which trypanosomes had never before been isolated. Up to July 1968, there have been added to the trypanosome bank isolates from six species of opossums, 11 species of bats, seven species of monkeys, four edentate species, eight rodent species, one rabbit and four species of carnivores.

Malaria Studies: Prevalence studies were carried out in six villages, which were surveyed from 4 to 6 times during the year. *Plasmodium vivax* was the only species encountered. The following were the results of the surveys:

Place	No. of examinations	Percent positive
Escobal	1,401	4.6
Piña	450	0.9
Achiote	398	3.2
Altos del Jobo	1,137	0.0
Río Chagres Villages	911	1.7
Mendoza	1,152	0.4

Investigations were continued during the year on the behavior of human malaria parasites in Panamanian monkeys. The evidence indicated that *Plasmodium vivax* can be continuously passed through monkeys by the inoculation of infected blood. One strain, the Achiote, since its original isolation has been through a total of 56 passages over a period of 2 years. Higher parasitemias were produced in splenectomized and drug-treated monkeys than in those unaltered and untreated. The night monkey, *Aotus trivirgatus,* is the most susceptible to human malarias. The marmoset, *Saguinus geoffroyi,* also continued to show susceptibility to *P. vivax* malaria. Previously, only low grade infections of *P. vivax* could be obtained in black spider and red spider *(Ateles)* monkeys but during the past year it has been shown that certain strains can be adapted to these animals and will grow well. This raises to four the number of Panamanian monkey species which appear to be good experimental hosts for human malarias. Attempts to standardize infections have been encouraging and will be pursued further.

A fifth monkey, *Cebus capucinus,* also was susceptible to *P. vivax,* but so far has not shown high parasitemias.

Of various species of mosquitoes fed on infected monkeys, only *Anopheles albimanus* became infected. For the first time *P. vivax* transmission from monkey to monkey was accomplished through the bites of mosquitoes.

In order to provide adequate numbers of mosquitoes for transmission experiments, seven species were colonized in the laboratory. These included *Anopheles apicimacula, aquasalis, argyritarsis, eiseni, punctimacula, pseudopunctipennis* and *triannulatus. A. pseudopunctipennis* was colonized for the first time and has been carried through two laboratory generations. This species seems to be less susceptible than *A. albimanus* to the human malarias in monkeys.

Studies on Other Parasitic Infections: The little known tapeworm, *Echinococcus oligarthrus,* which was shown to be the cause of a fatal case of hydatid disease in man in Panama, was studied further. A natural infection was found in 1 of 15 agouties, *Dasyprocta punctata,* from the endemic area of Achiote. Adult worms were recovered from experimental hosts following the feeding of the material from the agouti. Experimental infection was produced for the first time in the cotton rat, *Sigmodon hispidus,* the white mouse, *Mus musculus,* (CFW strain), the Wistar albino rat, *Rattus rattus,* and the gerbil. Several lines of *E. oligarthrus* have been established in the laboratory, including a cat-rodent-cat cycle, a line of intraperitoneal secondary hydatidosis (rodent to rodent cycle), and a line of intramuscular secondary hydatidosis (rodent to rodent cycle).

Examinations for intestinal parasites were conducted on three population groups. A survey of 52 children, 2-6 years old, from the Red Cross Orphanage, revealed 54.3 percent positives on the basis of an average of 1.5 samples per individual. *Giardia, Ascaris* and *Trichuris* were the dominant species found. An average number of samples of 2.5 from 167 Peace Corps Volunteers revealed 30.5 percent of the individuals to be positive for intestinal parasites. *Giardia* was the most common parasite but *Entamoeba histolytica,* hookworm, *Ascaris* and *Trichuris* were also encountered. About 25 percent of the individuals with *E. histolytica* showed some symptomatic involvement. A third group consisting mainly of rural inhabitants from Panama and Colon Provinces comprised referrals from Santo Tomás Hospital and private physicians together with Gorgas Memorial Laboratory clinic patients. Of 475 persons, 51.2 percent were positive on the basis of 1.2 samples per person. The most common findings included *Trichuris,* hookworms, *Ascaris, E. histolytica* and *Giardia.*

Bacteriological Studies: Surveillance for enterobacterial pathogens in the rural population was continued on a reduced scale. Of 530 persons examined, 88 had diarrhea but only five harbored pathogens. Twenty-three other individuals yielded pathogens but had no diarrhea. Among the 28 isolations, nine different pathogens were represented, of which *Edwardsiella tarda, Salmonella oslo* and *Shigella sonnei* were the most common.

Rectal swabs from recently captured monkeys yielded five species of pathogens, including two serotypes of enteropathogenic *E. coli* and two of *Salmonella* from three species of monkeys. A high proportion of lizards and snakes harbored *Salmonella* and *Arizona* organisms.

Agglutination tests on the sera from 2,360 individuals in 31 communities in Panama provided *Brucella* antibodies in 1.2 percent; symptoms of brucellosis were not noted in any of the positive individuals.

Taxonomic Entomology: Work was continued on the identification and classification of various arthropods involved in disease transmission or as external parasites of man and lower animals. A Catalogue of Neotropical Tabanidae was completed and will soon be submitted for publication. It lists some 92 valid genera and subgenera and 987 species with about half that number of synonyms.

Interoceanic Canal Studies: Last year feasibility studies were inaugurated along proposed sea-level canal Route 17 in Panama and Route 25 in Colombia. The extent of the project was materially reduced because of the lack of funds; the medico-ecological program was terminated on January 31, 1968 while the disease surveillance program continued through June 30, 1968. The studies were designed to assess the disease hazards with the object of preparing for the control of diseases in order to maintain health standards during canal construction. During the medico-ecological studies over 280,000 specimens of various kinds were brought to the laboratory and processed. There were 2,759 attempts to isolate viruses from vertebrates and mosquitoes; in addition over 2,000 blood specimens from animals captured on Route 17 were tested for antibodies by hemagglutination inhibition and complement fixation tests.

The following viruses were isolated or were shown serologically to be present in the Route 17 area:

Group A: Venezuelan equine encephalitis*, Mayaro and Eastern equine encephalitis.

Group B: Ilhéus, St. Louis encephalitis and Bussuquara.

Group C: Madrid*, Nepuyo*, Ossa*, Patois* and Zegla.

Guamá Group: Guamá.

Bunyamwera Group: Wyeomyia.

Phlebotomus Group: Chagres.

Other Groups: Changuinola and Vesicular stomatitis (Indiana Type)*.

Although a relatively short time was spent working on Route 25 in Colombia, results indicated a fairly high level of viral activity in that area. VEE, Una, Ossa, Madrid and Guamá viruses were among several isolates obtained from sentinel and wild animals and human fever cases.

Blood parasites were found in 21 percent of the mammals collected on Route 17 in Panama and in 25 percent of those on Route 25 in Colombia. Six species of trypanosomes were recovered. Microfilariae were noted in all orders of mammals except Edentata; rabbits were negative. A total of 17,590 ectoparasites taken were distributed among 71 different species. Blood sucking flies and bugs were represented to the extent of 68,380 identified as belonging to 294 species. The majority of the specimens were mosquitoes of 153 species. *Phlebotomus* sandflies were represented by 18,787 specimens belonging to 45 species.

Malaria was present along both routes. Of 258 blood smears made from fever cases, 15 percent were positive; *Plasmodium falciparum* was the most prevalent species among the native Indians, followed by *P. vivax* and *P. malariae*. *P. vivax* was the species most commonly acquired by employees. In a special study at the Pacific end of Route 25 in Colombia, natives showed a high rate of malaria. *P. falciparum* was shown to be resistant to
* Represents isolates

chloroquine. The usual weekly suppressive doses of this drug failed to prevent the acquisition of malaria by North Americans working in the area, one of whom developed a very severe case. The finding represented the point farthest north in the Western Hemisphere that chloroquine resistant malaria has been noted.

In connection with a serious malaria outbreak among Indians along Route 17, VDRL positive tests ranged from 6 to 96 percent in three groups examined. Final determinations need to be made but it is believed that the diseases involved are yaws and pinta.

Complement fixation tests for Chagas' disease in natives along Route 17 indicated rates up to 17 percent in some of the Indian villages. One suspected case occurred in an individual from the United States. *T. rangeli* was found among native workers and residents. *Mansonella ozzardi* was prevalent at rates ranging up to 16 percent in native Indians.

Leishmaniasis transmission was active along Route 17. Over 80 percent of the natives showed intestinal parasites. Foreign workers on the routes had an average infection rate of 27 percent. Eighteen percent of the natives along Route 17 showed either *Salmonella* or *Shigella* but diarrheal symptoms were present in only 3 of the 15 persons harboring enteropathogens. The native labor force had a 5 percent rate of enteropathogens and the foreign workers 2.5 percent.

A total of 379 native laborers or residents on Route 17 were tested with 21 different arboviral antigens. Antibody rates of 60 percent were encountered to one or more arboviruses. Results indicated past infections with viruses in Groups A, B, C, Bunyamwera, Changuinola, California encephalitis, Phlebotomus fever or VSV. Only 13 percent of 493 foreigners engaged in the surveys were positive for arbovirus antibodies. Subsequent testing for antibody conversions indicated that in four cases native workers were positive with one or more of the following viruses: VEE, Mayaro, Ilhéus and Changuinola. Seven additional cases were detected among the foreign group while on duty; one case represented Mayaro, and the others Ilhéus, Bussuquara or SLE viruses. Two strains of VEE virus were isolated from foreigners while on duty on Route 25. The first isolation of VSV (Indiana) virus from man in Panama was made from a native worker on a cattle farm on Route 17.

It is apparent that among the important disease hazards along contemplated canal routes are malaria, arbovirus infections, Chagas' disease and leishmaniasis.

Studies by the U. S. Naval Medical Science Unit: This Unit under the direction of Lt. Commander Ralph D. Comer continued malaria drug studies in the Sambu River Valley, in cooperation with the Pan American

Health Organization and the Ministry of Health of Panama. The 2-year trial ended in May 1968.

The inhabitants of the above river valley, consisting of about 2,300 individuals the majority of whom were Choco Indians, were given a combination of pyrimethamine and primaquine every 2 weeks by a team going from house to house. Persons with febrile illnesses consistent with malaria were treated with 600 mg. chloroquine base. If the blood proved positive, the patient was later given 1.5 gm. chloroquine base regimen. During the first year the combined pyrimethamine-primaquine tablet consisted of 50 mg. of the former and 25 mg. of the latter. During the second year, the dose was 75 mg. of pyrimethamine and 40 mg. of primaquine. No toxic reactions were noted. The participation of the population averaged 72 percent.

The malaria prevalence rate fell from 17.4 percent at the start of the treatment regimen to 2.5 percent in 8 weeks. Subsequently, it came down to 1.0 percent or less. Clinical malaria disappeared quickly and never reappeared. A total of 201 proved cases of malaria remained negative. The *P. falciparum-P. vivax* ratio was 3:1. *P. vivax* disappeared for a period of 32 weeks at the beginning of the second year but reappeared subsequently, apparently having been reintroduced by visitors.

It was concluded as a result of the trials that the administration of the combined pyrimethamine-primaquine therapy every 2 weeks to a remote group of individuals greatly reduced the prevalence of malaria in the absence of any other control measure and eliminated the clinical disease.

Visiting Staff: The visiting staff consisted of the following persons:

Dr. Leslie A. Stauber, Rutgers, The State University of New Jersey, from January 16 to June 12, 1968.

Lt. Commander Ralph D. Comer, Medical Corps, U. S. Navy, until May 25, 1968.

William T. Lynch, HM-1 U. S. Navy, until August 16, 1968.

Visiting Scientists: The following individuals spent varying periods of time at the Gorgas Memorial Laboratory during 1968:

Dr. Paul Williams, Dermal Leishmaniasis Unit, British Honduras, spent a month working mainly on the taxonomy of *Phlebotomus* sandflies.

Dr. J. E. Frenkel, University of Kansas Medical School, used the facilities of the Laboratory for investigating pentastomid worms in reptiles.

Dr. Willard H. Wright was in residence for 4 weeks obtaining source materials for the history of the Gorgas Memorial Institute and the Gorgas Memorial Laboratory.

Dr. Alfred Logan, University of Washington, spent a week at the Laboratory in connection with problems of public health epidemiology.

Professional Personnel on Duty as of December 31, 1968:
Martin D. Young, Sc.D., Director.
Carl M. Johnson, Sc.D., M.D., Director Emeritus, pathologist.
Graham B. Fairchild, Ph.D., Associate Director, entomologist.
Roberto Blandón-Calderón, M.D., assistant cardiologist.
David C. Baerg, Ph.D., entomologist.
Howard A. Christensen, Ph.D., entomologist.
John H. Edgcomb, M.D., pathologist.
Pedro Galindo, M.S., medical entomologist.
Margaret A. Grayson, Ph.D., virologist.
José Félix Guevara, M.D., cardiologist (part time).
Aristides Herrer, Sc.D., entomologist.
Ernesto Jonás, M.D., medical intern.
Miguel Kourany, M.P.H., Ph.D., bacteriologist.
Eulo Lupi, M.D., medical intern.
Eustorgio Méndez, M.S., vertebrate zoologist.
Manuel E. Núñez, M.D., medical resident.
Cutberto Parillón, M.D., medical intern.
Octavio E. Sousa, Ph.D., parasitologist.
Sunthorn Srihongse, M.D., M.P.H.T.M., Dr. P.H., virologist and epidemiologist.
Sam R. Telford, Jr., Ph.D., ecologist.
Vernon E. Thatcher, Ph.D., ecologist.
Manuel A. Vásquez, M.D., physician, fourth category.
Lt. Col. Alfred K. Cheng, Medical Corps, U. S. Air Force.
Roberto Reyna, M.D., medical intern.

The Gorgas Memorial Laboratory
The Research Program 1963-1968
A Summation

Yellow Fever Surveillance: This activity was continued throughout the period. The only evidence concerning the presence of the virus was obtained in 1966 when the howler monkey population in Cerro Cana in the Pirre Mountain range in Darien Province was apparently decimated. One young animal had positive serology. In the same year serological tests disclosed positive reactors among juvenile black spider monkeys and a white-faced monkey in the Río Mono area of the Upper Tuira River basin in southern Darien Province. No evidence was obtained of the virus in other areas surveyed. The data indicate that yellow fever virus was probably widespread in southern Darien Province between June 1963 and July 1966. No human cases were reported. This was the first indication of yellow fever in Panama since the 1957 outbreak. The medico-ecological survey of Canal Routes 17 and 25 failed to disclose yellow fever virus activity in those areas in 1967 and 1968.

Ecology of Arboviruses Other Than Yellow Fever: Studies in the Almirante area were continued during the period when the following virus isolations were made from the indicated sources:

Venezuelan equine encephalitis: Man, rodents, birds, mosquitoes.

Eastern equine encephalitis: Mosquitoes.

Una: Mosquitoes.

Ilhéus: Man, birds, mosquitoes.

Bussuquara: Rodents, mosquitoes.

Ossa: Man, sentinel mice and hamsters, and mosquitoes.

Guaroa: Mosquitoes.

Vesicular stomatitis (Indiana): Phlebotomus sandflies.

Mayaro: The mosquito, *Psorophora ferox.*

Wyeomyia Complex: Mosquitoes.

Madrid: Man, sentinel mice and hamsters.

Nepuyo: The spiny rat and mosquitoes.

Patois: The cotton rat and sentinel mice and hamsters.

Zegla: The cotton rat and sentinel mice.

Guamá Group Viruses (Untyped): Mosquitoes and sentinel mice and hamsters.

Additional studies were made on sera obtained from various sources during and following the outbreak of Venezuelan equine encephalitis in the Almirante area in 1960 to 1962. Not only was VEE virus widespread among the human population but was equally so among lower animals.

The cotton rat and the spiny rat appeared to be important reservoir hosts of VEE and Group C arboviruses in the Almirante area. Experimentally, the tree rat, *Tylomys panamensis,* the heron, *Butorides striatus,* and the opossum, *Didelphis marsupialis,* proved susceptible to VEE virus and presumably could serve as efficient reservoir hosts. The scarlet-rumped tanager, *Ramphocelus passerinii,* would also appear to serve in this capacity.

Investigations of arbovirus activity in areas of Panama other than Almirante indicated widespread occurrence of members of Groups A, B and C viruses. Low percentages of antibodies were found for Bunyamwera, Phlebotomus and Turlock groups. One virus strain, "Salterin," recovered from a worker on the Pan American Highway, represented the first isolation of Wyeomyia subgroup of viruses from man. Two other viruses, Bussuquara and Changuinola, were also found in man for the first time. Other isolates from human febrile cases included VEE and Chagres viruses. The mosquito, *Deinocerites pseudes,* was found in nature to be infected with St. Louis encephalitis (SLE) virus.

In view of the above-mentioned isolation, intensive studies were undertaken to evaluate the potential role of *Deinocerites* mosquitoes as vectors of arboviruses. Formerly considered to seldom attack man or to take any vertebrate blood, these mosquitoes were thought to be little involved in this regard. Taxonomic studies indicated the presence of at least seven species in Panama, with two seemingly new to science. *D. pseudes, D. melanophyllum* and *D. epitedeus* were colonized and produced large numbers of adults for experimental use. Precipitin tests on engorged female *Deinocerites* indicated a wide range of feeding preferences. *D. pseudes* proved to be a good transmitter of VEE virus in the laboratory but failed to transmit SLE virus.

Several other major findings in arbovirus studies were obtained during the last 5 years. Eastern equine encephalitis virus was isolated from mosquitoes *(Culex taeniopus)* for the first time in Panama. Outbreaks of EEE virus in horses were recorded previously but no human cases were recognized. The technique of exposing adult hamsters in the field, as demonstrated to be effective for VEE virus in Mexico, was successfully used for detection of at least five viruses in the Almirante area even during the low period of virus transmission. Wild-caught mosquitoes, after species identification, were shown to be able to transmit virus to clean animals in the laboratory. Thus, vector species for particular viruses were readily recognized. The discovery of Group C hemagglutinins in serum of infected adult hamsters provided a better tool for serological work, since prior to this study HI antigens for this group of viruses had to be prepared from serum of baby mice. The detection of high VSV antibody rates in monkeys and other arboreal vertebrates and the demonstration of antibody conversion in sentinel monkeys provided supportive evidence that these animals may be involved in VSV cycles in the forest canopy.

Leishmaniasis Studies: Observations were continued on the occurrence of leptomonad flagellates in wild-caught sandflies. *Phlebotomus trapidoi* and *P. ylephiletor* had the highest infection rates and *P. panamensis* the lowest. Most of the leptomonad flagellates from wild-caught sandflies failed to survive at the site of inoculation in hamsters for as long as 7 days and none could be recovered from the viscera.

Continued search was made for natural leishmanial infections in wild-trapped animals. Over 1,400 mammals and 549 lizards were taken and examined during the period. Skin and visceral cultures were made from many animals that showed no gross alteration of the skin. In some cases skin smears were also made. Positive results (presence of L-D bodies) were obtained from skin scrapings of a kinkajou and a porcupine, and leptomonad flagellates were cultured from the skin of porcupines, sloths and one each of marmoset, opossum and olingo. Sloths and porcupines also yielded positive visceral cultures. A high percentage of porcupines, and a lower proportion of sloths, from different areas were positive by the culture method. Late in 1968, two more forest mammals were found with natural leishmanial infections, i.e. the rice rat *(Oryzomys capito)* and the spiny rat *(Proechimys semispinosus)*. In the case of the rice rat conspicuous skin lesions were observed on the tail. While the strain obtained from the opossum was lost before identification, all other strains proved to belong to the genus *Leishmania.*

Studies were made on various strains of *Leishmania.* A considerable integration was noted in the characteristics of geographical strains; Guatemalan and some Panamanian strains reacted differently in hamsters. After miniaturized Ouchterlony agar-gel diffusion tests, it seemed certain that in Panama at least there are two distinct immunological groups of *Leishmania* which are capable of causing disease in man. *Leishmania* from the skin of the porcupine produced no lesions after intradermal inoculation into hamsters. On the other hand, the strains from the skin of the marmoset, kinkajou, olingo and sloths produced typical swellings with abundant L-D bodies after introduction into the nose of hamsters. The same results were obtained with the strains isolated from the rice rat and the spiny rat in 1968.

In a search for a suitable experimental animal, a strain of *Leishmania* from a human patient in Panama was inoculated into hamsters, cotton rats, tree rats, a kinkajou and a spiny rat. After an incubation period of 12 to 19 days, lesions appeared at the site of inoculation in all animals. The infection in the spiny rat was the first after numerous previous attempts.

Trials were conducted with pyrimethamine for the treatment of leishmaniasis in a total of 169 patients, of whom 81 completed treatment. Of these, 74, or 91.4 percent, were healed completely. In many patients it was found necessary to administer supplemental antibiotic therapy to control the secondary bacterial infection. The duration of treatment was governed by the time required to clear the lesions. As a rule, healing occurred in 3 to 6 weeks. Severe toxic reactions were encountered in only one instance.

Further chemotherapeutic trials were conducted with dihydrotriazine pamoate (Camolar®). Dosage ranged from 350 mg. for patients 11 years and older down to 140 mg. for those 6 months to 4 years of age. The drug was administered intramuscularly in a single dose. Patients studied were those in whom a parasitological diagnosis of leishmaniasis had been made without evidence of chronic illness. Of a total of 34 patients, 9 failed to return for completion of the study. Of the 25 remaining, 18 were considered cured and 7 were judged to be failures. A single case of mucocutaneous leishmaniasis was one of the failures. Healing was usually completed within 100 days; however, one case healed in 44 days and one required 128 days.

American Trypanosomiasis: Studies on the epidemiology of American trypanosomiasis were carried out by the U. S. Naval Medical Science Unit under the direction of Commander Alan C. Pipkin. A field survey of domiciliary reduviid bugs in central Panama over a 3-year period indicated that *Rhodnius pallescens* was overwhelmingly predominant over other hematophagous Reduviidae frequenting native houses. *Triatoma dimidiata* mentioned prominently in the literature as an important vector of Chagas' disease, while occurring next in frequency, was comparatively rare. Other species were taken so uncommonly that they can be considered as only occasionally present in native houses. An average of 36.58 percent of 3,283 bugs (virtually all *R. pallescens*) taken in the house collections contained trypanosomes; 32.71 percent of the total contained *Trypanosoma cruzi* in the feces, while from 4.2 to 8.1 percent were infected with the non-pathogenic *T. rangeli*. In a search for bugs in peridomestic and sylvatic surroundings, *R. pallescens* was found most frequently in chicken houses and pig pens, although only bugs from the former location contained trypanosomes. In sylvatic surroundings, bugs were collected only in trees harboring animals or animal nests. Most frequent findings were in opossum nests. Laboratory studies on defecation time after feeding indicated that *R. pallescens* is a tardy defecator as compared to *R. prolixus*. It would seem that this factor might account for the apparent inefficiency of *R. pallescens* as a vector of Chagas' disease in Panama.

In a study of potential reservoir hosts by the U. S. Naval Medical Science Unit, 209 animals of eight species were taken in forests around native houses. Of these animals, 41 of 128 opossums, or 32.03 percent, were positive for *T. cruzi*. None of 43 armadillos harbored trypanosomes. Marmosets, anteaters, coatis and sloths were found infected occasionally.

In a blood survey conducted by the regular staff of the Laboratory, 70 pigs, 16 horses and four mules were negative for trypanosomes. However, 19 of 82 dogs were positive as were 22 of 108 rats *(Rattus rattus)*. Some of the dogs and rats carried both *T. cruzi* and *T. rangeli*. *T. cruzi* was isolated from the anteater, *Tamanda tetradactyla,* which was found susceptible to *T. rangeli* of human origin. The agouti, *Dasyprocta punctata,* was also found infected with *T. cruzi*. Numerous other animals were shown to harbor trypanosomes; in addition to *T. cruzi* and *T. rangeli,* the isolates included at least five other species.

In other studies, *T. rangeli* of human origin developed well in *Rhodnius pallescens,* with massive infection of the salivary glands. Development failed to take place in *R. prolixus*. In an attempt to reduce the natural resistance of the latter species, specimens were subjected to radiation with various dosages of Cobalt-60, but susceptibility was not altered by this means.

T. rangeli and *T. cruzi* differ basically in their behavior in triatomid bugs. The former invades the body cavity and the salivary glands and is transmitted through the bite. The latter develops wholly within the intestinal tract and transmission is through the feces.

Treatment of Chagas' disease was carried out with a new 8-amino-quinoline compound designated as C-349-C-59 (Burroughs-Wellcome, London) administered in a dose of 15 mg. daily for as long as the complement fixation test remained positive. The chronic form of the disease is considered to be resistant to therapy but six cases became negative for the CF test. It would seem that the drug had eradicated the parasites.

In 1961, studies on esophageal function were conducted to determine whether patients with Chagas' disease in Panama demonstrated dysfunction connected with the disease in Brazil. Further observations were made on 32 patients. There was no evidence of esophageal pathology; the transit time was normal and no megaesophagus was present.

Of patients admitted to Santo Tomás Hospital with a positive serology for Chagas' disease, 101 were carefully studied. Forty-eight of these showed cardiac abnormalities with one or more of the following types: Arrhythmias, right bundle branch block, left bundle branch block, ventricular enlargement, atrial enlargement, myocardial lesions and A/V block. There were four deaths, two with acute and two with chronic Chagas' disease. One of the fatal cases was 46 years of age; this was the first death from this disease in Panama in anyone over 30 years of age. In South America acute fatal Chagas' disease deaths are said to occur only in children. Ventricular aneurysms were found in the heart in two fatal cases, lesions which had not been reported previously in Chagas' disease patients in Panama. Contrary to previous concepts, it would appear that apical lesions may be commonly associated with the chronic disease in Panama.

Xeno-diagnosis was found to be of little value for the detection of chronic cases of Chagas' disease but was of some value in acute cases. Blood culture was also of value in the more acute infections. The complement fixation test has been employed for prevalence studies but cross reactions between *T. cruzi* and *T. rangeli* were not uncommon. Preliminary trials with the hemagglutination test were promising. Abnormally high levels of Serum Glutamic Oxalacetic Transaminase and Serum Glutamic Pyruvate Transaminase were observed in acute cases but not in chronic cases. However, about 28 percent of the latter showed abnormally high urea nitrogen in the blood.

Malaria Studies: Noteworthy findings concerned the establishment of the human malarias in various species of Panamanian monkeys, thus providing for the first time a laboratory model in New World primates. The night monkey, *Aotus trivirgatus,* proved most susceptible to *Plasmodium vivax* but the marmoset, *Saguinus geoffroyi,* also demonstrated susceptibility. Certain strains of the parasite have been adapted to black and red spider monkeys (*Ateles* spp.). Higher parasitemias were produced in drug-treated and splenectomized animals than in those unaltered or untreated.

One strain of *P. vivax* (the Achiote), since its original isolation, has been through 56 blood passages over a period of 2 years. Of various species of mosquitoes fed on infected monkeys, only *Anopheles albimanus* became infected. Transmission of *P. vivax* from monkey to monkey was accomplished for the first time by the bites of this mosquito.

In contrast to Panamanian strains of *P. falciparum* which produced only low grade infections in *Aotus* and *Saguinus* monkeys, strains of foreign origin grew well in several monkeys. *P. falciparum* from Uganda and Malaya produced heavy infections in the *Aotus* monkey and has been passed serially. These foreign strains grew also in *Ateles fusciceps* and *Cebus capucinus* and were passed serially in the latter.

For the first time *falciparum* malaria was grown in the white-faced monkey *(Cebus capucinus)* and the black spider monkey *(Ateles fusciceps)*.

A third species of Panamanian primate, the black spider monkey, was found to be susceptible to sporozoite-induced infection of *vivax* malaria.

The natural host range of *Plasmodium brasilianum* was extended to include the marmoset *(Saguinus geoffroyi)*.

In studies on the chemotherapy of malaria, trials were carried out with a pyrimethamine-primaquine combination in the La Represa and Mendoza areas. Malaria was effectively controlled when the drugs were given weekly on a mass basis. One hundred percent participation of the population was not essential. The drugs were administered once a week for 2 years or more without evidence of toxicity or development of resistance on the part of the parasites.

The U. S. Naval Medical Science Unit under the direction of Lt. Commander Ralph D. Comer, in cooperation with the Pan American Health Organization and the Ministry of Health of Panama, conducted a 2-year study with a combination of pyrimethamine and primaquine in a remote area in the Sambu River Valley. During the first year, the combined tablet consisted of 50 mg. of pyrimethamine and 25 mg. of primaquine. During the second year, the respective doses were 75 mg. and 40 mg. Acute fever cases were given 600 mg. of chloroquine base and those with blood parasites received 1.5 gm. chloroquine base. The malaria prevalence rate fell from 17.4 percent at the start of the treatment regimen to 2.5 percent in 8 weeks. Subsequently, it came down to 1.0 percent or less. Clinical malaria disappeared quickly and never reappeared. A total of 201 proved cases of malaria remained negative. The *P. falciparum-P. vivax* ratio was 3:1. *P. vivax* disappeared for a period of 32 weeks at the beginning of the second year but reappeared subsequently, apparently having been reintroduced by visitors.

It was concluded as a result of the trials that the administration of the combined pyrimethamine-primaquine therapy every 2 weeks to a remote group of individuals greatly reduced the prevalence of malaria in the absence of any other control measure and eliminated the clinical disease.

Studies on Other Parasitic Infections: The first human infection with a little known tapeworm, *Echinococcus oligarthrus,* was reported from a fatal case. Adult worms were recorded from the intestinal tract of the puma, jaguar and jaguarundi. The first natural hydatid cyst of this species was recovered from the agouti. Local rodents were easily infected by feeding eggs or proglottids. Several lines of the infection cycle were established in the Laboratory, including a cat-rodent-cat cycle, a line of intraperitoneal secondary hydatidosis (rodent to rodent cycle), and a line of intramuscular secondary hydatidosis (rodent to rodent cycle).

Studies under the direction of Lt. Col. Bryce C. Walton of the U. S. Army Medical Research Unit indicated that toxoplasmic chorioretinitis is a hitherto unrecognized health problem of appreciable importance in Panama. Evidence was obtained that toxoplasmic infection, as indicated by the indirect fluorescent antibody test (IFAT), was more prevalent in school children living at a level of 700 feet as opposed to those dwelling at 4,200 to 6,200 feet above sea level.

In further studies by the above-mentioned Unit on the effect of wandering *Trichinella spiralis* larvae in animals exposed to EEE, Ilhéus and Japanese B encephalitis, it appeared that an ordinarily benign infection with a viral agent would result in an almost invariably fatal outcome, if it should happen to coincide with the presence in the body of wandering nematode larvae.

A species of protozoan parasite, *Besnoitia,* was found in the lizard, *Basilicus basiliscus.* Natural infections were observed also in other species of lizards and in the opossum, *Didelphis marsupialis.* The HI test disclosed positive reactors in 31 percent of 527 cattle. However, the specificity of the test has not been established. The species of *Besnoitia* was determined to be *B. darlingi.* Mouse-adapted *B. darlingi* produced acute, fatal infections in white mice, hamsters, marmosets, squirrels, a woolly opossum *(Caluromys derbianus)* and a four-eyed opossum *(Philander opossum).* Chronic infections with cysts were produced in opossums *(Didelphis marsupialis)* and one lizard *(Ameiva ameiva).*

A number of surveys indicated that the common intestinal protozoa and helminths are extremely prevalent in various population groups in Panama.

Bacteriological Studies: Examinations for enteropathogenic bacteria in various population groups revealed a high prevalence of these organisms which, however, were not always associated with diarrheal symptoms. Conversely, diarrheal cases did not always harbor enteropathogens. *Salmonella, Shigella, Edwardsiella* and enteropathogenic *E. coli* were of common occurrence. In an outbreak of diarrheal disease among Indian children on one of the offshore islands, there was only 1 month in the year in which diarrhea was absent in children of 3 years and younger. *Shigella sonnei* was the most prevalent pathogen.

Isolations of enteropathogenic bacteria were made from 47 percent of 72 lizards, *Ameiva ameiva;* of 5 other species of lizards, 2 also harbored Salmonellae. Of a total of 228 monkeys of eight species examined, enteropathogenic bacteria were found in 14 percent of black howler monkeys, 6 percent of marmosets, 5 percent of night monkeys and 3 percent of spider monkeys.

Agglutination tests on the sera from 2,360 individuals in 31 communities in Panama provided *Brucella* antibodies in 1.2 percent; symptoms of brucellosis were not noted in any of the positive individuals.

Interoceanic Canal Studies: In connection with feasibility studies of two proposed sites for a sea-level canal in Panama and Colombia, the Gorgas Memorial Laboratory cooperated with the U. S. Army in a medico-ecological reconnaissance and a disease surveillance program. In the former program, over 280,000 specimens of various kinds were brought to the Laboratory and processed. There were 2,759 attempts to isolate viruses from vertebrates and mosquitoes; in addition over 2,000 blood specimens from animals captured along Route 17 were tested for antibodies by hemagglutination inhibition and complement fixation tests. The following viruses were isolated or were shown serologically to be present in the Route 17 area:

Group A: Venezuelan equine encephalitis*, Mayaro and Eastern equine encephalitis.

Group B: Ilhéus, St. Louis encephalitis and Bussuquara.

Group C: Madrid*, Nepuyo*, Ossa*, Patois* and Zegla.

Guamá Group: Guamá.

Bunyamwera Group: Wyeomyia.

Phlebotomus Group: Chagres.

Other Groups: Changuinola and Vesicular stomatitis (Indiana type)*.

A more limited period was spent in studies on Route 25 but the results indicated a fairly high level of viral activity in that area. VEE, Una, Ossa, Madrid and Guamá viruses were isolated from different sources.

Malaria was present along both routes. Of 258 blood smears from fever cases, 15 percent were positive. *Plasmodium falciparum* was the most prevalent species among the native Indians, followed by *P. vivax* and *P. malariae*. *P. vivax* was the species most commonly acquired by employees. In a special study on the Pacific end of Route 25 in Colombia, natives showed a high rate of malaria and *P. falciparum* was shown to be resistant to chloroquine. The usual weekly suppressive doses of this drug failed to prevent

* Indicates isolates.

the acquisition of malaria by North Americans engaged in the survey area; one of these developed a very severe case. The finding represented the point farthest north in the Western Hemisphere that chloroquine resistant malaria has been noted.

Complement fixation tests for Chagas' disease in natives along Route 17 indicated rates up to 17 percent in some of the Indian villages. *T. rangeli* was also encountered. Intestinal parasites were a common finding. Leishmaniasis transmission was active along Route 17. Enteropathogenic bacteria were present in 18 percent of the natives along this route.

As a result of the surveys, it was apparent that among the important disease hazards along the contemplated routes are malaria, arbovirus infections, Chagas' disease and leishmaniasis.

Medical Entomology: The identification and taxonomic work, so essential in the conduct of the other studies of the Laboratory, was maintained as usual. In addition, the collection of thousands of specimens along the canal routes mentioned above added to the responsibilities of this Department. Because of the important role of *Culex* mosquitoes of *Melanoconion* and allied subgenera, in disease transmission, special studies were being conducted on the taxonomy, biology and ecology of this group. A Catalogue of Neotropical Tabanidae was nearing completion.

In 1966 an important publication appeared under the sponsorship of the Field Museum of Natural History of Chicago, Ill. The "Ectoparasites of Panama" contained 17 chapters under the editorship of Rupert L. Wenzel and Vernon J. Tipton. Three staff members of the Gorgas Memorial Laboratory, viz: Graham B. Fairchild, Phyllis T. Johnson and Eustorgio Méndez contributed materially to this outstanding work.

Visiting Staff Members: During the period in question, a number of visiting scientists conducted research in the Laboratory and made important contributions. The following are the individuals involved and the subject matter of their projects:

Dr. Sarah B. Pipkin: The taxonomy, ecology and genetics of Neotropical Drosophilidae.

Dr. William A. Summers, Indiana University Medical School: The infectivity, morphology and growth rates of *Toxoplasma* and *Besnoitia* in tissue culture.

Mr. Charles Myers and Dr. William Duellman, University of Kansas: The distribution and ecology of amphibians and reptiles in Panama.

Dr. John M. Legler and Mr. Edward O. Moll, University of Utah: The life history and ecology of a neotropical slider turtle.

Dr. Leslie A. Stauber, Rutgers University: Studies on leishmaniasis.

Activities of the Gorgas Memorial Institute 1963-1968

1963

Executive Committee Meetings: At a meeting of the Executive Committee on February 13, 1963 President Streit stated that the new laboratory building was nearing completion. After several postponements, the date for dedication was set for April 27.

The occupancy and use of the new building would entail a considerable increase in operating costs of the Gorgas Memorial Laboratory. In view of this fact, the Committee discussed the desirability of an increase in the enabling Act to provide an additional $250,000 and agreed that efforts should be made to secure additional support from Congress.

A recent memorandum from Dr. James A. Shannon, Director, National Institutes of Health, was presented and discussed. The memorandum mentioned the need for a "broader base" for the Gorgas research program, improvements in administration and increased salaries for professional personnel. Dr. John Parks was of the view that further affiliation with the University of Panama would be advantageous for both institutions. Other universities were mentioned also as possibilities.

The Executive Committee met again on May 10, 1963. Dr. John Parks, Chairman of the Dedication Ceremonies Committee, presented a report of the dedication exercises for the new laboratory building which were held on April 27, 1963. The other members of the Committee were Governor Maurice H. Thatcher, Dr. L. L. Williams, Jr. and Dr. Fred L. Soper.

President Streit discussed the Darien Gap project and stated he was hopeful that necessary research funds would be made available by the National Institutes of Health in June. The project-site visit team which visited the Gorgas Memorial Laboratory in April had been impressed with the quality of research being conducted.

President Streit emphasized the need for high quality scientists in various disciplines for augmenting the Laboratory staff. A discussion followed concerning this point and also the need for administrative changes. A motion was made and adopted to establish a committee to develop necessary plans for future staffing. The President appointed Doctors Parks, Williams and Soper to serve on this Committee.

A meeting of the Executive Committee was called for August 6, 1963 to discuss job descriptions for the positions of Administrative Director and Director for Research for the Gorgas Memorial Laboratory. After considerable discussion and exchange of views, it was decided not to establish the position of Administrative Director. President Streit stated that a research grant for the Darien Gap project had not been approved but that the work was being continued and was being financed from general funds.

The next meeting of the Executive Committee was convened on the morning of November 1, 1963, prior to the annual meeting on that day.

It was announced that the grant-in-aid application for the Darien Gap project had been disapproved on August 6, 1963 because of the objections of the Director, National Institutes of Health.

President Streit reported on his visit to Panama on September 22, 1963 in connection with possible changes in administration of the Gorgas Memorial Laboratory.

Due to the serious illness of Mr. Clarence W. May, engineering consultant for the Gorgas Memorial Institute, it was necessary to select a successor. Mr. Lloyd M. Runkle was selected for the post.

It was stated that Senator Hill had introduced on August 26, 1963, a bill (S. 2080) increasing the authorization for Gorgas from "not to exceed $250,000" to "not to exceed $500,000." Dr. Justin M. Andrews, Director, National Institute of Allergy and Infectious Diseases, was asked to use his influence on behalf of Gorgas to secure passage of the bill. He was pessimistic concerning the financial future of the Gorgas Memorial Laboratory and expressed the view that non-governmental support should be solicited for creating a fiscally independent organization.

Annual Meeting: The annual meeting of the Corporation was held in Washington on November 1, 1963 with President Streit in the chair. After the election of directors, the meeting adjourned to be followed by the annual meeting of the Board of Directors.

President's Report: President Streit reported that a contract had been let to Díaz & Guardia, S.A. for the construction of the new insectary. The contract was in the sum of $117,512 and called for completion of the insectary by July 1, 1964. This amount was exclusive of architectural fees for planning and supervision and for equipment. The total cost was estimated to be $150,000, a figure considerably in excess of the original estimate of $80,000. President Streit stated that effort had been made to reduce costs but that it was found that no real economies could be effected without seriously impairing the usefulness of the structure. The total contribution for the building amounted to $132,387.

The President announced plans for administrative changes for the Gorgas Memorial Laboratory in view of the greatly increased demands occasioned by the new building program and staff additions. It was stated that Dr. Carl M. Johnson would remain with the Laboratory devoting full time to research, especially in the field of pathology.

On the retirement of Mr. Clarence W. May on account of ill health, a resolution was passed expressing appreciation for his services as consulting engineer since 1960. Mr. May's services had been of great value to the Institute and the Gorgas Memorial Laboratory in the planning and construction of the new research building and the preliminary planning of the new insectary.

Treasurer's Report: The Assistant Treasurer, Mr. Donald A. McCormack, presented his report which indicated that the new research building was completed at a cost of $376,880 and that a total of $97,186 had been expended during the years 1962 and 1963 for new equipment. The total value of the Gorgas Memorial Laboratory installations was carried on the books at $866,416. The securities in the Endowment Fund had a current market value of $60,555, an appreciation of $11,803 over cost.

President Streit presented the budget for fiscal year 1965 which called for a total expenditure of $609,764, which represented a prospective deficit of $114,314.

Major General Paul H. Streit, USA, (Ret.) was reelected President and Governor Maurice H. Thatcher Vice President.

The Treasurer, Mr. John M. Christie, who had served in that capacity since 1959, was unable to continue in this position. Mr. Donald A. McCormack, Vice President, and Mr. John C. Gibbons, Assistant Vice President of the Riggs National Bank, were elected Treasurer and Assistant Treasurer, respectively.

1964   *Appointment of Dr. Young:* A meeting of the Executive Committee was held on January 10, 1964 for the purpose of considering the appointment of Dr. Martin D. Young as Director of the Gorgas Memorial Laboratory. After extended discussion, it was agreed that the President and Dr. L. L. Williams, Jr. should confer with Dr. Young further concerning the terms of a contract.

In another meeting of the Committee on January 28, 1964, a "letter of agreement" with Dr. Young was approved with minor changes. This agreement was signed by President Streit and Dr. Young on January 28 and called for the appointment of the latter for a period of 2 years beginning on April 1, 1964.

Another meeting of the Executive Committee was held on April 14, 1964. Because of potential unrest in connection with the forthcoming elections in Panama, it was thought advisable to postpone the arrival of the Director Elect until June 1.

It was decided to retain Dr. Johnson as Director of the Gorgas Memorial Laboratory until June 30, 1964, which would mark 10 years of duty in that post. On retirement from the directorship, Dr. Johnson was designated Director Emeritus.

President Streit announced the sudden death on April 8 of Dr. Henry K. Beye, Director of the Middle America Research Unit of the National Institutes of Health. He was requested to send a letter of condolence to the Director of NIH and to the widow of Dr. Beye.

Executive Committee Meeting: The Executive Committee met on September 25, 1964. It was reported that S. 2080 introduced by Senator Hill to lift the appropriation ceiling would probably not pass in the then current session of Congress. A discussion considered alternative means of meeting the prospective deficit in the 1965 fiscal year.

The insectary, scheduled to be completed by July 1, was still unfinished. It was voted to name the building the "Rand Insectary" in honor of Mr. James H. Rand, who contributed so generously to the financing of its construction.

Salary increases for the professional staff at the Gorgas Memorial Laboratory have been approved in the past as Civil Service pay raises occurred. It was voted in the future to follow the U. S. Civil Service General Schedule.

Dr. Hertig's service was extended for 1 year only to November 1965 contingent on favorable action on the NIH research grant in support of the leishmaniasis studies.

Benefits for Panamanian Employees: It was voted to provide life and medical insurance benefits to Panamanian employees of Gorgas Memorial Laboratory. Such benefits were requested by a small group of the employees in lieu of their current annuity contributions. Salary schedules were adopted for internes and residents on duty at the Laboratory.

Annual Meeting: The annual meeting of the Corporation was held in Washington on October 30, 1964. Following the election of directors, the meeting adjourned, after which the annual meeting of the Board of Directors took place. President Streit reviewed the work of the Gorgas Memorial Laboratory during the current year. Miss King consented to remain on duty in the Washington Office for another year. Personnel policies were reviewed and it was stated that certain positions at the Gorgas Memorial Laboratory had been up-graded so as to make positions more attractive for qualified scientists.

The President reported that Dr. Martin D. Young had assumed the directorship of the Laboratory on July 1. Working relations with the University of Panama had been maintained on a cordial basis. Three medical graduates of the University of Panama were currently on duty at Gorgas.

Mr. John C. Gibbons, Assistant Treasurer, presented his report. Of a total of $632,388 in the building fund, $573,154 had been expended for construction and $32,592 for equipment, leaving a balance of $26,642. Endowment fund investments, representing a cost of $48,753 were valued on June 30, 1964 at $65,698.

The budget for fiscal year 1966 called for a total expenditure of $662,328, which exceeded by $52,325 funds in prospect.

A resolution of appreciation for the services of Dr. L. L. Williams, Jr. was adopted on his retirement from the secretaryship of the Gorgas Memorial Institute at the conclusion of the meeting.

Major General Paul H. Streit, USA, (Ret.) was reelected President and Governor Maurice H. Thatcher, Vice President.

1965   *Executive Committee Meetings:* The Executive Committee held a meeting on January 12, 1965, at which time President Streit announced that the new insectary was nearing completion. Plans were being made for dedication exercises in February or March.

Justifications had been prepared for new legislation to replace S. 2080 which had failed passage in the last session of Congress.

Benefits for Employees: The group insurance plan for Panamanian employees of the Gorgas Memorial Laboratory approved by the Committee on September 25, 1964, became effective on January 1, 1965. The Pan American Life Insurance Plan provides for life insurance, AD&D hospitalization, surgical and medical, and major medical benefits. The new plan covered 92 Panamanian employees and was also applicable to U. S. and foreign nationals and to employees of the Washington Office, provided such employees elected to contribute the total cost.

President Streit stated that the TIAA-CREF retirement plan, adopted in 1954, was no longer adequate because of increasing social security taxes. Motion was adopted to revise the present agreement with TIAA in accordance with the preference of the participants, any revision to be made effective as of January 1, 1965.

Other Actions: Approval was given for the appointment of Dr. Aristides Herrer of Peru effective on or about February 1. Dr. Herrer, an entomologist, will be assigned to the leishmaniasis project under Dr. Hertig.

Dr. Fred L. Soper presented a summary of his findings relative to the establishment of the Gorgas Memorial Institute.

The Executive Committee met again on May 27, 1965.

A resolution was adopted approving the modified TIAA-CREF retirement plan.

A discussion was held regarding the desirability of reconstituting membership on the Board of Directors and the Advisory Scientific Board.

A motion was adopted authorizing the President to appoint a group of three scientists to evaluate the present research program of the Gorgas Memorial Laboratory.

Personnel Actions: The following personnel matters were acted upon:
Dr. Herrer's appointment as head of the leishmaniasis project as of

December 1, 1965 and Dr. Hertig's continuance on the project at one-half salary.

The appointment of Dr. José Felix Guevara, chief of the Cardiology Clinic at Santo Tomás Hospital, as "cardiologist ad honorem."

The appointment of a veterinarian, Dr. James A. Porter to be effective on June 1. Dr. Porter will be engaged on the Monkey Malaria project.

The President announced that Lt. Commander Ralph D. Comer, MC, USN, was being assigned to the Gorgas Memorial Laboratory on July 1, to conduct malaria studies.

It was announced that the Bureau of the Budget had waived objections to the enactment of the bill S. 511 to raise the ceiling on the annual appropriation.

Grant for Malaria Studies: Announcement was made of the receipt of a grant by the U. S. Army Medical Research and Development Command for a 5-year project to determine the susceptibility of monkeys to human malaria. The amount allocated for the first 2 years was $110,304.

Rand Insectary Dedication: The Rand Insectary was dedicated on March 4, 1965, although the building had not yet been accepted because of needed adjustments in the air conditioning and humidity control systems.

The Executive Committee was convened again on October 7, 1965. President Streit reported on his visit to Panama last June and his discussions with President Robles, other Panamanian officials and Dr. Ricardo J. Alfaro concerning problems related to the Gorgas Memorial Laboratory. Officials of the National Heart Institute accompanied President Streit for the purpose of reviewing possibilities for the establishment of a Heart Center at the Gorgas Memorial Laboratory.

The appointment of Mr. Ramiro Walker Mendoza as Executive Officer of the Gorgas Memorial Laboratory effective August 16 was approved.

President Streit attended a conference with officials of the National Institute of Allergy and Infectious Diseases and Dr. Karl Meyer, Director of the Plague Center in San Francisco concerning the possibilities of developing such a center at the Gorgas Memorial Laboratory.

Removal of the Gorgas Memorial Institute Office: On July 1, 1965 a lease was signed with the Medical Society of the District of Columbia for office space of 828 sq. ft. in suite number 4 of the new headquarters building under construction at 2007 Eye Street, N.W. in Washington, D.C. effective December 15, 1965 at an annual rental of $3,726.

Public Law 89-181: It was reported that Bill S. 511 was signed by President Johnson on September 11, 1965 and became Public Law 89-181 (89th Congress). This Bill authorized funds for the support of the Gorgas Memorial Laboratory from "not to exceed $250,000" to "not to exceed

$500,000." Senator Hill, Congressman Selden and Governor Thatcher were active in support of this legislation.

Gorgas Memorial Regional Medical Library: The President reported that discussions had been underway for several months for the establishment in Panama of a central library to serve Panama and the Central American countries. Dr. Martin M. Cummings, Director, National Library of Medicine, attended a meeting of the Ministers of Health of these countries in Panama City last August, at the request of President Streit and presented the matter. The presentation met with an encouraging response and Dr. Roderick Esquivel, Minister of Labor, Social Welfare and Public Health of Panama, stated that his government would furnish land near the present site of the Gorgas Memorial Laboratory and assist in the costs of the construction of the library. It was estimated that the cost of the building would be about $500,000 and the operating budget $150,000 per annum.

Annual Meeting: The annual meeting of the Corporation was held in Washington on November 9, 1965.

President's Report: The deaths of Major General Julian L. Schley, USA (Ret.), a member of the Board of Directors since 1952, and of Rear Admiral Charles S. Stephenson, USN (Ret.), a member of the Advisory Scientific Board since 1956, were noted with deep sorrow. After the election of directors, the meeting adjourned and was followed by that of the Board of Directors.

President Streit reviewed matters which had received the attention of the Executive Committee during the year. Among these were the passage of S. 511 (P.L. 89-191—89th Congress), the dedication of the Rand Insectary, grants from the National Institutes of Health for research projects at the Gorgas Memorial Laboratory, the proposed Plague Center and Heart Center and the Gorgas Memorial Regional Medical Library. With regard to the latter project, President Streit stated that the National Library of Medicine had offered to assist Gorgas in many ways and that the Director, Dr. Cummings, had visited Panama and had presented the matter to the Ministers of Health of Panama and the Central American Republics.

The budget for fiscal year 1967 ($781,450) was presented and called for a deficit of $100,000 which it was hoped would be covered by the increased support ceiling under Public Law 89-191, 89th Congress.

Major General Paul H. Streit, USA (Ret.) was reelected President and Governor Maurice H. Thatcher Vice President.

1966   *Executive Committee Meeting:* The Executive Committee met on April 12, 1966. On November 22, 1943, the Board of Directors had authorized the transfer of $2,116.46 in the Canal Zone Endowment Fund to the regular endowment accounts. The amount was raised by residents of the Panama Canal Zone in 1926 and the interest from it was to be used solely for research purposes in Panama. The Comptroller General at that time failed to approve the action of the Board of Directors because of the wording of the resolution. A new resolution was adopted to meet the objections of the Comptroller General.

Action was taken to amend the TIAA-CREF retirement plan for Gorgas Memorial Laboratory employees to handle contributions of non-United States nationals.

The contract of Dr. Martin D. Young as Director of the Gorgas Memorial Laboratory was renewed for 3 years at the same salary.

Personnel Actions: The following personnel appointments were approved:

Dr. Manuel A. Vásquez for 2 years in the Department of Bacteriology, effective May 1, 1966.

Dr. Roberto Blandón-Calderón for 6 months, effective April 1, 1966, as assistant cardiologist in the Chagas' disease project.

Mrs. Dolas M. Grosjean as bookkeeper-accountant in the Washington office, effective May 1, 1966.

A request of Dr. Young was approved for Dr. William A. Summers of the University of Indiana School of Medicine to spend his 6-months' sabbatical leave at GML.

Gorgas Memorial Regional Medical Library: President Streit reported on progress of the Gorgas Memorial Regional Medical Library project. Negotiations were in progress with the University of Panama School of Medicine for temporary storage of 10,000 volumes offered by the National Library of Medicine. A candidate for librarian was in prospect.

President Streit announced that he had received no replies to numerous letters addressed to Mr. James H. Rand asking for the payment of the amount of $300,000 pledged to the Gorgas Memorial Laboratory in 1962.

Other Items: The President reported on a meeting held the previous month with officials of the National Institute of Allergy and Infectious Diseases (NIAID) concerning a proposal that the Gorgas Memorial Laboratory acquire rights from the Panama Canal Company to the building in the Canal Zone presently occupied by the Middle America Research Unit. Various phases of the matter were discussed but action was postponed pending a definite proposal on the part of NIAID.

Fig. 12. The Executive Committee of the Gorgas Memorial Institute of Tropical and Preventive Medicine, 1966.

Standing left to right: Dr. Alexander Wetmore, Dr. Fred L. Soper, Dr. James Watt, Mr. Donald L. Simpson, Secretary, and Dr. Martin D. Young (non-member).

Seated left to right: Major General Paul H. Streit, USA (Ret.), Admiral Calvin B. Galloway, MC, USN (Ret.), President, Governor Maurice H. Thatcher, Honorary President and General Counsel, and Dr. John Parks.

Executive Committee Meeting: The Executive Committee met again on June 21. Several personnel actions were taken.

The salary of the Executive Officer, Mr. Ramiro Walker Mendoza, was increased.

Dr. Manuel E. Núñez and Dr. Alfredo Tablete were appointed as internes to fill two vacancies.

Dr. Sunthorn Srihongse was offered a permanent position on the staff effective July 1, 1966.

Dr. Young submitted data to show that non-professional salary levels at the Gorgas Memorial Laboratory were below those of the Panama Public Health Department and Social Security Administration, and the Health Department of the Canal Zone. During the last 5 years there had been an increase of 74 percent in the number of non-professional employees at the Gorgas Memorial Laboratory and an increase of 121 percent in personnel costs.

Other Items: With further reference to the proposed amalgamation of the Middle America Research Unit (MARU) with the Gorgas Memorial Laboratory it was announced that Dr. James A. Shannon, Director of the National Institutes of Health, had failed to approve the proposal.

At the request of President Streit, Dr. Young went to Freeport, Grand Bahama, in an effort to obtain from Mr. James H. Rand his unpaid pledge of $300,000. It was reported that Mr. Rand was sympathetic but felt that he could not release the funds until current litigation against him was settled.

Another meeting of the Executive Committee was held on November 8, 1966 to approve Dr. Young's recommendation for new salary schedules.

Annual Meeting: The annual meeting of the Corporation was held in Washington on November 8, 1966. After the election of directors, the meeting adjourned to be followed by that of the Board of Directors.

President's Report: President Streit reported on administrative changes at the Gorgas Memorial Laboratory and approval for non-professional salary increases to bring levels to those of similar positions in the Republic of Panama.

The Foreign Ministry of the Republic of Panama, at the request of the Gorgas Memorial Institute, instituted a new simplified procedure for admission of foreign scientists to be employed by that institution.

Current projects were reviewed. The U. S. Naval Medical Science Unit at Gorgas had been re-established in July 1965 by the assignment of Lt. Commander Ralph D. Comer, MC, USN and Corpsman Paul H. Campbell. A cooperative program for mass malaria therapy was initiated in cooperation with the Pan American Health Organization and the Government of Panama, under the immediate direction of Commander Comer.

The Laboratory had begun a project on disease surveillance of employees engaged in feasibility studies on Canal Route 17 (Sasardi-Morti) in Panama. Also a 2-year contract in the sum of $117,634 had been signed with the U. S. Army for participation in a medico-ecological survey of proposed Route 17 in the Darien Region for a sea-level canal. The United Fruit Company had announced a substantial donation to assist in the arbovirus studies in Almirante.

Proposals for collaboration with the University of Alabama were reviewed. Several joint programs were under discussion.

The status of the Gorgas Memorial Regional Medical Library was reviewed. It was stated by President Streit that the Minister of Labor, Social Welfare and Public Health of Panama was investigating available land sites for the building.

The National Library of Medicine offered to assist Gorgas in the above project in the following manner:

(1) Contribution of 50,000 book credits (books and journals).

(2) Technical assistance for studies of area needs and plans.

(3) Medical literature tapes from January 1, 1961 on a continuing low-cost purchase basis.

(4) Back-stop service of additional books needed.

(5) Assistance in training medical librarians.

The President reviewed the financial outlook for the Gorgas Memorial Laboratory and foresaw need in the near future for additional funding. He pointed out that salaries for para-medical personnel had increased 12.3 percent during the current year. Rising operational costs were foreseen. The hope was expressed that additional private funds might be obtained to supplement the Congressional appropriation.

Treasurer's Report: Mr. Donald A. McCormick submitted his report as Treasurer, showing net current assets of $86,756 and the sum of $72,418 in the Endowment Fund.

Budget for 1968: The budget for fiscal year 1968 called for $756,966. Of this amount, $523,926 would be covered from regular sources and $233,040 by research grants.

Resolutions: Two resolutions were passed. One authorized the Executive Committee to negotiate with governments of the United States and Latin America in an effort to secure additional support for the Gorgas Memorial Laboratory. The other resolution expressed deep appreciation of the Board of Directors to Miss Helen A. King for her 34 years of devoted and outstanding service to the Gorgas Memorial Institute. Miss King was presented with a hand-lettered copy of the resolution and a gift of a Panamanian "mosqueta" on a gold chain. Miss King assumed complete charge of the Gorgas Memorial Institute office on March 1, 1935, when Miss Gladys R. Newman followed Admiral Grayson to the American Red Cross. During her long period of service, Miss King functioned in many capacities. She was steeped in the lore of the Gorgas Memorial Institute and the Gorgas Memorial Laboratory and there was little in the history of these organizations that she could not recall. Her devotion to duty during these long years was extraordinary and her services were sorely missed after her retirement.

Election of Officers: Rear Admiral Calvin B. Galloway, Medical Corps, U. S. Navy (Ret.) was elected President to succeed General Streit who expressed a desire to retire from that position. Governor Maurice H. Thatcher was reelected Vice President.

Ambassador Ricardo M. Arias of Panama then decorated General Streit and Dr. John Parks with the Order of Vasco Núñez de Balboa of Panama with the rank of Grand Officer.

Admiral Galloway is the fourth of a group of distinguished Naval Medical Officers who have served as President of the Gorgas Memorial Institute. Born in Wyandotte, Michigan, on January 10, 1903, he obtained his academic education at Michigan State College 1919-1920 and the College of Detroit 1921-1922. He attended the University of Michigan 1923-1930 from which he received his M.D. degree. He successfully passed a competitive examination for entrance into the Medical Department of the United States Navy and was commissioned as a Lieutenant Junior Grade on June 3, 1930, following which he completed his internship at the Norfolk Naval Hospital, Portsmouth, Virginia.

In the summer of 1931 he returned to the University of Michigan for post-graduate study. In October of that year he was assigned to the USS Panay on the Yangtze River Patrol. From September 1932 to September 1934, Dr. Galloway served with the Fourth Marine Regiment at Shanghai, China. Following this tour of duty, he returned to the United States and was assigned to the Naval Hospital at New York and served as Liaison Officer with Memorial Hospital, where he undertook post-graduate studies in cancer. From 1935 to 1938, he was in charge of the Cancer Service at the New York Naval Hospital.

Admiral Galloway's next tour of duty comprised a year's service as Medical Officer of the USS Badger of Squadron Forty-T in European waters. The Badger was one of the ships which were under heavy bombing attack in the harbor of Barcelona, Spain in 1939. Brief tours of duty followed on the USS Dickenson and the USS Arkansas, after which he was assigned to the Marine Barracks, Quantico, Virginia from December 1940 to April 1941.

At the outbreak of World War II, Admiral Galloway was in charge of the Cancer Service of the New York Naval Hospital. In November 1942 he was assigned to the U. S. Embassy, Río de Janeiro, Brazil, as Assistant Naval Attaché and Medical Officer. At the same time he served as Medical Officer of the U. S. Operating Base at that port.

Following his return to the United States in June 1944, he attended the Command Course Naval War College, Newport, Rhode Island, for 6 months. In January 1945, he became Division Surgeon of the Second Marine Division and participated in the military operations at Saipan and Okinawa. After V-J Day he remained with the Division during the occupation of Kyushu, until September 1946.

Following his return to the United States, for 3 years he was Senior Medical Officer at the Marine Barracks, Camp Lejeune, North Carolina. In September 1949 he was assigned for post-graduate studies at the Skin and Cancer Unit of New York University following which he was certified by the American Board of Dermatology and Syphilology in 1950. In 1948, he completed the Basic Course in Atomic Medicine at the Naval Medical School.

Following his post-graduate studies, Admiral Galloway commanded the Medical Field Research Laboratory at Camp Lejeune, North Carolina. In June 1954, he was ordered to Cairo, Egypt, to assume command of Naval Medical Research Unit No. 3 for 2 years. From August 1956 to December 1958, he was Commanding Officer of the Naval Medical School, National Naval Medical Center, Bethesda, Maryland. Until April 1963, he served as Assistant Chief of the Bureau of Medicine and Surgery for Research and Military Medical Specialties. In April 1963, he became Commanding Officer of the National Naval Medical Center, Bethesda, Maryland. In that year also he served as President of the Association of Military Surgeons. He was retired in 1965.

Admiral Galloway received the Bronze Star Medal for meritorious service as Division Surgeon of the Second Marine Division during the training and planning phases of the operations on Okinawa and for his outstanding efforts in disease prevention and maintenance of health standards during the occupation of Kyushu. During his long service he received the Yangtze Service Medal (1932); Marine Corps Expeditionary Medal (1932-34); American Defense Service Medal, Fleet Clasp; American Campaign Medal; Asiatic-Pacific Campaign Medal; World War II Victory Medal; Navy Occupation Service Medal, Asia Clasp; National Defense Service Medal; Korean Service Medal; the United Nations Service Medal and the Legion of Merit.

Admiral Galloway was uniquely fitted for the post of President of the Gorgas Memorial Institute. His varied service in many of the hot-beds of tropical disease provided him with an unusual experience not often obtained by American physicians. Furthermore, during the latter part of his

Navy career, he was responsible for formulating research policies and in a command position was able to bring the objectives to successful fruition. At one time or another, he held nearly all of the important posts associated with naval medical research and his record in these assignments was indubitably outstanding.

1967   *Executive Committee Meeting:* A meeting of the Executive Committee was held on March 17, 1967. Dr. Young was present.

President Galloway reported on his visit to the Gorgas Memorial Laboratory on March 4-14 and his discussions with President Robles, other Panamanian officials, and various United States representatives in Panama and the Canal Zone.

The President reported that the Government of Panama had ceded to the Gorgas Memorial Institute approximately 6,000 sq. meters of land as a site for the proposed Gorgas Memorial Regional Medical Library and additional laboratory facilities. A brief ceremony was held at the site. The plot of land is located near the present site of the Gorgas Memorial Laboratory, immediately to the rear of the office building of the U. S. Embassy and between 37th and 38th Streets, and Chile and Mexico Avenues in the so-called Exposición suburb. It was estimated that the cost of the building would be approximately $650,000. Sources for financing were being explored.

It was reported that the architects Díaz & Guardia, S.A. had been unable to complete the Rand Insectary and that the sum of $6,326.23 had been withheld. There was claim on the part of the architects that specifications for the humidity control system had been faulty. As a result of a conference during Admiral Galloway's visit to Panama, a compromise was reached for a final settlement of $3,868.54. Authorization was given for immediate payment of this amount.

The urgent need for a primate center was discussed. The National Cancer Institute had shown interest in participating in such a project. It was stated that a certain tract of land in the Canal Zone might be available. Preliminary conversations with Canal Zone and Panamanian officials indicated some encouragement for the development of the project. However, transfer of the land to Gorgas was influenced by then current U. S.-Panama treaty negotiations.

Personnel Actions: Personnel and administration items were discussed, as follows:

Dr. Curt R. Schneider was separated from Gorgas Memorial Laboratory on December 15, 1966.

Mr. Ramiro Walker Mendoza, the Executive Officer, resigned effective

February 20, 1967. The Committee approved in principle the appointment to this position of Mr. Alexander Clark.

Authorization was granted for Dr. Leslie A. Stauber of Rutgers University to spend his sabbatical leave at the Gorgas Memorial Laboratory.

Miss Helen A. King, whose retirement became effective on January 1, 1967, was requested to remain in office until further notice.

Certain changes were recommended in inventory policy to eliminate small items and to charge off items over 20 years of age.

The employment of Mr. William R. Furrey as consultant on administrative procedures was authorized.

The Treasurer and Assistant Treasurer reviewed and recommended adoption of certain changes in the TIAA-CREF retirement plan which provided more flexibility in pension planning. The changes carried no increased costs to Gorgas Memorial Institute or the participants. The proposed amendment was adopted.

Review of Financial Support: The President reviewed funds available to the Gorgas Memorial Laboratory for the current fiscal year through grants and contracts, which would be as follows:

From the National Institutes of Health:

Transmission of Leishmaniasis in Panama (grant AI01251-11)	$ 92,293
Ecology of Arthropod-borne Viruses in Panama (grant AI02984-8)	88,076

From U. S. Army Medical Research and Development Command:

Monkeys as Hosts of Human Malaria (grant DA-MD-49-193-65-G165)	55,152
Disease Surveillance Studies on Route 17, Sasardi-Morti (contract DADA 17-67-C-0020)	35,354

From Panama Canal Company:

Laboratory Studies for Medico-Ecological Survey of Inter-Oceanic Canal Studies, Route 17 (contract PC-2-1096)	59,606

From the Pan American Health Organization (PAHO):

Mass Drug Trial for Control of Malaria	35,339
TOTAL	$365,820

The President offered information concerning the status of other funds, as follows:

The Army grant, Monkeys as Hosts of Human Malaria, has been renewed for one additional year, at $129,283.

PAHO's contract, Mass Drug Trial for Control of Malaria, has been renewed for one additional year, at $27,530.

The United Fruit Company Foundation has donated, for the support

Fig. 13. The last five presidents of the Gorgas Memorial Institute of Tropical and Preventive Medicine.
Upper row left to right: Hugh S. Cumming, M.D., Surgeon General, USPHS (Ret.), President and Chairman of the Board of Directors 1940-1941. Joseph F. Siler, Colonel, MC, USA (Ret.), President and Chairman of the Board of Directors 1941-1957.
Center: Walter A. Bloedorn, M.D., President and Chairman of the Board of Directors 1957-1961.
Lower row left to right: Paul H. Streit, Major General, USA (Ret.), President and Chairman of the Board of Directors 1961-1966. Calvin B. Galloway, MC, USN (Ret.), President and Chairman of the Board of Directors 1966-   .

of Gorgas Memorial Laboratory work, $10,000 per annum, for both 1967 and 1968.

Negotiations are proceeding for an additional Army contract to conduct disease surveillance studies on Route 25 (Truando-Atrato River Basin, Colombia) at an approximate cost of $27,000 for the first year.

Secretary Donald F. Simpson distributed a draft document covering a 5-Year Plan for the expansion of the Gorgas Memorial Laboratory. The document was designed as a justification for an increase in the congressional ceiling on the annual appropriation.

The President was authorized to explore sources of funds for the construction of the Gorgas Memorial Regional Medical Library and additional research facilities.

Executive Committee Meeting: The Executive Committee convened again on November 7, 1967. Dr. Young was present at this meeting.

The President reported on the success of the cooperative malaria project with PAHO and the Government of Panama. A reduction of the malaria rate from 17 percent to less than 1 percent had taken place during the year in the Sambu River villages in Darien Province.

The status of the project on disease surveillance and medico-ecological studies on the proposed new canal routes was somewhat in doubt.

The acute need for additional laboratory space at the Gorgas Memorial Laboratory was discussed. It was proposed that the space problem be assigned high priority and that further avenues for solution be investigated. It had been determined that the main research building would not support an additional floor.

Admiral Galloway reviewed the present status of negotiations with the Government of Panama for the transfer of a library site and read Resolution No. 209 which had been signed on August 22, 1967 by President Robles of Panama and the Minister of the Treasury, David Samudio A.

Copies of a report on a project site visit in Panama by Dr. Fritz Gluckstein of the National Library of Medicine were presented. He provided suggestions for strengthening the library facilities of the Gorgas Memorial Laboratory and the School of Medicine of the University of Panama.

Serious consideration was given to the publication in Spanish of the Annual Report of the Gorgas Memorial Laboratory.

Discussions were held concerning the desirability of preparing a bibliography on Chagas' disease. Preliminary cost estimates were to be obtained.

The President was authorized to enter into an agreement with Dr. Willard H. Wright for preparation of a history of the Gorgas Memorial Institute and the Gorgas Memorial Laboratory.

Annual Meeting: The annual meeting of the Corporation was convened in Washington on November 9, 1967 with President Galloway presiding.

Following the roll call and the election of directors, the meeting was adjourned to be followed by the 45th annual meeting of the Board of Directors.

President's Report: The President reported on progress and achievements during the year. The first item concerned the transfer of a plot of land in Panama City for the site of the proposed Gorgas Memorial Regional Medical Library. Legal representatives of Gorgas were in the process of searching the title and preparing the necessary documents. It was hoped to have possession by the end of the year or by the spring of 1968.

The following personnel actions were reported:

Dr. David C. Baerg joined the staff of the Laboratory in July. He is assigned to the Malaria Research Program.

Dr. Samuel R. Telford, Jr. will join the staff in December of this year and will be assigned to the Leishmaniasis Project.

Dr. John H. Edgcomb, former staff member of the National Cancer Institute, National Institutes of Health, will join the staff of the Chagas' Disease Program on the first of January 1968.

Dr. José Félix Guevara joined the Gorgas Memorial Laboratory staff as part-time Senior Cardiologist in June. Dr. Roberto Blandón-Calderón became a permanent member of the staff in June 1967 as Assistant Cardiologist.

Dr. Leslie A. Stauber, Chairman, Department of Zoology, Rutgers University, will spend 6 months of a sabbatical year at GML, beginning on or about January 1, 1968.

Mr. Alexander Clark joined the Laboratory as Executive Officer.

Dr. William A. Summers, Professor, Department of Microbiology, Indiana University School of Medicine, honored the Gorgas Memorial Laboratory by spending there 6 months of a sabbatical year.

The President commented on the retirement of Dr. Marshall Hertig from the staff of the Gorgas Memorial Laboratory and commended Dr. Hertig for his long and outstanding services and his contributions to the Laboratory program.

It was reported that the National Library of Medicine had made available book credits to the Gorgas Memorial Laboratory and that the Executive Committee had approved the allotment of $5,000 for the expansion of existing library facilities. The Library had been authorized to remain open during evening hours for the benefit of the staff of Santo Tomás Hospital and the students and staff of the University of Panama School of Medicine.

The President reviewed monies available to the Gorgas Memorial Laboratory from grants and contracts. The amounts totalled $738,783. In addition, the United Fruit Company had contributed $10,000 and had promised an additional amount. Also funds had been received as a memorial to the late Dr. L. L. Williams, Jr. and had been deposited in the Endowment Fund.

It was reported that Senator Lister Hill had introduced Senate bill 1922 to remove the legislative ceiling on the annual appropriation for the Gorgas Memorial Laboratory.

Treasurer's Report: Treasurer Donald A. McCormack presented his report. Costs had increased 13.2 percent during the year. A document was presented to show the remarkable gain in fixed assets of the Gorgas Memorial Institute which had increased in the last 10 years from $274,649 to $1,132,664.

The budget for fiscal year 1969 was approved in the sum of $1,080,000.

Dr. Abraham Horwitz, Director of the Pan American Health Organization, presented a eulogy in memoriam of the late Dr. L. L. Williams, Jr.

Commander Alan C. Pipkin, U. S. Navy, presented the President with the up-dated plaque containing the names of all Navy personnel assigned to the Gorgas Memorial Laboratory since 1931.

Admiral Galloway was reelected President and Governor Maurice H. Thatcher Vice President.

1968   *Executive Committee Meeting:* The Executive Committee met on June 26, 1968. Admiral Galloway made a number of announcements, as follows:

(a) An announcement has been received of support by the United Kingdom Foundation for the International College of Tropical Medicine, to permit the establishment of post-graduate tropical medicine centers, bringing to international focus the increasing need for training in this field. The first center will be established in Uganda and it is anticipated others will follow in Asia and Latin America.

(b) Dr. Antonio González Revilla has been reelected Dean of the Medical School of the University of Panama.

(c) The Director of the Gorgas Memorial Laboratory, Dr. Young, has been appointed an Extraordinary Professor of Tropical Medicine and Clinical Hematology (ad Honorem), for the academic year 1968-69, at the University of Panama Medical School.

(d) A new cost-reimbursement contract has been signed with the Army for a total of $23,661, for the period July 1, 1968 thru December 31, 1969, to conduct studies on a research project entitled "Stabilization Pond Operation in Tropical Areas." The principal investigator is Dr. Young and the principal professional assistants are Major Karl E. Langley, USA, Sanitary

Engineer, and Dr. Miguel Kourany of the Gorgas Memorial Laboratory staff.

1. *Personnel Actions at the Gorgas Memorial Laboratory:*

(a) *Assignment of U. S. Air Force personnel at the Gorgas Memorial Laboratory.* The Surgeon General of the Air Force has announced the assignment for 1 year at the Gorgas Memorial Laboratory of Major Albert K. Cheng; hopefully, this will be extended to a full tour of duty. The collaborative program to be undertaken will be determined in consultation with Dr. Young. Also, under Air Force orders, Second Lieutenant Dennis Cannon, a second-year medical student at The George Washington University, will receive 2-months' research training at the Gorgas Memorial Laboratory. This initiates at the Laboratory a long sought collaboration with the U. S. Air Force medical services.

(b) *Malaria Program.* Dr. Young has secured the temporary services of Dr. Rudolph Johnson, a graduate of Stanford University Medical School, to assist in the primate malaria program during the summer months. This assistance is particularly required due to the resignation of Dr. James A. Porter, project co-investigator, effective May 31, 1968. Dr. Porter's replacement is being sought.

(c) *Leishmaniasis Program.* The vacant position of entomologist in this program has been filled, effective June 21, by Dr. Howard A. Christensen, a graduate of the University of California.

(d) *Training Program.* On a 2-months' training period at the Gorgas Memorial Laboratory during the summer will be Mr. John Emmett, second-year medical student at The George Washington University, sponsored by the Department of Epidemiology and Environmental Health, and Mr. Andrew Balber, a Rockefeller University graduate student. Mr. Balber has been recommended by Doctors William Trager and Leslie Stauber and will devote full time to the leishmaniasis program.

(e) *U. S. Naval Medical Science Unit at the Gorgas Memorial Laboratory.* Commander Ralph D. Comer, MC, USN, terminated his 3-year tour of duty at the Laboratory on May 25. The Navy is making every effort to replace him with a competent medical officer interested in tropical disease research. Unfortunately, requirements of the Vietnam War have prevented the assignment to the Laboratory of an active duty officer. The Gorgas Memorial Laboratory will retain the services of First Class Corpsman William T. Lynch who continues to work on a project concerning the diagnosis of malaria by the use of the fluorescent antibody technique. Dr. Comer directed a major research project in the Sambu River Valley on mass drug administration for malaria control funded by the Pan American Health

Organization. This project has yielded excellent results and will serve as a model for other areas in Central America.

Dr. Comer's performance and standard of work have been outstanding. The American Board of Preventive Medicine and Public Health considered his experience at the Laboratory as meeting his Board requirements for residency. This action by the Board establishes a precedent for the Gorgas Memorial Laboratory.

2. The Classified Personnel System at the Gorgas Memorial Laboratory; Salary Increases.

(a) A classified system for non-professional personnel was established in 1966 at the Laboratory and had proved satisfactory. Some of the best employees, however, are already at the top of their grades. To permit an annual increment without establishment of new grades, Dr. Young proposes the addition of three steps to each grade; this would give a total of 10 steps to all grades, the same as the U. S. Civil Service schedules. The Committee approved this recommendation.

(b) President Johnson has signed the Pay Increase legislation for Federal employees. The Executive Committee provided in September 1964 that salaries of GML professional and Washington Office personnel would equal those of the U. S. Civil Service General Schedule. In line with this provision, the Committee approved, effective July 1, 1968, this increase which amounts to approximately $13,163 annually, or 6.34 percent.

3. Financial Status at Close of F.Y. 1968; Gorgas Memorial Laboratory Short-term Projects.

The Chairman indicated there would be an unexpended balance of $107,331 at the close of the fiscal year. A general discussion followed

Dr. Watt proposed that the Gorgas Memorial Laboratory develop a series of short-term projects for possible implementation by means of contracts or agreements with U. S. universities. This would generate a tremendous amount of goodwill and would permit a sound investment of Gorgas Memorial Laboratory excess funds when available.

4. The Teheran Meetings.

The Gorgas Memorial Laboratory has been invited to participate in the 8th International Congresses on Tropical Medicine and Malaria to be held in Teheran, September 7-15, 1968. Several Laboratory scientists have been invited. Dr. Martin D. Young will present two papers on malaria and act as Chairman of a session; Dr. Carl M. Johnson has been invited to organize a section on Chagas' disease; Mr. Pedro Galindo and Drs. Herrer and Fairchild have been invited to present papers on leishmaniasis and the control of *Phlebotomus*.

5. *Gorgas Memorial Laboratory Fire Insurance Policy.*

The Committee approved a 5-year renewal of the fire insurance policy through Thren & Zarek, and requested that a professional appraisal be made to determine the current valuation. Further, the Executive Committee recommended estimates be obtained for extended perils coverage.

6. *Management and Accounting Procedures and Policies.*

Mr. William R. Furrey, management and fiscal operations consultant, made a 2-week site visit to the Laboratory last fall. His management audit report and recommendations were distributed to the Executive Committee on October 13 and received the Committee's unanimous approval.

The Committee noted progress has been made in management and recommended that the above procedures and policies be continued at the Gorgas Memorial Laboratory.

The Gorgas Memorial Laboratory has also established plant account, equipment and library records. Two categories for equipment and supplies have been established as capitalized and expendable. Basis for capitalization and provisions for exceptions used by the U. S. Army and the U. S. Public Health Service, and those suggested by Mr. Furrey and by Dr. Young have been reviewed. Proposed policies for implementation at GML were considered. A general discussion followed. The Committee approved a policy for capitalization, effective F.Y. 1968.

It was noted that the fixed assets policy approved by the Executive Committee at its March 17, 1967 meeting was never implemented. The Committee concurred in the view that this policy is superseded by the new proposals. In line with adopted policies, the June 30, 1968 inventory will drop equipment and books by report of survey, permitting, hopefully, that the 1968 audit will offer a realistic fixed assets statement.

A 1-week follow-up visit to the Laboratory was made by Mr. Furrey on April 29, 1968. His survey report and comments on the Gorgas Memorial Laboratory and the Washington business office, as well as Dr. Young's comments, have been distributed to the Executive Committee. A general discussion followed.

Mr. Furrey recommended delaying the transfer of the accounting responsibility to the Gorgas Memorial Laboratory for another year. The Executive Committee concurred.

The Executive Committee approved bringing the Gorgas Memorial Laboratory's accountant, Mrs. Victoria Tasón, to the Washington Office for 30 days, to correlate accounting procedures and receive additional training which will prepare her for future responsibilities when this transfer is accomplished.

To assist with the accounting and fiscal work load in the Washington

Office, the Committee authorized the services for 1 year of one additional person. The incumbent, Mrs. Georgia MacKrill, whose 6-months' temporary employment has been satisfactorily completed, was approved for this period.

7. *Transfer to the Gorgas Memorial Institute of the Library Site.*

Governor Thatcher reviewed recent correspondence and documents relating to the transfer to the Gorgas Memorial Institute of a site in Panama for the construction of a Library. A general discussion followed. Motion was made, seconded and carried that a mutually agreeable, non-restrictive, bilateral agreement is desirable and should be sought, prior to Panamanian congressional approval of this transfer; this will be pursued with the new Panamanian Administration which will take office October 1, 1968.

8. *Status of Bill S. 1922.*

The Chairman offered recent information regarding Bill S. 1922 introduced by Senator Hill to remove the ceiling from the annual congressional appropriation for the maintenance and operation of the Gorgas Memorial Laboratory. Time is running short for action by the Congress. Governor Thatcher was requested to explore with Congressman Selden the House reaction to this legislation. It developed later that this Bill was never passed.

The Committee was reminded that Senator Hill will retire at the end of this calendar year. They agreed to recognize, probably at the annual meeting in October, his numerous and valuable contributions to the Gorgas Memorial Institute.

Annual Meeting: The 46th annual meeting of the Gorgas Memorial Institute was held in Washington on October 29, 1968, with the President, Rear Admiral Calvin B. Galloway, MC, USN (Ret.) in the chair. After the roll call of the members, the President recognized Mrs. Alzora Hale Eldridge, who brought greetings from Hon. Galo Plaza, the new Secretary General, Organization of American States. Mrs. Eldridge announced that her organization was engaged in a regional scientific and technological development program for the purpose of strengthening a number of multinational research and training centers in Latin America. She expressed the hope that the new program might be of continuing mutual interest to the Gorgas Memorial Institute.

The President paid tribute to the memory of the late James H. Rand, Chairman, Colonial Research Institute of the Bahamas, as a friend and benefactor of the Gorgas Memorial Institute, and for his humanitarian efforts and his medical philanthropies. Mr. Rand made a number of major gifts to the Institute and one of his contributions made possible the construction of the Rand Insectary at the Gorgas Memorial Laboratory.

After the election of directors, the meeting of the Corporation was adjourned to be followed by the annual meeting of the Board of Directors.

President's Report: The President, Admiral Galloway, reported on the activities of the Gorgas Memorial Institute during the year past. It was recalled that at the annual meeting on November 9, 1967, it had been announced that the President of Panama had authorized and directed the transfer of approximately 6,000 sq. meters of public land to the Gorgas Memorial Institute as a site for a regional medical library and the expansion of existing laboratory facilities. Subsequently, an error was discovered in the description of the plot of designated land. Efforts had been made to correct the error, which had delayed transfer of the land. In the meantime, the replacement of the duly elected President of Panama by a military-civilian junta on October 10, 1968, had brought the proceedings to a standstill. President Galloway, however, announced that continued efforts would be made to negotiate the transfer of the property.

Certain personnel actions were announced. Dr. Howard A. Christensen, formerly associated with the University of California, joined the staff of the Gorgas Memorial Laboratory on June 21, 1968, for participation in the leishmaniasis program.

The United States Air Force had assigned Lt. Col. Alfred K. Cheng, MC, USAF, to the Gorgas Memorial Laboratory for a tour of duty. Colonel Cheng was present and was introduced. In addition, the Air Force assigned a second-year medical student with the rank of 2nd Lieut. to the Laboratory for a training period of 60 days. These assignments marked the initiation of a long sought and hopefully productive collaboration.

It was announced also that the U. S. Navy had indicated its intention to reactivate the U. S. Naval Medical Science Unit at the Gorgas Memorial Laboratory with the assignment of Commander Robert J. Kinney, MC, USN. Commander Kinney was in the audience and was introduced by President Galloway.

The President noted that Dr. Graham B. Fairchild, Associate Director of the Gorgas Memorial Laboratory, had received the signal honor of being nominated to serve as the Memorial Lecturer at the Dallas meetings of the Entomological Society of America, to be held on December 2, 1968.

During the year, the following consultants visited the Gorgas Memorial Laboratory for reviewing and advising on various programs and projects:

(a) Dr. Gustave J. Dammin, Friedman Professor of Pathology, Harvard Medical School; President, Armed Forces Epidemiological Board.

(b) Dr. James Watt, Assistant Surgeon General, United States Public Health Service.

(c) Mr. William R. Furrey, Administrative Services Director, Department of Mental Hygiene and Hospitals, Commonwealth of Virginia.

(d) Dr. Donald Heyneman, Head, Division of Parasitology, Department of Epidemiology and International Health, University of California.

(e) Dr. Willard H. Wright, Veterinary Director, USPHS, (Ret.) visited the Gorgas Memorial Laboratory in connection with a history of the Gorgas Memorial Institute and Laboratory which he is writing. The history is proceeding on schedule and the manuscript to date comprises over 300 typewritten pages. Completion is set for the end of the current year. With illustrations and appendices, it is estimated that the book will print out between 150 and 170 pages. It is hoped that publication may be effected sometime during 1969, marking the 40th anniversary on April 2.

(f) It was announced that Dr. Leslie A. Stauber, Professor of Zoology, Rutgers University, had spent 5 months of his sabbatical leave at the Gorgas Memorial Laboratory participating in the leishmaniasis studies. During the year, visitors to the Laboratory included 21 fellows from Louisiana State University Medical School, 10 medical students from other institutions, and 140 other individuals.

The President expressed appreciation to the United Fruit Company for a grant of $10,000 for the year 1967 and a similar grant for 1968 to assist in financing the arbovirus studies in the Almirante area of Panama.

The President stated that the 90th Congress provided an increase in the ceiling authorization of appropriations for the Gorgas Memorial Laboratory from $500,000 to $1,000,000 for the fiscal year ending June 30, 1970. This authorization was contained in Public Law 90-574 (90th Congress, H. R. 15758). It was proposed to justify appropriation for approximately $200,000 of this additional amount and to seek extension of the authorization for an additional 2 years.

Treasurer's Report: Mr. Donald A. McCormack presented the report of the Treasurer. He remarked that the Endowment Fund was progressing modestly; based on cost the income from stock investments during the year was at the rate of 9.9067 percent. He commented on the chart presented by the President showing the growth and productivity of the Gorgas Memorial Laboratory for the past 10 years and remarked that for the first time the total income exceeded $1,000,000.

The Secretary, Mr. Donald F. Simpson, presented the proposed 1970 budget which called for a total of $1,222,636.

Lister Hill Graduate Fellowship Program: Governor Maurice H. Thatcher presented a resolution calling for the establishment of the Lister Hill Graduate Fellowship program in honor of Senator Lister Hill of Alabama, who was expected to retire from the United States Senate in January 1969. Governor Thatcher recalled the great service which Senator Hill had rendered to the Gorgas Memorial Institute over a long period of years.

He stated that a fellowship program would represent an expression of the great indebtedness which the Institute owed to Senator Hill for the unfailing support which he had accorded it ever since the enactment of the original legislation making possible the establishment of the Gorgas Memorial Laboratory. A motion was made, seconded and carried that the Fellowship Plan be authorized, that the administration of the Plan be committed to the jurisdiction of the Executive Committee, that the Plan be financed with income derived from the Endowment Fund, and that Senator Hill be furnished a copy of the Resolution, which was as follows:

WHEREAS, the GORGAS MEMORIAL INSTITUTE OF TROPICAL AND PREVENTIVE MEDICINE, INCORPORATED, takes notice of the fact that the HONORABLE LISTER HILL of Alabama will retire from the United States Senate on January 3, 1969, after a distinguished, long-continuing and unbroken congressional service of 46 years—15 years in the House and 31 years in the Senate; and the Institute fully mindful of the preeminent achievements of Senator Hill in sponsoring and obtaining in the Congress enactment of much important legislation (a) in general, in behalf of the sanitation and health of the nation, and (b) in particular for the benefit of the cause of tropical and preventive medicine in obtaining increased congressional authorization for the maintenance, operation, and expansion of the Gorgas Memorial Laboratory; and

WHEREAS, the Institute deems it fitting and proper that it should create something tangible, adequate, and enduring of a memorial character, in recognition, honor, and appreciation of Senator Hill's highly important achievements thus mentioned—such memorialization to be compatible with, and in furtherance of, the aims and purposes of the Institute and Laboratory; and

WHEREAS, it is believed that the best and most appropriate method of such memorialization can be obtained thru the creation of graduate fellowships—to be designated as the Lister Hill fellowships—for selected persons to enter and be associated with the Laboratory and its activities as students or scientists dealing with research and other labors of the Laboratory; and

WHEREAS, the cost of administering such memorialization and graduate fellowships—the holders of the graduate fellowships to be known as fellows—will require substantial outlays, and the cost thus to be incurred must be paid solely from income received by the Institute from investment of its endowment funds and/or from private gifts and contributions wholly exclusive of any congressional appropriations for the maintenance, operation and expansion of the Laboratory and its activities; and

WHEREAS, the direction of the Lister Hill fellowship plan, because of the numerous and continuous details to be encountered and the practical

232

situation which will obtain, can only be effectively met by the Executive Committee of the Institute: in consideration of the premises,

BE IT RESOLVED by the GORGAS MEMORIAL INSTITUTE OF TROPICAL AND PREVENTIVE MEDICINE, INCORPORATED, at its regular annual meeting held in Washington, District of Columbia, on October 29, 1968, as follows:

1. That the Institute, because of the considerations and premises, and in order to carry out in timely and effective manner the plan or design of memorialization and graduate fellowships hereinbefore described, and in harmony with the aims and purposes of the Institute and the Laboratory, hereby vests the Institute's Executive Committee with full and complete authority, power, and responsibility to take charge of and conduct the administration of the indicated plan or design of memorialization and graduate fellowships, and to do all and everything which the Executive Committee may, in its discretion, consider necessary or desirable to achieve the needs and aims of the said plan or design; and the acts of the Executive Committee in these connections shall be and become the acts of the Institute, and binding on all concerned.

2. That the Executive Committee make to the Institute annual reports of the Committee of its actions hereunder, and any interim reports which to the Committee or the Institute may seem desirable.

3. That the Executive Committee shall have full authority and power to solicit and receive contributions, gifts, and grants for the said fellowship plan.

4. That the General Accounting Office shall have the right to examine the accounts and the records hereunder, and to make any recommendations and reports deemed necessary or desirable.

5. That these resolutions be incorporated in the minutes of today's proceedings of the Institute's regular annual meeting, and a copy furnished to Senator Hill.

Rear Admiral Calvin B. Galloway, MC, USN (Ret.) was re-elected President and Governor Maurice H. Thatcher Vice President.

By-Law Changes: Two minor changes in Article III, Section 2 and Article IV, Section 3 of the By-Laws were authorized to bring the date of the annual meeting into consonance with the time frame for the annual audit and the orderly submission of annual budgets to officials of the National Institute of Allergy and Infectious Diseases, and to increase the authorized Related Directors by one to a total of 14 to provide representation of the National Institutes of Health.

Chapter 7.

The Gorgas Memorial Laboratory
1929-1968

Epochs of Changing Patterns; Types of Research; Basis for Selection; Short and Long Term Trends; A Review of Projects and Achievements

*"Every advantage in the past is judged in the light
of the future issue."*
—DEMOSTHENES

Research planning and research accomplishment are influenced materially by the adequacy of facilities, the extent of financial support and the availability of qualified personnel dedicated to program objectives.

The research programs of the Gorgas Memorial Laboratory have expanded over the period of 40 years in accordance with provision for these essential elements. During this period, the annual Congressional appropriation for the operation of the Laboratory has been multiplied 10 times. In addition, during more recent years, funds have been made available from other sources for specific projects. Because of dollar erosion, it would be inappropriate to claim that research output has increased proportionally to increased financial support. In the early days when funds were at a bare minimum, accomplishment may be said to have run ahead of support. This may have been due in part to the enthusiasm and dedication of the small staff and in part to the fact that little was known concerning the epidemiology, control and treatment of tropical diseases endemic in Panama. Under such circumstances, any finding was of importance and represented a distinct contribution to the knowledge of the day.

Epochs of Changing Patterns: The 40 years of the Gorgas Memorial Laboratory seem to have been marked by distinct periods or epochs in which circumstances provided opportunities for significant expansion of research into new fields of endeavor. Most of these new epochs were marked by the introduction of new, highly competent and enthusiastic personnel who injected a new purpose and a new spark into the Laboratory programs.

Historically, the initial change took place in 1934, when Dr. Carl M. Johnson, Protozoologist, Dr. A. O. Foster, Helminthologist, and Dr. L. E. Rozeboom, Medical Entomologist, came on duty. These individuals inaugurated new studies in their respective fields and thus broadened the activities and horizons of the Laboratory. This group was augmented on October 1, 1938, when Dr. Graham B. Fairchild reported for duty.

The second of these epochs had its beginnings in 1943 when a cadre of U. S. Army Sanitary Corps officers was assigned to carry out studies on insect repellents and insecticides. Major Marshall Hertig arrived on June 15, 1943 to take charge of this endeavor. Subsequently, Capt. Graham B. Fairchild, Capt. W. C. McDuffie, Capt. Charles D. Michener, First Lieut. Roy Melvin, Lieut. Harold Trapido and First Lieut. Dale W. Jenkins reported for duty under this program. This was a highly successful venture which brought added prestige to the Laboratory and resulted in the addition to its permanent staff of Dr. Hertig and Dr. Trapido after their discharge from the Army.

The third epoch of significant change began in 1949 when research objectives were materially altered by the recognition in January of that year of yellow fever as the cause of death of 5 patients in Santo Tomás Hospital in November and December of 1948. This diagnosis led to the formation of a Yellow Fever Service in Panama by Dr. Fred L. Soper, Director of the Pan American Sanitary Bureau. Gorgas personnel were destined to play a large and important role in the studies on the epidemiology of this disease. Fortunately the Laboratory was well prepared to assume this role. Dr. Harold Trapido had joined the staff. In 1947, Medical Entomologist Pedro Galindo, Chief of the Anti-Malarial Campaign of the Department of Public Health of Panama became associated with the Laboratory as a liaison member on malaria control. Dr. Enid C. de Rodaniche, a virologist and an employee of the Republic of Panama, was assigned to the staff in February 1947. Together with Dr. Herbert C. Clark, these individuals contributed incalculably to the success of the yellow fever campaign. Their studies constituted one of the major highlights in the history of the Gorgas Memorial Laboratory and led to research on other arboviruses.

The fourth epoch began in 1956. In that year the appropriation from Congress was increased to $150,000, representing a tripling of the amount of the original authorization. Also in 1956, the Laboratory received the first substantial grant-in-aid from the National Institutes of Health. This grant was for studies on leishmaniasis under the direction of Dr. Marshall Hertig and Dr. Graham B. Fairchild. Subsequently, other personnel were added to the project. Leishmaniasis had received a certain amount of attention previously but the funds provided by the grant-in-aid permitted a material expansion of the program. The outstanding success of these studies established the Laboratory as a worthy recipient of outside support.

The fifth epoch had its inception in 1960, when Congress appropriated $500,000 for plant improvement. The budget ceiling had been raised to $250,000. In 1962, gifts totaling $132,387 were received for the construction of a modern insectary. A portion of these funds was donated by Mr. James H. Rand of the Colonial Research Institute. Part came from the International Research Foundation, Inc. through the instigation of Mr. Rand. The latter also gave $100,000 to cover Gorgas budget deficits. The new facilities and increased allotment allowed for the acquisition of new personnel, the extension of some previous programs and the establishment of separate Departments of Vertebrate Zoology, Bacteriology, Serology, Parasitology and Pathology, and a unit on clinical tropical medicine research in cooperation with the Hospital del Niño and Santo Tomás Hospital.

Types of Research: The major contributions have been in the fields of epidemiology, treatment and control. Laboratory activities for the most part have been aligned with and carried out in support of field studies. Undoubtedly this coordination has led to a well rounded program and has contributed materially to the success of the major research endeavors.

The location of the Laboratory was well adapted for the pursuit of field problems, many of which were still in need of elucidation at the time of its establishment. Outstanding progress has been achieved in the epidemiology of malaria, yellow fever and other arbovirus infections, Chagas' disease, leishmaniasis and equine trypanosomiasis. Throughout such studies, the problems of reservoir hosts received utmost attention.

Chemotherapeutic studies were initiated very early in the history of the Laboratory. Malaria treatment investigations have been pursued almost continuously and notable contributions have been made to this as well as to the chemotherapy of Chagas' disease and leishmaniasis. Treatment of equine trypanosomiasis received considerable attention in the early days. The control of malaria was one of the first projects, both by means of chemotherapy and larviciding. Later basic studies on residual insecticides provided the pattern for a country-wide control effort.

It is obvious that much of the progress in epidemiology and control was attributable to coordinated studies in medical entomology. From the very beginnings of the Laboratory, considerable stress has been placed on this field of endeavor. Studies have embraced identification, taxonomy and ecology of vectors, as well as means of control through herbicides, repellents, larvicides and insecticides.

Numerous studies have been carried out on the occurrence and prevalence of helminth and protozoan parasites both in the human and animal host. The immunology of these parasitic infections has been studied at various times and more recently has received increased emphasis. In recent years, a project has been inaugurated on the diarrheal diseases, one of the most troublesome health problems in Panama. The ecology of arboviruses continues to be an important part of the research program. That on geographical pathology is a promising means of throwing additional light on disease occurrence and distribution. In the past, many other research problems have received attention; these have included a wide variety of subjects ranging from tropical climatology to herpetology and to the genetics of *Drosophila.*

The fields of research have thus been wide and varied. The one little represented to date has been that of so-called "pure" or academic research. As time goes on, this field may receive more attention not only because of its far-reaching fundamental importance but because of the distinct possibility that it may contribute to the solution of problems heretofore resisting elucidation.

Basis for Selection of Research Projects: It is not always rewarding to delve into past history in an effort to fathom the reasons for the adoption of any piece of research. Undoubtedly some of the research at the Gorgas Memorial Laboratory was carefully planned and some was casual and spontaneous arising out of unforeseen events. Malaria is an example of the first. Not only had the Scientific Committee of the Gorgas Memorial Institute agreed that it should receive initial attention but in Dr. Clark's judgment as well it represented the tropical disease of greatest importance in Latin America. In the annual report for 1929, malaria problems constituted six of the ten proposed for study in the immediate future. The demonstration of the life cycle of the warble fly, *Dermatobia hominis,* is an example of the second type and resulted from the casual alighting of an insect carrying a mat of eggs of the fly on the knee of Major Dunn during a brief rest on a field trip. The unforeseen occurrence of yellow fever in Panama in the latter months of 1948 was the means of launching the extensive studies on the epidemiology of this disease. An outbreak of equine trypanosomiasis among horses of the United States Army in 1930 led to the establishment in 1931 of the Miraflores Veterinary Station. This station was utilized for many years for study of a variety of parasitic infections in domestic animals.

The availability of qualified personnel played a large role in the selection of research projects. No doubt at most times, the staffing was the result of planned objectives, as was the case in 1934. At other times, the staffing was already fortuitously available when the need arose, as was the case at the appearance of yellow fever in 1948.

The doors of the Gorgas Memorial Laboratory have always been open to outside investigators and many of these have contributed materially to the research output. Especially so is the case of officers from the Uniformed

Services of the United States. Visiting scientists have been welcomed freely. In these cases, research conducted by such individuals has been usually along the lines of individual interest but many times their interests have coincided with established programs of the Laboratory.

In retrospect, it may be said that the selection of research projects which have constituted the program of the Gorgas Memorial Laboratory over this long period of years has been made with a considerable degree of wisdom and in keeping with the relative health importance of diseases in Panama and Middle America. When unforeseen and unanticipated problems arose, for the most part qualified personnel were already available to meet the challenge and to carry the research to a successful conclusion.

Short and Long Terms Trends: Circumstances no doubt governed the course of various research endeavors over the long period. Some projects received continuous attention over 40 years. Others were pursued intermittently while some were completed and permanently closed out.

Studies on equine trypanosomiasis received considerable attention during the 1930's but were abandoned in 1946 on the retirement of Col. H. S. Eakins, Veterinary Corps, U. S. Army, who had carried on many of the studies. The gradual disappearance of the horse as a medium of transport was probably a factor in the cessation of the project. The studies on the equine helminthiases which began in 1934 were discontinued in 1939 with the departure of Dr. A. O. Foster, the Helminthologist. Cattle trypanosomiasis was first diagnosed in 1940 and limited studies continued until 1943, when the project was abandoned because of the exigencies of the war.

During the early years, surveys for human intestinal helminths and protozoa were conducted mainly by attached Service personnel or by visiting scientists. These were short term investigations and were at no time an important phase of the Laboratory program. During recent years there has been a renewed interest in this subject. Tropical climatology was studied briefly in 1941. A project which, because of circumstances, proved to be of relatively short duration was that on the value of BCG vaccination. Established early in 1949, the work was continued until December 1951, when it was taken over by the Servicio Cooperativo Interamericano de Salud Pública, and its research aspects abandoned.

Research on some of the most important human diseases in Panama has been of the long term variety. Various phases of the malaria problem have received continuous attention since the founding of the Laboratory in 1929. Chagas' disease was first diagnosed in Panama by Laboratory personnel in 1931. Research on this condition was actively pursued until the resignation of Dr. Carl M. Johnson in December 1944. There was a brief revival of studies in 1950 and 1951, when the Laboratory cooperated with Dr. Johnson, then with the Canal Zone Board of Health Laboratory.

An apparent gap existed in this project between 1951 and 1956. The problem was attacked intensively after the receipt of a grant-in-aid in 1967.

Investigations on leishmaniasis were inaugurated in 1944 and have received continuous attention since that time. Taxonomic studies of insects affecting man and animals had their inception at the opening of the Laboratory and have been pursued intensively.

A Review of Projects and Achievements
Parasites and Parasitic Diseases

Protozoa and Protozoal Diseases of Man: Malaria: This has been one of the main research efforts. Studies have been conducted on chemotherapy, immunology, vector taxonomy and ecology, natural and human infection in primates and control.

The Santa Rosa Field Station was established in 1931 to be followed by initial surveys for prevalence in five Chagres River villages. Treatment was instituted with quinine in 1931 and was followed by various regimens over a long period of years. By 1935, methods of treatment included atebrin and plasmochin, quinine and plasmochin and quinine alone. Infection rates were materially reduced. In that year, malaria reached epidemic proportions in the five villages and continued at a high level for 4 months. Subtertian parasite rates rose almost simultaneously in all towns. Over the 5-year period (1930-35) it was demonstrated that prevalence rates could be materially reduced by drug therapy with marked abatement in clinical symptoms, but that such therapy failed to prevent relapses and did not prevent the disease from reaching epidemic proportions. In 1945, residual house spraying with DDT was started and in 1948 was extended to all towns, following which malaria rates were materially reduced further. The project was continued for 32 years. Transmission at the end of that time was still taking place. Dr. Herbert C. Clark and Mr. W. H. W. Komp headed these studies, which were finally completed by Dr. Carl M. Johnson.

In 1947, treatment experiments were undertaken in three Gatun Lake villages, with chloroquine and paludrine. After 3 years, the malaria rate in the two towns receiving chloroquine once a week had been reduced from 26.5 to 0.7 percent and the rate in the town receiving paludrine weekly had been reduced from 34.8 percent to 1.5 percent.

In June 1960, Dr. Carl M. Johnson began chemotherapeutic trials with a pyrimethamine and primaquine combination in a holoendemic area to test the value of these drugs as an adjunct to eradication programs based on residual insecticides which had not produced expected results in certain Latin American countries. Two villages, La Represa and Mendoza, were selected and drugs were supplied for voluntary treatment. After August

1960 no malaria occurred in the study area. Treatment was maintained for 2 years. Between June 1962 and June 1964, 24 cases of malaria occurred in La Represa and 29 in Mendoza; some of these cases represented importation of the infection. Results indicated that this drug combination taken weekly on a mass basis halted transmission and was without any untoward reactions or evidence of toxicity.

Similar studies with a pyrimethamine-primaquine combination were carried out among Indians in a remote area in the Sambu River Valley by the U. S. Naval Medical Science Unit under direction of Lt. Commander Ralph D. Comer, in cooperation with the Pan American Health Organization and the Ministry of Health of Panama. The administration of the combined therapy every 2 weeks greatly reduced the prevalence of malaria in the absence of any other control measure and eliminated the clinical disease.

Primate malaria was studied at various times beginning in 1930, when experimental transmission of *Plasmodium brasilianum* to eight human volunteers was unsuccessful. The following year, Dr. William H. Taliaferro and associates began studies on acquired immunity in monkey malaria and attempted the transmission of *P. falciparum* to monkeys.

In 1966, new studies were inaugurated by Dr. Martin D. Young to determine the susceptibility of primates to human malaria. Dr. James A. Porter joined the program later that year and Dr. David C. Baerg, an entomologist, came on duty in 1967. Early success was achieved when *Aotus trivirgatus* inoculated with *P. vivax* of human origin was found susceptible. By the end of 1968, five species of Panamanian monkeys had been shown to be susceptible to *P. vivax*. The *Aotus* (night monkey), *Ateles* (spider monkey) and *Saguinus* (marmoset) all appeared to be good hosts. By 1968, one strain (Achiote) of *P. vivax* had been through 56 blood passages in the night monkey and another strain (Santa Rosa) through 17 transfers. About 90 percent of *Aotus* monkeys exposed became infected. Parasitemias were higher in splenectomized and drug-treated animals. The parasitemias reached high levels and a few persisted for over 90 days. Monkey to monkey transmission through bites of infected mosquitoes, *Anopheles albimanus*, was accomplished.

Inoculations of *P. falciparum* blood of Panamanian origin produced only temporary infections in *Saguinus* (marmoset). However, strains of *P. falciparum* of African and Malayan origin grew well in *Aotus, Cebus* and *Saguinus* monkeys and less well in other species.

After the employment of DDT in the Chagres River villages for 8 years, changes were noted in the behavioral pattern of *Anopheles albimanus*. Gross numbers of mosquitoes in dwellings were no longer drastically reduced and selective killing of engorged females was no longer evident. If changes were due to DDT resistance, it was of a very low order and not detectable by standard methods. Apparently a strain had evolved which was hyperirritant to DDT and possessed an enhanced positive phototropism, since the mosquitoes no longer rested on the walls of the houses but congregated around kerosene lamps. The studies were conducted by Dr. Harold Trapido.

American Trypanosomiasis: Chagas' disease investigations have concerned diagnosis, prevalence, clinical manifestations, treatment, epidemiology, reservoir hosts, and vectors and vector ecology. Trypanosomes other than *T. cruzi* have been studied also. Dr. Carl M. Johnson has been in charge of this project. Dr. John H. Edgcomb joined the project on January 1, 1968.

Prevalence rates have been determined from time to time. The complement fixation test was first employed for diagnosis of Chagas' disease in 1936. Of 1,251 individuals tested in 12 communities in Panama in that year, 3.83 percent were positive. In 1951, the CF test on 2,000 blood specimens indicated a spotty distribution of the infection in 10 localities in five Provinces. In 1966, it was estimated that there were 40,000 cases of Chagas' disease in Panama.

In 1967, intensive surveys by CF test, direct examination of blood smears, blood culture and xeno-diagnosis gave the following results:

Source of blood	No. specimens tested	Percent positive
Blood bank	6,253	2.0
Other surveys	399	12.5
Outpatient clinics	1,294	11.4

On the basis of reports from South America that *T. cruzi* infection was associated with delayed esophageal transit time and megaesophagus, in 1961 studies were conducted on 98 individuals, about one-half of whom were infected. The negative group served as controls. The number showing delayed esophageal transit time was approximately the same in both groups. Further observations in 1968 on additional patients gave the same results.

Of individuals admitted to Santo Tomás Hospital with a positive serology for Chagas' disease, 101 were carefully studied. Forty-eight of these showed cardiac abnormalities with one or more of the following types: Arrhythmias, right bundle branch block, left bundle branch block, ventricular enlargement, atrial enlargement, myocardial lesions and A/V block. Four deaths occurred, two with acute and two with chronic Chagas' disease. Ventricular aneurysms were found in two cases, a lesion not previously reported from Panama. It would appear that apical lesions may be commonly associated with the chronic disease in the area.

In the treatment of the disease, some promising results were obtained in a limited number of chronic cases with an 8-aminoquinoline compound

Fig. 14. Dr. Carl M. Johnson, an authority on Chagas' disease, examining the heart of a patient succumbing to the disease for evidence of gross pathology.

(Burroughs-Wellcome 349-C-59). The drug was administered in a dose of 15 mg. daily for as long as the complement fixation test remained positive. The chronic form of the disease is considered to be resistant to therapy but six cases became negative for the CF test. It would seem that the drug had eradicated the parasites.

T. cruzi was found to be widely disseminated in various animals and was recorded from 33 species representing six different orders. The course of *T. cruzi* infection in the dog simulated closely that in man. Cardiac lesions were noted in acute fatal cases in this animal. In a blood survey, 70 pigs, 16 horses and four mules were negative for trypanosomes. However, 19 of 82 dogs were positive as were 22 of 108 rats *(Rattus rattus).* Some of the dogs and rats carried both *T. cruzi* and *T. rangeli,* demonstrated through blood culture procedures and isolate characterizations.

Xeno-diagnosis and blood culture were found to be of little value for the detection of chronic cases of Chagas' disease but were of some value in acute cases. The complement fixation test, which has been employed for prevalence studies, was found to give cross reactions between *T. cruzi* and *T. rangeli.* In 1968, preliminary trials with the hemagglutination test proved promising. Abnormally high levels of Serum Glutamic Oxaloacetic Transaminase and Serum Glutamic Pyruvate Transaminase were observed in acute cases of Chagas' disease but not in chronic cases. However, about 28 percent of the latter showed abnormally high urea nitrogen in the blood.

In studies on trypanosomes other than *T. cruzi, T. rangeli* was found for the first time in Panama in 1957. Human infections were encountered in endemic areas of *T. cruzi;* the infections varied from 2.3 to 6.0 percent. Research conducted by Dr. Octavio E. Sousa provided information on the natural occurrence of *T. rangeli* in Panama, on its biological characteristics in experimental and wild mammals, and on the behaviour of this trypanosome in natural and experimental vector hosts. *Rhodnius pallescens* was found to be an efficient vector but *R. prolixus,* not native to Panama, could not be infected with the local strains of the parasite. *T. rangeli* could be transmitted to CFW* mice by bites of naturally or experimentally infected *R. pallescens.* Natural infections were discovered in both *Tamandua tetradactyla* and *Procyon lotor.* Several other wild mammal species have been recorded as local reservoir hosts of *T. rangeli.* A strain isolated from *Tamandua tetradactyla* was transmitted to the pigmy anteater, *Cyclopes didactylus.* Human strains in this animal produced a lower grade infection.

A natural infection with *T. legeri* was found in *T. tetradactyla* and a similar type of infection with *T. minasense* was discovered in *Saguinus geoffroyi. T. rangeli* was also found in the latter animal.

Natural infections with trypanosomes have been encountered in various Reduviidae bugs including *Panstrongylus geniculatus, Triatoma dimidiata,*

---

* A Swiss-Webster strain of albino mouse.

and *R. pallescens*. The latter species appears to be the chief vector. It is predominantly present in native houses. In studies of the ecology of reduviid bugs conducted by Commander Alan C. Pipkin of the U. S. Naval Medical Science Unit, of 3,283 bugs (nearly all *R. pallescens*) taken from houses, 32.71 percent were infected with *T. cruzi* and 4.1 to 8.1 percent with the non-pathogenic *T. rangeli*.

Leishmaniasis: Leishmaniasis has been one of the most intriguing and at the same time one of the most difficult problems in the program of the Gorgas Memorial Laboratory. When first given attention in 1944, little was known concerning the occurrence and distribution of the disease, its treatment, vectors and vector ecology and patterns of transmission. Great progress has been made in solving some of these problems.

Leishmaniasis in Panama is mainly a forest disease and tends to be markedly reduced or to virtually disappear when forests are cleared.

Considerable success has been achieved in the treatment of the disease. Pyrimethamine administered orally has been followed by cures in approximately 90 percent of the cases which have been followed adequately. Toxic reactions have been minimal except in one instance. In trials with dihydrotriazine pamoate (Camolar®), 18 of 25 patients were cured. The drug failed in the single case of the mucocutaneous form.

Differences in geographic strains of *Leishmania braziliensis* were demonstrated by types and extent of lesions in hamsters. Immunologic variations were revealed also by the agar-gel diffusion technique of Ouchterlony. Two distinct forms capable of producing human disease apparently exist in Panama.

Natural infections in wild-caught Panamanian *Phlebotomus* sandflies with leptomonad flagellates, consistant morphologically with *Leishmania,* were first found in 1961. Many thousands of these sandflies have been dissected with an overall infection rate of approximately 8.4 percent.

In studies on sandfly ecology, breeding places of wild sandflies were first discovered in 1957, when a few young stages were recovered from topsoil at the buttresses of forest trees. Larvae of some species were later found in rotting leaves covered by vegetation on the forest floor. It was possible to rear young forms to the adult stage by methods developed previously in the Gorgas Memorial Laboratory. Some of the species thus reared were maintained through many generations.

In further studies on sandfly ecology, aboreal trapping of the insects was rewarded by large catches, most of which belonged to five of the commoner man-biting species. The bulk of the catches was composed of *Phlebotomus trapidoi* and *P. panamensis*. There was an almost complete vertical separation of these two species, with nearly all of the *P. trapidoi* being taken in the canopy and nearly all of the *P. panamensis* at ground level. It was

Fig. 15. The *Hertig* pipette technique for the artificial feeding of *Phlebotomus sandflies*. (*Greatly enlarged*).

suggested by this result that *P. trapidoi* might be breeding in the forest canopy. Samples of dead leaves and litter from branches and tree holes 20 to 50 feet above ground revealed a single *Phlebotomus* larva, which was taken 22 feet above ground. This finding represented the first recovery of a sandfly larva ever found in the forest canopy and may prove of great significance as a factor in the epidemiology of the disease.

A unique pipette technique was used for the artificial feeding and infection of sandflies. A high percentage of infections was secured in hundreds of the flies. Infected flies were employed in transmission experiments by feeding on or by injection into various animals and by feeding on human volunteers.

Intensive effort was made to find a suitable laboratory host susceptible to *L. braziliensis*. Spiny rats failed to develop evidence of infection. Localized infections followed intradermal injection of the organisms in suckling white mice but the parasites disappeared shortly after weaning. More success was had with hamsters and visible lesions have been produced by injection into the nose of these animals. In a continued search, cotton rats gave results comparable to hamsters. Cutaneous infections were obtained in the tree rat, *Tylomys panamensis,* the kinkajou, *Potos flavus,* and the olingo, *Bassaricyon gabbii.* After numerous attempts, infection was finally obtained in a spiny rat, *Proechimys,* and in 1 of about 60 spiny rats of the genus *Hoplomys.* However, no additional infections were subsequently encountered in cultures of heart blood in over 2,000 animals representing at least 35 genera.

It was not until January 1965 that lesions were observed in a wild animal host, in this case a kinkajou which had a small papule on the ear. Leishman-Donovan bodies were isolated from this lesion and produced infection in hamsters. This was the first time that a cutaneous leishmanial infection with a grossly demonstrable lesion, contracted in nature, had been found in a non-human host in Panama.

In a further search for reservoir hosts, a skin-biopsy culture technique was tried and proved successful in isolating the organism. Skin cultures from several hundred animals of 25 genera resulted in positive findings in biopsies from the skin of porcupines, an opossum, a marmoset, an olingo and many sloths. A high percentage of porcupines from some areas were positive. *Leishmania* from the skin of the porcupine produced no lesions after intradermal inoculation into hamsters. On the other hand, the strains from the skin of the marmoset, the olingo and sloths produced typical swellings with abundant L-D bodies.

Differences were noted in the growth pattern of *Leishmania* in artificially infected sandflies. In most Old World species growth of the leptomonad stage takes place chiefly in the anterior part of the midgut or cardia. Panamanian strains also exhibit growth in the cardia but in addition there is usually growth in the hind-gut, especially in the thin-walled portion just posterior to the Malpighian tubules. A human strain and one from the marmoset followed this growth pattern in *Phlebotomus sanguinarius*. However, the strain isolated from the porcupine failed to become established in the gut of this sandfly. This feature, as well as the fact that the strain produces no external sign of infection in the normal host and in hamsters, raises the question of the identity of this *Leishmania*.

The leishmaniasis studies were under the direction of Dr. Marshall Hertig until his retirement in 1967. Since then, Dr. Aristides Herrer has directed the project. Dr. G. B. Fairchild has had an active role in the investigations throughout. Others involved in the research have been Dr. Phyllis T. Johnson, Mr. Wilford J. Hanson, Dr. Ellicott McConnell, Miss Mary Lou Morrow, Dr. Vernon E. Thatcher, Dr. Carl M. Johnson, Dr. Curt R. Schneider, Dr. Sam R. Telford and Dr. Howard Christensen.

Other Protozoa and Protozoal Diseases of Man: At various times attention was given to certain human protozoal diseases other than malaria, Chagas' disease and leishmaniasis. In the main, the research was carried on sporadically.

A number of studies were conducted on amoebiasis. Various surveys were undertaken on the prevalence of infection with *Entamoeba histolytica*. In 1930, Dr. Ernest Carroll Faust of Tulane University together with two associates examined over 2,000 individuals representing all social and economic levels; infection rates varied between 2.8 and 72.7 percent with highest rates in inhabitants of river villages. Clinical manifestations were infrequent. However in five autopsies, extensive ulceration was encountered in two cases.

In 1931, Dr. Hamilton H. Anderson of the University of California examined a group of patients in Santo Tomás Hospital but found a prevalence rate of only 13.9 percent. Experimental therapy with carbarsone was administered to 88 patients. Of 37 who could be followed for a month after treatment, all were cleared of the infection.

In 1937, Dr. Harry E. Wright of Baylor University conducted a survey of 478 inhabitants of Chagres River villages and encountered *E. histolytica* in 32.4 percent. In the same year, Lt. James J. Sapero, Navy Medical Corps, and Dr. Carl M. Johnson studied the role of the food handler in the transmission of *E. histolytica*. The study comprised 14 groups of Navy personnel with a total of 919 persons. No evidence was found to support the belief that infected food handlers were important agents in the transmission of the parasite. Additional examinations brought the total to 1,021, of whom 11.6 percent were positive for the parasite. Highest rates were encountered in Navy personnel returning from the Orient. *Dientamoeba fragilis* was found in 17.1 percent of the individuals in one group.

In another study by Lt. Sapero, 216 cases of non-dysenteric amoebiasis were investigated. Of 106 apparently healthy men harboring *E. histolytica,* 46, or 43.4 percent, registered complaints. A control group of 108 negative for intestinal protozoa revealed but 8, or 7.4 percent, to have complaints. Of 236 individuals harboring intestinal protozoa other than *E. histolytica,* the percentage with symptoms was similar to that found in the control group with the exception of persons harboring *D. fragilis,* of whom 27.3 percent of 44 cases presented symptoms.

In 1937, during a tour of duty at the Gorgas Memorial Laboratory, Lt. Commander E. G. Hakansson conducted therapeutic trials with carbarsone in cases of amoebiasis and amoebic dysentery. Relatively small doses of the drug failed to eliminate *E. histolytica* in carrier cases. However, a dose of 0.025 gm. per kilogram of body weight administered twice daily for 10 days resulted in clinical cure in frank cases of dysentery and in some cases was effective in eradicating the infection.

In 1943, Dr. Carl M. Johnson reported a prevalence rate of 12.0 percent of *E. histolytica* in some 600 stool examinations.

In 1944, Dr. Johnson, in cooperation with Dr. Bliss C. Shrapnel and Dr. J. H. Sandground, treated 20 cases of amoebiasis with emetine hydrochloride provided with an "Enseals" coating, which was designed to release the contents in 3 to 4 hours after ingestion. Total dose rates varied between 3 grains for the youngest to 22 grains for the oldest patient. Amoebae disappeared from the stools in 3 to 4 days. Fifteen of the patients were freed of amoebae as disclosed by rigorous follow-up examinations over a period of 1 to 7 months. Four patients who were not freed of the organism remained free of symptoms. No side effects were observed.

In recent years it has been suggested that the so-called small race of *E. histolytica* is actually another species which has been designated as *E. hartmanni,* as well as by other names. This so-called species is believed by some authorities to be non-pathogenic. While the validity of *E. hartmanni* is at present *sub judice,* it is probable that in many instances at least some of the organisms identified as *E. histolytica* in the above-mentioned studies may have fallen within the specifications claimed for *E. hartmanni.*

In 1944, *Isospora hominis,* a human coccidial parasite, was found for the first time in Panama.

In 1963 and 1964, the U. S. Army Medical Research Unit under the direction of Lt. Col. Bryce C. Walton carried out studies on toxoplasmosis which indicated that toxoplasmic chorioretinitis is a hitherto unrecognized health problem of appreciable importance in Panama. Evidence was obtained that toxoplasmic infection, as indicated by the indirect fluorescent antibody test (IFAT), was more prevalent in school children living at a level of 700 feet as opposed to those dwelling at 4,200 to 6,200 feet above sea level.

Helminths and Helminthic Diseases of Man: The first survey for intestinal helminths was conducted by Visiting Scientist Ernest Carroll Faust and associates in 1930. *Ascaris lumbricoides* and *Necator americanus* were relatively common. *Trichuris trichiura* ranged from 1.0 to 21.0 percent. Of 1,662 native patients in Santo Tomás Hospital, 348 were positive for *Strongyloides stercoralis;* 10.5 percent of the positives exhibited symptoms due to this infection.

Mansonella ozzardi was shown by different investigators over a period of time to be of fairly frequent occurrence among Indians in Darien Province. The first survey by Dr. Oliver R. McCoy in 1932 disclosed infection in 9.9 percent of 244 natives. Lt. Commander Paul W. Wilson found 109, or 5.8 percent, of 1,885 persons in the above province to have this parasite. In the Interoceanic Canal studies in 1967 and 1968 the parasite was found in up to 16 percent of inhabitants of certain native villages.

Dr. Harry E. Wright in 1937 noted ova of *Capillaria hepatica* in 16 of 194 persons examined in a Chagres River village. The frequency of these eggs in human stools was observed by other investigators. It was found, however, that their occurrence did not represent infection with the parasite but that the eggs were taken in when livers of certain lower animals were consumed.

Later parasite surveys from 1964 to 1968 indicated heavy prevalence of most intestinal helminths. Hookworm was the predominant helminth; about 80 percent of several thousand persons harbored this species. There is no record of studies on the degree of infection or on clinical manifestations, if any. Data on the public health significance of this infection are therefore lacking.

Although comparable groups were not represented in early and late surveys, there was no evidence to indicate that any appreciable reduction had taken place in the prevalence of intestinal helminths in the human population in Panama.

The first human infection with a little known tapeworm, *Echinococcus oligarthrus,* was reported from a fatal case. Adult worms were recorded from the intestinal tract of the puma, jaguar and jaguarundi. The first natural hydatid cyst of this species was recovered from the agouti. Local rodents were easily infected by feeding eggs or proglottids. Several lines of the infection cycle were established in the Laboratory, including a cat-rodent-cat cycle, a line of intraperitoneal secondary hydatidosis (rodent to rodent cycle) and a line of intramuscular secondary hydatidosis (rodent to rodent cycle). Dr. Octavio E. Sousa and Dr. Vernon E. Thatcher have been involved in these studies.

In studies by the U. S. Army Medical Research Unit on the effect of wandering *Trichinella spiralis* larvae in animals exposed to EEE, Ilhéus and Japanese B encephalitis viruses, it appeared that an ordinarily benign infection with a viral agent would result in an almost invariably fatal outcome, if it should happen to coincide with the presence in the body of wandering nematode larvae.

Parasites and Parasitic Diseases of Lower Animals: During the period of 40 years, numerous observations have been made on various parasites and parasitic diseases of lower animals. Some of these studies have already been mentioned in connection with the reservoir host problem concerned with American trypanosomiasis and leishmaniasis. Other studies are noted in the following paragraphs.

In 1930, Dr. William H. Taliaferro and his associates from the University of Chicago studied malaria in various species of monkeys. The species in Panamanian monkeys resembled morphologically the human quartan parasite. Many young *Ateles* and *Cebus* monkeys were found to succumb to the disease. In 1966, records of 1,994 primates examined since 1931 were analyzed. Four of 7 species of Panamanian primates were found to be naturally infected with *Plasmodium brasilianum,* the only species encountered; the highest rate was 30 percent in the red spider monkey, *Ateles geoffroyi.*

In 1930, a new species of spirochaete was discovered in a marmoset monkey and was transmitted to a human volunteer who became acutely ill as a result. Subsequently, this relapsing fever strain was transmitted through ticks from monkeys to man. In this year also, an outbreak of equine trypanosomiasis due to *Trypanosoma hippicum* was studied among horses of the Quartermaster Corps of the U. S. Army. The disease was almost invariably fatal to horses and mules; cattle retained the parasite for long periods without clinical involvement. Later, transmission by the bites of the vampire bat, *Desmodus rotundus murinus,* was demonstrated and infected bats were found in nature. Transmission was shown to be of a mechanical and not of a biological nature. Various methods of treatment were tried; the most successful proved to be a combination of Bayer 205 (Suramin) and Tarter emetic.

In 1934, Dr. Oliver R. McCoy conducted a survey of filariid parasites of monkeys in three areas in Panama. Eighty-seven percent of 72 monkeys harbored seven different species of these parasites. *Acanthocheilonema gracile* was the parasite most frequently encountered. Two new species, *Tetrapetalonema atelensis* and *T. parvum,* were discovered.

In 1940, *Trypanosoma vivax* was found for the first time in cattle in the Republic of Panama. The trypanosome was well established in local animals, since surveys of a number of herds revealed infection rates from 5 to over 50 percent. Symptoms exhibited by infected animals consisted of fever, anemia and emaciation. A number of different animals were inoculated with the parasite but infections were established only in calves, goats and horses.

In 1939, a survey was conducted of internal and external parasites in racing greyhounds, hunting dogs and mongrel animals in Chagres River villages. The heartworm, *Dirofilaria immitis,* was present in 45 percent of the greyhounds, 8 to 61 percent of three packs of hunting dogs, and 22.5 percent of the mongrels. There was a high prevalence of hookworms in all groups of animals.

During the 1930's, a new and economically important parasite was found in captive monkeys. This species was believed to be *Protospirura muricola,* normally parasitic in the stomach of rats. The cockroach, *Leucophaea maderae,* was found to serve as the intermediate host. A considerable number of deaths in monkeys were attributed to this parasite, which occurred in the stomach and other portions of the digestive system. Lesions were particularly severe in the stomach and perforations of the wall resulted fatally.

Between 1934 and 1939, Dr. A. O. Foster carried out extensive studies on equine parasites, as well as some studies on parasites of other animals. Observations on numerous horses and mules revealed infection with 44 species of worm parasites. The most frequently occurring forms belonged to the Subfamily Strongylinae Railliet, 1893. Fifteen of the species accounted for about 98 percent of the Strongylid parasites. Active verminous arteritis or aneurysm was found in about 80 percent of the animals. The lesions were due to the larvae of *Strongylus vulgaris* and were confined to the anterior mesenteric artery. *Trichostrongylus axei* was recovered from equines in Panama for the first time. Seven percent of house flies, *Musca domestica,* were found to carry the larvae of equine stomach worms, *Habronema muscae* and *Drascheia megastoma.*

Toxoplasma was reported for the first time from Panama in 1943. The organism was isolated by Dr. Johnson from Army carrier pigeons and was responsible for epizootic illness with a fatal outcome in many instances. The organism was transferred to guinea pigs by intraperitoneal inoculation and caused acute illness followed by death in 6 to 10 days. In 1955, Dr. Rodaniche found that the marmoset, *Saguinus geoffroyi,* and the night monkey, *Aotus trivirgatus,* were extremely susceptible to *Toxoplasma* infection. Thirty-one marmosets and 15 night monkeys developed a uniformly fatal illness with death in 3 to 11 days after exposure by various inoculation routes. The marmoset proved highly susceptible also to inoculation by dropping the organisms on the conjunctiva.

In 1961, a survey was inaugurated by Dr. Octavio E. Sousa on blood parasites of birds taken in connection with the arbovirus studies in the Almirante area. Subsequently, birds from other parts of Panama were examined. Numerous parasites were encountered including five species of

Plasmodium, Haemoproteus spp., *Leucocytozoan* sp., *Trypanosoma* spp. and four types of microfilariae, both sheathed and unsheathed. Overall infection rates varied but usually exceeded 20 percent. The prevalence of malaria parasites was especially noteworthy.

Studies on *Besnoitia,* a protozoan parasite, were inaugurated in 1964 by the finding of the organism in the lizard *Basilicus basiliscus.* Dr. Curt R. Schneider was responsible for most of the studies. Natural infections were observed also in other species of lizards and in the opossum, *Didelphis marsupialis.* The HI test disclosed positive reactors in 31 percent of 527 cattle; however the specificity of the test was yet to be established. The species of *Besnoitia* was determined to be *B. darlingi,* first described in Panama by Darling in 1910 and assigned to the genus *Sarcocystis.* Mouse-adapted *B. darlingi* produced acute, fatal infections in white mice, hamsters, marmosets, squirrels, a woolly opossum *(Caluromys derbianus)* and a four-eyed opossum *(Philander opossum).* Chronic infections with cysts were produced in opossums *(Didelphis marsupialis)* and one lizard *(Ameiva ameiva).*

Dr. William A. Summers, a visiting scientist, investigated the infectivity, morphology and growth rates of *Toxoplasma* and *Besnoitia* in tissue culture. Infection and growth were obtained in both the human monocyte and monkey kidney cell lines. Differences observed were primarily concerned with the rate of growth and cytopathogenesis. *Toxoplasma gondii* reproduced faster than any of the three species of *Besnoitia* employed. Cytopathogenesis and the rapidity of host cell destruction were directly proportional to the rate of parasite growth. The effect of homologous and heterologous antibody on infectivity suggested the possibility that growth inhibiting properties of the antiserum may reside in different forms of the antibody globulin.

Virus and Rickettsial Diseases

Studies on arboviruses were initiated following the appearance of yellow fever in Panama in 1948. Over the years, these studies have assumed increasing importance and have been pursued vigorously. In order to demonstrate succinctly the results of these widespread investigations, the record of virus isolations by the Gorgas Memorial Laboratory up to 1969 is summarized in Table 1.

Yellow Fever*: The yellow fever studies constituted one of the most successful research activities ever undertaken by the Gorgas Memorial

---

* Throughout this history the term yellow fever has been employed. In no case during the extension of the disease from Panama northward was transmission due to *Aedes aegypti,* the agent responsible for the passage of the urban type of epidemic. The epidemiological type of disease in the present instance has been referred to as "sylvan" or "jungle" yellow fever. The latter term is the one originally used and is more descriptive of the conditions under which transmission took place between 1948 and 1957 in Panama and Central America.

Table 1. Record of Isolation of Arboviruses in Panama by the Gorgas Memorial Laboratory up to 1969.*

Antigenic Group and Virus	Initial Isolation			Total Isolations					
	Date	Place	Source	Number	Man	Sentinel Rodents	Wild Vertebrates	Diptera
Group A								
Venezuelan Equine Encephalomyelitis	June 1961	Almirante	Man	111	+	+	+	+
Eastern Equine Encephalomyelitis	Sept. 1964	Almirante	*Culex taeniopus* (z)	1				+
Una	July 1960	Almirante	*Psorophora albipes* (z)	8				+
Mayaro	Aug. 1961	Almirante	*Psorophora ferox* (z)	1				+
Group B								
Yellow Fever	April 1951	Almirante	Man	33	+			+
St. Louis Encephalitis	July 1957	Buena Vista Colon	*Sabethes chloropterus* (z)	9	+			+
Ilhéus	June 1958	Cerro Azul	*Haemagogus capricornii falco* (z)	16	+		+	+
Bussuquara	May 1961	Almirante	Sentinel mouse	10	+	+	+	+
Group C								
Nepuyo	Sept. 1961	Almirante	*Proechimys semispinosus* (x)	5			+	

252

Virus	Date	Location	Host	No.				
Ossa (a)	Jan. 1961	Almirante	Man	54	+	+	+	+
Madrid (a)	March 1961	Almirante	Man	32	+	+	+	+
Patois (a)	June 1961	Almirante	*Sigmodon hispidus* (x)	6		+	+	
Zegla (a)	June 1961	Almirante	*Sigmodon hispidus* (x)	7		+	+	
Bunyamwera Group								
Wyeomyia	July 1960	Almirante	*Psorophora ferox* (z)	4	+			+
Guaroa	Sept. 1960	Almirante	*Aedes (Ochlerotatus)* spp. (z)	2				+
Guamá Group								
Guamá	June 1961	Almirante	Sentinel mouse	95		+	+	+
VSV Group								
Vesicular Stomatitis-Indiana	Jan. 1960	Almirante	*Phlebotomus* spp.	2	+			+
Phlebotomus Group								
Chagres	July 1964	Las Cumbres	Man	2	+			
Changuinola Group								
Changuinola	May 1960	Almirante	*Phlebotomus* spp.	10	+			+

(a) = New virus
(x) = Rodent
(z) = Mosquito

* The Gorgas Memorial Laboratory and the Middle America Research Unit conducted cooperative arbovirus studies in the Almirante area of Panama between September 1959 and July 1961. Many of the above-mentioned viruses were isolated by workers in both laboratories during this period. The material was shared and data on certain isolations from it have not yet been published.

Laboratory. They were comprised of several objectives including the determination of vectors and potential vectors and their distribution, life cycles, biting habits and ecology. The role of arboreal animals as reservoir hosts of the virus was an important objective. Since 1948, when the disease appeared in Panama, continued surveillance has been maintained. The yellow fever program, first instituted in Panama under the auspices of the Pan American Sanitary Bureau, took Gorgas investigators into all countries of Central America and as far north as the United States.

In the vector studies, aboreal mosquitoes were collected from tree platforms; pools of these mosquitoes were injected intracerebrally into mice for virus isolation; mosquitoes were fed on susceptible monkeys; and later many species were colonized for biting transmission experiments. Over the period of the studies, nearly 200,000 mosquitoes were collected and processed.

Taking part in these studies were Dr. Herbert C. Clark, Dr. Enid C. de Rodaniche, Dr. Harold Trapido, and Mr. Pedro Galindo. Lt. Col. Stanley J. Carpenter of the U. S. Army cooperated actively in the investigations.

Tree-top collections in Panama, Central America and Mexico indicated that vectors and potential vectors of jungle yellow fever were prevalent in many areas. *Haemagogus spegazzinii falco* (= *Haemagogus capricornii falco*), a tropical rain-forest mosquito, was found to range through Panama and as far north as the northern coast of Honduras. *H. lucifer* was recovered from the forests of Panama at elevations below 3.500 feet. It was replaced near the Costa Rican border by the closely related species, *H. iridicolor*, which extended into northern Nicaragua. The *H. mesodentatus* complex was found in deciduous tropical forests as far north as Tapachula, Mexico. *H. anastasionis* was common on the Pacific coast of Nicaragua.

Aedes leucocelaenus was recovered in the forests of Panama but became uncommon in Costa Rica and rare in Nicaragua and Honduras. *Sabethes chloropterus* was common below 3000 ft. in the region covered by the investigations and appeared epidemiologically to be involved in transmission in certain areas, although its ability in this respect was not demonstrated until later. *Trichosprosopon magnum* was common on the north coast of Honduras.

Early in 1956, yellow fever appeared in the Motagua River valley in Guatemala and the virus was isolated from captured *Haemagogus mesodentatus mesodentatus, H. equinus* and *Sabethes chloropterus* mosquitoes. In July 1957 the disease made its appearance in the Buena Vista area of Panama and virus was isolated from pools of *H. spegazzinii falco* (= *H. capricornii falco*) and *H. lucifer* captured in that area.

In efforts to determine the geographical limits of the species of *Haemagogus* responsible for yellow fever transmission in Middle America and

Mexico, *H. equinus* was found as far north as Brownsville, Texas. The northernmost record of the genus on the Pacific side was a single female of *H. mesodentatus gorgasi* taken near the southern border of the State of Sinaloa, Mexico. The northernmost collection of *H. equinus* on the Pacific side was near San Blas in the State of Nayarit, Mexico. On the Caribbean side *H. mesodentatus mesodentatus* was taken near Ciudad Santos, north of Tamazunchale, Mexico.

Following the appearance of yellow fever in Panama, studies were initiated on distribution, annual cycle of abundance, the vertical stratification in the forest, and the possible relationship of the forest mosquitoes attacking man in the transmission of jungle yellow fever. Particular attention was directed toward species which had been shown to be vectors of the disease in South America, *Haemagogus spegazzinii falco* (= *Haemagogus capricornii falco*) and *Aedes leucocelaenus*. *A. leucocelaenus* was relatively indiscriminate in vertical distribution but favored the ground level. On the other hand, *H. equinus, H. spegazzinii falco* (= *H. capricornii falco*) and *Sabethes chloropterus* were predominantly aboreal.

H. equinus and *H. lucifer* proved to be considerably more abundant than *H. spegazzinii falco* (= *H. capricornii falco*) or *A. leucocelaenus*. At the time, it was considered that the first named species might not be involved in transmission of the virus to man because of the small number of cases and the large non-immune human population. All of the above species virtually disappeared as adults during the dry season. However, *Sabethes chloropterus* appeared to be better adapted to carry over during the dry season.

Following the laboratory colonization of the chief suspected vectors of yellow fever, transmission experiments from monkey to monkey were undertaken by means of bites of the mosquitoes. Transmission was effected in the case of *H. equinus, H. mesodentatus gorgasi, H. mesodentatus mesodentatus* and *Sabethes chloropterus*. However, in check tests the virus could not be transmitted to mice by the latter species. Further tests failed to effect bite transmission by *S. chloropterus*. These failures led to a reevaluation of the conditions of the experiment and further studies on the life cycle of this species. It was found that females of the species did not begin to suck blood before the sixth day after emergence; in fact most females did not take a blood meal until 10 to 15 days after emergence. The mean life span after the first blood meal was over 30 days and females were kept alive in the laboratory colony for as long as 5 months.

Experimental procedures were altered in keeping with new facts concerning the life cycle of *S. chloropterus* and yellow fever was successfully transmitted to a clean monkey 37 days after the infective blood meal. In additional experiments with rhesus monkeys *(Macaca mulatta)*, transmission occurred but experiments with *Ateles* monkeys were all negative. The conclusion was reached that *S. chloropterus* is capable of transmitting yellow fever, although a high titer of the virus in the infective meal, a prolonged incubation period and a highly susceptible host are required.

Surveys for reservoir hosts of yellow fever contributed materially to the epidemiological studies. The surveys comprised sacrifice of animals in the wild and animals trapped or purchased and brought alive to the laboratory. In the case of those killed in the field, each animal was weighed, measured, the sex noted and relative age recorded. Autopsies were performed and two sets of tissues preserved for histological examination. Skulls and selected skins were forwarded to the U. S. National Museum for identification purposes. Serum samples were sent to the Carlos Finlay Institute, Bogotá, Colombia, for mouse-protection tests for yellow fever. Sera from animals taken in Mexico were processed at the Gorgas Memorial Laboratory and the National Yellow Fever Service, Río de Janeiro, Brazil. In the case of animals brought alive to the Laboratory, the mouse-protection test was first employed but was later superseded by the intracerebral technique.

Killed animals were taken in nine areas in eastern Panama from the Canal Zone to the border of Colombia and in six areas in western Panama from the Canal Zone to the Costa Rican border. In addition, animals were obtained from two areas in the State of Chiapas, Mexico.

A total of 201 monkeys were taken in eastern Panama, of which 104, or 51.7 percent, were positive on the mouse-protection test. In western Panama, 224 animals were sacrificed, of which 68, or 30.4 percent, were positive. In both areas the howler monkey, *Alouatta villosa,* showed the highest percentage of positive reactions, followed by the white-faced monkey, *Cebus capucinus,* and the red spider monkey, *Ateles geoffroyi.* Positive tests were also obtained in black spider monkeys, *Ateles fusciceps,* the squirrel monkey, *Saimiri oerstedii,* the marmoset, *Saguinus geoffroyi,* and the kinkajou, *Potos flavus.*

Positive findings were also registered in certain non-primates, including sloths, ocelots, opossums and the conejo pintado. Positive reactions in the non-primates were probably questionable since the specificity of protection tests in such animals has been shown to be affected by a number of variables.

In 1951, 77 howler and spider monkeys were sacrificed in the State of Chiapas, Mexico. Blood specimens from 34 were unsatisfactory for testing. The same three of the remaining specimens proved to be positive in tests in each of two laboratories.*

The tests in live animals were of greater significance because it was difficult to preserve blood samples from animals killed in remote areas of the jungle. On the other hand, the live animals came from areas relatively

---

* In 1953, Boshell and Groot (Bol. Of. San. Panamericana, v. 43, p. 309, 1957) conducted neutralization tests for yellow fever on monkeys taken in the region of Shupá, Palenque, Chiapas and obtained negative results.

close to the Laboratory and thus were not representative of the coverage afforded by the animals taken in the jungle.

Of a total of 505 live monkeys tested, 33 gave positive reactions. These included 17 positives among 183 marmosets, 15 among 145 spider monkeys and 1 among 82 night monkeys; 46 howler and 49 white-faced monkeys were negative. Antibody titers were usually high; 17 of 21 specimens showed the capacity to neutralize 500 LD_{50} of virus. Positive reactions were obtained in juvenile monkeys in areas of eastern Panama during the time when human cases of yellow fever developed.

A review article by Dr. Trapido and Mr. Galindo in May, 1956 (Exper. Parasitology, v. 5 (3), pp. 285-323) sketched the history of yellow fever in Middle America and the events associated with the passage of the wave of the jungle form of the disease from Panama to Honduras during the period 1948 to 1954. On the basis of their studies, they suggested the following epidemiological conclusions: "(1) It is proposed that in the past there have been circumscribed and self-limiting episodes of sylvan yellow fever in Middle America, which were seeded from urban *Aedes aegypti*-transmitted epidemics. These epizootics were limited in extent and duration because of the marginal effectiveness of the sylvan mosquito fauna as vectors. (2) Localized outbreaks, by reducing the size of the susceptible primate pool, precluded the possibility of any general sustained wave of sylvan yellow fever. The elimination of urban yellow fever at about the end of the first quarter of this century permitted the susceptible primate host population to build up to densities capable of maintaining the recent wave of yellow fever during a 6-year period. (3) The passage of virus across the Canal Zone on to the Atlantic slope of western Panama, and so into Central America, is attributed to the coincidence of the arrival of a virus wave at this zone of marginal ecology during a period of climatic conditions particularly favorable for forest canopy mosquitoes. (4) It was suggested that transmission of yellow fever by *Sabethes chloropterus,* which persists through the dry season, was the key to the survival of virus during this unfavorable time of year. (5) The apparent end of the yellow fever wave in northern Honduras in 1954 was thought most likely to have been due to a severe and unusual drought during the first half of 1955."

However, before the publication of the above-mentioned paper, monkey mortalities were reported during December 1955 and January 1956 on the north coast of Honduras near Esparta, and the lower part of the Motagua River valley in adjacent Guatemala. Histological diagnosis of yellow fever in howler monkeys, *Alouatta,* from the two areas was made by Dr. Carl M. Johnson.

The reappearance of the disease in the two areas invalidated the working premise adopted in conclusion No. 5 above and led the authors in an addendum to their paper to revise their thinking. The Honduras locality in which the disease reappeared was within a few miles of La Masica where monkeys died in July and August 1954. Thus an unforeseen special concatenation of circumstances enabled the virus to persist in a locality for almost a year and a half, a state of affairs known in some areas of South America but novel insofar as recent observations in Middle America were concerned. The locality in which the disease reappeared in Guatemala was beyond the limit of the range of *Haemagogus spegazzinii falco* (= *Haemagogus capricornii falco*), as it was then known. Dr. J. Boshell M. and his assistants could find only *Haemagogus equinus* and *H. mesodentatus* in the area. The authors concluded there was an increased probability that these other species of *Haemagogus,* already known to transmit yellow fever in the laboratory, may under some circumstances also be vectors in nature.

Following the appearance of yellow fever in the Cerro Azul area in 1956 and the Buena Vista area in 1957, no further evidence concerning the presence of the virus in Panama was obtained until 1966. In that year, the howler monkey population in Cerro Cana in the Pirre Mountain range in Darien Province was apparently decimated. One young animal had positive serology. In the same year, HI tests disclosed positive reactors among young black spider monkeys and a white-faced monkey in the Río Mono area of the Upper Tuira River basin in southern Darien Province. No evidence was obtained of the virus in other areas surveyed. The data indicated that yellow fever virus was probably widespread in southern Darien Province between June 1963 and July 1966. No human cases were reported. The medico-ecological survey of Canal Routes 17 and 25 failed to disclose yellow fever virus activity in those areas in 1967 and 1968.

Virus Diseases Other Than Yellow Fever: As indicated previously, the establishment in February 1947 of studies on virus and rickettsial diseases was a step of far reaching importance. As the yellow fever investigations slackened off, more attention was given to other virus diseases, which have received increasing emphasis over the intervening years.

Soon after Dr. Enid C. de Rodaniche came on duty many cases of nervous diseases of unknown etiology occurred and were thought to be associated with equine encephalomyelitis. However, protection tests in mice against the eastern strain of this virus proved negative, as did attempts to isolate a neurotropic virus from spinal fluid and autopsy material.

The recognition in January 1949 of yellow fever as the cause of death of five patients in Santo Tomás Hospital in November and December of 1948 and the demand for full attention to this disease precluded for a considerable time any material amount of research on other virus diseases. However, in 1951, during the first recorded epidemic of poliomyelitis in Panama, Dr. Rodaniche isolated three strains of the virus. The disease was transmitted to local monkeys, *Alouatta villosa* and *Cebus capucinus.*

The monkeys were found susceptible to all three of Type I strains but were completely refractory to Type II and Type III strains.

In 1954 and 1955, experiments on dengue fever were conducted by Dr. Leon Rosen on assignment from the Laboratory of Tropical Diseases of the National Institutes of Health. Various serological tests indicated that the epidemic of "dengue-like" disease which occurred in Panama in 1941-42 was in all probability due to dengue Type II virus. Some evidence was obtained that dengue Type I virus had been present in Panama many years previously. Apparently, dengue had not been endemic in Panama since 1942.

A total of 30 monkeys were inoculated with strains of Type I and Type III dengue virus which had never been passaged in laboratory animals. Although none of the monkeys showed overt signs of illness, almost all developed hemagglutination (HI) or neutralizing antibodies. Viremia was demonstrated in four species of monkeys of three different genera 4 to 6 days after inoculation. This experiment provided the first data on the susceptibility of New World monkeys to this virus.

Interest in arboviruses other than yellow fever was no doubt stimulated by isolations from mosquitoes collected during the yellow fever studies. In 1956, Ilhéus virus was isolated for the first time in Central America from species of the genus *Psorophora* and in 1957 St. Louis encephalitis virus was isolated for the first time in Panama. Other viruses were detected and their identification provided an undeniable challenge. Outbreaks of equine encephalitis at Pacora in 1958, Tocúmen in 1959, Cañito in April 1961 and Almirante in June 1961 clearly indicated the public health importance of arbovirus infections in Panama and warranted increased emphasis on their ecology. Following the Almirante outbreak, Venezuelan equine encephalitis virus was isolated from human patients, sentinel mice and hamsters, birds, mosquitoes and wild rodents. The first mosquito isolation was from *Culex vomerifer*. Early it appeared that the cotton rat, *Sigmodon hispidus,* was an important reservoir host.

The Almirante area has continued to be a rich field for arbovirus studies. Up to the end of 1968, the following viruses had been isolated in this area from the sources indicated. Some of the identifications were made at the Middle America Research Unit.

Venezuelan Equine Encephalitis: Man, sentinel mice and hamsters, rodents, birds and mosquitoes.

Eastern Equine Encephalitis: Mosquitoes.

Una: Mosquitoes.

Mayaro: The mosquito, *Psorophora ferox.*

Ilhéus: Man, birds and mosquitoes.

Bussuquara: Man, sentinel mice, rodents and mosquitoes.

Ossa: Man, sentinel mice and hamsters, the spiny rat and mosquitoes.

Madrid: Man, sentinel mice and hamsters, the spiny rat and mosquitoes.

Nepuyo: The spiny rat.

Patois: Sentinel mice and hamsters and the cotton rat.

Zegla: Sentinel mice, the cotton rat and the rice rat.

Guaroa: Mosquitoes.

Wyeomyia: Man and mosquitoes.

Guamá: Sentinel mice and hamsters, the cotton rat and mosquitoes.

Changuinola: Man and *Phlebotomus* sandfles.

VSV-Indiana: Man and *Phlebotomus* sandflies.

Additional studies were made on sera obtained from various sources during and following the outbreak of Venezuelan equine encephalitis in the Almirante area in 1961 to 1962. Of 1,343 human sera tested by HI, antibodies were obtained to two Group A Viruses, viz: VEE and Una. Not only was VEE virus widespread among the human population but was equally so among lower animals. HI tests indicated the following antibody findings:

Source	No. examined	Percent positive for VEE antibodies
Domestic animals	82	69.5
Rodents	269	67.5
Marsupials	140	29.3
Reptiles	101	2.0
Birds	803	2.4

The cotton rat and the spiny rat appeared to be important reservoir hosts of VEE and Group C arboviruses in the Almirante area. Experimentally, the tree rat, *Tylomys panamensis,* the heron, *Butorides striatus,* and the opossum, *Didelphis marsupialis,* proved susceptible to VEE virus and presumably could serve as efficient reservoir hosts. The scarlet-rumped tanager, *Ramphocelus passerinii,* also appears to serve in this capacity.

An important phase of the Almirante studies involved determination of the role of migrant birds in the epidemiology of arboviruses. Many hundreds of birds were taken for virus isolation attempts and serological studies; population observations were carried out and involved a banding program and a census of nests, eggs, nestlings and fledglings.

Investigations of arbovirus activity in areas of Panama other than Almirante indicated widespread occurrence of members of Groups A, B and C viruses. Low percentages of antibodies were found for Bunyamwera, Phlebotomus and Turlock groups. St. Louis virus was isolated in a number of localities. Eastern equine encephalomyelitis virus was identified by HI tests on bird sera and immune bodies to A and B Group viruses were detected in bats by similar tests. Venezuelan encephalitis virus was isolated from man in another area in Panama and Ilhéus virus was isolated from humans. One virus strain, "Salterin," recovered from a worker on the Pan

American Highway, represented the first isolation of Wyeomyia subgroup of viruses from man.

The mosquito, *Deinocerites pseudes,* was found in nature to be infected with St. Louis encephalitis (SLE) virus. A large percentage of mosquitoes of this species became infected when fed on VEE infected guinea pigs and in turn transmitted the virus to other guinea pigs and to hamsters. VEE virus was also isolated from a member of the genus *Deinocerites* in Mexico.

In view of the above-mentioned isolations, intensive studies were undertaken to evaluate the potential role of *Deinocerites* mosquitoes as vectors of arboviruses. These crab-hole breeding mosquitoes were formerly considered to seldom attack man or to take any vertebrate blood. Because of these assumptions, mosquitoes of this genus had not been thought to be involved in disease transmission. Taxonomic studies indicated the presence of at least seven species in Panama, with two seemingly new to science. *D. pseudes, D. melanophyllum* and *D. epitedeus* were colonized and large numbers of adults were produced for experimental use. Precipitin tests on engorged female *Deinocerites* indicated a wide range of feeding preferences. *D. pseudes* proved to be a good transmitter of VEE virus in the laboratory but failed to transmit SLE virus.

A tissue culture laboratory was initiated in 1964. This technique replaced to some extent the employment of experimental animals in the isolation and characterization of viruses. Certain cell lines were found to be susceptible to almost all of Panamanian virus strains. Isolations were made from tissue culture when suckling mice were not susceptible. Plaque formation of some important viruses was found useful in serological surveys for these viruses.

During the past 3 years (1966-1968) observations have been made on the pathology of Group C viruses in sentinel and other animals, a subject which has been little studied. Infection with Madrid and Ossa viruses was found to be associated with lesions in the liver and lymphoid tissues, whereas VEE virus caused demonstrable changes only in the latter tissues. Ossa virus produced diffuse liver necrosis while Madrid infection was marked only by small focal necrotic areas. All three viruses were responsible for practically the same alterations in lymphoid tissues. The spleens were not notably enlarged but hemorrhages were noted in the pulp tissue along with large numbers of phagocytes containing nuclear remnants. The peripheral sinuses of the lymph nodes showed phagocytic cells with engulfed nuclear debris; the medullary cords were inconspicuous and the follicles were reduced in size.

In 1968, in cooperation with the Middle America Research Unit, tests were undertaken to evaluate the susceptibility of the golden hamster, *Mesocricetus auratus,* to infection with 37 New World arboviruses. Most Group C arboviruses were found to induce illness and death in this animal. High titered hemagglutinins were detected in serum of hamsters infected with this group of viruses. Lethal infections also were produced by VEE, EEE, WEE and Chagres viruses. Others did not result in fatalities, although antibodies were developed during convalescence. Thus, adult hamsters may prove to be valuable sentinel animals for detection of arbovirus activity.

Personnel engaged in the arbovirus studies included Dr. Enid C. de Rodaniche, Mr. Pedro Galindo, Dr. Margaret A. Grayson, Dr. Sunthorn Srihongse, and Dr. Carl M. Johnson.

Rickettsial Diseases: A limited amount of attention was paid to these diseases during the time Dr. Rodaniche was a member of the Laboratory staff. In 1947, the second case of Q fever in Panama was diagnosed and a strain of *Rickettsia prowazeki* (= *R. typhi*) was isolated from a sporadic case of endemic typhus fever. In 1949, two new strains of *Rickettsia mooseri* (= *R. typhi*) were isolated from human blood and experimental transmission of *R. burneti* (= *Coxiella burnetii*) was accomplished through the nymphal and larval stages of *Amblyomma cajennense*. *Rickettsia rickettsii* was isolated from a fatal case of Rocky Mountain spotted fever in 1951. A third fatal case of this disease was recognized in 1952 and a highly virulent strain of *R. rickettsii* was recovered from adult *A. cajennense*.

Bacterial Diseases

Tuberculosis: Investigations on the prevalence of tuberculosis in rural Panama were inaugurated in 1948 under the direction of Sra. Teresina P. de Pinzón, in cooperation with the Department of Health of the Republic of Panama. The project was designed as a 5-year study to include BCG vaccination of tuberculin negatives. In 1951, the investigations were assumed by the Servicio Cooperativo Interamericano de Salud Pública.

Tests were begun in the cities of Colon and Panama and later extended to Bocas del Toro Province, the city of Chorrera, Chitré in Herrera Province and the Gatun Lake villages of Ciricito, Cuipo and Lagarterita. During the period in question, a total of 32,804 tuberculin tests were conducted, of which 13,554 were positive and 19,250 were negative, not including doubtful reactions. A total of 28,967 BCG vaccinations were administered not including those done in the Province of Bocas del Toro by Dr. Gustav Engler, the Medical Superintendent of the Chiriqui Land Co. at Almirante.

Diarrheal Diseases: This study was begun in 1964 under the direction of Dr. Miguel Kourany. Examinations for enteropathogenic bacteria in various rural population groups revealed a moderate prevalence of these organisms which, however, were not always associated with diarrheal symptoms. Salmonellae were demonstrated to be the most frequent pathogens.

The rates varied according to the community. Conversely, diarrheal cases did not always harbor enteropathogens. *Salmonella, Shigella,* enteropathogenic *Escherichia coli, Edwardsiella,* and *Arizona* were isolated.

Among outpatients seen at the Children's Hospital in Panama City, there was considerable diarrheal disease not related to specific bacterial pathogens. Over 90 percent had no enteropathogenic bacteria; 5.3 percent had enteropathogenic *E. coli,* 1.7 percent *Shigella,* and 1.2 percent *Salmonella.*

Isolations of enteropathogenic bacteria were made from 50 percent of 96 lizards, *Ameiva ameiva;* of five other species of lizards, two harbored Salmonellae. Of a total of 671 monkeys of eight species examined, enteropathogenic bacteria were found in 11 percent of black howler monkeys, 2 percent of marmosets, 3 percent of night monkeys and 5 percent of spider monkeys.

Brucellosis: Agglutination tests carried out in 1968 by Dr. Kourany on the sera from 2,360 individuals in 31 communities in Panama revealed *Brucella* antibodies in 1.2 percent. Symptoms of brucellosis were not noted in any of the positive individuals.

Medical Entomology

Entomological activities have been pursued continuously since the founding of the Gorgas Memorial Laboratory. These activities have embraced many fields of endeavor and have represented an important segment of the research program over the period of 40 years. Many of the studies have been intimately associated with and have formed an integral part of other projects, including malaria, arboviruses, leishmaniasis and American trypanosomiasis. As a result, a considerable number of the research findings applicable to medical entomology have been included in the summaries of these diseases. Initial studies concerned the elucidation for the first time of the life cycle of *Dermatobia hominis* by Major Dunn in 1929.

Vectors and Vector Ecology: This part of the summary deals mainly with malaria vectors, inasmuch as data on other insects in this category have been mentioned under various other specific diseases.

In 1931 and the years following, Dr. D. P. Curry, Honorary Assistant Director of the Gorgas Memorial Laboratory, initiated studies on anopheline breeding. Mr. W. H. W. Komp cooperated in this investigation because of its relation to the malaria treatment project in the Chagres River villages. The growth of aquatic plants around the borders of Gatun Lake afforded excellent breeding conditions for anopheline vectors, including *Anopheles albimanus.* Evidence was gathered that this vector is able to make flights by interrupted stages for distances of 12 or more miles.

The aquatic flora of Gatun Lake included several species of *Chara* and the bladderwort, *Utricularia mixta. A. albimanus* favored exposed patches of *Chara* while *A. albitarsis* preferred exposed *Utricularia.* During the dry season, the water in the lake receded thus providing a canopy of these plants, a situation extremely favorable for anopheline breeding.

In 1935, Dr. Lloyd E. Rozeboom was able to experimentally infect *Anopheles bachmanni* (= *A. triannulatus*) with *Plasmodium vivax.* The mosquito was found to attack man in the jungle during daylight hours. Dr. Rozeboom established a laboratory colony of *A. albimanus* and elucidated the details of the life cycle. Ovarian development took place in approximately 7 days at a temperature of 80° to 86° F. and a relative humidity of around 80 percent. Six females deposited an average of 435 eggs; each female oviposited from 2 to 6 times; oviposition took place during the night. Eggs usually hatched after an incubation period of 40 to 48 hours in water at a temperature of 27° to 30° C. The larval stage usually consumed 8 to 13 days, the pupal stage usually 30 to 33 hours. Of 10,003 adults that survived emergence, 42.7 percent were males and 57.3 percent were females. Approximately 3 weeks were required for the development of one generation.

In 1936, Dr. Rozeboom observed differences in the blood feeding habits of Brazilian and Panamanian *Anopheles albitarsis,* and a marked dissimilarity in the morphology of the eggs of strains in the two countries. It was apparent that the species is divided into at least two separate races. The egg of *A. pseudopunctipennis* was also described and compared with that of the species in other countries.

In 1937, studies were conducted by Dr. Rozeboom on the eggs of the *Nyssorhynchus* group of *Anopheles* in Panama. In most instances specific identification could be made on the basis of egg structure. However, the presence of three types of *A. strodei* (= *A. evansae*) eggs indicated that egg structure alone is not a dependable criterion for distinct races of species in this group. In further studies, the Nearctic species *A. quadrimaculatus* and *A. punctipennis* exhibited a high degree of susceptibility to infection by strains of *Plasmodium vivax* and *P. falciparum* derived from their own as well as the Neotropical region. On the other hand, representatives of the Neotropical species *A. albimanus* from Cuba and Panama showed high susceptibility to infection with these malaria parasites from their own region but were distinctly refractory to certain strains of the malaria species from the Nearctic region.

In experiments on the infectibility of Panamanian anophelines fed on *P. falciparum* gametocyte carriers, 4.0 percent of *A. albitarsis* became lightly infected, as compared to 32.7 percent of *A. albimanus.* *A. bachmanni* (= *A. triannulatus*) could be infected with human parasites but its preference for animal blood would indicate that it is not a vector of importance in Panama. *A. punctimacula* was found to feed on both man and lower animals; it was rarely encountered, however, in the Chagres River villages and was apparently not a factor in transmission.

In 1938, an entomological field station was established at Juan Mina. In 1939, observations conducted by Mr. Daniel M. Jobbins indicated that a low water level in the Chagres River resulted in a buildup of *Cabomba* vegetation and enhanced opportunities for mosquito breeding in the early spring. *A. albimanus* breeding reached a peak in late April. Adult emergence occurred at a slightly lower rate for the next 3 months but sufficient to maintain quantities of anophelines in Santa Rosa and Guayabalito, two of the Chagres River villages in which malaria control was being carried out by drug treatment.

In 1942, Mr. Komp's monograph on "The Anopheline Mosquitoes of the Caribbean Region" was published and supplied an authoritative reference work on the subject, which had become of increasing importance because of war efforts in Middle America and the Caribbean Region. For 6 months of 1942, Mr. Komp was detailed to the Office of the Coordinator for Inter-American Affairs, as a consultant on its malaria program.

The studies on leishmaniasis in Panama were initially embraced in 1944 and were extended in 1945 when Major Marshall Hertig and Capt. G. B. Fairchild made the first sustained observations on the occurrence and distribution of sandflies, *Phlebotomus* spp., in Panama. Four species previously reported from Panama were taken. In addition, the collections included 30 other species which remained to be identified. Only five species were taken biting man. *P. suis* (= *P. gomezi*) and *P. panamensis* were by far the most common ones attacking man and animals. The sandfly collections were made from various types of habitat, including houses, horse-baited traps, masonry ruins, tree buttresses and hollow trees. By 1952, 60 species of *Phlebotomus* had been identified from Panama, and more have been recognized since then. Knowledge was accumulating concerning the habits of these various species in relation to the epidemiology of leishmaniasis. Of the 80-odd Central American species known at that time, 12 were known to bite man and 5 of these were of rather common occurrence in forested areas. Three species extended from the northern to the southern limits of the endemic areas of leishmaniasis in the Western Hemisphere.

Insect Repellents: The first insect repellent studies were initiated in 1939. Over the next 2 years, Mr. Jobbins continued these investigations under a contract with the Committee on Medical Research, Office of Scientific Research and Development. Field and laboratory tests under controlled conditions disclosed a number of new synthetic compounds far more effective as mosquito repellents than previously known substances.

Beginning in 1943, the repellent investigations were greatly intensified with the assignment to the Gorgas Memorial Laboratory of a cadre of U. S.

Army Sanitary Corps Officers. Major Marshall Hertig arrived on June 15 of that year to take charge of the studies. Initially of eight substances, all gave adequate protection for an average time of at least 160 minutes against *Anopheles albimanus, A. punctimacula* and several species of *Mansonia.* Interesting observations were made on the biting habits of mosquito species, the attractiveness of the human bait subjects and the efficacy of the repellents in relation to different body surfaces. The repellent activity was of less duration against *Mansonia* as compared with other species. *Mansonia* tended to bite more frequently on the arms while the legs were preferred in the case of *A. albimanus.* Repellent protection persisted longer in old subjects than those in the late teens and early twenties. *A. albimanus* bit the young subjects more frequently. Repellent action was affected adversely in heavily perspiring subjects.

Good protection against mites was obtained by uniform cloth impregnated with certain chemicals. One compound was still lethal to mites after seven washings of the cloth. Subjects wearing treated clothing were protected against chiggers until five washings and 6 weeks of wear rendered the cloth unprotective.

The mite protection tests were conducted by Capt. Charles D. Michener, who extended the studies in 1945. Of five different compounds employed to impregnate uniform cloth, 2-phenyl cyclohexanol killed chigger mites more quickly but washed out more easily. Best results were obtained with dibutyl phthalate and benzyl benzoate which retained some activity even after eight washings. When impregnated clothing was worn by test subjects, a 4 percent emulsion of benzyl benzoate proved to be the most effective and retained some activity through four washings.

In tests with the above-mentioned repellents against larvae and nymphs of *Amblyomma cajennense,* one of the most common ticks occurring in Panama, benzyl benzoate gave better results than did the other chemicals; treated clothing protected after 8 days of regular wear. However, thorough laundering greatly reduced or eliminated the protective qualities. In addition to carrying out the protection tests with various repellents, Capt. Michener published a number of papers on life histories and bionomics of chiggers.

Larvicides and Insecticides: Prior to the advent of DDT, little attention had been paid at the Gorgas Memorial Laboratory to vector control by larvicides or insecticides. Beginning in 1943, Capt. W. C. McDuffie conducted a series of tests with DDT, both in dusts and in oils, as an anopheline larvicide under various breeding conditions. Dosages of as little as 0.02 pounds of DDT per acre in dust and 0.01 per acre in oils or emulsions gave perfect to near perfect kills of anopheline larvae in 24 hours, provided there was adequate coverage of the area by the diluent and that weather conditions were optimum. Under river margin conditions, DDT remained effective for a maximum of only 6 weeks under the most favorable conditions. Decreases in effectiveness in time were associated with the action of wind, currents, wave movement and type of vegetation. Culicine larvae were not killed by DDT applied in dusts or oils unless very heavy doses were used. However, emulsions were effective against both types of larvae. Comparative tests of Paris green-talc and DDT-talc dusts indicated that DDT was 5 to 10 times as toxic to anopheline larvae.

In studies on the control of sandflies in Peru in 1944, Major Hertig and Capt. Fairchild found that certain repellents gave 100 percent protection for at least 3 hours. In a small number of tests, Army Freon-pyrethrum aerosol bombs and 2.5 percent DDT in kerosene rid houses of sandflies and rendered daytime resting places untenable for several days. These preliminary investigations were so promising that they led to the assignment of Major Hertig to Italy and Palestine during the latter part of 1944. The observations in the Mediterranian area indicated that area control of *Phlebotomus* might be possible and accordingly Major Hertig and Capt. Fairchild carried out further studies in Peru during June to August 1945. A number of project sites were sprayed with DDT and a high degree of area control was achieved.

The first recorded attempts to control *Simulium* spp., vectors of *Onchocera volvulus,* were carried out in Guatemala in 1945 by Capt. Fairchild and P. A. Engineer E. A. Barreda, USPHS. Using an emulsion containing 4 percent DDT prepared from a stock concentrate containing 20 percent DDT, 20 percent Triton X-100 and 60 percent Xylene, complete eradication of *Simulium* larvae from streams for distances up to 10 kilometers was effected at concentrations of 1 part DDT to 10 million parts of water.

Experiments conducted by Lieut. Harold Trapido indicated that protection against bites of *Culicoides* spp. could be afforded by painting the inside and outside of screens in a room with a 5 percent solution of DDT in kerosene. In the same year (1945), Lieut. Trapido conducted trials with 5 percent DDT in kerosene as a residual spray in houses in Gatuncillo, one of the Chagres River villages. Applications were made at intervals of 4 months. Marked reductions occurred in anophelines in the treated village. After the third spraying in July 1945, the ratio of anophelines in the treated village was 0.004, or only 4 anophelines versus 1,000 in two control villages.

The DDT house spraying program inaugurated by Lieut. Trapido was continued by him after his separation from the Army in 1946. It was found that DDT in kerosene was not as effective on the clay surfaces of the quincha walls of houses, and search was made for other more effective formulations. Water suspensions proved to be more suitable and as effective as DDT in kerosene. However, it was necessary to modify the Lofstrand sprayer to obviate clogging of the nozzle with the water suspensions. This, Dr. Trapido was able to do. Following these initial trials with various formulations of DDT, Dr. Trapido cooperated with Medical Entomologist Pedro Galindo in the national malaria control campaign in Panama.

From June to October 1948, Dr. Hertig carried out sandfly studies in Greece and Crete under the sponsorship of the World Health Organization for the purpose of evaluating the extent of *Phlebotomus* control achieved during malaria control with DDT. He also reviewed programs for the control of oriental sore in the Abruzzi, Italy area, where the use of DDT had brought about a marked reduction in the sandfly population. From observations in Sardinia, it was apparent that treatment of house interiors with this insecticide gave immediate and virtually complete protection against sandflies.

In 1948, Dr. Trapido conducted studies on the normal feeding habits of *Anopheles albimanus* because of his observations on the modified behavior of this species in DDT sprayed houses. He also used new herbicides on aquatic vegetation which favored breeding of malaria vectors. The herbicide 2,-4-D gave variable results with different plant species. It was most effective against the water hyacinth, *Eichornia crassipes*.

In 1950, Dr. Trapido was assigned to the International Health Division of the Rockefeller Foundation for the period April 20 to September 28, for the purpose of advising on the program for the eradication of *Anopheles l. labranchiae* from Sardinia. Subsequently, he served at other times as consultant on this project.

During the period February to May 1950, Dr. Hertig conducted a survey for leishmaniasis and vectors in Paraguay under the auspicies of the International Health Division, U. S. Public Health Service.

From 1952 to 1955, Dr. Hertig served as Field Director of the Commission on Hemorrhagic Fever of the U. S. Army in Korea.

Taxonomy of Insects: Studies on the taxonomy of various insects have been an important feature of the Gorgas Memorial Laboratory research program from the very beginning. The work has continued without interruption over the period of 40 years. Its prominent place in respect to research output is best exemplified by the fact that of 500 papers emanating from the Laboratory from 1930 to 1968, 150 dealt with the taxonomy of various insects. Over the years, many staff members have published on the subject and the coverage includes many different insects of medical importance. A cursory examination of publications indicates that papers have appeared on the taxonomy of mosquitoes, ticks, horse flies, black flies, mites, sandflies, fleas and lice.

Many of the taxonomic determinations have been of inestimable assist-

Fig. 16. Dr. Graham B. Fairchild, Associate Director of the Gorgas Memorial Laboratory, examining part of the extensive insect collection of the Laboratory.

ance in other research projects, especially in malaria, leishmaniasis, American trypanosomiasis and the ecology of arboviruses.

The following is a list of staff members who have contributed most to insect taxonomy, together with their respective fields of interest:

W. H. W. Komp—Mosquitoes (Culicidae).

P. Galindo—Mosquitoes (Culicidae).

G. B. Fairchild—Horse flies (Tabanidae), sandflies (Phlebotominae), ticks (Ixodoidea) and black flies (Simuliidae).

M. Hertig—Sandflies (Phlebotominae).

C. D. Michener—Mites (Trombiculidae).

E. Méndez—Fleas (Siphonaptera) and biting lice (Mallophaga).

P. T. Johnson—Fleas (Siphonaptera) and sucking lice (Anoplura).

Miscellaneous Research Activities

Herpetology: Shortly after the establishment of the Gorgas Memorial Laboratory, the Director, Dr. Herbert C. Clark, undertook a snake census of the Republic of Panama. Initial surveys were inaugurated in 1929 in cooperation with the Antivenin Institute of America. In 1932, the Museum of Comparative Zoology of Harvard University, under Dr. Thomas Barbour, became actively interested in the studies and supported them in part. The work was continued almost up to the time of the retirement of Dr. Clark in 1954. Between January 1929 and September 1953, a total of 13,745 snakes had been collected, of which 3,275, or 23.82 percent, were poisonous varieties, comprising 16 species.

Climatology: In 1941, cooperative laboratory experiments were conducted by Dr. C. A. Mills and Dr. Carl M. Johnson on the effect of temperature on certain animals. Experimental animals were maintained at a constant temperature of 68° F., with controls at usual prevailing outside temperatures. Results were based on a comparison of antibody production, growth rates, reproduction and hemoglobin levels. It was found that the "cold room" animals consumed more food, grew better, were more active, and had a higher birth rate with more rapid maturity of the young than did the control animals. Hemoglobin values were considerably higher in the experimental group than in the control group.

While at the Gorgas Memorial Laboratory, Dr. Mills studied the effects of tropical climate on growth and development in children in the Panama Canal Zone. Growth and sexual development appeared to have progressed more rapidly in those children who had only recently left temperate climates to enter the Canal Zone. With prolongation of residence in the tropics, more and more of the advantages of the former temperate zone residence were lost.

In another study, Dr. Mills and Robert W. Chapin, D.D.S. determined that the occurrence of dental caries in children in the Canal Zone was exceptionally high as compared with most areas in the United States. The rate was significantly higher in children born in the Canal Zone, as compared to those who had migrated from the United States. It was suggested that the high rates might be associated with low fluorine content of Gatun Lake water which supplied the Canal Zone.

Interoceanic Canal Studies: In cooperation with the U. S. Army, the Gorgas Memorial Laboratory took part in medico-ecological reconnaissance and disease surveillance programs along the proposed Route 17 (Sasardi-Morti) in Panama and Route 25 (Atrato-Truando) in Colombia. The operations on Route 17 started in November 1966 and those on Route 25 in April 1967. The Gorgas Memorial Laboratory acted as the base laboratory for the identification of all animals, insect vectors and other material bearing on disease occurrence and transmission, served as a consultant on the general organization of the programs and aided in the evaluation of results. The disease surveillance activity included examination of all persons going into the area to work, reexamination at intervals and observation on any illnesses which occurred.

A great bulk of material was collected and processed and observations on workers along the routes disclosed the occurrence of infections which developed as a result of exposure in the area. It was apparent from the results of the surveys that among the important disease hazards along the contemplated routes were malaria, arbovirus infections, Chagas' disease and leishmaniasis.

Geographic Pathology: This activity represents a continuing service as a reference and consulting center for the medical and allied professions in the Republic of Panama and Central America. Pathological diagnoses are made for local hospitals and physicians and service is available to other medical agencies.

Epidemiological Surveillance: Outpatient medical care is provided for all of the field areas in which the Laboratory is conducting special studies. Staff teams enter various communities at intervals in connection with research projects on various diseases and hold clinics for the benefit of the local population. A clinic is also maintained at the Laboratory to provide service for patients referred by government and private physicians for consultation and for patients from the field areas who wish to present themselves at the Laboratory. Through a cooperative arrangement, patients requiring hospitalization are referred to Santo Tomás Hospital or the Hospital del Niño.

Department of Vertebrate Zoology: This activity was established in 1959 and has been directed by Mr. Eustorgio Méndez. It has functioned effectively as an ancillary operation to many other research endeavors and has conducted studies in its own right. The importance of vertebrate hosts and potential vertebrate reservoirs of various disease agents in Panama emphasizes the value of the activity. A comprehensive reference collection of birds, mammals, reptiles and amphibians has been established and has been augmented year by year. The collection is not only of value to staff members but is utilized by visiting scientists and serves for teaching purposes for students from Panama and the Canal Zone.

Department of Serology: This department was established in 1963 with two main objectives, viz: Serological surveys of humans and wild vertebrates to determine arbovirus activities among vertebrate hosts and to conduct mass complement fixation and hemagglutination tests for Chagas' disease, in order to acquire baseline information on the distribution of the disease in Panama. The department is also concerned with the immunological identification of arboviruses and carries out tissue culture and virological studies. The department represents a valuable adjunct to the research projects on arboviruses, Chagas' disease and other protozoal infections.

Research by Visiting Scientists: Ever since its establishment, the Gorgas Memorial Laboratory has been a mecca for visiting scientists not only from the United States but from many foreign countries. Some of these visitors have remained for only a short time but others have spent weeks or months working in the Laboratory on specific projects, some of which have been closely allied to the research program of the Laboratory and others of which have been of a more alien character. Much of the research conducted by these visitors has been summarized in the various chapters of this history and certain of it has been mentioned in this chapter. The bibliography of publications emanating from the Laboratory, as presented in the Appendices, contains references to the papers which have resulted from visitor research.

The Future of the Gorgas Memorial Laboratory

It would be remiss to conclude this record of achievement without commenting on the future of the Gorgas Memorial Laboratory. After 40 years of productive research, the Laboratory can undoubtedly look forward not only to maintaining its past record but to increasing its contributions to the advancing field of tropical medicine. Its unique position as a private institution located at the crossroads of the Americas with an autonomous shelter from political manipulation would seem to offer assurance of additional research opportunities and achievements. Its past record can be regarded as remarkable when it is considered that many of its major accomplishments were realized with a small professional staff and meager financial resources.

At the end of the Laboratory's 40th year, new projects and new avenues were being explored. Proposals for a new building to house a regional medical library have had an initial encouraging response and would seem to be possible of fruition within the next few years. This library would augment facilities currently available to medical students and physicians in Panama and its services would be extended to the medical profession and to biomedical scientists of Middle America. Thus the new facility would not only be of benefit to the professional staff of the Laboratory but would promote harmonius relations and enhance opportunities for liaison with local and regional colleagues.

The establishment of a primate colony is contemplated and initial inquiry into the feasibility of the project has aroused the interest of a number of agencies which are hopeful of cooperating in such a venture. Such a colony would offer distinct advantages for the research program of the Laboratory. Panamanian monkeys have been utilized in many research studies in the past. More precise interpretation of research results would be possible if the experimental animal could be raised under controlled conditions. In this way, it would be protected from the hazards of jungle life and its medical and immunological history would be known.

The Gorgas Memorial Laboratory promises to become of increasing importance as a training center. The Directors of the Gorgas Memorial Institute at their annual meeting on October 29, 1968 voted to establish a post-graduate fellowship program at the Laboratory in honor of former Senator Lister Hill who for many years was a strong supporter of the Institute and the Laboratory. This formal program will further opportunities which have been available in the past and will help to emphasize the advantages which the Laboratory has to offer in this field.

The Gorgas Memorial Laboratory has excelled in certain types of research, notably in problems involving the epidemiology of certain diseases endemic in Panama. In this area, numerous surveys have delineated the scope of the various problems, the modes of disease transmission, the insect vectors and their taxonomic status, ecology and behavioral characteristics and the reservoir hosts in lower animals. After 40 years it might be thought that further opportunities for epidemiological research would be distinctly limited. However, such is not the case. There are still many unsolved problems. Furthermore, from a geographical standpoint, much of Panama remains to be surveyed for the purpose of delineating disease problems. The Darien Gap area, for instance, constitutes one of the last remaining primitive regions in Middle America. It includes vast tracts of tropical

Fig. 17. *Some of the buildings of the Gorgas Memorial Laboratory. In the foreground a corner of the Administration Building; in the background the new Research Building; and in the center the one-story Animal House.*

rain forest which are virtually inaccessible by ordinary means of transportation, and its inhabitants have had little contact with the outside world. Conditions in the area offer an unusual opportunity for a study of its medical ecology before the region is permanently opened to the outside world by the proposed extension of the Pan American Highway. The introduction of new diseases will undoubtedly follow and living conditions of the inhabitants will probably eventually undergo marked changes.

As the Gorgas Memorial Laboratory opens its 41st year of endeavor, the above are a few of the prospective new programs which it is hoped to embrace. With an expanded physical plant, more modern equipment, increased personnel and augmented financial support the Laboratory is in a position to contribute even more abundantly than in the past to the solution of world health problems and especially those of Middle and South America. The Laboratory will continue to serve as an important sentinel post for the surveillance of yellow fever and other exotic diseases which are an ever present threat to much of the Western Hemisphere and even to the United States of America itself.

Acknowledgments

Appreciation is accorded Rear Admiral Calvin B. Galloway, MC, USN (Ret.), President of the Gorgas Memorial Institute of Tropical and Preventive Medicine, Inc., and Dr. Martin D. Young, Director of the Gorgas Memorial Laboratory, for encouragement and assistance. Several members of the Executive Committee of the Institute read certain chapters of the history and offered valuable suggestions. Miss Gloriela Calvo of the Washington Office has been most helpful in securing data from the files and in assisting in the preparation of the manuscript.

Dr. Carl M. Johnson and Dr. Graham B. Fairchild, staff members, and Dr. Marshall Hertig, retired staff member, of the Gorgas Memorial Laboratory, have kindly supplied information concerning the early days of the Laboratory and have read and made suitable alterations in the manuscript. On a number of occasions other staff members have contributed specific data.

The writer acknowledges his indebtedness to Miss Eleanor K. Grimm, Sarasota, Florida, former secretary to Dr. Franklin H. Martin, for her many courtesies in furnishing data concerning Dr. Martin's activities in connection with the Institute. Miss Helen A. King and Miss Gladys R. Newman, who were for so long connected with the Institute, graciously provided data which otherwise might not have been available. Mrs. Aileen Gorgas Wrightson, daughter of General Gorgas, has also been most helpful in this regard. Miss Laura Louise Kuhl, Editor of the Bulletin of the American College of Surgeons, kindly supplied information concerning the career of Dr. Bowman C. Crowell, former President of the Gorgas Memorial Institute. Mr. Mayer Mathis of the American Red Cross was helpful in furnishing biographical material of Rear Admiral Cary T. Grayson, USN (Ret.).

In Panama, Dr. Ricardo J. Alfaro, long a member of the Board of Directors of the Institute, ex-President of Panama, distinguished jurist and former member of the International Court of Justice, The Hague, kindly granted an interview concerning the early days of the Gorgas Memorial Laboratory. Similarly, Sr. Camilo Antonio Porras, eldest son of ex-President Porras, the founder of the Gorgas Memorial Institute, supplied recollections of his father's career. Also Sr. Roberto Chiari, ex-President of Panama, and aide-de-camp to his father, ex-President Rodolfo Chiari, kindly granted an interview regarding President Chiari's efforts in providing the building for the Gorgas Memorial Laboratory. Sr. Luis Carlos Noli arranged for access of the writer to the files of the Panama newspapers, Estrella de Panamá and the Star and Herald. Thanks are due Sra. Carmen D. de Herrera, Librarian of the University of Panama, for permitting access to the papers of Dr. Porras and for a copy of his biography.

The writer is indebted to Dr. Edgar A. Bocock, first superintendent of Santo Tomás Hospital, for recollections of his close association with Dr. Porras. Mrs. Dorothy Hanks of the Historical Section, National Library of Medicine, kindly furnished biographical material.

The Honorable Maurice H. Thatcher reviewed for the writer his association with President Porras during the time he was Governor of the Canal Zone and Dr. Porras was a young member of the Foreign Office of Panama. Governor Thatcher also provided a detailed account of the legislation which led to the first appropriation for the Gorgas Memorial Institute and the establishment of the Gorgas Memorial Laboratory.

Dr. Edward I. Salisbury, retired Medical Director of the United Fruit Company, kindly supplied historical data concerning the early days of the Gorgas Memorial Institute.

Dr. Colvin L. Gibson, Editor of Tropical Medicine and Hygiene News, went to a great deal of trouble to search back issues of that publication for information concerning the award of the Richard Pearson Strong Medal to Dr. Herbert C. Clark.

Dr. James M. Brennan, Rocky Mountain Laboratory, National Institute of Allergy and Infectious Diseases, and Dr. E. W. Baker, Agricultural Research Service, U. S. Department of Agriculture, were helpful in updating the synonymy of certain of the Trombiculidae of Panama. Dr. Alan Stone also of the U. S. Department of Agriculture kindly supplied similar advice concerning mosquito synonymy.

Dr. Fred L. Soper kindly reviewed and made corrections in the Spanish-English and English-Spanish translations of documents.

Special thanks are due Honorable J. Rufus Bealle, Attorney, Land Commissioner and Secretary of the Board of Trustees of the University of Alabama, for detailed information and copies of all documents relating to the disposition of the funds raised in Alabama in the 1922 campaign for providing a memorial to General Gorgas. My appreciation is accorded Mrs. Aileen Gorgas Wrightson for putting me in touch with Mr. Bealle.

Credit is due Lic. Manuel Víctor De Las Casas, Librarian of the Gorgas Memorial Laboratory, for his preparation of the bibliography of papers emanating from that Laboratory through December 31, 1969.

—The Author

APPENDICES

Appendix 1

A Brief Biographical Sketch of Dr. Belisario Porras, Three Times President of Panama, and Founder of the Gorgas Memorial Institute of Tropical and Preventive Medicine

Dr. Belisario Porras was one of the most eminent and progressive of the constitutional presidents of the Republic of Panama. Considered by many to be the greatest Panamanian of his time, his fame transcended the frontiers of the small nation to earn him a place as one of the outstanding leaders of the American Republics, distinguished not only in politics but in the fields of jurisprudence and diplomacy.

Dr. Porras had long been a friend of General William Crawford Gorgas and following the death of General Gorgas in 1920, Dr. Porras was the first to suggest the establishment of an institute of tropical medicine in his memory. He was one of the incorporators of the Gorgas Memorial Institute of Tropical and Preventive Medicine and supplied funds for the initial operating expenses of that organization.

Belisario Porras was born at Las Tablas, Province of Los Santos, on November 28, 1856. His primary schooling was obtained at Las Tablas under the direction of several tutors. His secondary education followed in the College of San Bartolomé in Bogotá, after which he entered the National University of Colombia, which conferred upon him the degree of Doctor of Laws in 1881.

Not long after his graduation from the University, he plunged into a career of public service. In 1876, he became the provisional secretary of the Civil Tribunal of Panama. In 1883, he served as a deputy in the National Assembly from Los Santos and in 1884 as attorney for the Panama Canal Company. He became a local magistrate in 1886 and the following year a professor in the College of La Esperanza. The year 1889 found him serving as an official in the Colombian Legation in Rome. During the next decade he became increasingly involved in local politics. His partisan activities in behalf of the Liberal cause met with growing disfavor on the part of the Conservative regime in power at that time so that he was forced into exile. He found refuge first in El Salvador where he served as Professor of Law in the National University and later in Nicaragua where he also became a university professor. Later he served as Professor of Psychology in the Colegio de Sión of Guatemala. However, he found Nicaragua most to his liking and nearest in accord with his political tenets.

While in exile Dr. Porras maintained his image before the people of the Isthmus and his popularity even increased during his absence from his native land. Thus it was inevitable that he should be destined to lead the revolution of 1899-1902, better known as the "War of a 1,000 days."

In March of 1900 he reappeared on the Isthmus at the head of a revolutionary expeditionary force which he had organized in Central America. Landing on the coast of Chiriquí, he launched a movement which brought him a succession of victories to the very gates of Panama City. In the battle for the city, his forces met with total defeat which resulted in a temporary halt in the revolutionary movement. He was forced to flee again to exile in Central America.

After the establishment of the Republic in 1904, Dr. Porras returned to his home land and was elected to the Municipal Council of Panama. In 1907, he was a delegate to the Hague Peace Conference. After serving as Minister to Brazil in 1908, the following year he was transferred to Costa Rica as Minister to that country.

In 1911, he became Minister to the United States and in 1912 was elected to his first term as President of the Republic. He devoted a considerable part of his energies to developing public works, especially projects in the interior of the country. Near the end of his term in 1915, he organized an international exposition in Panama City to commemorate the opening of the Panama Canal to world traffic.

At the end of his first term in the Presidency, Dr. Porras was succeeded by Dr. Ramón M. Valdés, who unfortunately died in office a little over a year and a half after his inauguration. Porras entered the list of candidates and was elected First Designate to serve the remaining years of the Valdés term. He was re-elected and on October 1, 1920 was inaugurated as the Fifth Constitutional President of Panama.

The third administration of President Porras was one of great activity. One of his prime objectives was the development of a highway system, a project which he had actually instituted during his previous short term of office. With unusual business acumen, he engaged the services of an American economist, Addison T. Ruan, to whom he entrusted the task of reorganizing the Nation's finances. As a result, when his third term began more than $2,000,000 was available for the road building program. In addition to this program, he was responsible for the erection of many public buildings, the establishment of a number of additional educational facilities, and the institution of many public works throughout the interior of Panama.

After leaving the Presidency in 1924, Dr. Porras was appointed Envoy Extraordinary and Minister Plenipotentiary to Great Britain and France. From 1931 to 1932, he was Ambassador to Italy, and from 1932 to 1935, again Ambassador to Great Britain and France. In 1933, he represented Panama in the Council and Assembly of the League of Nations; in 1935 he was a Delegate to the Fourteenth Assembly of that Organization, and in 1938, a Delegate to the Fifteenth Assembly. His last diplomatic post was that of Ambassador to attend the inauguration of the President of Costa Rica in 1940.

Dr. Porras was a member of many learned societies in Latin America and throughout the world. He received many decorations including the Grand Cross of Isabel La Católica of Spain, the Grand Cross of the Legion of Honor of France, the Grand Cross of Saint Maurice and Lazarus of Italy, the Grand Cordon of the Order of Leopold of Belgium, the Grand Cross of Serbia, the Grand Cross of Roumania, the Grand Cross of the Order of Santiago da Espada of Portugal, and finally the Grand Cross of the Order of Vasco Núñez de Balboa of his native Panama. In addition to these awards, he was the recipient of a number of honorary degrees as well as diplomas from many organizations.

Dr. Porras was the author of a number of works on political science and jurisprudence. He was an avid reader with catholic interests. His extensive collection of books and his private papers rest in the library of the University of Panama.

Dr. Porras died in Panama City on August 28, 1942, in his 85th year. On that day, the newspapers of the capital city rightly referred to him as "The Grand Old Man of Panama."

Appendix 2,a

Discurso del Excelentísimo Señor Dr. Belisario Porras, Presidente de la República de Panamá, en Ocasión de la Colocación de la Primera Piedra del Instituto Conmemorativo Gorgas de Medicina Tropical y Preventiva en Panamá, República de Panamá, 18 de Febrero de 1923

Experimento una profunda satisfacción al ver que me corresponde el alto privilegio de colocar la piedra fundamental del Instituto de Medicina Tropical que Panamá dedica a William Crawford Gorgas, para perpetuar su memoria aquí en las orillas del turbulento Pacífico y en íntima proximidad a esa vía pública que—precipitadamente en épocas pasadas como perseguida por el fantasma de la muerte, y lentamente hoy día como si lamentara la brevedad del tiempo que los obliga a renunciar a los encantos de nuestro clima benigno y uniforme, a la inalterable belleza de nuestros verdes campos y al incomparable azul de nuestro cielo—ha sido utilizada por los hombres de todas las nacionalidades para quienes Gorgas sólo abrigó sentimientos de profunda humanidad que prevalecieron siempre por sobre todo prejuicio de raza, nacionalidad, cuna o alcurnia.

Este sentimiento de satisfacción que experimento ahora se deriva primordialmente del hecho de que fui un amigo de este noble hombre cuya memoria veneramos en esta ocasión, y que como tal estuve en una posición admirable para juzgar de lleno la fuerza de su noble y buen corazón; y, además, siendo uno de los hombres de aquellos días que vivió en nuestro medio ambiente, estoy en mejor capacidad de apreciar de lleno la grandiosa obra de sanidad, vida y felicidad que este noble hombre llevó a cabo en mi país.

El monumento que erigiremos aquí, será una expresión de la gratitud de Panamá hacia el hombre que demostró, más allá de los límites de la duda, que los trópicos podían convertirse en sitios habitables para todas las razas de la tierra. Nosotros tenemos una deuda de gratitud para con el genio de Gorgas por haber transformado a Panamá de una región asolada por las fiebres, en el paraíso en que vivimos hoy día. Por lo tanto, consideramos que Gorgas hasta cierto punto nos pertenece también, puesto que fue en esta tierra donde vió coronado por el éxito su gran esfuerzo de aliviar a una humanidad doliente.

Es privilegio de los grandes hombres, sabios, descubridores, héroes y mártires cuyas actividades, enseñanza y ejemplos no están circunscritos a los estrechos confines del país de su nacimiento, y cuyas hazañas en el mundo han sido benéficas para la mayoría, si no para toda la humanidad, que se les ame universalmente. Tales hombres, y Gorgas fue uno de ellos, no pueden ser ciudadanos de una ciudad, población o villa en particular, puesto que todas las ciudades y todas las naciones los reclaman; ellos son los verdaderos ciudadanos del mundo.

En el caso de Esculapio, cuando consideró necesario apelar a los servicios de un oráculo para determinar cuál de las ciudades de la antigua Grecia que se disputaba el honor había sido cuna de su nacimiento, y en el caso de Cristóbal Colón que había sido declarado italiano, español y más recientemente judío, el lugar del nacimiento de Gorgas, según se me ha informado, se lo disputan los Estados de Alabama y Georgia. Sin embargo, Gorgas no pertenece exclusivamente a los Estados Unidos de Norte América donde recibió su educación. Cuba y Serbia, Bulgaria y el Ecuador, Panamá y el Africa del Sur, todos lo reclaman como resultado de haber vivido y trabajado entre ellos para beneficio de la familia humana.

La obra llevada a cabo en el mundo por el eminente Gorgas, es inmensa, inconmensurable. De Hipócrates puede decirse que fue el primero en divorciar la medicina de la superchería y del misticismo eclesiástico de sus tiempos; de Galeno, que fue un gran médico y escritor al cual se le atribuyó la publicación de unas 500 obras que tendían a popularizar la práctica de la medicina; del sabio Pasteur, de Kock, Ramón Cajal y Cajal, Ehrlich, Finlay y Rose, que penetraron hondamente dentro de los cultos secretos de lo invisible; el mundo infinitesimal de Metchnikoff que desarrolló la famosa teoría del fagocito y que en compañía con Roux, Chamberland y Calmette coadyuvó y continuó la obra del gran Pasteur; pero ¿ cómo podríamos describir a Gorgas, que solucion el parente imposible problema de hacer habitables los trópicos y que vino a complementar la maravillosa obra de Dios que nos creó para que viviéramos en la tierra y fuéramos felices en ella? Gorgas destruyó las moradas de la muerte, nos proporcionó agua para beber, purificó el aire de nuestros exhuberantes bosques tropicales y de nuestras ciudades coloniales. En una palabra Gorgas redimió los Trópicos.

Todavía recuerdo, y aún me parece como horrible pesadilla, cuando hace 50 años en que me dirigía a Bogotá a terminar allí mis estudios tuve que pasar una noche en Colón. Me fue imposible conciliar el sueño debido a las continuas y atormentadoras picaduras de los mosquitos, cuyo incesante zumbido hería mis oídos como las notas discordantes de una serenata infernal. Estos diminutos tormentos eran tan numerosos que sacando la mano los podía agarrar a montones. Tampoco puedo olvidar las condiciones que prevalecían cuando regresé del colegio diez años más tarde y entré a prestar mis servicios en la compañía francesa del Canal. Desde ese momento pude darme cuenta, o a lo menos sospechar, la causa predominante del fracaso de dicha compañía al tratar de contruir esta vía transístmica. Ellos construyeron lindas residencias, hermosas avenidas de árboles, y organizaron muy bien sus oficinas, pero no hicieron nada, en efecto no conocían nada, acerca de la sanidad tropical y probablemente nunca sospecharon lo que valía.

En esos días del pasado era costumbre muy natural pasearse en los alrededores de la ciudad llevando un pañuelo en la nariz para evitar el olor que resultaba de la vegetación podrida, de los pozos de agua estancada y putrefacta, y de las alcantarillas primitivas o defectuosas. A cada momento se encontraba uno con amigos que iban apresurados a la casa, víctimas de los escalofríos del paludismo o de cualquiera otra fiebre perniciosa; en cada calle se encontraban personas vestidas de luto, con las señales de tristeza y de desesperación hondamente impresas en sus facciones; y diariamente se oía el lúgubre tañir de las campanas de la iglesia que anunciaban la muerte de un amigo o de un pariente; o con frecuencia se le llamaba para asistir a los servicios religiosos por el descanso del alma de un amigo que había desaparecido víctima de los miasmas mortíferos de nuestra insalubre tierra tropical.

Sin embargo, gracias a William Crawford Gorgas aquellos días han desaparecido para no volver y nuestra tierra tropical se ha convertido en uno de los lugares más saludables del mundo.

En los días de la antigua Grecia se erigían templos y monumentos en las montañas y en los arroyos de la salud, en honor de Esculapio, el dios de la Medicina. A estos sitios de veneración y acción de gracias acudían infinidad de personas enfermas y afligidas a ofrecer sacrificios y a depositar ofrendas en sus altares. Y es un templo como estos el que levantaremos aquí a manera de un testimonio imperecedero a la memoria del hombre que trajo tantos beneficios a los habitantes del Istmo y al mundo tropical en general.

Sobre esta primera piedra se elevará un grandioso templo dedicado a este hombre, a él acudirá una incesante cadena de peregrinos, compuesta no sólo de nuestros compatriotas enfermos, sino también de todos los miles de afligidos que vendrán de todos los países tropicales a buscar salud con absoluta fé en el nombre de Gorgas. Y luego regresarán a sus hogares sanos y felices con lágrimas de gratitud en sus mejillas y bendiciendo a nuestro querido país y a la noble y humanitaria obra de William Crawford Gorgas, benefactor de la humanidad y redentor del mundo tropical.

Appendix 2,a

Address of His Excellency Dr. Belisario Porras, President of the Republic of Panama, on the Occasion of the Laying of the Cornerstone of the Gorgas Memorial Institute of Tropical and Preventive Medicine in Panama, Republic of Panama, February 18, 1923

I take deep satisfaction in the fact that I am privileged to lay the cornerstone of the Institute of Tropical Medicine that Panama dedicates to William Crawford Gorgas, to perpetuate his memory here, on the shores of the murmuring Pacific and in close proximity to that thoroughfare which—precipitately in the past as if pursued by the phantom of death and lingeringly today as though regretting the brevity of the time in which to enjoy the delights of our benign and equable climate, the beauty of our country's unchanging verdure and the incomparable blue of our sky—has been used by men of every nationality for whom Gorgas cherished only sentiments of compassion that prevailed always over any prejudice of race, nationality, birth, or class.

The satisfaction I feel today comes from the fact that I was a friend of this man to whose memory we are today assembled here to pay tribute, and as such, I was in an admirable position to judge fully the strength of his great and noble heart; and, further, being a man in the days when he lived in our midst, I am better able to appreciate to the full the great work of health, life, and happiness which this great man accomplished for my country.

The monument which we will erect here will be an expression of Panama's gratitude to the man who proved beyond the peradventure of a doubt that the Tropics could be made habitable for all the races of the earth. We are indebted to the genius of Gorgas for the transformation of Panama from a fever-ridden land to the Paradise we now enjoy. Therefore, we consider that Gorgas, to a certain extent, belongs to us also, because it was here he saw his great effort to lighten the burden of suffering humanity crowned with success.

It is the privilege of great men, sages, discoverers, heroes and martyrs, whose activities, teachings, and examples are not circumscribed within the narrow confines of the land of their birth, and whose achievements in the world have been beneficial to the majority, if not to all their fellow-beings, to be universally loved. Such men—and Gorgas was one of them—cannot be citizens of one particular city, town, or village, for every city and every nation of the earth claims them; they are the real citizens of the world.

As in the case of Aesculapius, for whom it was found necessary to enlist the services of an oracle to determine which of the cities of ancient Greece that disputed the honor to have been his birthplace; in the case of Christopher Columbus, who has been declared an Italian, a Spaniard, and more recently a Jew, the birthplace of Gorgas, I am informed, is disputed, both Alabama and Georgia claiming this honor. However, Gorgas does not belong exclusively to the United States of North America where he was educated. Cuba and Serbia, Bulgaria and Ecuador, Panama and South Africa, all have claims to him as a result of his having lived and worked in them for the good of the human family.

The work accomplished in the world by the eminent Gorgas is immense, immeasurable. Of Hippocrates it may be said that he was the first to divorce medicine from the witchcraft and the ecclesiastical mysticism of his times; of Galen, that he was a great physician and writer to whom is attributed the authorship of some 500 books to popularize the practice of medicine; of the great Pasteur, de Koch, Ramon Cajal y Cajal, Ehrlich, Finlay, and Rose, that they penetrated far into the hidden secrets of the invisible; the infinitesimal world of Metchnikoff who evolved the famous phagocyte theory and with Roux, Chamberland, and Calmette, collaborated in and continued the work of the great Pasteur; but how can we describe Gorgas, who solved the apparently impossible problems of making the Tropics habitable, and who came to us to complement the marvelous work of God who created us to live on the earth and be happy on it? Gorgas destroyed the abodes of death and gave us pure drinking water and purified the air of our exuberant tropical forests and our colonial cities. Gorgas redeemed the Tropics.

I can still remember, and it still seems a horrible nightmare to me, the time, 50 years ago, when, on my way to Bogota to complete my education,

I had to spend a night in Colon. Sleep during that night was impossible for me because of the constant and tormenting bites of the mosquitoes, whose incessant buzzing smote on my ears like the discordant notes of an infernal serenade. These minute tormentors were so numerous that by clutching at the apparently empty air I caught handful after handful of these pests. Neither can I forget the conditions that prevailed when I returned from college 10 years later and entered the employ of the French canal company. From that time I was able to realize, or at least suspect, the underlying cause of the Frenchmen's failure in their attempt to construct the transisthmian waterway. They constructed beautiful residences and tree-lined avenues and admirably organized their workshops and offices; but they did nothing, in fact they knew nothing, about tropical sanitation, and apparently never suspected its worth.

In those days of long ago, it was the most natural thing for one to visit the environs of the city holding a handkerchief to one's nostrils, to keep out or lessen the stench contaminating the air as a result of decaying vegetation, of stagnant and putrid puddles, and of primitive or defective sewerage. Continually one encountered friends hastening home in the grip of malarial chills or some other pernicious fever; one encountered on every street, people clothed in the somber black garb of mourning with the marks of grief and despair deeply impressed on their features; or daily heard the lugubrious tolling of church bells announcing the death of a friend or a relative; or was frequently summoned to attend the last rites for a departed friend laid low by the deadly miasmas of our unsanitary tropical land.

However, thanks to William Crawford Gorgas, those days have passed never to return, and our tropical home has become one of the world's health resorts.

In the days of ancient Greece, shrines and temples were erected in the mountains and at the springs of health in honor of Aesculapius, the god of medicine. To these places of worship and thanksgiving an endless stream of sick and afflicted persons came to offer sacrifices and deposit votive tablets on his altars. And it is a temple such as these that we will erect here as a living testimonial to the memory of the man who brought so much comfort to the Isthmian family and the tropical world in general.

On this first stone, there will arise a great temple dedicated to this great man, and to this shrine of Gorgas will come in a never-ceasing pilgrimage, not only our sick compatriots, but also the afflicted thousands from other points of the Tropics to seek health with undying faith in the name of Gorgas. And shortly they will depart hence for their homes healed and happy, with tears of gratitude in their eyes and blessing our beloved country and the great and humane work of William Crawford Gorgas, the benefactor of humanity and the redeemer of the tropical world.

Address by Dr. Franklin H. Martin, Acting President of the Gorgas Memorial Institute of Tropical and Preventive Medicine, on the Occasion of the Laying of the Cornerstone of the Institute in Panama, Republic of Panama, February 18, 1923

It is fitting that we, surgeons from Canada and from the United States, many of whom served in the uniform of our chief, traveling to pay our respects to the Central and South American countries, should assemble with our families and yours in this garden Paradise to honor the memory of William Crawford Gorgas, whose genius brought to it its worth, its beauty, and its charm.

Gorgas, simple in character, a lover of men, with a vision of the fundamentals of the intricate discoveries of science, by the simple application of a formula conceived by him, wrought a miracle that for all time will enrich the world, as Lister revolutionized surgical progress from the discoveries of Pasteur, and as the lowly Nazarene brought forth from the wisdom of the prophets His pronouncement that Christianized the world.

We, assembled here, are the apostles of Gorgas, brought together by our mutual admiration for him, to build on this place a monument that will be to us and to all people a symbol of his greatness, and that will enable his devoted followers to continue his work as he himself would have desired. It can not add one iota to the monument that he created in his modest way, by his honest character, his gentle persistency, his unostentatious industry, and his enduring patience.

For, in 1 century, in 10 centuries, or in 20 centuries, it will be known that it was in this little country between two seas, that he went about and did his work, and citizens of great commonwealths of the future, on the Orinoco, on the Amazon, on the Ganges, and in all the Tropics of the earth will tell how Gorgas was their savior; how he brought to them a physical blessing that transformed their regions from the lands of death to the living communities of civilization; and it will be remembered then, in those far off days, that we, his contemporaries, loved him and sought to honor him.

President Porras, you know, and I know, how our friend loved this, his beloved Isthmian country, and how, in the evening of his life, when upon him rested the enormous responsibility of presiding over a great corps of the greatest war, in his moments of contemplation, his vision was turned toward Panama, the place which was selected by him to be his final earthly home when retirement should come. And we, here gathered to pay tribute to him, the great benefactor, may be assured, if the screen is not too impenetrable, that around us, in approbation, is his genial presence in spirit, and over us is shed his love and his benediction.

Discurso de Su Excelencia Luis Felipe Clement, Secretario de Agricultura y Obras Públicas, en la Inauguración del Edificio del Laboratorio Conmemorativo Gorgas, Panamá, República de Panamá, 2 de Abril de 1929

Excelentísimo Señor Presidente;
Señor Doctor Martin;
Señores:

Nos hallamos congregados hoy en este recinto para declarar formalmente inauguradas las actividades científicas de este Laboratorio que lleva el nombre del eminente Gorgas.

A la tesonera y fecunda labor del Doctor Martin, se debe en gran parte el feliz resultado de esta gran obra que enaltece, de una manera digna, la memoria del distinguido médico que saneó el Istmo, haciéndose así acreedor al título de Benefactor de la humanidad.

Otro buen amigo de Panamá, que sirvió en la Comisión del Canal Istmico como Jefe de la administración civil, el Honorable Maurice H. Thatcher, miembro hoy de la Cámara de Representantes de los Estados Unidos de América, hizo cristalizar en Ley la noble y generosa idea, votándose por el Congreso de aquel país una partida de cincuenta mil dólares ($50,000) anuales, para atender al funcionamiento de este Laboratorio.

Ha querido el Gobierno de Panamá, hábilmente presidido por el Excelentísimo Señor Don Florencio Harmodio Arosemena, aprovechar la oportunidad en que comienzan estas labores como también la feliz circunstancia de encontrarse entre nosotros el Doctor Martin, médico de fama y de prestigio que preside el Comité Ejecutivo de esta noble Institución, poniendo así de relieve la inmediata colaboración de Panamá, para cuyo efecto hace donación formal y efectiva de este edificio que, aunque modesto en su forma, está más de acuerdo con nuestras posibilidades para que funcione de manera permanente este Laboratorio destinado a servir a la gran causa de la humanidad, previniendo y curando las enfermedades tropicales.

Al efectuar esta donación, el Gobierno de Panamá confía haber asegurado la permanencia del Instituto y espera que el acto solemne que aquí nos congrega sea el punto de partida de la realización de la obra que inspirara la mente de los iniciadores del homenaje que hoy se tributa al recuerdo de William Crawford Gorgas.

Nada más justo, señores, que sea esta ciudad donde se levante en honor de Gorgas este Laboratorio de investigaciones científicas. Fue precisamente Panamá el campo donde desarrolló sus mayores actividades y en donde conquistó mayor renombre por haber culminado con éxito ruidoso su feliz labor.

Este tributo de admiración y de reconocimiento que ofrendamos hoy a la memoria del gran Gorgas, consagrando el edificio que contiene el Laboratorio de investigaciones científicas de las enfermedades del trópico, honra a Panamá, y por extensión a todos los países del Continente.

Nuestra gratidud para con el eminente Benefactor es tan grande, tan sincera y tan pura, como lo son también nuestros anhelos porque su nombre se perpetúe a través de la eternidad en esa obra, como justo merecimiento a la grandeza de su alma!

Esta Institución desde hoy queda abierta a la laboriosidad de los hombres de ciencia para facilidad de sus investigaciones, especialmente a los médicos de todas las razas y de todos los pueblos de la tierra que quieran cooperar a esta causa de la humanidad, con sus conocimientos y sus sabios consejos. Abrigamos la confianza de que ella será pródiga en los resultados de sus experimentos y fecunda en grandes hechos científicos como lo fue la obra del Benemérito Gorgas a quien muy respetuosamente dedicamos este Templo de la Ciencia.

Servíos aceptar, Doctor Martin, a nombre de la Institución que presidís, este edificio como también los terrenos comprendidos dentro de los linderos de este sitio, como la contribución del Gobierno de Panamá, para que en lo sucesivo sea la Sede permanente del Instituto.

Appendix 3,a

Address of the Honorable Luis Felipe Clement, Secretary of Agriculture and Public Works, Republic of Panama, at the Dedication of the Gorgas Memorial Laboratory Building, Panama, Republic of Panama, April 2, 1929

Your Excellency, Mr. President;
Doctor Martin;
Gentlemen:

We are gathered today in this edifice to inaugurate formally the scientific activities of this Laboratory, which bears the name of the eminent Gorgas.

To the persistent and fruitful efforts of Doctor Franklin H. Martin, is due in a great measure this creditable result—the memorial which honors in a dignified manner the distinguished physician who rid the Isthmus of disease, and thereby won for himself the title of Benefactor of Humanity.

Another good friend of Panama, who served in the Isthmian Canal Commission as Chief of Civil Affairs, the Honorable Maurice H. Thatcher, a member today of the House of Representatives of the United States of America, crystallized the noble and generous idea into a law, through which the U. S. Congress appropriates $50,000 annually toward the maintenance of this Laboratory.

The Government of Panama, ably presided over by His Excellency Florencio Harmodio Arosemena, desires to use this occasion when the work of the Laboratory is beginning, as well as the happy circumstance of the presence among us of Doctor Martin, a physician of fame and prestige, who presides over the Executive Committee of the noble Gorgas Institute, to signalize immediately the collaboration of Panama by making formal effective donation of this building, which though modest in form, is thoroughly in accord with our resources, so that this Laboratory may function in perpetuity for the service of mankind in the prevention and cure of tropical diseases.

Through this donation, the Government of Panama wishes to insure the permanency of the Institute, and hopes that this solemn occasion, for which we are here assembled, may be the starting point of the realization of the work which inspired the initiators of the homage today rendered to the memory of William Crawford Gorgas.

Nothing is more fitting nor just, gentlemen, than that this Laboratory of scientific research in honor of Gorgas should be located in this city. Panama was the very field where General Gorgas rendered his greatest service to humanity, and where he won his greatest fame by finishing his happy task with full success.

This tribute of admiration and recognition we offer today to the memory of the Great Gorgas, in consecrating the building which is to house the Laboratory of scientific investigation of tropical diseases, honors Panama and indirectly all the nations of the continent.

Our gratitude to the eminent Benefactor is as great, as sincere, and as pure, as are our earnest desires that his name be perpetuated eternally through this institution as a just tribute to the grandeur of his spirit.

This institution, from this day forward, is opened to men of Science, to facilitate their investigations, especially to those physicians of all races and of all peoples of the earth who wish to cooperate in this humanitarian cause with their knowledge and their able counsel. We are confident that this institution will be rich in the results of its research, and fertile in great scientific achievements, as was the labor of the worthy Gorgas, to whom we most respectfully dedicate this Temple of Science.

Do us the honor, Doctor Martin, to accept in the name of the Institute of which you are president, this building and the land upon which it stands, as the contribution of the Government of Panama, so that from this time forward it may serve as the permanent site of the Gorgas Institute.

Reply by Dr. Franklin H. Martin, Chairman, Board of Directors, Gorgas Memorial Institute of Tropical and Preventive Medicine, to the Presentation Address of the Honorable Luis Felipe Clement, Secretary of Agriculture and Public Works, Republic of Panama, on the Occasion of the Dedication of the Gorgas Memorial Laboratory Building, Panama, Republic of Panama, April 2, 1929

Your Excellency, Florencio Harmodio Arosemena;
Mr. Secretary:

In behalf of the Gorgas Memorial Institute of Tropical and Preventive Medicine, and its Board of Directors and Executive Committee over which I have the honor to preside as Chairman, may I acknowledge my sense of deep responsibility to you for the sympathetic and generous manner in which the Government of Panama has co-operated in establishing this Laboratory, and providing for its permanency.

We have dealt with three administrations of your Government. The same enthusiastic support and co-operation have been accorded to us by Doctor Porras and Doctor Chiari; and now we are met with the generous spirit of practical co-operation of your present distinguished Doctor Arosemena.

Mr. Secretary, the wishes of your present Government have been expressed through your tender of gift of the building in which we are now meeting and the site upon which it stands, as a permanent legal transfer to the Gorgas Memorial Institute, by the following words:

"The Government of Panama, ably presided over by His Excellency, Mr. Florencio Harmodio Arosemena, desires to take cognizance of the occasion of beginning work in the Laboratory. . . . To emphasize immediately the collaboration of Panama, our Government wishes to make formal and actual donation of this building, which, though modest in form, is thoroughly in accord with our possibilities, in order that this Laboratory may function in perpetuity for the service of mankind in the prevention and cure of tropical diseases. Through this donation the Government of Panama wishes to insure the permanency of the Institute. . ."

Mr. President, Mr. Secretary, I am sure that my distinguished Board of Directors would wish me, as its Chairman, to accept this generous offer in the spirit in which it is given, and to express to you and to your people our enthusiasm in receiving the gift as one more expression of your interest in the work of the Gorgas Memorial Laboratory, and your friendship for our people. Therefore, I formally accept the proffer of gift, with the hope that the legal formalities may be culminated during this, my present visit to your city.

Dedication of the Gorgas Memorial Laboratory

Mr. President, Mr. Secretary, Señores and Señoras, we have met today again to honor ourselves by paying tribute to William Crawford Gorgas, and dedicate to his memory the Laboratory that will, encouraged by his example, still further unravel the mysteries of the tropics—the tropics that he so greatly loved.

We are representatives in this present act of dedication, not only of this little land between the seas, made sacred by his labors, this land that has given us this beautiful building and its site; but we are also representatives of the Republic that gave him birth, and that is contributing toward the financial support of this memorial; and we are representatives as well of the other countries of America that, too, are privileged to call Gorgas their benefactor and to pay tribute to his memory.

Barely twenty-five years have lapsed since March of that eventful year, 1904, when Colonel Gorgas, who had it in his heart and in his will to work again the miracle by which he had redeemed Cuba from the greatest plague spot of the tropics, was ordered to accompany the Panama Commission of the United States to the Isthmus as its sanitary advisor, particularly for the purpose of drawing up a scheme of sanitation whereby "the laboring forces" would be protected during the construction of the Panama Canal.

Men, women and little children will ever marvel at that great feat. In June of the succeeding year, 1905, with his handsome but determined face at last upon the goal, the march of his greatest victory began; and in November of that same year, 1905, the last case of yellow fever in Panama, by his efforts, was banished from the land.

"This," remarked Gorgas, "was the high water mark of sanitary efficiency on the Isthmus, and more sanitation was at this time accomplished than during any other time during the construction of the Canal. One more case of yellow fever occurred in Colon during May, but since," (he added in 1913) "now more than eight years, not a case of yellow fever has originated in Panama."

It was that great victory he was thinking of in 1917, during the World War, when he was Surgeon General of the United States Army and had under his command a corps of more than 200,000 souls. Then this successful warrior on the scourges of the tropics, who had peace in his soul for his fellow men, said to me:

"I wish this horrible war were over." In reply to my question: "What is the first act you would perform if it suddenly ended?" he replied, quickly, with a far away, wistful expression: "Do? I would call New York City by long distance telephone, engage a passage on the first ship sailing to South America, to Guayaquil, Ecuador, where yellow fever is making its last stand, eradicate the pest, and then return to Panama, the garden spot of the world, and there write an elegy on yellow fever."

And so, with the co-operation of the people of these two continents, in the physical separation of which General Gorgas played a premier part, and which act of separation united us, morally and spiritually as never before, we, in our small way strive to continue his work of redeeming the tropics and maintain his much loved Panama as "the garden spot of the world."

Applied Science

This magnificent accomplishment, that marks one more epoch in applied science, was not an accident. Pure science reveals facts. Walter Reed and Carlos Finlay wrought as pure scientists, and discovered the method of transmission of yellow fever. It required the genius of a Gorgas to visualize a formula by which these facts could be applied in the practical eradication of yellow fever. This achievement is another outstanding mountain peak of history, peaks that mark the progress of mankind during the centuries, which include in medical science the work of Jenner, Pasteur, Lister, Koch, and Ross; and on our own continent Reed and Gorgas. The achievements of these benefactors, revealed by a study of their biographies, clarifies the reason for their success. Their accomplishments were not due to accidents, freaks of luck, or supernaturalism. Each, let us observe, was a normal man, a man of thought, vision, initiative, industry, perseverance, untiring energy, with courage to endure criticism and opposition, and with uncompromising belief in his vision.

These attributes all apply to our genius, Gorgas, as revealed through his daily life, his vision, his plans, his organization, his resistance to opposition, his industry, and his final accomplishments. And who that knew this man can say that there were about him any evidences of false prophecy, or supernatural assumption? Those who knew him saw in his daily life the revelation of a simple, loving heart; a mind devoted to his friends, to his family, to his work, and to his God.

No flights of oratory, no analysis of his character, no words of praise by his fellow men can adequately picture the heights and depths, or the beauty of life of this great, gentle man, who was our friend while he lived, and who now has become a friend and inspiration for the ages.

Our Heritage

Though the work of Gorgas belongs to the world, as does the inspiration of the humble Nazarene, Gorgas' life belongs to the Americas: and his workshop belongs to this little Republic between the seas that shall always be hallowed by his name, as is little Palestine by the Sea hallowed by the life and words of the Great Teacher.

How fitting it is, then, for us to build this model laboratory in beautiful Panama, where he went about and did his work. It will be an inspiration to those we have chosen to imitate and pursue his work; and their responsibility is paramount, for if this laboratory, situated at the cross-roads of commerce, in the heart of the tropics, is to become the model and inspiration of the tropical world, it must establish a leadership by genuine accomplishments that will compel the approval of science, and that will promote the wholesomeness of the tropics. This responsibility is the responsibility of the host left to administer the home of our benefactor; his house by the roadside which will become the Mecca for the scientists of the world; his house, whose stepping stones will be worn by the feet of myriads of reverent pilgrims who come on through the centuries to pay loving and grateful tribute to this genius who carved empires of wealth and culture from tropical jungles, and whose work made them habitable.

Their responsibility it is to make this workhouse no mere gesture of his example, but of such transcendent importance that the future ages will say: "There were giants in those days," who appreciated the accomplishments of Gorgas, and were worthy to become his friends, and the inheritors and promoters of his work. Their responsibility is the responsibility of executors upon whom the vision and generosity of the many nations of this American continent have placed a financial and scientific trust, which, because of its importance, must be maintained until its influence shall extend to all tropical and semi-tropical climes of the world.

Precautions Not Neglected

Nor have those of us who organized this Gorgas Memorial Institute of Tropical and Preventive Medicine neglected to observe every precaution in selecting the personnel for the Laboratory: first and foremost a Director was chosen as leader who has organized and will conduct the researches of this Laboratory, that has been so generously provided by this Republic.

The Scientific Board of the Institute consists of seven outstanding scientific authorities who have had special training in the study and treatment of tropical diseases. Each one of these seven was asked to submit three names of tropical experts, in the order of their importance, who would be most capable, personally, scientifically and temperamentally, to organize and conduct a Research Laboratory in tropical diseases. Without consultation, miraculously, of the seven men, four placed Dr. Herbert C. Clark first on their list, and each of the others included his name.

Most providential, from a practical standpoint, this scientist who was honored by this vote, and who for several years had been director of tropical work for the United Fruit Company, was magnanimously released to the Institute by that Company, though with a feeling of great loss and regret, and with an acknowledgement of their debt to General Gorgas and their interest in the contemplated laboratory.

The paramount factor of the acquisition of our Director cannot be over-estimated. His experience with the United Fruit Company in all of the Republics and islands surrounding the Caribbean Sea, has given him a practical knowledge of the problem of tropical sanitation.

Dedication

We have met in the presence of these friends of Gorgas, and distinguished citizens of the Americas to dedicate this temple of science. Its future work is in the hands of scientists; its jurisdiction extends to the tropics and semi-tropics of all the world; its authorizations under the Charter are unlimited; its research and clinical opportunities are unbounded; its prestige in tropical medicine is supported by the name and reputation of the greatest practical sanitarian of the age.

If this trust is well executed, the anniversary of this day will be celebrated each year, each hundred years, each thousand years, for all the future, by people in great countries of the tropics that were inaccessible and unin-habited before Gorgas lived and did his memorable work.

Appendix 4,a

Discurso del Dr. Antonio González Revilla, Decano de la Escuela de Medicina, Universidad de Panamá, en la Inauguración del Nuevo Edificio de Investigaciones del Laboratorio Conmemorativo Gorgas, Panamá, República de Panamá, 27 de Abril de 1963
Síntesis Histórica del Laboratorio Conmemorativo Gorgas

Su Excelencia Señor Ministro de Trabajo, Previsión Social
y Salud Pública, representante personal del Excelentísimo
Señor Presidente de la República;
Su Excelencia Reverendísima señor Arzobispo de Panamá;
Sus Excelencias Señores Ministros de Estado;
Sus Excelencias Señores Jefes de Misión Acreditados en Panamá;
Su Excelencia Señor Secretario Asistente de Defensa de los Estados
Unidos de América;
Autoridades de Panamá y la Zona del Canal;
Honorable Representante señor Selden;
Señor Rector de la Universidad de Panamá;
Señor Director y Miembros de la Junta Directiva del
Instituto Conmemorativo Gorgas;
Señor Director General de Salud Pública;
Señoras y Señores:

En el año de 1921 unos amigos y admiradores de aquel gran americano y eminente higienista cuyo nombre está tan íntimamente ligado a nuestra historia republicana y quien ha sido con justicia denominado el "Redentor de los Trópicos," William Crawford Gorgas, idearon la fundación de un Instituto como homenaje dinámico a sunombre. Así fué como el día 25 de Octubre de 1921 se legalizó en el Estado de Delaware la creación del Instituto Conmemorativo Gorgas de Medicina Tropical y Preventiva, Incorporado, con el objeto y propósito de "dirigir, asistir y estimular la investigación en la ciencia y en el arte de la higiene, de la medicina, la cirugía y materias afines, en la naturaleza y causa de las enfermedades, en los métodos de prevención y tratamiento, en difundir los conocimientos relacionados con estas materias para hacerlos disponibles en la protección de la salud de los pueblos y en mejorar el tratamiento de las enfermedades y traumatismos, particularmente aplicados a la Medicina Tropical y Preventiva."

El principal y más entusiasta propulsor de este proyecto fué el doctor Franklin H. Martin, Presidente del Colegio Americano de Cirujanos y él junto con personalidades sobresalientes de Estados Unidos y de Panamá fué signatario del certificado original de incorporación. Fueron ellas, además del Doctor Martin, el Doctor Belisario Porras, Presidente de la República de Panamá, el señor José E. Lefevre, Chargé d'Affaires de Panamá en Washington, en representación de la Junta Nacional de Higiene; el General Merritt W. Ireland, Cirujano General del Ejército de los Estados Unidos; el Vice-Almirante Edward R. Stitt, Cirujano General de la Armada de los Estados Unidos; el Dr. Leo S. Rowe, Director General de la Unión Panamericana; el Almirante William C. Braisted de la Armada de los Estados Unidos y el Honorable John Bassett Moore, Juez del Tribunal Permanente de Justicia Internacional de la Haya.

El objetivo inmediato del recién creado Instituto fué el de construír un Laboratorio Conmemorativo en el Istmo de Panamá dedicado al estudio y a la investigación de la Medicina Tropical y Preventiva. Hacia este fin era necesario conseguir el terreno adecuado, el dinero necesario para la edificación de su planta física y fondos suficientes para su mantenimiento. Su primera Junta de Directores, a través del Doctor Franklin H. Martin logró interesar a los gobiernos de la República de Panamá y de los Estados Unidos en este proyecto, aunque para ello se tomaron varios años antes de ver plasmado en alentadora realidad el esfuerzo conjunto de dos países hermanos.

El Doctor Belisario Porras, entusiasta alentador del Laboratorio, amigo personal y gran admirador del General Gorgas, en su carácter de Presidente de la República de Panamá, cedió al Instituto en 1923, un lote de terreno adyacente al actual Hospital Santo Tomás con la promesa de que Panamá aportaría la suma de 500.000.00 a 700.000.00 balboas para la construcción y dotación de la planta física del Laboratorio. En la ceremonia de colocación de la primera piedra el Doctor Porras hizo una emocionante apología del General Gorgas y no he podido resistir la tentación de citar uno de sus conceptos por parecerme el más elocuente tributo hecho por un panameño hacia ese insigne médico:

"Como podríamos describir a Gorgas, que solucionó el aparente imposible problema de hacer habitables los trópicos y que vino a complementar la maravillosa obra de Dios que nos creó para que viviéramos en la tierra y fuéramos felices en ella? Gorgas destruyó las moradas de la muerte, nos proporcionó agua para beber, purificó el aire de nuestros exhuberantes bosques tropicales y de nuestras ciudades coloniales. En una palabra Gorgas redimió los Trópicos."

Deplorablemente y debido a condiciones imprevistas de índole fiscal ese proyectado laboratorio nunca llegó a construirse. No fué sino hasta 1928 cuando se dió el primer paso efectivo: don Rodolfo Chiari, a la sazón Presidente de la República de Panamá, cedió al Instituto Gorgas, el edificio construído para una Escuela de Medicina que no llegó a funcionar, para que sirviese de sede al Laboratorio, edificio en el cual ha laborado hasta el presente. El 2 de abril de 1929 fué inaugurado el Laboratorio con la presencia del Ingeniero Florencio Harmodio Arosemena quien sucedió al señor Chiari en la Presidencia. El traspaso final en nombre del Gobierno Nacional lo hizo el señor Luis Felipe Clement, Secretario de Agricultura y Obras Públicas. El Doctor Franklin H. Martin lo recibió en nombre del Instituto como Presidente de su Junta de Directores.

Conjuntamente al desarrollo de estos eventos, el Honorable Maurice H. Thatcher, en ese entonces representante ante el Congreso de los Estados Unidos, presentó a la Cámara de Representantes un proyecto de ley conocido como el H. R. 8128 por el cual se autorizaba la erogación de una partida anual permanente de $50.000 para que fuese usada en el sostenimiento y manejo del Laboratorio Conmemorativo Gorgas, proyecto que fué aprobado finalmente el 28 de marzo de 1928 por la Cámara y el 24 del próximo mes por el Senado y sancionada por el Presidente de la República, el Honorable Calvin Coolidge, el 7 de mayo de ese mismo año. Esta ley ha sufrido diferentes modificaciones y gracias a los esfuerzos de los distintos presidentes del Instituto entre los cuales mencionaré singularmente al Dr. Franklin H. Martin, al Dr. Walter Bloedorn y a su actual Presidente el General Paul H. Streit, la partida original ha sido aumentada a $250.000. En 1960 el Congreso aprobó la suma adicional de $500.000 para la construcción y dotación del nuevo edificio que hoy inauguramos.

Por decisión unánime de su Junta de Directores, el Doctor Herbert C. Clark fué nombrado el primer Director del Laboratorio el primero de enero de 1929, cargo que desempeñó con dedicación, celo y con grandes rendimientos hasta 1954. El doctor Clark murió hace algunos años: es difícil para mí concentrar en cortas palabras su dinámica, abnegada y productiva labor durante el largo período en que el Laboratorio permaneció bajo su hábil dirección. A pesar de lo exiguo del presupuesto inicial para funcionamiento y de lo bajo de los salarios que hasta hace apenas unos escasos años eran muy inferiores a los pagados a otros investigadores fuera del país, pudo el Doctor Clark estimular a un selecto grupo de científicos quienes tesonera y silenciosamente han podido legarle al mundo grandes descubrimientos en la prevención y curación de varias enfermedades que se originan en los trópicos. Entre este grupo de investigadores recordamos a Fairchild, Komp, Trapido, Johnson, Dunn, Hertig, Miller, Foster, Rozeboom, Rodaniche, Michener y Galindo. En las etapas tempranas la primera gran contribución del laboratorio fué la de probar con estudios controlados la eficacia de drogas sintéticas en la curación y prevención de la malaria en masas de población, ya que el único medicamento efectivo que se conocía hasta ese entonces era la quinina. Gracias a estos estudios, drogas como la atebrina, la cloroquina, y la paludrina son hoy día de uso general y corriente. Para ello, el Doctor Clark hizo una encuesta de la incidencia de malaria entre los habitantes de las poblaciones aledañas al Río Chagres dividiendo las aldeas en grupos, de modo que ciertos grupos de población fueron tratados con quinina y otros con drogas sintéticas lográndose probar la eficacia indubitable de estas nuevas drogas en la prevención y tratamiento de la malaria. La importancia inmediata de estos trabajos se reflejó en Panamá y su tremenda influencia en el buen éxito de la Segunda Guerra Mundial en el Oriente, es de todos conocida.

Asimismo, el Doctor Clark y sus colaboradores fueron los primeros en probar la eficiencia de irrigación con insecticidas tanto en la ciudad como en el campo en el control de la malaria para la protección de grandes núcleos de población. Con el pasar de los años, fondos adicionales en forma de donaciones para la investigación fueron obtenidos de organizaciones internacionales. Con esta inyección económica pudo el Laboratorio ampliar sus valiosos trabajos como lo podemos verificar por la enorme publicación de sus aportes en más de trescientas monografías. Por ejemplo, se creía que la enfermedad de Chagas no existía en Panamá: el Laboratorio fué el primero en descubrir su existencia, en señalar los grupos de población donde esta enfermedad prevalece, en encontrar los insectos que la trasmiten y en orientar al clínico en su tratamiento. A pesar de que Miller fué quien la descubrió en el Istmo, no hay duda que las magníficas investigaciones sobre ella en Panamá han sido hechas por el Doctor Carl M. Johnson, hasta el punto de que casi pierde la vida en una ocasión, por haber contraído él mismo la enfermedad en el curso de sus experimentos. En este laboratorio también se hizo el importante descubrimiento de la trasmisión de la tripanosomiasis equina por murciélagos vampiros; la presencia de la tripanosomiasis en el ganado vacuno; la aparición de la fiebre Q y de la fiebre de las Montañas Rocosas en Panamá. Además se han practicado por primera vez estudios detallados del tórsalo en el hombre; clasificación de las serpientes venenosas y la incidencia de mordeduras de serpientes en Panamá, lo cual condujo a la preparación de sueros curativos adecuados; la primera clasificación de las garrapatas e insectos que pican al hombre, muchos de los cuales son transmisores de mortales enfermedades; el descubrimiento del *Anopheles darlingi,* el peor vector de la malaria en el nuevo mundo; la primeras pruebas de control del *Phlebotomus papatasi,* en fin, centenares de estudios y descubrimientos que han tenido una influencia tan benefactora en la vida de los trópicos y que no sigo detallando debido al tiempo limitado de esta síntesis histórica.

Al retirarse el Doctor Clark a la edad de 72 años lo reemplazó el insigne hombre de ciencia, el Doctor Carl M. Johnson, actual Director del Laboratorio. Bajo la dirección del Dr. Johnson esta institución cobró nuevos impulsos, no solamente en la ampliación de investigaciones iniciadas en años anteriores sino también en el estudio cuidadoso de las enfermedades producidas por virus y sus medios de transmisión. A pesar de que la labor e importancia del Laboratorio es poco conocida en Panamá, su fama es casi legendaria en el exterior y muchas instituciones internacionales han pedido su colaboración no sólo en el campo de consultas sino también en el adiestramiento de investigadores. La Organización Mundial de la Salud ha usado las facilidades del Laboratorio y su experto conocimiento en el control de programas de prevención sanitaria en la América Central. La unidad de investigación "Middle America" de los Institutos Nacionales de Salud Pública de los Estados Unidos lleva a cabo ciertos estudios conjuntos en bases cooperativas. Profesores y estudiantes de Universidades de las Américas, Europa, Asia y Africa vienen por períodos variables al Laboratorio a estudiar tópicos de especial y mutuo interés. Los Institutos Nacionales de Salud Pública de los Estados Unidos, a través de contínuas donaciones han ayudado al desarrollo de muchos de sus proyectos. En el campo nacional ha trabajado en contacto íntimo con nuestra Escuela de Medicina, y muy en especial con las autoridades sanitarias de Panamá en problemas tales como el de la Erradicación de la Malaria, en el control de brotes endémicos de fiebre amarilla selvática, en el estudio de control y prevención de la enfermedad de Chagas y en la actualidad está llevando a efecto un intenso programa en el Darién desde el punto de vista epidemiológico y ecológico paralelo a los estudios de la proyectada carretera Panamericana a través de esa importante región. Para el desarrollo de estos importantes programas los investigadores del Laboratorio están en contínuo movimiento en el campo y podemos decir sin temor a equivocarse que ellos conocen mejor el Istmo de Panamá que cualquier ciudadano panameño.

El Instituto Gorgas de Medicina Tropical y Preventiva a través del Laboratorio Conmemorativo Gorgas representa el ejemplo más elocuente del logro de objetivos de incalculable beneficio para la humanidad gracias al esfuerzo conjunto de dos países de América, los Estados Unidos y la República de Panamá. Los resultados obtenidos en sus treinta y cuatro años de existencia constituyen el homenaje dinámico más grande que ha podido ofrendársele a ese sabio redentor de los trópicos, William Crawford Gorgas.

Appendix 4,a

Address by Dr. Antonio González Revilla, Dean of the School of Medicine, University of Panama, at the Dedication of the New Research Building of the Gorgas Memorial Laboratory, Panama, Republic of Panama, April 27, 1963

Historical Brief: The Gorgas Memorial Laboratory

In the year 1921, a group of friends and admirers of that great American and eminent sanitarian whose name is intimately linked to our national history and has been justly called "Redeemer of the Tropics," William Crawford Gorgas, came with the idea of establishing an Institute as a dynamic tribute to the great man. Thus, on October 25, 1921, the establishment of the Gorgas Memorial Institute of Tropical and Preventive Medicine, Incorporated, was legalized in the State of Delaware "to conduct, assist and encourage investigations in the sciences and arts of hygiene, medicine and surgery and allied subjects, in the nature and causes of disease and the methods of its prevention and treatment, and to make knowledge relating to these various subjects available for the protection of the health of the public and the improved treatment of disease and injury, particularly as applied to Tropical and Preventive Medicine."

The most enthusiastic among this group of men was Dr. Franklin H. Martin, President of the American College of Surgeons, who together with outstanding citizens of the United States and Panama was a signer of the original Certificate of Incorporation. Others were: Dr. Belisario Porras, President of the Republic of Panama; Mr. José E. Lefevre, Charge d'Affaires of Panama in Washington, representing the National Board of Health; General Merritt W. Ireland, Surgeon General of the Army; Vice Admiral Edward R. Stitt, Surgeon General of the Navy; Dr. Leo S. Rowe, Director General of the Pan American Union; Admiral William C. Braisted of the

United States Navy; and the Honorable John Bassett Moore, Judge of the International Court of Justice in the Hague.

The immediate goal of the recently established Institute was to build a Memorial Laboratory on the Isthmus of Panama for the study and research of Tropical and Preventive Medicine. To this end, it was necessary to obtain an adequate plat of land, necessary funds for the construction of its physical plant, and sufficient funds for its maintenance. Its first Board of Directors, thru Dr. Franklin H. Martin, interested the Governments of the Republic of Panama and the United States of America in the project, but only after several years did the joint efforts of these two sister nations become a reality.

Dr. Belisario Porras, enthusiastic backer of the Laboratory project, personal friend and great admirer of General Gorgas, as President of Panama ceded to the Institute in 1923 a plat of land adjacent to the present Santo Tomás Hospital, and promised also that Panama would contribute B/. 500,000 to 700,000 (balboas) to build and equip the Laboratory. At the dedication ceremony Dr. Porras made a highly moving speech praising General Gorgas. I quote a concept expressed by him then, as it seems to me the most eloquent tribute paid that eminent doctor by a citizen of Panama:

"How can we describe Gorgas, who solved the apparently impossible problem of making the tropics habitable, and who came to us to complement the marvelous work of God who created us to live on the earth and be happy on it? Gorgas destroyed the abodes of death and gave us pure drinking water and purified the air of our exuberant tropical forests and our colonial cities. Gorgas redeemed the Tropics."

Very unfortunately, due to unforeseen fiscal problems, the proposed Laboratory was never built. It was not until 1928 when the first effective move was made: Don Rodolfo Chiari, then President of Panama, ceded to the Gorgas Memorial Institute the building previously constructed to house a School of Medicine which had never been used, to serve as headquarters for the Laboratory. This is the same building which has housed the Laboratory to this date. The Laboratory was thus dedicated on April 2, 1929, by H. E. Florencio Harmodio Arosemena who succeeded President Chiari. The final transaction was made by Mr. Luis Felipe Clement, then Secretary of Agriculture and Public Works, on behalf of the Government of Panama. Dr. Franklin H. Martin accepted the building for the Institute, as President of its Board of Directors.

Meanwhile, the Honorable Maurice H. Thatcher, then member of the House of Representatives of the United States of America, had introduced to the House bill HR 8128, authorizing a permanent annual appropriation of $50,000 for the maintenance and operation of the Gorgas Memorial Laboratory. The bill was passed in the House on March 28, 1928, in the

Senate on April 24, and was signed into law by President Calvin Coolidge on May 7, 1928. The law has been amended several times and, more recently, to increase the authorization to $250,000, thanks to the efforts of the various Presidents of the Institute of which I will name especially Dr. Franklin H. Martin, Dr. Walter A. Bloedorn, and Major General Paul H. Streit, USA (Ret.), President at this time. In 1960, Congress also authorized the additional sum of $500,000 for the construction of this new building which we dedicate today.

By unanimous decision of the Institute's Board of Directors, Dr. Herbert C. Clark was appointed first Director of the Laboratory on January 1, 1929, a position he held with dedication and zealousness until 1954. Dr. Clark died a few years after his retirement. It is difficult to describe in a few words the dynamic productive output and achievements of the Laboratory during the long period of time Dr. Clark remained as its able Director. Regardless of the small initial budget Dr. Clark had for operation and maintenance, and the very low salaries paid to scientists until very recent years, he encouraged and guided a select group of investigators who unpretentiously and with dedication bequeathed the world great findings in the prevention and cure of various diseases originating in the tropics. We remember particularly Fairchild, Komp, Trapido, Johnson, Dunn, Hertig, Miller, Foster, Rozeboom, Rodaniche, Michener and Galindo. In the early stages, the first great contribution made by the Laboratory was the evidence of the effectiveness of synthetic drugs in the cure and prevention of malaria in mass populations, since the only known effective medicine at the time was quinine. Due to studies made in the Laboratory drugs like atabrine, chloroquine, and "paludrine" are commonly and generally used today.

To bring about this finding, Dr. Clark made a survey of malaria incidence among residents in villages bordering the Chagres River, dividing villages in groups, so that some were treated with quinine while others were being treated with synthetic drugs, proving the effectiveness of these new drugs in the prevention and treatment of malaria. The result of this finding was of immediate importance to Panama, but is also well known the important role played in the Far East to end successfully the Second World War.

Likewise, Dr. Clark and his collaborators were the first to prove the effectiveness of insecticide spraying, in cities as well as in rural areas, for protection of the great majority of the population in malaria control programs. Through the years, additional funds were made available in grants received from international organizations for furthering research in this area. With this economic injection the Laboratory was able to increase its valuable research as may be confirmed by the large output of publications, totalling more than 300 monographs. For example, it was believed there was no Chagas' disease in Panama. The Laboratory was the first to find it, the first to indicate places where the disease prevails, the first to find the vectors and to guide clinicians in treatment of this disease. Without any doubt, the excellent investigational studies on Chagas' disease have been made in Panama by Dr. Carl M. Johnson, although it was Miller who first discovered it on the Isthmus. At one time, Dr. Johnson almost lost his life when he contracted the disease during the course of some of his experiments. The no less important transmission of equine trypanosomiasis by vampire bats was also found in this Laboratory. Other findings have been the presence of trypanosomiasis in cattle, the appearance in Panama of Q-fever and of Rocky Mountain Fever. For the first time, detailed studies were made of screw-worm in man; the classification of venomous snakes and the incidence of snake bites in Panama, the latter leading to preparation of suitable curative sera; the first classification of ticks and insects which bite man, many of which are vectors of deadly diseases; the discovery of *Anopheles darlingi,* worst vector of malaria in the new world; the first control tests of *Phlebotomus papatasi,* and so many hundreds of more studies and findings of importance in the tropics which I do not name here because of time limitations for this historical brief.

When Dr. Clark retired at age 76, he was replaced by the eminent scientist, Dr. Carl M. Johnson, present Director of the Laboratory. Under Dr. Johnson's direction, the institution has not only enlarged the research activities initiated in early years, but it has also initiated careful studies in diseases produced by viruses and their vectors.

Although the work and the importance of this Laboratory is little known in Panama, its prestige overseas is almost legendary, many international institutions requesting collaboration not only for consultation and advice, but also for training scientists. The World Health Organization has used the facilities of the Laboratory and its expert knowledge in programs of sanitary prevention and control in Central America. The Middle America Research Unit of the United States Public Health Service's National Institutes of Health carries out joint cooperative studies. Professors and students of universities in the Americas, Europe, Asia and Africa come to the Laboratory, for various periods of time, to study problems of special and mutual interest. The National Institutes of Health, through grants, have assisted in the development of many of its projects. In the national level, the Laboratory has worked closely with our School of Medicine and, very especially, with Panamanian sanitary officials in problems such as the eradication of malaria, the control of endemic outbreaks of jungle yellow fever, studies for control and prevention of Chagas' disease and, presently, an epidemiological and ecological program in Darien running parallel to studies being made on the proposed Pan American Highway. To develop these important programs scientists at the Laboratory move about with ease and knowledge all over the countryside, to the extent we can assert they know the Isthmian territory better than any Panamanian citizen.

The Gorgas Memorial Institute of Tropical and Preventive Medicine, through the Gorgas Memorial Laboratory, is the most eloquent example of service to humanity made possible by the joint effort of two countries of America, the United States and the Republic of Panama. The accomplishments of its 34 years of existence constitute the greatest tribute possibly paid to that wise Redeemer of the Tropics, William Crawford Gorgas.

Appendix 4,b

Remarks by Dr. John Parks, Member, Executive Committee, Representing Major General Paul H. Streit, USA (Ret.), President, Gorgas Memorial Institute of Tropical and Preventive Medicine, at the Dedication of the New Research Building of the Gorgas Memorial Laboratory, Panama, Republic of Panama, April 27, 1963

Doctor Parks speaking for General Streit:

His Excellency Doctor Bernardino González Ruiz, Minister of Labor, Social Welfare and Public Health;

Most Reverend Monsignor Francis Beckmann, Archbishop of Panama;

Their Excellencies Ministers of State;

Their Excellencies Heads of Missions accredited in the Republic of Panama;

His Excellency Dr. Frank B. Berry, Assistant Secretary of Defense for Health and Medical Affairs, USA;

Authorities of Panama and the Canal Zone;

Honorable Armistead I. Selden, Jr., Congressman, State of Alabama, USA;

Mr. Narciso Garay, Rector of the University of Panama;

Members of the Board of Directors of the Gorgas Memorial Institute;

Ladies and Gentlemen:

I bring Greetings from General Paul H. Streit, President of the Gorgas Memorial Institute of Tropical and Preventive Medicine.

A confining, but no longer serious illness prevents General Streit from being with us for these ceremonies. General Streit's greetings are as follows:

"It gives me much pleasure to welcome the Minister of Public Health of the Republic of Panama to these exercises.

"Likewise, I welcome Doctor Antonio González Revilla, the Dean of the Faculty of Medicine of the University of Panama and the Master of

Ceremonies on this occasion, who is visual evidence of the close ties between the University of Panama and the Gorgas Memorial Laboratory.

"I welcome, also, the many friends from medical installations, from research centers, and from the Governments of both the United States and of Panama, near and far, now assembled here for this ceremony.

"I must greet especially our benefactor, Mr. James H. Rand, and his gracious wife who have come from the Bahamas for this happy event.

"I have noted with great satisfaction the continued growth and mutual understanding and respect that has developed between the medical profession, the Government and the people of Panama and the Gorgas Memorial Laboratory. Our past relations are a key to our future relationships, which I hope will result in many contributions to Tropical Research. Truly, "Operation Friendship" has been at work at Gorgas for 35 years, and will continue to be the basic tenet of its expanding program.

"There have been notable advances in Tropical Medicine in recent decades to which Gorgas has contributed its share. Gorgas took part in the work which resulted in the eradication of the Yellow Fever Mosquito which is responsible for epidemics in cities. Furthermore, much important information has been obtained in work on Yellow Fever in its other quite different habitat, the jungle, where extensive studies have been made on the mosquitoes of the forest canopy and the forest animals which keep the disease going. Gorgas was one of the pioneers in testing DDT and putting into practice this method for the control of malaria under the tropical conditions of Panama. Notable success has been achieved in the prophylactic treatment of whole villages and districts with anti-malarial drugs, which have brought the malaria rate in the experimental areas to zero. Certain of the newer drugs still under study have proved to be remarkably effective in the treatment of American Leishmaniasis and Chagas' Disease. There are in progress, at present, the study of the insect groups, which transmit these two diseases and of the forest animals or other wildlife which harbor the infection and serve as reservoirs of these diseases. A number of viruses causing disease of man have been isolated from either the insects which transmit these diseases or from patients. Throughout the whole history of the Laboratory there have been under continual study various groups of insects and other arthropods of medical importance, such as the mosquitoes, sandflies, horseflies, reduviids, ticks, and their relations to the diseases of man.

"But much remains to be done before the tropics here and elsewhere will be free of the menace of serious disease. Basic, as well as clinical research, extending over many years is necessary before the major residual problems of illness will be overcome. Gorgas is planning an expanded research program and is even now gathering outstanding dedicated scientists in such fields as Pathology, Mycology, Bacteriology, Anthropology, Genetics,

Botany, and Virology. With this well-rounded team it is believed that additional victories over disease and disability may be won.

"The Government of Panama recently gave Gorgas Memorial Laboratory full responsibility in planning, initiating, and conducting a ten-year study of the medical ecology of both humans and animals in the underdeveloped jungle area of eastern Panama along the Route of the Inter-American Highway. This is further evidence of the confidence of the Government of Panama in the Gorgas Memorial Laboratory.

"The new Research Building which we are dedicating today is modern in the best sense of the word. Only a few of the latest buildings in other research complexes have the unique features of this fine building which will give our staff the essential tools to carry out the purpose. Basic design and special requirements, including specialized air-conditioning for our new research Laboratory Building and changes and renovation for the animal breeding building were supplied by Mr. Clarence W. May, Special Engineering Consultant, Bethesda, Maryland. Architects for the Project were Schay & Holzer, S.A., Panama, R. P. Contractors for the construction were Díaz & Guardia, S.A.

"And so it is with confidence that we approach our future challenges. Together we will succeed. I am proud to be here to celebrate this great occasion with you."

Appendix 4,c

Address by the Honorable Armistead I. Selden, Jr., United States House of Representatives, at the Dedication of the New Research Building of the Gorgas Memorial Laboratory, Panama, Republic of Panama, April 27, 1963

It is indeed an honor to be here today to take part in the dedication of this important new structure—a structure that symbolizes the common humanitarian goals of the people of Panama and of the United States.

We are dedicating more than a structure, however. This institution represents nothing less than a joint humanitarian venture—one in which Panama and the United States can share great pride.

Although these are troubled times for our hemisphere and for the world —in the humanitarian work that is conducted by this institution—the people of Panama and the United States are as one.

As chairman of the Inter-American Affairs Subcommittee of the House of Representatives, I had a part in securing the enactment of legislation to maintain and operate this great research institution. This is especially true of the Act of 1960 which authorized the appropriation of $500,000 to build and equip the structure we are now dedicating.

We meet here today not only to dedicate a building, but to pay homage to one whose great name is borne by these institutions—the Gorgas Memorial Institute of Tropical and Preventive Medicine, Inc., and the Gorgas Memorial Laboratory.

Not only do we pay honor to the greatest practical sanitarian of the ages, but also to all those who, through the years, have given so much of their time and talents to the work of the Institute and the Laboratory. In addition, we today recognize and honor all the personnel—scientific and non-scientific, on the Isthmus and in Washington—who have effectively and loyally performed their exacting duties in behalf of this Institution.

The Gorgas Memorial Institute of Tropical and Preventive Medicine, a non-profit institution created by an act of the Congress of the United States was incorporated under the laws of the State of Delaware on October 25, 1921. The work of the Institute was limited to the United States until the Act of May 7, 1928, authored by Congressman Maurice H. Thatcher, formerly a member of the Isthmian Canal Commission and a great friend of Panama, created the Gorgas Memorial Laboratory to be located in the Republic of Panama. The measure also authorized an annual appropriation of $50,000 for its maintenance and operation.

The activities of the Laboratory began January 1, 1929, under the immediate direction of Dr. Herbert C. Clark. The Institute restricted its labors to the field of tropical disease as it does today. In connection with the origin of the Institute, it is interesting to note that Dr. Belisario Porras, President of the Republic of Panama, and Joseph E. Lefevre, representing the Panama National Health Board, are both signers of the articles of incorporation. The other incorporators were citizens of the United States. As provided by its By-Laws, the Institute has always had an Honorary President, the President of the United States.

This valuable site, and its original buildings, were donated to the Institute as the home of the Laboratory by the Panamanian Government.

I shall not attempt in the time allotted to me this morning to give a detailed account of the splendid achievements of the past century in the study and conquest of many of the more deadly diseases, which throughout all the ages have plagued the human race. Ross, Manson, Pasteur, Jenner, Lister, and Reed have been among those who have successfully dealt with our human ills.

However, it remained for William Crawford Gorgas of the Medical Corps of the United States Army to plan and execute the first campaign to eradicate "Yellow Jack" as a centuries-old plague throughout Cuba. By similar methods he also greatly reduced malaria there. This was during the years of United States occupation of that island following the Spanish-American War. Then he was sent here to Panama, where the great Canal was being constructed, and here he achieved successful results similar to those he brought about in Cuba. Had the work of Gorgas on the Isthmus been unsuccessful, the Canal probably would not have been built. Sanitation and the establishment of order were indispensable to the success of the engineering labors that made possible that historic undertaking.

I have mentioned in general terms the great achievements of Gorgas in Cuba and the Isthmus of Panama. As a fellow Alabamian, I feel it would be appropriate on this occasion to remind you of a few of the more interesting details of the life of this great physician.

William Crawford Gorgas was born October 3, 1854, in the environs of Mobile, Alabama. He was the eldest son of Josiah Gorgas and Amelia Gayle, daughter of an early Governor of Alabama. Josiah Gorgas, a graduate of the military academy at West Point, was of Pennsylvania birth, but he chose Alabama as his home. Young William Crawford Gorgas spent his earlier years in Richmond, Virginia, where his father was located as chief ordnance officer of the Confederate military forces. His father's army career greatly influenced the youthful Gorgas to wish for a military career. After the close of the War Between the States, young Gorgas sought an appointment to West Point, but failed to obtain it. His ambition then turned to medicine and a career in the Medical Corps of the United States Army. He was a student at the University of the South at Sewanee, Tennessee, graduating there in 1876, 66 years before I graduated from the same institution. At the time young Gorgas attended the University of the South, his father was serving as its president.

Gorgas became a student in Bellevue Medical College in New York City in 1876, graduating three years later. The years at Bellevue intensified his ambition for a career in the Army Medical Corps. He successfully passed the examination required and became a member of the Corps. For the next ten years he served in the Army Medical Corps chiefly in Texas, North Dakota, and Florida.

During these years, he volunteered and was sent to Fort Brown, near Brownville, Texas, where for the first time he came to grips with yellow fever—the great enemy he was afterwards to know so well and to finally master.

It was at Brownville he met a Miss Marie Doughty of Cincinnati, Ohio, who was visiting her sister, the wife of the commanding officer of the post. There was an epidemic of yellow fever at the Fort, many were dying, and panic was everywhere. Miss Doughty became stricken. Dr. Gorgas ministered to her, and, when her death seemed imminent, he was asked to attend her burial and to read the accustomed service. This he agreed to do, but fate intervened. The young woman began to recover, and recover she did. In turn, the courageous young physician was stricken, but he too survived. Out of these dramatic circumstances a romance sprang, which ripened into marriage. Having experienced yellow fever, both were immune

306

to it. Thus, they were especially fitted to go anywhere it might strike, to live with it, to fight it, and to finally master it. In later years, Mrs. Gorgas remarked: "It would be untrue to say that Yellow Jack was the best man at our wedding, but it would be perfectly true to say that, in a sense, he was an usher."

Then came the Spanish-American War with Gorgas, a Medical Corps officer with the rank of major, in charge of the yellow fever camp at Siboney in fever-ravaged Cuba. Later in the year 1898, he was back in Havana and was soon made its Chief Sanitary Officer. Gorgas instituted an overall plan for the removal or destruction in the Havana area of every receptacle in the entire region which might be the breeding site of the Stegomyia mosquito and its larvae. Drainage and fumigation practices were maintained. These processes and strict quarantine in a few months destroyed the presence of yellow fever, and the city became one of the healthiest anywhere to be found. To the extent necessary, similar sanitary practices were followed elsewhere on the Island, and yellow fever was banished from the whole of Cuba.

Then, in 1904, the United States took up the challenge to build the Panama Canal. Gorgas was appointed Chief Sanitary Officer of the Canal Zone, and assumed his duties as such in the early summer of 1904. He served in this capacity until his appointment in 1907 as a member of the second Isthmian Canal Commission in charge of the health and sanitary work on the Isthmus.

He accomplished in Panama what he had accomplished in Cuba. The Isthmus, which had come to be considered one of the plague spots of the world, became a region of health. Yellow fever was eradicated and malaria greatly reduced. The centers of population on the Isthmus became as healthful as cities of the United States.

Thus Gorgas had again proved to the world that the people of the temperate zones could live and thrive in the tropics if proper sanitation were provided.

In the fall of 1913, Col. Gorgas went to South Africa, on invitation of the Transvaal Chamber of Mines, to investigate and report on the subject of pneumonia then raging among the laborers in the gold and diamond mines in that region. He accepted the call, made the required trip and studies, and submitted recommendations for methods to be employed in the situation presented based on his handling of the same problem among the laborers on the Canal project.

The adoption of these recommendations was followed by a gratifying lower death rate from pneumonia in the affected South African areas.

Then, on the invitation of the Government of Rhodesia, in 1914, he visited Salisbury, and suggested methods for handling malaria, which was ravaging that country. While there, he learned by cable that he had just become General Gorgas, through his appointment on January 16, 1914, by President Wilson, as Surgeon-General of the United States Army with the rank of Brigadier General. A year later, by an act of Congress, he became a Major General.

As Surgeon-General, Gorgas was called on to perform an unprecedented task in arranging the assembly of a mighty army of fit soldiers following our nation's entry into World War I in April, 1917.

In the summer of 1916 he had served as Chief of the Special Yellow Fever Commission of the Rockefeller Foundation, and had visited various countries in Central and South America which were potential or actual yellow fever centers. He had given advice to local authorities on methods to be employed to eradicate these sources of peril. Everywhere he received the evidences of affection and esteem. The great mission of his life was to aid in the complete extermination of this frightful disease. He found in various places his measures against yellow fever and malaria were being carried out with complete success.

When he retired his post as Surgeon-General in 1918 at the age of 65, he promptly accepted the directorship of the yellow fever work of the International Health Board of the Rockefeller Foundation. On May 30, 1920, he sailed for West Africa to make a study of yellow fever conditions there. Then came the stop in London, his illness and death on July 4.

The death of General Gorgas was mourned throughout the British Isles, as well as the United States, Panama, Cuba, and in the world-at-large. At the command of the British King and by order of the British Government, there was provided for him a funeral service in St. Paul's Cathedral, with the highest military honors. In the historic sanctuary—which is the last resting place of some of the greatest soldiers and sailors known to British history—impressive homage was paid to one who had walked humbly, but had so long successfully labored for his fellow man. He died in the faith in which he had ever lived—that there would be a better tomorrow, and that all should be given an opportunity to live healthy, fruitful lives.

His remains were carried by ship back to his beloved country, and laid in the sacred soil of Arlington National Cemetery in Washington.

General Gorgas was the recipient of an ever-increasing list of accolades and honors, but one of the greatest was the last-bestowed at his bedside in a London Hospital by King George the Fifth himself—the insignia of Knight Commander of the Most Distinguished Order of St. Michael and St. George. The King had come to the hospital because, as he said, General Gorgas could not come to the Palace to receive the honor.

Today, the fame of this Laboratory bearing his name is known far beyond the boundaries of this Hemisphere. Its findings were, in large measure, used for the benefit of the Allied Forces in World War II, especially in the

South Pacific areas. Its work is collaborative, not duplicative; its malarial techniques are of the first order.

Panama is an ideal site for the location and operation of a tropical research laboratory. Situated at a center of international traffic and a crossroads of the world—the Gorgas Memorial Laboratory is unrivalled in its opportunity for service to humanity in the field of tropical medicine.

This new building that we today are dedicating is destined to serve its purpose to the benefit of all mankind.

We gratefully acknowledge the splendid aid and cooperation which the Government and the people of Panama have always accorded the Gorgas Memorial Laboratory. This institution has ever been a common denominator of friendship and goodwill between our two countries.

The conquest of human disease and misery brings our countries and our people together—and so may the Gorgas Memorial Laboratory continue to symbolize that which unites, rather than separates, good neighbors of the Western Hemisphere.

Appendix 4,d

Address by Dr. Frank B. Berry, Assistant Secretary for Health and Medical Affairs, Department of Defense, United States of America, at the Dedication of the New Research Building of the Gorgas Memorial Laboratory, Panama, Republic of Panama, April 27, 1963

In 1826 Bolívar wrote that it was his desire that peace should reign in the Americas and that the spiritual communion of our peoples should find expression in the actual political situation in the New World. This—"would consist of independent nations, bound together by a common set of laws which would govern their foreign relations and afford them a right to survival through a general and permanent congress."

On April 14, 1890, representatives of eighteen free nations met in Washington. Since then there have been frequent similar meetings. Although the initial results were very modest, a simple organization was designed to provide an information agency for commercial transactions. It was named the international Union of American Republics. As the result of this 1890 conference, in 1930, April 14 was officially designated Pan American Day. The Alliance for Progress is the culmination of this series of meetings and undertakings dating back to 1890.

To quote from an address by Dr. Franklin H. Martin at the Dedication of the Memorial Laboratory, "William C. Gorgas is the man whose work made the Panama Canal possible, the economic savior of Cuba and whose accomplishments as the world's physician made all the world his debtor. He was a servant of mankind and benefactor of humanity." And in the words of President Porras at the laying of the cornerstone of the Gorgas Memorial Institute of Tropical and Preventive Medicine, "General Gorgas was truly a citizen of the world."

Assigned to his task in Panama in April 1904, in November 1905 he reported that the highwater mark had been reached, that there was no more yellow fever in Panama. His application of the scientific proof by Carlos Finlay and Major Walter Reed that yellow fever was carried by the *Aedes aegypti* mosquito transformed Panama from one of the worst areas in the world for yellow fever to a pleasant tropical area free of yellow fever and with malaria under control. This was accomplished by his thorough knowledge of hygiene, preventive medicine and sanitation. With the establishment of the Memorial Laboratory in 1929, Dr. Herbert C. Clark became the first Director.

In World War I, I was assigned to the Central Medical Department Laboratory in Dijon, France. Colonel Joseph Siler, commanding all the laboratories in the American Expeditionary Force, had his Headquarters here and Lieutenant Colonel Herbert C. Clark was in charge of the museum and all gross specimens that were received. Drs. Franklin H. Martin and Jeff Miller were on the original Board as officers of the Gorgas Laboratory and Colonel Siler and Dr. Goodpaster were on the Scientific Board.

Early in World War II, I was again associated with Colonel Siler for a short period at the Walter Reed Army Hospital. Between the Wars, I had maintained my contact with Dr. Clark and saw him in both New York and Panama.

The work and interest of the Gorgas Laboratory in mosquito control, originally with yellow fever, and continually with malaria, were extended to include studies of the sylvan form of yellow fever beginning in 1948. Dr. Clark continued his own outstanding work with animal diseases and zoonoses and the interest of the various sections of the Laboratory in Chagas' disease, leishmaniasis, and diseases carried by sandflies and bats. With the expansion of the Laboratory it became a teaching center not only for Latin America but also for visitors from the United States and other countries, and added opportunities were afforded through cooperation with the Middle America Research Unit and the Gorgas Hospital in the Canal Zone. Because of the juxtaposition of the laboratories, the Gorgas to Santo Tomás Hospital and the Middle America Unit to Gorgas Hospital, the potential of these two laboratories was greatly enhanced for the study, prevention and cure of tropical diseases, their epidemiology and epizoology, and the close interplay between animal and human disease—zoonoses.

Because of our increasing speed in communications, greater amount of human travel and transportation, shipment of animals and birds, and shipments of disease and insect bearing vegetables and fruits, the need for these laboratories has greatly increased along with a greater opportunity for them to work together as training centers. Finally, there are the important functions of coordination and training for other branches of the medical, dental, veterinary, pharmacological and other biological professions for work in this wide field of diseases.

As our knowledge increases so does our need for those well educated and well trained in the application of the basic sciences, hygiene and preventive medicine, and in the medical and paramedical professions and in biology.

Appendix 5,a

Discurso del Dr. Ricardo J. Alfaro, Miembro de la Junta Directiva del Instituto Conmemorativo Gorgas, en la Inauguración del Insectario Rand del Laboratorio Conmemorativo Gorgas, Panamá, República de Panamá, 4 de Marzo de 1965

Excelentísimo y Reverendísimo Monseñor Tomás A. Clavel, Arzobispo de Panamá;
Excelentísimo señor Ministro de Trabajo, Previsión Social y Salud Pública;
Señor Director del Laboratorio Gorgas;
Distinguidos huéspedes;
Señoras y señores:

Con honda complacencia y alto sentido de honor doy cumplimiento al grato encargo que se me ha hecho, de decir unas cuantas palabras en este acto. Con la inauguración de su insectario, el Laboratorio Gorgas pone un jalón más en su ya largo y honroso historial de institución científica exclusivamente consagrada al bien de la humanidad.

A principios de 1921, los deberes de mi cargo de Secretario de Gobierno y Justicia de la República me retuvieron por algún tiempo en la ciudad de Washington, consagrado a la defensa de los derechos de Panamá en un conflicto internacional de ingrata recordación en que nos vimos envueltos en aquellos días. Pero en medio de las amarguras de aquella situación recayó sobre mí el privilegio de colaborar en nombre de mi Gobierno en las gestiones y labores que culminaron con la fundación del Instituto Conmemorativo Gorgas de Medicina Tropical y Preventiva, que tiene en este Laboratorio el centro de sus actividades científicas. De allí el interés sentimental con que participo en este programa.

Se concibió la fundación del Instituto como monumento viviente consagrado a honrar la memoria del insigne benefactor del género humano que fue el General William Crawford Gorgas, el hombre que con el antecedente de su resonante triunfo en Cuba extirpó definitivamente de nuestro suelo, y virtualmente de la faz de la tierra, la espantosa amenaza de la fiebre amarilla, azote de los trópicos, estorbo del progreso en las regiones ubicadas dentro o cerca de ellos, y factor trágicamente conocido como una de las varias causas que dificultaron en el Istmo de Panamá los primeros trabajos acometidos por los franceses para llevar a cabo la obra gigantesca del Canal Interoceánico. La erección de este monumento fue idea que lanzó el entonces Presidente de la República, Doctor Belisario Porras, quien ofreció como contribución de Panamá la construcción de este Laboratorio y sus terrenos, y el Gobierno de los Estados Unidos contribuyó y sigue contribuyendo a su sostenimiento con liberalidad que ha permitido el notable desarrollo de sus actividades científicas que ha alcanzado durante los cuarenta y cuatro años de su fecunda existencia. Así tiene asiento en la tierra panameña una admirable manifestación de cooperación internacional que impulsa la ciencia de la medicina y que favorece singularmente el vasto ámbito de la humanidad tropical.

La obra del Laboratorio Gorgas no es por su naturaleza de aquellas que llaman la atención de la mayoría de las gentes. No son muchos los que pueden percatarse de lo que ha significado y significa para Panamá y el resto del mundo la labor silenciosa de esos hombres que con las armas del microscopio, de los caldos de cultivo, y de la observación y estudio de numerosas especies de animales, están librando una batalla incesante contra las bacterias productoras de dolencias que son flagelo del género humano. Buscar, descubrir, aislar, estudiar y someter a experimentos de todas clases los microorganismos vectores de las diferentes enfermedades; y luego buscar y encontrar las sustancias químicas, sueros o drogas que destruyan esos microorganismos o que les impidan invadir el cuerpo humano, no son ciertamente, hazañas espectaculares. Pero el efecto benéfico de ellas lo disfrutan millares y centenas de millares de seres humanos y de animales amigos del hombre a quienes se les protege preventivamente o se les salva terapéuticamente merced a la acción tesonera de los soldados de la ciencia.

Las realizaciones del Laboratorio Gorgas, por razón de su alto tecnicismo, se hallan sin duda más allá del alcance de la mayoría de las personas. Por tal razón a mí, como lego en la ciencia médica, me sería imposible describirlas cumplidamente. Pero puedo afirmar sin vacilación y con pleno convencimiento, que aquí se han estudiado con provecho y se han resuelto con éxito gran cantidad de problemas relativos a la medicina, higiene y sanidad de los trópicos. El resultado de esos estudios se encuentra en más de trescientas monografías o informes de que son autores no solamente los competentísimos técnicos de la institución sino también afamados sabios extranjeros que la han visitado y que han colaborado con sus actividades. Debe mencionarse en primer lugar la lucha por la extirpación de la malaria, que aunque sensiblemente disminuída en las ciudades de Panamá y Colón en comparación con lo que fue en otros tiempos, todavía hace estragos en las regiones rurales de la República. En prosecución de ese alto fin se han hecho experimentos de largo alcance—algunos de ellos los primeros— acerca del efecto de ciertos medicamentos antimaláricos en las regiones tropicales del continente; acerca de la eficacia de la impregnación de habitaciones con la droga llamada DDT como preventivo del paludismo; y acerca del uso de sustancias ahuyentadoras de insectos en la faja tropical del hemisferio. Se ha establecido por vez primera, para estudios y experimentos de laboratorio, una colonia de una nueva especie de mosquitos reconocida como el principal transmisor de la malaria en la América Central y se ha descubierto otra especie que es también vehículo de esa enfermedad en todo el continente. De igual manera se debe a este Laboratorio el descubrimiento del papel que desempeña el murciélago en la transmisión de la enfermedad que afecta a los caballos, llamada *trypanosomiasis,* como también el descubrimiento de ese mismo mal en el ganado panameño. Asimismo debemos a esta institución una extensa monografía sobre las serpientes venenosas de Panamá y sobre la incidencia de sus mordeduras; el primer estudio sobre la presencia del mal de Chagas en Panamá y sus vectores; los primeros estudios completos sobre la larva del estro en el ser humano; sobre los parásitos del caballo; sobre las garrapatas y demás insectos que pican; sobre aislamiento del virus de la encefalitis equina venezolana, procedente de pájaros de Panamá, acompañado de estudios ecológicos y epidemiológicos sobre el mismo mal y otras formas de encefalitis; sobre el uso de la droga DDT para combatir diferentes especies de insectos perniciosos de los que nos torturan en nuestras playas, en nuestros bosques y aun en nuestras áreas urbanas. Y sobresaliendo por su importancia entre todos estos trabajos, debo mencionar especialmente las valiosas investigaciones, experimentos y descubrimientos llevados a cabo en relación con la presencia de la fiebre amarilla en las selvas de Centro América y de Panamá y las especies de mosquitos que la transmiten, y en relación con la aparición en nuestro medio de varios de los virus que, como nos decía hace un rato el Dr. Soper, han hecho explosión en todo el orbe.

Imposible es para el lego, como lo soy yo y como lo somos la mayoría de los aquí presentes, comprender en toda la magnitud de su valor científico la obra realizada por el Laboratorio Gorgas, pero una idea siquiera sea vaga, de su honda y vasta significación, debe hacer vibrar en todos los ciudadanos de Panamá el sentimiento de la gratitud y de la admiración hacia los hombres de ciencia que aquí realizan obra de tanta importancia mundial. No nos es posible tampoco dejar de sentir un bien fundado orgullo por el hecho de que en suelo panameño, por iniciativa panameña y con la eficaz cooperación técnica y económica del Gobierno de los Estados Unidos y de meritorios filántropos de aquel país, fructifique aquí de manera magnífica esta benemérita institución. Y no es posible, en fin, olvidar que este Laboratorio constituye, como lo dije antes, un monumento viviente a la memoria del eximio sabio que fue el General William Crawford Gorgas, a quien la posteridad reconoce como el hombre que llevó a cabo la transformación sanitaria de las ciudades de Panamá y Colón y de la faja territorial por donde se extiende el canal interoceánico.

Tarea magna fue aquella en los primeros años de nuestra nacionalidad, cuando la República no poseía aún las fuerzas económicas y técnicas que se requerían para llevarla a cabo, y cuando era necesario combatir hábitos y herir intereses provenientes del atraso en que vivíamos. Las labores del saneamiento exigían la eliminación de las tradicionales tinajas, tanques y otros depósitos de aguas donde los mosquitos depositaban sus larvas y se producían así los vehículos de la fiebre amarilla y del paludismo; la destrucción de las canales de los techos y de toda estructura susceptible de producir el estancamiento de aguas y los consiguientes criaderos de mosquitos; la fumigación de las casas para la destrucción de insectos, ratas y otros animales higiénicamente peligrosos; la adopción de reglas de construcción que aseguraran en las viviendas mejores condiciones de salubridad; y en fin, una serie de medidas que significaban para nuestra población molestias y gastos que muchas personas consideraban injustificados.

Fue privilegio mío conocer personalmente al Doctor Gorgas y presenciar en sus comienzos el proceso lento pero firme, difícil pero eficaz, del saneamiento del Istmo. Era yo en aquella época un modesto funcionario de la Secretaría de Gobierno y Relaciones Exteriores, y el Doctor Gorgas venía con frecuencia al Despacho para tratar con nuestro ilustre Secretario, el inolvidable General Santiago de la Guardia, acerca de los métodos que debían acordar los dos gobiernos para la acción sanitaria. Tuve así ocasión de admirar de cerca las cualidades del ínclito caballero y hombre de ciencia que realizaba en nuestra patria tan trascendental misión.

En Marzo de 1921 la Southern Society de Washington obsequió un retrato al óleo del General Gorgas a la Biblioteca del Cirujano en Jefe del Departamento de Guerra, y en el discurso que se me invitó a pronunciar en aquel acto dije:

"El arduo problema del saneamiento fue acometido y resuelto por el General Gorgas de manera eficiente y completa. Al propio tiempo fue él tan cuidadoso, tan considerado y tan cortés en sus métodos, que no obstante verse obligado a afectar en cierta medida los intereses de la población para eliminar costumbres y prejuicios que habían existido por generaciones, logró llevar a cabo sin fricción alguna su estupenda tarea. Suavidad era el rasgo predominante de su idiosincracia. No pertenecía él a esa laya de hombres que creen que es necesario ser grosero y áspero para el desempeño de una función de importancia. La urbanidad fue el factor que abrió el camino al éxito de sus trabajos. Su voz era suave; sus maneras llenas de gentileza y de dignidad, y una afable sonrisa ponía un toque de luz a la severa regularidad de sus funciones."

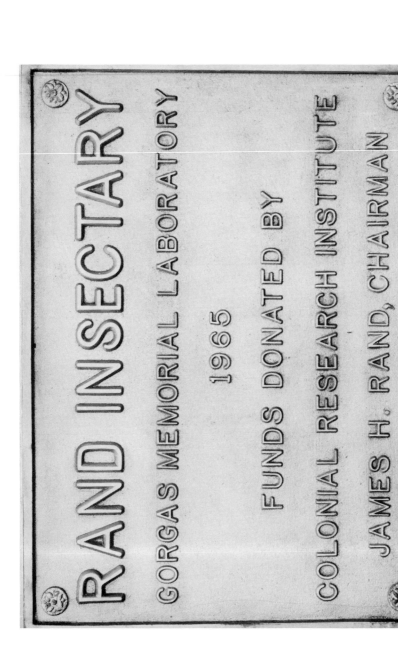

Fig. 18. The plaque commemorating the dedication of the Rand Insectary of the Gorgas Memorial Laboratory.

Señoras y señores, al inaugurar el Laboratorio Gorgas el Insectario que constituye su última y más brillante realización, yo os invito a que tributemos un devoto recuerdo al esclarecido sabio que le dio su nombre, y un cálido aplauso al eminente Mayor General Paul H. Streit, Presidente del Instituto, quien desde su sede de Washington vino a honrar este acto con su presencia y su palabra pero por causa de enfermedad no ha podido estar presente y ha sido reemplazado con lucimiento en el programa por el Secretario General del Instituto, Dr. Fred L. Soper; al generoso filántropo señor James H. Rand, donador del espléndido insectario que hoy inauguramos y que llevará su nombre en reconocimiento de su munificencia; al distinguido Director del Laboratorio, Doctor Martin D. Young, y a todos los hombres y mujeres de los Estados Unidos y de Panamá que colaboran en esta Institución, enlazados por el doble vínculo del amor a la ciencia y de la solidaridad universal.

He dicho.

Appendix 5,a

Address by Dr. Ricardo J. Alfaro, Member of the Board of Directors, Gorgas Memorial Institute of Tropical and Preventive Medicine, on the Occasion of the Dedication of the Rand Insectary of the Gorgas Memorial Laboratory, Panama, Republic of Panama, March 4, 1965

The Very Reverend Monsignor Tomás A. Clavel, Archbishop of Panama;
His Excellency the Minister of Labor, Social Welfare and Public Health;
The Director of the Gorgas Memorial Laboratory;
Distinguished guests, Ladies and Gentlemen:

It is with profound pleasure and a keen sense of the honor bestowed upon me that I fulfill the pleasant task of saying a few words at this ceremony. With the inauguration of this Insectary, the Gorgas Memorial Laboratory marks one more stage in its already long and honored record as a scientific institution devoted exclusively to the good of mankind.

Early in 1921, my duties as Secretary of Government and Justice of the Republic kept me in the city of Washington for some time, spent in defending the rights of Panama in an international disagreement of unhappy memory in which we were then embroiled. But in the midst of the bitterness of that situation, I had the privilege of taking part, in the name of my Government, in the negotiations and labors that culminated in the establishment of the Gorgas Memorial Institute of Tropical and Preventive Medicine, whose center of scientific activity is in this Laboratory. Hence my sentimental interest in participating in this program.

The establishment of the Institute was conceived as a living monument to honor the memory of that outstanding benefactor of the human race, General William Crawford Gorgas, the man who, fresh from his resounding triumph in Cuba, definitely rid our land, and virtually the face of the earth, of the frightful threat of yellow fever, the scourge of the tropics, a stumbling-block to progress in the regions lying in or near them, and a tragic factor recognized as one of the various obstacles on the Isthmus of Panama to the initial work of the French in the gigantic task of building the Interoceanic Canal. The construction of this monument was the idea of the then President of the Republic, Dr. Belisario Porras, who offered to build this Laboratory and give the land on which it stands as the contribution of Panama, and the Government of the United States contributed and still contributes to its support with a generosity that has made possible the noteworthy development of the scientific activities it has carried out during the forty-four years of its fruitful existence. Thus there is located on Panamanian soil an admirable expression of international cooperation, which gives impulse to medical science and is of particular benefit to those who dwell within the tropics.

By its very nature, the work of the Gorgas Memorial Laboratory is not one that attracts the attention of a large part of the public. Not many are aware of what has been, and still is, the significance to Panama and to the rest of the world, of the quiet labor of those men who, armed with microscopes, culture broths, and the observation and study of many species of animals, are waging a ceaseless war against the bacteria producing ailments that afflict mankind. To seek, discover, isolate, and study the microorganisms that are the vectors of the different diseases, and to subject them to all kind of tests; and then to seek and find the chemical substances, sera, or drugs that will destroy these microorganisms or keep them from invading the human body, are not, it is true, spectacular achievements. But their beneficial effect is enjoyed by thousands and hundreds of thousands of human beings and of animals friendly to man, who are given preventive protection or life-saving remedies, thanks to the tenacious activities of the soldiers of science.

The accomplishments of the Gorgas Memorial Laboratory, because they are on so high a technical plane, are unquestionably beyond the ken of most people. That is why it would be impossible for me, a layman in medical science, to describe them fittingly. But I can, unhesitatingly and with complete conviction, say that a great many problems relative to tropical medicine, hygiene, and sanitation have been studied to advantage and successfully solved. The results of these studies are to be found in more than three hundred monographs or reports, whose authors are not only the extremely competent technicians of the institution, but also famous foreign scientists who have visited it and participated in its activities. Mention should be made, in the first place, of the effort to wipe out malaria, which, although now appreciably less in the cities of Panama and Colon than it was in other times, still ravages the rural regions of the Republic. In pursuit of that lofty aim, long-range experiments—some of them the very first —have been undertaken on the effect of certain antimalarial medicines in the tropical regions of the continent; on the efficacy of impregnating dwellings with DDT as a malaria preventive; and on the use of insect-repellent substances in the tropical belt of the continent. For the first time there has been established, for study and laboratory experiment, a colony of a new species of mosquito recognized as the principal carrier of malaria in Central America, and another species has been discovered that also is the vector of this disease throughout the continent. Likewise, we are indebted to this Laboratory for the discovery of the role played by bats in the transmittal of the disease affecting horses, called trypanosomiasis, and also the discovery of this disease in Panamanian livestock. We owe to this institution an extensive monograph on the poisonous snakes of Panama and on the incidence of snake bites; the first study on the presence of Chagas' disease in Panama and its vectors; the first complete studies on the botfly larvae in human beings; on horse parasites; on ticks and other biting insects; on the isolation of the Venezuelan equine encephalitis, from birds of Panama, accompanied by ecological and epidemiological studies on that disease and other forms of encephalitis; on the use of DDT to combat different species of harmful insects that torture us on our beaches, in our forests, and even in our urban areas. And because it is outstanding in importance, among all these papers, I should make special mention of the valuable investigations, experiments, and discoveries with respect to the presence of yellow fever in the jungles of Central America and Panama and the species of mosquito that transmit it, and with respect to the appearance in our midst of various viruses that, as Dr. Soper told us a little while ago, have been exploding throughout the world.

It is impossible for a layman, such as I am and as most of us here present are, to understand the full magnitude of the scientific value of the work done by the Gorgas Memorial Laboratory, but even a vague idea of its wide and deep significance should make every citizen of Panama feel gratitude to and admiration for the men of science who are accomplishing a work of such world importance. Nor can we fail to feel a well founded pride in the fact that on Panamanian soil, on Panamanian initiative, and with the effective technical and economic cooperation of the United States and of praiseworthy philanthropists from that country, this laudable institution should flourish here. Nor is it possible, in fine, to forget that this Laboratory is, as I have already said, a living monument to the memory of that eminent savant who was General William Crawford Gorgas, whom posterity recognizes as the man who brought about the sanitary transformation of the cities of Panama and Colon and of the strip of land through which the Inter-oceanic Canal runs.

That was an immense task in our first years as a nation, when the Republic did not yet have the technical and economic resources needed to carry it out, and when it was necessary to contend with custom and to do damage to existing interests based on the backwardness in which we lived. The work of sanitation required the elimination of the traditional "tinajas," large earthen jars, tanks, and other water repositories where mosquitoes laid their eggs, and thus bred the vectors of yellow fever and of malaria; the destruction of roof gutters and of all structures capable of collecting stagnant water and so becoming mosquito breeding places; fumigation of dwellings for the destruction of insects, rats, and other animals that are menaces to health; the adoption of building regulations that would ensure better health conditions for dwellings; and, in fine, a series of measures that meant for our people, trouble and expense that many persons considered to be unjustified.

It was my privilege to know Dr. Gorgas personally and to witness at the outset the slow but firm, difficult but effective, progress of the sanitation of the Isthmus. At that time I was a minor employee of the Department of Government and Foreign Affairs, and Dr. Gorgas often came there to discuss with our illustrious Secretary, the unforgettable General Santiago de la Guardia, the methods that the two Governments should agree upon for sanitation activities. So I had occasion to admire at first hand the personality of the renowned gentleman and scientist who performed such a vital mission.

In March 1921 the Southern Society of Washington presented an oil portrait of General Gorgas to the Library of the Surgeon General of the War Department, and in the speech I was asked to make at that ceremony I said:

> "The great problem of sanitation was undertaken and solved by Gorgas in a most efficient and thorough manner. At the same time he was so careful, so considerate, and so gentle in his methods that notwithstanding being obliged to damage to a certain extent the people's interests, to destroy customs and prejudices that had existed for generations, he succeeded in carrying out without friction his stupendous task. Suavity was the predominant trait of this personality. He did not belong to that class of men who believe it is necessary to be rough and harsh for the performance of a great duty. Courtesy was the means that paved the way for the easy going on of his work. His voice was soft; his manners were gracious and dignified, and a kind smile gave a touch of light to the severe regularity of his features."

Ladies and Gentlemen:

As the Gorgas Memorial Laboratory inaugurates the Insectary that is its latest and most brilliant achievement, I ask that we recall with devotion the memory of the brilliant savant whose name the Laboratory bears, and give warm applause to the eminent Major General Paul H. Streit, President of the Institute, who was coming from his headquarters in Washington to honor this occasion with his presence and his remarks, but who, for reasons of illness, was unable to be present, and whose place on the program has been taken with distinction by the Secretary of the Institute, Dr. Fred L. Soper; to the generous philanthropist James H. Rand, the donor of the splendid Insectary we are inaugurating today, which will bear his name in recognition of his munificence; to the distinguished Director of the Laboratory, Dr. Martin D. Young; and to all the men and women in the United States and in Panama who are working in this Institution, bound by the twofold ties of love for science and of universal solidarity.

Thank you.

Appendix 5,b

Remarks by Dr. Fred L. Soper, Secretary, Representing Major General Paul H. Streit, USA (Ret.), President, Gorgas Memorial Institute of Tropical and Preventive Medicine, at the Dedication of the Rand Insectary of the Gorgas Memorial Laboratory, Panama, Republic of Panama, March 4, 1965

On behalf of the Gorgas Memorial Institute of Tropical and Preventive Medicine, its Board of Directors, and the Executive Committee, whose Chairman I have the honor to represent, may I express my pleasure in being here with this distinguished audience at the dedication of a most important addition to the physical resources of the Gorgas Memorial Laboratory. In the name of Dr. Streit, I bid you welcome.

The Gorgas Memorial Laboratory, established on this site in 1929, has completed 36 years of research. But the Gorgas Memorial Institute, the parent organization, antedates the Laboratory by almost a decade.

The initiative for the creation of the Gorgas Memorial Institute came from the President of the Republic of Panama, Dr. Belisario Porras. In November 1920, the President wrote to Surgeon General William C. Braisted asking his collaboration in creating a Gorgas Memorial Laboratory in Panama.

At its first meeting in Washington in January 1921, Dr. Porras was declared President and Founder of the Provisional Board of Directors of the Gorgas Memorial Institute.

The President of Panama was one of the nine incorporators of the Gorgas Memorial Institute; among the others were the Surgeons General of the U. S. Public Health Service, U. S. Army, U. S. Navy, Dr. Leo S. Rowe, the Director General of the Pan American Union, and the Honorable John Bassett Moore, the first United States jurist to serve on the International Court at The Hague. Moore, was personally involved in the legal proceedings leading to the incorporation of the Gorgas Institute; to him we owe the text of the Institute's charter which even today could not be bettered for its purposes.

Once the Institute was created in October 1921, the President of Panama caused its charter to be registered and legalized in this Republic before the end of the same year.

The Gorgas Memorial Institute is deeply indebted to President Porras for without his initiative and persistence the Gorgas Memorial Institute might not have been born. On the basis of existing records in its files, Dr. Belisario Porras can truly be designated the Father of the Gorgas Memorial Institute.

The incorporators of the Gorgas Memorial Institute, under the leadership of the President of Panama, envisaged it as a research center supported by philanthropic contributions from Gorgas' fellow countrymen with the participation of Panama and other American nations.

In its early years the Gorgas Institute failed to get adequate endowment from private sources; in 1928, an appeal was made to the United States Congress. The Congress responded with Public Law 350 (70th Congress) committing the United States to permanent annual contributions to the Gorgas Memorial Institute for the operation of the Gorgas Memorial Laboratory, provided a suitable building and site could be provided from other resources.

This condition was met the following year when the Republic of Panama ceded to the Gorgas Memorial Institute in perpetuity the present site of the Gorgas Laboratory, so long as it continues to be used as such. This action was confirmed by the National Assembly in 1930.

This Laboratory then was created through indirect collaboration of Panama and the United States through a private agency, without resort to direct negotiation and in the absence of any over-all agreement between the two nations. It has operated from the beginning as a technical institution, free of diplomatic and political pressures.

The ample terms of the charter of the Gorgas Memorial Institute, issued by the State of Delaware, are strengthened for international purposes by United States Public Law 350 of the 70th Congress, as amended, which provides that "the said Gorgas Memorial Institute be, and it hereby is, authorized within its discretion, henceforth to accept from any of the Latin American Governments, or from any other sources, any funds which may be offered or given for the use of the Gorgas Memorial Institute for the maintenance and operation of the Gorgas Memorial Laboratory, and for carrying on the work of said Laboratory wherever deemed by the said Institute to be necessary or desirable."

This constitutes, in effect, a Federal Charter for the Gorgas Memorial Institute in its dealings with individuals, organizations, and nations in financing the Gorgas Memorial Laboratory.

I have traced this historical development that you may know the solid basis of legal position of the Gorgas Laboratory before attempting to look at its future potential.

I make no pretense of foresight; I have no crystal ball. My attempt is to analyze the present situation on which the future potential of the Gorgas Laboratory must depend.

As has been pointed out, the legal position of the Gorgas Memorial Institute is an ideal one. It is free from diplomatic and political pressures, free from the bureaucratic restrictions of any government. It is free to negotiate directly, at the technical level, with any government, government agency, intergovernmental agency, private organization, or individual.

Within the Republic of Panama, the Gorgas Memorial Laboratory has an established position after more than three decades of operation, with ready acceptance by Government and by the people of the areas worked in the Interior.

The Gorgas Memorial Laboratory has an international staff; citizens of Panama, of the United States, and of other nations working harmoniously together under identical conditions of employment.

The Gorgas Memorial Laboratory is located in a large metropolitan center with unexcelled facilities of communication to tropical areas in the Republic of Panama and in other countries of Central American, Caribbean, and South American areas. This metropolitan area has all the amenities for the social and cultural development of the families of staff members very close to the tropical problems to be studied.

The site of the Laboratory, adjacent to the grounds of the Santo Tomás Hospital, gives it access to clinical material coming from underdeveloped, but developing, tropical areas. Also nearby, in the Panama Canal Zone, is the Middle America Research Unit, a medical research laboratory of the United States National Institute of Allergy and Infectious Diseases, operated in collaboration with the Walter Reed Army Institute of Research.

At the present moment in history, with the penetration of the Inter-American Highway and with preparatory studies for the digging of an inter-oceanic canal, the Gorgas Memorial Laboratory is most strategically located for studies of biomedical importance. The opportunity is unique and should not be neglected.

The Gorgas Memorial Laboratory is located at the narrow point where the two land-funnels forming the natural biocommunication route between North and South America come together.

At this critical time the Gorgas Memorial Laboratory finds itself with adequate physical resources for its immediate program. The three buildings in this compound, significantly, have been financed from three different sources. The parent building has been ceded by the Republic of Panama; the modern laboratory unit, dedicated two years ago, was financed by the United States; and the third, the Insectary, which we are here to dedicate today, is the fruit of private philanthropy.

The receipt of funds for the erection of this Insectary from a private individual is a gratifying milestone in the progress of this effort. As mentioned earlier, the initial plan for the Gorgas Memorial Laboratory called for its support by private endowment. This recent gift for capital improvement is but part of the considerable assistance the Laboratory has received from Mr. James H. Rand, the first philanthropist to become actively interested in it. Mr. Rand, who discovered the Gorgas Laboratory only a few years ago, is a most successful and dynamic business man, long a friend of medicine, now keenly interested in the problems of tropical diseases. Mr. Rand's interest has grown as his knowledge of the needs and opportunities has increased.

For the first time, the Gorgas Memorial Laboratory is equipped to meet its current needs. But the current needs of the Gorgas Memorial Laboratory are not in accord with the needs and opportunities in its chosen field of endeavor.

The tropical disease problems of Panama may vary in detail but are essentially the same as those of neighboring countries. Just as the United States has found it impossible to properly study its encephalitis virus diseases within its own borders, so it is necessary, if one is to understand the problems of Panama, that studies be conducted in other countries.

Modern medical research is much more sophisticated and costly than medical research of a past generation. Small individual countries cannot easily meet the requirements of highly trained technical personnel and financial support required for national research units. From its strategic position, the Gorgas Memorial Laboratory should be collaborating with, and receiving some support from, other countries accessible to it.

Various departments and agencies of the United States Government freely admit their need to study problems in other countries for the benefit of its own citizens. United States support in tropical-medical research is quite considerable. The amount of such support to programs at the Gorgas Memorial Laboratory should increase rapidly as this Laboratory becomes prepared to do research in depth on some of the problems now under survey.

In no other tropical area of the world are there opportunities and facilities for biomedical research comparable with those provided in the Panama area as a result of the location here of the Gorgas Memorial Laboratory and the Middle America Research Unit. This unique situation results in a multi-disciplinary team, with modern research facilities, capable of conducting concentrated investigations on any major micro-biological problem in the tropics. These two laboratories, together provide research opportunities that should be better known and more fully utilized by the countries of this Hemisphere.

The Pan American and World Health Organizations, with the responsibility of advising and assisting all of the nations in the Western Hemisphere, have their own divisions of research for the support and stimulation of work on certain special problems. Problems of special interest to these Organizations, in which the Gorgas Memorial Laboratory might well be involved internationally, are malaria, yellow fever, and plague. The international health agencies should come to depend more and more on the Gorgas Memorial Laboratory as it develops and intensifies its activities.

There is a very real need and opportunity for programs involving the collaboration of the Gorgas Memorial Laboratory with research departments of universities in the United States and elsewhere. Many universities with interest in certain phases of tropical medicine lack the opportunity for observation and training in contact with the problems of their interest. If the Gorgas Memorial Laboratory is to develop cooperative programs with such university departments having special interest in the tropics, this Laboratory must be ready to service workers in the field and at the same time get the benefit of service from the more sophisticated centers of research elsewhere.

Research in tropical medicine was a relatively simple operation 35 years ago when this Laboratory was founded, in comparison with this field today. At that time the known virus diseases were very limited in number, the best known of which were rabies, smallpox, yellow fever, and poliomyelitis. Since then our knowledge of identifiable viruses has developed at an explosive rate; of the arthropod-borne viruses, about 175 are known. The whole field of adeno and entero-viruses has developed since that time.

The increasing incrimination of viruses as the activating agents in the development of various types of cancer inevitably forces intensified studies in this field.

I have mentioned particularly the virus field, but it must be remembered that the Gorgas responsibility is to a broad field of tropical problems. I have failed to touch on the problem of training of technical workers at various levels in the field of tropical medicine which is essential if this Laboratory is to make its major contribution to the solution of the tropical disease problems of the Americas.

In closing I would emphasize once more that I have not really attempted to look at the future, rather have I attempted to analyze the basic resources of the Gorgas Memorial Laboratory and to indicate some of the needs and opportunities which exist. The elements we have and the needs and opportunities together create a potential for an unlimited future. Let us begin to plan and work in accord with that potential.

Appendix 6

Address by Major General Paul H. Streit, USA (Ret.), President, Gorgas Memorial Institute of Tropical and Preventive Medicine, at the Dedication of the Gorgas House Historical Marker, University of Alabama Campus, Tuscaloosa, Alabama, May 29, 1966

William Crawford Gorgas—In Appreciation

It is a pleasure indeed for me to join you today in this ceremony honoring the Gorgas family, the most notable of which were General Josiah Gorgas, his wife, Amelia Gayle Gorgas, and their son, William Crawford Gorgas. These wonderful people left an indelible mark on the University of Alabama, the State of Alabama, and in the case of their son William, on the whole world.

Young Amelia Gayle, the daughter of Governor John Gayle of Alabama, could not have foreseen the events that were to occur in the years ahead, when in the summer of 1853, she journeyed to Mt. Vernon, Alabama, and there met Captain Josiah Gorgas. He was a handsome bachelor, a West Point graduate, and the Commander of the Arsenal. Marriage followed, and soon thereafter, the Civil War. Captain Gorgas served as Chief of Ordnance for the Confederate Forces, and was promoted thru grades to the rank of General.

After the War, he was elected as Vice Chancellor of the University of the South at Sewanee, Tennessee, and served for nine years in this capacity. In 1878, he became President of the University of Alabama. His tenure was short lived. Tragic illness forced his untimely retirement, but not before he had made an indelible imprint on the University.

The Gorgas family first occupied, in 1879, the now famous Gorgas House before which we are gathered today to dedicate this historical monument. In the difficult times following the death of General Josiah Gorgas, Amelia Gayle Gorgas continued to live on at the Gorgas House, having two important responsibilities. Supervising the health of the students at the University dispensary, and acting as the University Librarian won Amelia Gayle Gorgas the love and respect of the students and faculty, and all others connected with the University. It is most appropriate that her memory should live on today with the University Library bearing her name as the "Amelia Gayle Gorgas Library."

William Crawford Gorgas, their son, became an international character, and his professional career in the military service involved great responsibilities and accomplishments of importance to human welfare. He was the world's first great sanitarian, and "the most internationally honored American who ever lived." It is entirely fitting that we honor his memory today, together with that of his parents, on the soil of Alabama where he was born, and which he loved with passionate devotion.

William graduated from the University of the South in 1875. He aspired to a military career. Failing to get a West Point appointment, he entered the Army through the back door, by studying Medicine, over the protests of his father. Said he: "It is not in the Army that the sphere of the doctor is ennobling." William was awarded the degree of Doctor of Medicine in 1879 from Bellevue Hospital Medical College in New York, and following an internship, entered the Army.

For almost 20 years Gorgas lived the life of an Army doctor of that period. In those days, an Army doctor's activities extended beyond the post; anyone with medical skills was compelled, for humanitarian reasons alone, to respond to calls from the native population. Such practice was comprehensive and inclusive: an infant ill with diphtheria, a woman in childbirth, a frontiersman with a gangrenous leg. Army life was more than an education in Medicine; it was training in those fine virtues of patience and sympathy, and self-sacrifice, so essential to the good practitioner.

There was something fatalistic in the way yellow fever dogged Gorgas' life, yet served to further him in his great career. Had it not been for the terrible yellow fever epidemic in Mobile in 1853, his mother would not have fled to Mt. Vernon and there met his father; nor would there have occurred the marriage of Doctor Gorgas to Marie Doughty, herself stricken with yellow fever in 1882 at Fort Brown, Texas, and attended by him. Gorgas also contracted the disease at Fort Brown. Later, being immune, the Army frequently sent him to posts where yellow fever existed.

Following the occupation of Havana by American troops in 1898, Gorgas was sent there as Chief Sanitary Officer. After five years of civil war, the city was in a highly unsanitary condition. Though yellow fever was infrequent, it was always a chief concern.

Yellow fever inspired terror equalled by few other diseases. People who constantly associated with the disease did not necessarily contract it, while others, who had never been near a patient, fell victim to it. Men and women could sleep near and feed yellow fever patients and never catch the disease. Meanwhile, craven souls locked in their rooms fell victims and died. Such was the disease whose elimination became the chief duty of Gorgas.

Like most medical men of his time, Gorgas believed that yellow fever was a filth disease, and the way to protect a city was to make it clean. Gorgas set to work to do just that. At the end of several months, this tropical city became the pride of America. The general death rate declined; dysentery, typhoid and the like all but disappeared. But yellow fever increased, and especially in areas that were cleanest.

Yellow fever had been the subject of serious inquiry by scientists for generations, but no progress was made until Walter Reed and his courageous associates and volunteers came to Cuba in 1900, and dramatically proved its transmission by the *Stegomyia* mosquito. In six months, Walter Reed, Lazaer, Carroll and Agramonte solved the mystery of yellow fever with an inescapable finality which sometimes makes science as much a thing of beauty as art itself. To a skeptical world Reed proved that the yellow fever parasite was carried only by the *Stegomyia fasciata*.

Most scientists regarded Reed's experiments as a brilliant academic performance but could not see how it lessened the yellow fever peril. We now knew that the *Stegomyia* mosquito conveyed the disease, but how to control these pests which existed by the billion in every street, house and nook in Havana?

Gorgas followed the experiments of Walter Reed with wonder and skepticism, but when the truth was there for all to see he arrived at a simple conclusion. Said he: "If the *Stegomyia* mosquitoes cause yellow fever, I will eradicate them." Governor General Wood, a physician, gave him unqualified support.

In six months, yellow fever which had been endemic for centuries disappeared. The entire scientific world was tremendously impressed. Gorgas' success in Havana brought him international fame.

The triumph of Reed and Gorgas in Havana came at a particularly fortunate time. From the day when Balboa crossed the Isthmus, the linking of the Atlantic and Pacific oceans had been one of the great dreams of civilization. Near the end of the 19th century, the French undertook the work of making this dream come true, but their efforts resulted in abject failure.

Soon after the turn of the century, the American Government prepared to undertake this great adventure. By 1904 the digging began. America plunged into the task with assurance and cheerfulness, forgetting that it was yellow fever and malaria that caused the French failure.

Gorgas was appointed as Chief Sanitary Officer, but encountered almost insurmountable administrative difficulties from the Isthmian Canal Commission. He was not able to secure even the most essential sanitary supplies, and these administrative problems were long continued and endured. It was 1907 before he was finally made a member of the Canal Commission and obtained adequate authority.

The sad truth is that the work by Walter Reed and Gorgas in Havana had made little impression on the members of this commission or the Government. The first chairman of the commission was convinced that the whole idea of mosquito transmission of yellow fever was tommyrot. Gorgas' pleas for screening, crude oil and inspectors stirred him to laughter and scorn.

Despite this lack of cooperation, Gorgas patiently labored on, and, by his persistence, in time rid the Canal Zone of yellow fever, greatly reduced malaria, and made the cities of Colon and Panama models of sanitation. Morbidity and mortality rates in the Zone compared favorably with the best of the American cities. In the eyes of the world, it was Gorgas alone who made possible the construction of the Panama Canal.

Gorgas was amiable and optimistic. To this was added a strong determination and persistence. It was this combination of seemingly opposite qualities that contributed so much to his success over all obstacles in this project.

In late 1913, while yet a member of the Isthmian Canal Commission, Colonel Gorgas went to Rhodesia and South Africa, upon invitation of the Chamber of Mines in Johannesburg, to advise as to better methods of controlling malaria and pneumonia among the native mine workers. Pneumonia especially had been taking a tremendous toll of life among these laborers. His suggestions resulted in prompt alleviation of these serious problems.

In 1914, he was notified of his appointment as Surgeon General of the Army. He served during a time when our forces expanded overnight to great armies, and he served with notable distinction.

In the same year, Gorgas persuaded the newly created Rockefeller Foundation to undertake the eradication of yellow fever from the whole world. He became the head of the Rockefeller Yellow Fever Commission, and from 1915 to his death in 1920, was the guiding force in its work.

Three days after the signing of the Armistice, he retired from the service for age, and returned to his labor of love—the elimination of yellow fever from the world. By the end of 1919, he had eliminated yellow fever from Guayaquil, Ecuador, the notorious pesthole of the Pacific, and then turned his attention to Africa. In London, enroute there, he became ill and died. The funeral, at the wish of the British Government, took place in St. Paul's Cathedral.

Dr. William Welch of Johns Hopkins, in conferring a degree on Gorgas said: "It was he, who by the application of the discoveries of Walter Reed, was mainly instrumental in freeing Cuba of yellow fever—and it was he, who in spite of embarrassments and obstacles, made the construction of the canal possible without serious loss of life or incapacity from disease— a triumph of preventive medicine."

327

At a convocation at Oxford University, preparatory to conferring the honorary degree of Doctor of Science, the orator said: "Those are most to be honored by us who have increased knowledge and thereby promoted the welfare of the world. It was Gorgas who cleansed Havana; it was he who put fever and pestilence to flight in the Isthmus of Panama, and made possible the long-thwarted construction of the Panama Canal. The result has been an amelioration of the condition of human life in the tropics where it is now possible to live in comfort."

General Raymond W. Bliss, a former Surgeon General of the United States Army, in an address in the Hall of Fame in New York University on May 24, 1951, said: "He achieved great things but did this by methods so simple and logical that in retrospect they seem almost obvious. It would be easy to forget that they were not obvious at the time, and that he created them. He dreamed and planned great things but they were attainable. He was an international crusader against disease but a crusader in the entirely practical sense of the term. He was the first great preventive medicine officer. His character and life remain an inspiration to those who must fight disease throughout the world."

I heard General Gorgas address thousands of physicians in a medical officers' training camp in 1917, and later met him personally. He had a trim figure, and luminous eyes. His white hair and mustache contributed much to a distinguished appearance. He was mild, firm, kind and direct, and he made a profound impression on me.

Soon after his death, the Gorgas Memorial Institute of Tropical and Preventive Medicine, Incorporated, was organized to memorialize his name in a vital and effective way.

The initiative for the creation of the Gorgas Memorial Institute came from the President of the Republic of Panama, Dr. Belisario Porras. In 1928, Congress committed the United States to a permanent annual contribution to the Gorgas Memorial Institute for the operation of the Gorgas Memorial Laboratory.

The site and original building of the Laboratory were contributed by the Republic of Panama. Other agencies have contributed funds. Though small at first, the Gorgas Memorial Laboratory has grown in capacity and influence, and has made notable contributions to human knowledge, especially in the ecology and etiology of tropical diseases.

Efforts are under way now to bring about close working relationships between the Laboratory and the University of Alabama because of our common aims. Good progress is being made.

Yes, the State of Alabama and the Nation have a right to be proud of this man and his family. I am very happy to be present with you for the dedication of this tangible and historical memorial as a lasting recognition of their ideals and their work.

List of Professional Staff Members of the Gorgas Memorial Laboratory, 1929-1968

Herbert C. Clark, M.D., Director, 1928-1954.

Carl M. Johnson, Sc.D., M.D., Assistant Director 1934-1944; Director 1954-1964; Director Emeritus 1964-.

Martin D. Young, Sc.D., Director, 1964-.

Lawrence H. Dunn, B.S., Assistant Director, 1928-1934.

L. E. Rozeboom, Sc.D., 1934-1937.

A. O. Foster, Sc.D., 1934-1939.

Daniel Jobbins, M. Sc., 1938-1943.

Graham B. Fairchild, Ph.D., 1938-1943; 1946-; Assistant Director 1957-1961; Associate Director 1962-.

Harold Trapido, Ph.D., 1946-1956.

Enid C. de Rodaniche, Ph.D., 1947-1961.

Pedro Galindo, M.S., 1947-.

Marshall Hertig, Ph.D., 1948-1965.

Teresina P. de Pinzón, M.S., 1948-1951.

Phyllis T. Johnson, Ph.D., 1957; 1959-1963.

Mary Lou Morrow, B. A., 1957-1958.

Wilford J. Hanson, M.S., 1957-1961.

Ellicott McConnell, Ph.D., 1957-1962.

Eustorgio Méndez, M.S., 1959-.

Margaret A. Grayson, Ph.D., 1961-.

Octavio E. Sousa, Ph.D., 1961-.

César Pinilla, M.D., 1961-1962.

Vernon E. Thatcher, Ph.D., 1963-1967.

Manuel A. Vásquez, M.D., 1962-.

Curt R. Schneider, Ph.D., 1962-1967.

Sunthorn Srihongse, M.D., M.P.H.T.M., Dr. P.H., 1962-.

Manuel Palau, M.D., 1963-1967.

Alfredo Suescum, M.D., 1963-1964.

Katsuji Nagai, D.V.M., D.M.Sc., 1964.

Miguel Kourany, M.P.H., Ph.D., 1964-.

Aristides Herrer, Sc.D., 1965-.

Carlos E. Ortiz, M.D., 1964-1966.

James A. Porter, Jr., D.V.M., Ph.D., M.P.H., 1965-1968.

José Félix Guevara, M.D., part time, 1967-.

Roberto Blandón-Calderón, M.D., 1966-.

Manuel E. Núñez, M.D., 1967-.

Alvaro Tomás, M.D., 1965-1966.

Alfredo Tablete, M.D., 1966-1967.
Ernesto Jonás, M.D., 1967-1968.
David C. Baerg, Ph.D., 1967-.
Howard A. Christensen, Ph.D., 1968-.
John H. Edgcomb, M.D., 1968-.
Abdiel Goytía, M.D., 1968.
Eulo Lupi, M.D., 1968.
Cutberto Parillón, M.D., 1968-.
Sam R. Telford, Jr., Ph.D., 1968-.
Roberto Reyna, M.D., 1968-.

Appendix 8

List of Officers of the Uniformed Services Assigned to the Gorgas Memorial Laboratory 1931-1968

United States Army

	Period of Service
Major George Callender, M.C.	1932
Major H. S. Eakins, V.C.	1931–1935
Major Marshall Hertig, Sn.C.	1943–1947
Capt. G. B. Fairchild, Sn.C.	1943–1946
Capt. W. C. McDuffie, Sn.C.	1943–1944
Capt. Charles D. Michener, Sn.C.	1945–1946
1st Lieut. Roy Melvin, Sn.C.	1943–1944
1st Lieut. Harold Trapido, Sn.C.	1944–1946
1st Lieut. Dale W. Jenkins, Sn.C.	1945–1946
T4g Edson H. Fichter, Jr.	1945
Lt. Col. Bryce C. Walton, M.S.C.	1963–1964

United States Navy

Commander G. F. Clark, M.C.	1931–1932
Lt. Commander Paul W. Wilson, M.C.	1932–1934
Acting Chief Pharmacist Mate Charles E. Martin	1932–1933
Lt. Commander E. G. Hakansson, M.C.	1934–1937
Pharmacist Mate J. F. Buckner	1934–1935
Pharmacist Mate H. A. Down	1934–1937
Pharmacist Mate L. E. Boston	1936–1938
Lt. (j.g.) James J. Sapero, M.C.	1937–1939
Pharmacist Mate M. H. Williams	1938–1939
Commander Alan C. Pipkin Sr., M.S.C.	1959–1964
Hospitalman Chief William C. Coles	1959–1960

Chief Hospital Corpsman Barton S. Halderman   1960–1963
Commander Ralph D. Comer, M.C.   1966–1968
Chief Hospital Corpsman Paul E. Campbell   1965–1967
First Class Corpsman William T. Lynch   1968–

United States Air Force

Lt. Col. Albert K. Cheng, M.C.   1968–

United States Public Health Service

Sanitary Engineer Director W. H. W. Komp   1931–1947
Passed Assistant Surgeon Leon Rosen   1954–1955

Outstanding Pioneer Accomplishments of the Gorgas Memorial Laboratory

1. *Protozoal Diseases of Man and Lower Animals:*
   Malaria:
   1933 and Subsequently—First long range, large scale field tests of the antimalarial drugs, atebrin, chloroquine, and paludrine under controlled conditions in the New World tropics.

   1945—First long range field tests of DDT house spraying to control malaria.

   1960—Field demonstration of the effectiveness of weekly doses of pyrimethamine-primaquine drugs in combination in the eradication of *Plasmodium falciparum* malaria from a tropical area.

   1966—Demonstration that certain common human malaria parasites could be grown in certain species of Panamanian monkeys and could be transferred to man and other monkeys by blood inoculation and by bites of mosquitoes.

   American Trypanosomiasis:
   1931—First report of Chagas' disease in Panama and discovery of the vectors.

   1959—First report of *Trypanosoma rangeli* from man and wild vertebrates in Panama and demonstration of the development of the human strain in the salivary glands of *Rhodnius pallescens*.

   1965—Demonstration that the Panamanian strain of *T. rangeli* differs from the South and Central American strains in its behavior of development in the insect vector.

   Leishmaniasis:
   1965—Incrimination of seven wild vertebrates as reservoir hosts of human leishmaniasis.

1966—Demonstration that leishmania infection may commonly occur in the apparently normal skin of some feral animals without producing lesions.

1945-1968—Recognition of over 70 species of *Phlebotomus* in Panama, of which 4 or 5 have been found infected with leishmania.

Animal Trypanosomiasis:

1932—Discovery of the vampire bat transmission of equine trypanosomiasis.

1932—Discovery of bovine trypanosomiasis in Panama.

Intestinal Protozoa:

1944—First finding of *Isospora hominis* in Panama.

2. *Helminthic Diseases of Man and Lower Animals:*

1934-1935—First comprehensive survey of the worm parasites of equines in Panama.

1966—Finding of a new human disease entity caused by *Echinococcus oligarthrus,* a little known cestode parasite of pumas and other large felines; description of the first known human case which terminated fatally; and demonstration of the life cycle of the parasite.

3. *Rickettsial Diseases:*

1946—First report of Q fever in Panama.

1947—First report of murine typhus in Panama.

1951—First recognition of Rocky Mountain spotted fever in Panama.

4. *Virus Diseases:*

1949—First demonstration of the mosquito vectors of yellow fever in Panama and Central America and the inauguration of comprehensive studies on vector ecology and transmission capabilities.

1957—First recovery of St. Louis encephalitis virus and recognition of human cases in Panama.

1958—First isolation of Ilhéus virus in Central America.

1960—First isolation of Changuinola virus from man.

1961—Discovery of four new arboviruses: Madrid, Ossa, Patois, and Zegla.

1963—First isolation of Wyeomyia subgroup of arboviruses from man.

1964—First isolation of Bussuquara virus from man.

1964—Recognition of the first human case of Ilhéus encephalitis.

1964—First isolation of Eastern equine encephalitis virus from mosquitoes in Panama.

1965—Finding of crab-hole mosquitoes *(Deinocerites)* as hosts for St. Louis encephalitis virus.

1968—First isolation of Vesicular Stomatitis virus (Indiana) from man in Panama and detection of virus transmission by the use of sentinel monkeys.

5. *Medical Entomology:*

1929—First elucidation of the life cycle of the human botfly, *Dermatobia hominis,* in man.

1935—First establishment of a laboratory colony of *Anopheles albimanus,* the main vector of malaria in Central America.

1944—First tests of DDT to control Phlebotominae sandflies.

1945—First experimental trials of DDT for the control of *Simulium* spp., the vectors of *Onchocerca volvulus,* the blinding filariid parasite of man.

1945—First experiments with DDT for the control of *Culicoides* sandflies.

1945—First observations in Panama on the habits and life histories of chigger mites (Trombiculidae), potential vectors of disease.

1966—First comprehensive survey of the ticks and biting insects of Panama.

6. *Miscellaneous Projects:*

1930-1954—Comprehensive survey of the poisonous snakes of Panama and the incidence of snake bites.

Appendix 10

Bibliography of Papers Emanating from the Gorgas Memorial Laboratory Through December 31, 1969, with Author Index and Subject Headings Index

Prepared by Lic. Manuel Víctor De Las Casas, Librarian,
Gorgas Memorial Laboratory

Publ. No.

1930

1.   CLARK, H. C.—1930.
          A Preliminary Report on Some Parasites in the Blood of Wild Monkeys of Panamá.
          American Journal of Tropical Medicine, *10*(1): 25-42. (Repr. No. 2)

2.   CLARK, H. C.—1930.
          Some Records Concerning Traumatism and Malaria in Central America.
          Surgery, Gynecology & Obstetrics, *50*: 329-330. (Repr. No. 1)

3.*   DUNN, L. H.—1930.
          Rearing the Larvae of *Dermatobia hominis* Linn., in Man.
          Psyche, *37*(4): 327-342. (Repr. No. 4)

---

* The asterisk following the number of the citation indicates that reprints of the paper in question were available at the time of the preparation of the bibliography.

4.   FAUST, E. C.—1930.
      The Panamá Strains of Human Strongyloides.
      Proceedings of the Society for Experimental Biology and Medicine,
      28(3): 253-255. (Repr. No. 2a)

5.   WISLOCKI, G. B.—[1930]
      On a Series of Placental Stages of a Platyrrhine Monkey (Ateles geof-
      froyi) with Some Remarks Upon Age, Sex and Breeding Period in
      Platyrrhines.
      Contributions to Embryology, No. 133, pp. 173-192. (Repr. No. 2b)

1931

6.*   BATH, C. H.—1931.
      The Practical and Research Value of Mosquito Traps.
      American Journal of Tropical Medicine, 11(2): 147-150. (Repr. No. 5)

7.*   CLARK, H. C.—1931.
      Progress in the Survey for Blood Parasites of the Wild Monkeys of
      Panamá.
      American Journal of Tropical Medicine, 11(1): 11-20. (Repr. No. 9)

8.   CLARK, H. C., and DUNN, L. H.—1931.
      Experimental Efforts to Transfer Monkey Malaria to Man.
      American Journal of Tropical Medicine, 11(1): 1-10. (Repr. No. 10)

      CLARK, H. C., and DUNN, L. H.—1931.
      Experimental Efforts to Transfer Monkey Malaria to Man.
      Surgery, Gynecology & Obstetrics, 52(2A): 428-429. (Repr. No. 10a)

9.*   CLARK, H. C., DUNN, L. H., and BENAVIDES, J.—1931.
      Experimental Transmission to Man of a Relapsing Fever Spirochete in
      a Wild Monkey of Panamá, Leontocebus geoffroyi (Pucheran).
      American Journal of Tropical Medicine, 11(4): 243-257. (Repr. No.
      11)

10.* CURRY, D. P.—1931.
      Anopheles (Anopheles) neomaculipalpus. A new Species of the Arri-
      balzagaia Group of Anopheles from Panamá.
      American Journal of Hygiene, 13(2): 643-647. Repr. No. 7)

11.* CURRY, D. P.—1931.
      Recognition of Anopheles argyritarsis by the Characteristics of the Male
      Genitalia.
      American Journal of Hygiene, 13(2): 648. (Repr. No. 6)

12.   DUNN, L. H.—1931.
      Notes on the Tick Ornithodoros talaje (Guer.) Infesting a House in the
      Canal Zone.
      Psyche, 38(4): 170-173. (Repr. No. 18)

13. DUNN, L. H.—1931.
A Simple Method for Collecting Adult Filarial Parasites from Muscle
Tissues of Monkeys.
Journal of Parasitology, *18*(2): 111-112. (Repr. No. 17)

14. FAUST, E. C.—1931.
Human Strongyloidiasis in Panamá.
The American Journal of Hygiene, *14*(1): 203-211. (Repr. No. 14)

15. FAUST, E. C.—1931.
The Incidence and Significance of Infestation with *Endamoeba histoly-
tica* in New Orleans and the American Tropics.
American Journal of Tropical Medicine, *11*(3): 231-237. (Repr. No. 3)

16. FAUST, E. C.—1931.
Investigations in Panamá During the Summer of 1930.
Science, *73*(1880): 43-45. (Repr. No. 3a)

17. JORDAN, E. O., and HALL, J. R.—1931.
A Case of Food Poisoning Apparently Due to Staphylococcus.
Journal of Preventive Medicine, *5*(5): 387-389. (Repr. No. 15)

18.* MILLER, J. W.—1931.
Chagas' Disease in Panamá: Report of Three Cases.
Southern Medical Journal, *24*(7): 645-647. (Repr. No. 12)

1932

19. ANDERSON, H. H.—1932.
Amebiasis in Panamá and California with Special Reference to Incidence and Treatment.
American Journal of Tropical Medicine, *12*(6): 459-466. (Repr. No.
16a)

20.* CLARK, H. C., and DUNN, L. H.—1932.
Experimental Studies on Chagas' Disease in Panamá.
American Journal of Tropical Medicine, *12*(1): 49-77. (Repr. No. 19)

21. CLARK, H. C., and KOMP, W. H. W.—1932.
Observations on Malaria Incidence in Some Unsanitated River Villages
in the Republic of Panamá, with Special Reference to Proposed Construction Projects in the Canal Zone. (Symposium on Malaria—Part 2).
Southern Medical Journal, *25*(6): 642-647. (Repr. No. 16)

22. CLARK, H. C., and KOMP, W. H. W.—1932.
A Second Year's Observations on Malaria in Some Unsanitated Chagres
River Villages with Special Reference to the Use of Quinine and Plas-
mochin. Published by the Gorgas Memorial Laboratory.
(Privately Printed). (Repr. No. 33)

23. CURRY, D. P.—1932.
Some Observations on the *Nyssorhynchus* Group of the *Anopheles*
(Culicidae) of Panamá.
American Journal of Hygiene, *15*(2): 566-572. (Repr. No. 13)

24. DUNN, L. H.—1932.
An Effective Method for Collecting Ectoparasites from Live Animals and Birds.
Psyche, *39*(1-2): 26-29. (Repr. No. 20)

25.* DUNN, L. H.—1932.
Experiments in the Transmission of *Trypanosoma hippicum* Darling with the Vampire Bat, *Desmodus rotundus murinus* Wagner, as a Vector in Panamá.
Journal of Preventive Medicine, *6*(5): 415-424. (Repr. No. 23)

26. DUNN, L. H.—1932.
A Simple Method of Immobilizing Animals for Laboratory Purposes.
American Journal of Tropical Medicine, *12*(2): 173-179. (Repr. No. 21)

27. DUNN, L. H.—1932.
Susceptibility of Bats to Infection with the Horse Trypanosome, *Trypanosoma hippicum* Darling, in Panamá.
Journal of Preventive Medicine, *6*(3): 155-160. (Repr. No. 22)

28. HEGNER, R.—1932.
Studies on Amoebiasis in Panamá.
The Journal of Parasitology, *18*(3): 153-158. (Repr. No. 16c)

29. HEGNER, R., JOHNSON, C. M., and STABLER, R. M.—1932.
Host-Parasite Relation in Experimental Amebiasis in Monkeys in Panamá.
American Journal of Hygiene, *15*(2): 394-443. (Repr. No. 16b)

30. JORDAN, E. O., and McBROOM, J.—1932.
The Occurrence of *Brucella* Agglutinins in Cattle in the Panamá Canal Zone.
Journal of the American Veterinary Medical Association, *81*, n. s. *34*(3): 401-404. (Repr. No. 26)

31. KOMP, W. H. W.—1932.
A New *Culex, Culex vomerifer,* from Panamá (Dipt., Culicidae).
Psyche, *39*(3): 79-82. (Repr. No. 29)

32. KOMP, W. H. W., and CURRY, D. P.,—1932.
A New *Culex* from Panamá (Dipt., Culicidae).
Psyche, *39*(3): 82-84. (Repr. No. 28)

33. TALIAFERRO, W. H.—1932.
Experimental Studies on the Malaria of Monkeys.
American Journal of Hygiene, *16*(2): 429-449. (Repr. No. 25)

1933

34.* CLARK, H. C., CASSERLY, T. L., and GLADISH, I. O.—1933
Equine Trypanosomiasis—"Murrina" or "Derrengadera." Some Notes on the Disease in Panamá.
Journal of the American Veterinary Medical Association, *83*, n.s. *36*(3): 358-389. (Repr. No. 35)

35.*   CLARK, H. C., and DUNN, L. H.—1933.
       Animal Susceptibility to *Trypanosoma hippicum,* the Equine Trypano-
       some of Panamá; with Special Reference to Cattle as an Unharmed
       Host and Probable Reservoir of Importance.
       American Journal of Tropical Medicine, *13*(3): 273-281. (Repr. No.
       34)

36.   DUNN, L. H.—1933.
       A Natural Infection of *Trypanosoma cruzi* Chagas Found in *Rhodnius
       pallescens* Barber in Panamá.
       American Journal of Tropical Medicine, *13*(5): 471-473. (Repr. No. 43)

37.   DUNN, L. H.—1933.
       A New Snake from Panamá.
       Copeia, No. 4, 193-194. (Repr. No. 37a)

38.*   DUNN, L. H.—1933.
       Observations on the Carnivorous Habits of the Spear-Nosed Bat, *Phyl-
       lostomus hastatus panamensis* Allen, in Panamá.
       Journal of Mammalogy, *14*(3): 188-199. (Repr. No. 39)

39.*   DUNN, L. H.—1933.
       Observations on the Host Selection of *Ornithodorus talaje* Guern., in
       Panamá.
       American Journal of Tropical Medicine, *13*(5): 475-483. (Repr. No.
       42)

40.   DUNN, L. H.—1933.
       Two New Species of Ticks from Panamá (*Amblyomma tapirellum* and
       A. pecarium).
       Parasitology, *25*(3): 353-358. (Repr. No. 30)

41.*   DUNN, L. H., and CLARK, H. C.—1933.
       Notes on Relapsing Fever in Panamá with Special Reference to Animal
       Hosts.
       American Journal of Tropical Medicine, *13*(2): 201-209. (Repr. No.
       31)

42.   HEGNER, R.—1933.
       Specificity in the Genus *Balantidium* Based on Size and Shape of Body
       and Macronucleus, with Description of Six New Species.
       American Journal of Hygiene, *19*(1): 38-67. (Repr. No. 43a)

43.   HEGNER, R., and REES, CHAS. W.—1933.
       Taliaferria clarki, a New Genus and Species of Ciliate from the Cecum
       of the Red Spider Monkey, *Ateles geoffroyi* Kuhl.
       Transactions of the American Microscopical Society, *52*(4): 317-321.
       (Repr. No. 78)

44.   McCOY, O. R.—1933.
       The Occurrence of *Microfilaria ozzardi* in Panamá.
       American Journal of Tropical Medicine, *13*(3): 297-310. (Repr. No. 27)

1934

45. BENAVIDES, J.—1934.
Comments and Procedure on Thick Blood Film Technic.
Journal of Laboratory and Clinical Medicine, 20(3): 289-295. (Repr. No. 51)

46.* BUCKNER, J. F.—1934.
An Improved Technique for Mounting Mosquito Larvae.
American Journal of Tropical Medicine, 14(5): 489-491. (Repr. No. 60)

47. CLARK, H. C.—1934.
The Gorgas Memorial Laboratory and Problems Engaging its Attention.
Transactions of the College of Physicians of Philadelphia, 4th Series, 2(2): 140-149. (Repr. No. 77)

48.* CLARK, H. C.—1934.
The Incidence of Tonsillar Tuberculosis.
(Read August 17, 1922, before the Medical Association of the Isthmian Canal Zone). Published by GML (Workman Printery, July 1934), pp. 1-8. (Repr. No. 59)

49. CLARK, H. C.—1934.
Medical Research, 1932-1933. Report of the Sub-Committee. (Symposium on Malaria—Part 3).
Southern Medical Journal, 27(7): 642-644. (Repr. No. 44a)

50. CURRY, D. P.—1934.
Breeding of Anopheline Mosquitoes Among Aquatic Vegetation of Gatun Lake, Accompanied by Periodic Long Flights of A. albimanus Wied.
Southern Medical Journal, 27(7): 644-651. (Repr. No. 45)

51.* DUNN, L. H.—1934.
Attempts to Transmit Trypanosoma cruzi Chagas with Ticks of the Genus Ornithodoros.
American Journal of Tropical Medicine, 14(3): 283-289. (Repr. No. 55)

52.* DUNN, L. H.—1934.
Entomological Investigations in the Chiriquí Region of Panamá.
Psyche, 41(3): 166-183. (Repr. No. 32)

53. DUNN, L. H.—1934.
Notes on the Little Bulldog Bat, Dirias albiventer minor (Osgood) in Panamá.
Journal of Mammalogy, 15(2): 89-99. (Repr. No. 56)

54.* DUNN, L. H.—1934.
Notes on the Occurrence of Gigantorhynchus echinodiscus Diesing in the Anteater of Panamá.
Journal of Parasitology, 20(4): 227-229. (Repr. No. 41)

55.* DUNN, L. H.—1934.
Notes on the Reduviid Bug, *Eratyrus cuspidatus* Stal., Naturally Infected with *Trypanosoma cruzi* Chagas Found in Panamá.
American Journal of Tropical Medicine, *14*(3): 291-292. (Repr. No. 54)

56.* DUNN, L. H.—1934.
Notes on the Water Lettuce, *Pistia stratiotes* Linn., as a Nursery of Insect Life.
Ecology, *15*(3): 329-331. (Repr. No. 46)

57. DUNN, L. H.—1934.
Prevalence and Importance of the Tropical Warble Fly, *Dermatobia hominis* Linn., in Panamá.
Journal of Parasitology, *20*(4): 219-226. (Repr. No. 40)

58.* DUNN, L. H.—1934.
Ticks from Tapirs of Panamá.
Journal of Parasitology, *20*(5): 312. (Repr. No. 57)

59. JORDAN, E. O., and McBROOM, J.—1934.
Notes on Intestinal Flora in the Tropics.
American Journal of Tropical Medicine, *14*(1): 27-32. (Repr. No. 52)

60. JORDAN, E. O.—1934.
An Outbreak of Food Poisoning Apparently Caused by a New Serologic Type of *Salmonella, (S. panamá)*.
Journal of Infectious Diseases, *55*(Sept.-Oct.): 224-227. (Repr. No. 167)

61.* KOMP, W. H. W., and CLARK, H. C.—1934.
A Third Year's Observation in Panamá, with Special Reference to Control with Atabrine.
American Journal of Tropical Medicine, *14*(5): 381-406. (Repr. No. 37)

62. TALIAFERRO, W. H., and CANNON, P. R.—1934.
The Transmission of *Plasmodium falciparum* to the Howler Monkey, *Alouatta* sp. II. Cellular Reactions.
American Journal of Hygiene, *19*(2): 335-342. (Repr. No. 47a)

63.* TALIAFERRO, W. H., and TALIAFERRO, L. G.—1934.
Alteration in the Time of Sporulation of *Plasmodium brasilianum* in Monkeys by Reversal of Light and Dark.
American Journal of Hygiene, *20*(1): 50-59. (Repr. No. 49)

64.* TALIAFERRO, W. H., and TALIAFERRO, L. G.—1934.
Complement Fixation, Precipitin, Adhesion, Mercuric Chloride and Wasserman Tests in Equine Trypanosomiasis of Panamá (Murrina).
Journal of Immunology, *26*(3): 193-213. (Repr. No. 53)

65.* TALIAFERRO, W. H., and TALIAFERRO, L. G.—1934.
Morphology, Periodicity and Course of Infection of *Plasmodium brasilianum* in Panamanian Monkeys.
American Journal of Hygiene, *20*(1): 1-49. (Repr. No. 50)

66.* TALIAFERRO, W. H., and TALIAFERRO, L. G.—1934.
Superinfection and Protective Experiments with *Plasmodium brasilianum* in Monkeys.
American Journal of Hygiene, *20*(1): 60-72. (Repr. No. 48)

67.* TALIAFERRO, W. H., and TALIAFERRO, L. G.—1934.
The Transmission of *Plasmodium falciparum* to the Howler Monkey, *Alouatta* sp. I. General Nature of the Infections and Morphology of the Parasites.
American Journal of Hygiene, *19*(2): 318-334. (Repr. No. 47)

68. WILSON, P. W.—1934.
Atypical Yaws.
American Journal of Tropical Medicine, *14*(1): 1-25. (Repr. No. 36)

69.* WILSON, P. W.—1934.
Incidence of Yaws and Syphilis in Five Rural Villages, Republic of Panamá.
United States Naval Medical Bulletin, *32*(4): 391-401. (Repr. No. 58)

1935

70. CARPENTER, C. R.—1935.
Behavior of Red Spider Monkeys in Panamá.
Journal of Mammalogy, *16*(3): 171-180. (Repr. No. 73b)

71. CLARK, H. C.—1935.
Recent Research on Therapeutics of Malaria.
Southern Medical Journal, *28*(8): 746-749. (Repr. No. 62)

72. CLARK, H. C., and BENAVIDES, J.—1935.
The Cattle Reservoir for Equine Trypanosomiasis in Panamá. Additional Notes on the Subject.
American Journal of Tropical Medicine, *15*(3): 285-299. (Repr. No. 66)

73. DITMARS, R. L., and GREENHALL, A. M.—1935.
The Vampire Bat. A Presentation of Undescribed Habits and Review of its History.
Zoologica, *19*(2): 53-76. (Repr. No. 79a)

74. DUNN, E. R.—1935.
The Snakes of the Genus *Ninia*.
Proceedings of the National Academy of Sciences, *21*(1): 9-12. (Repr. No. 62a)

75. EAKINS, H. S.—1935.
Murrina.
Veterinary Bulletin (Supplement to the Army Medical Bulletin), *29*(4): 295-309. (Repr. No. 67)

76.* FAUST, E. C.—1935.
Notes on Helminths from Panamá. I. *Taxorchis schistocotyle* (Fischoeder, 1901), from the Panamanian Capybara, *Hydrochoerus isthmius* Goldman, 1912.
Journal of Parasitology, *21*(5): 323-331. (Repr. No. 8)

340

77. FAUST, E. C., and MARTÌNEZ, W. H.—1935.
Notes on Helminths from Panamá. II. Rare Human Nematode Eggs in the Feces of Individuals from Chagres River, Panamá.
Journal of Parasitology, *21*(5): 332-336. (Repr. No. 8a)

78. FAUST, E. C.—1935.
Notes on Helminths from Panamá. III. Filarial Infection in the Marmosets, *Leontocebus geoffroyi* (Pucheran) and *Saimiri orstedii orstedii* (Reinhardt) in Panamá.
Transactions of the Royal Society of Tropical Medicine and Hygiene, *28*(6): 627-634. (Repr. No. 8b)

79. FOSTER, A. O.—1935.
Further Observations on Prenatal Hookworm Infection of Dogs.
Journal of Parasitology, *21*(4): 302-308. (Repr. No. 70a)

80. FOSTER, A. O.—1935.
The Immunity of Dogs to *Ancylostoma caninum*.
American Journal of Hygiene, *22*(1): 65-105. (Repr. No. 73a)

81. FOSTER, A. O., and CORT, W. W.—1935.
Further Studies on the Effect of a Generally Deficient Diet Upon the Resistance of Dogs to Hookworm Infestation.
The American Journal of Hygiene, *21*(2): 302-318. (Repr. No. 70b)

82. HAKANSSON, E. G.—1935.
The Use of Aqueous Smears in the Study and Identification of the Amoebae of Man.
American Journal of Tropical Medicine, *15*(4): 439-453. (Repr. No. 87)

83. HEGNER, R.—1935.
Intestinal Protozoa from Panamá Monkeys.
The Journal of Parasitology, *21*(1): 60-61. (Repr. No. 77a)

84. HEGNER, R., and ESKRIDGE, L.—1935.
Influence of Carbohydrates on Intestinal Protozoa *in vitro* and *in vivo*.
American Journal of Hygiene, *21*(1): 121-134. (Repr. No. 79)

85. HILDEBRAND, S. F.—1935.
Trout Fishing in the Tropics. Rainbow Trout in the Río Chiriquí Viejo, Panamá.
Bulletin of the Pan American Union, *69*: 763-767. (Repr. No. 76)

86. JOHNSON, C. M.—1935.
A Rapid Technique for Iron-Hematoxylin Staining Requiring no Microscopic Control of Decolorization.
American Journal of Tropical Medicine, *15*(5): 551-553. (Repr. No. 68)

87. JOHNSON, C. M., and DE RIVAS, C. T.—1935.
La Enfermedad de Chagas en Panamá. *In:*
Novena Reunión de la Sociedad Argentina de Patología Regional, Mendoza, Oct. 1-4, 1935. Buenos Aires, Imp. de la Universidad, 1936.
Tomo 1, pp. 245-251. (Repr. No. 169)

88.   KOMP, W. H. W.—1935.

     Anopheles (Nyssorhynchus) anomalophyllus, a New Species of *Anopheles* from Panamá and Costa Rica, (Diptera, Culicidae).
     Proceedings of the Entomological Society of Washington, *38*(7): 160-164. (Repr. No. 171)

89.   KOMP, W. H. W.—1935.

     Malaria and Mosquito Survey at Caripito and Quiriquire, Venezuela, South America.
     Medical Bulletin of the Standard Oil Company, *2*(5): 204-216. (Repr. No. 170)

90.   KOMP, W. H. W.—1935.

     Notes on the Validity of the Types of the Species in the Sub-Genera *Mochlostyrax* and *Melanoconion* in the U. S. National Museum (Diptera Culicidae).
     Proceedings of the Entomological Society of Washington, *37*(1): 1-11. (Repr. No. 70)

91.   KOMP, W. H. W., and BROWN, C. G.—1935.

     Culex jubifer, a New Species of *Culex* from Panamá (Diptera: Culicidae).
     Annals of the Entomological Society of America, *28*(2): 254-255. (Repr. No. 71)

92.   KOMP, W. H. W., and CLARK, H. C.—1935.

     A Fourth Year's Observations on Malaria in Panamá, with Reference to Control with Atabrine and Plasmochin.
     American Journal of Tropical Medicine, *15*(2): 131-154. (Repr. No. 44)

93.   ROZEBOOM, L. E.—1935.

     Culex rooti, a New *Culex* from Panamá (Diptera Culicidae).
     Annals of the Entomological Society of America, *28*(2): 251-253. (Repr. No. 72)

94.   ROZEBOOM, L. E.—1935.

     Infection of *Anopheles bachmanni,* Petrocchi, with *Plasmodium vivax,* Grassi and Feletti, and Observations on the Bionomics of the Mosquito.
     American Journal of Tropical Medicine, *15*(5): 521-528. (Repr. No. 63)

1936

95.   CLARK, H. C.—1936.

     Recent Research on Prophylaxis and Treatment of Malaria. Report for 1935.
     Southern Medical Journal, *29*(7): 752-753. (Repr. No. 80)

96.   DUNN, E. R.—1936.

     Notes on North American Leptodeira.
     Proceedings of the National Academy of Sciences, *22*(12): 689-698. (Repr. No. 91c)

97.   FOSTER, A. O.—1936.
       Parasites of Equines in the Panamá Canal Zone.
       The Journal of Parasitology, 22(6): 528. (Repr. No. 91b)

98.*   FOSTER, A. O.—1936.
       Parasitic Worms of Equines in Panamá.
       Proceedings of the Helminthological Society of Washington, 3(2): 59-60.
       (Repr. No. 89)

99.   FOSTER, A. O.—1936.
       On a Probable Relationship Between Anemia and Susceptibility to
       Hookworm Infection.
       American Journal of Hygiene, 24(1): 109-128. (Repr. No. 91a)

100.* FOSTER, A. O.—1936.
       A Quantitative Study of the Nematodes from a Selected Group of
       Equines in Panamá.
       Journal of Parasitology, 22(5): 479-510. (Repr. No. 92)

101.   HAKANSSON, E. G.—1936.
       Dientamoeba fragilis; a Cause of Illness. Report of Case.
       American Journal of Tropical Medicine, 16(2): 175-185. (Repr. No.
       69)

102.* HAKANSSON, E. G.—1936.
       Observations on Chromatoid Bodies in the Cysts of *Entamoeba histo-
       lytica.*
       United States Naval Medical Bulletin, 34(4): 478-492. (Repr. No. 91)

103.   HURWITZ, E., and ANDERSON, H. H.—1936.
       Leprosy in Panamá; First Thirty Years of Segregation.
       American Journal of Tropical Medicine, 16(3): 353-369. (Repr. No.
       78a)

104.   JOHNSON, C. M.—1936.
       Further Studies on the Transmission of *Trypanosoma hippicum* Darling
       by the Vampire Bat *Desmodus rotundus murinus* Wagner.
       American Journal of Tropical Medicine, 16(2): 163-173. (Repr. No.
       64)

105.   JOHNSON, C. M.—1936.
       A Natural Infection of *Trypanosoma hippicum* Darling in the Vampire
       Bat *Desmodus rotundus murinus* Wagner.
       American Journal of Tropical Medicine, 16(1): 59-62. (Repr. No. 65)

106.   JOHNSON, C. M., and DE RIVAS, C. T.—1936.
       Six New Cases of Chagas' Disease in Panamá with Review of Previous
       Cases.
       American Journal of Tropical Medicine, 16(1): 47-57. (Repr. No. 88)

107.   KOMP, W. H. W.—1936.
       An Annotated List of the Mosquitoes Found in the Vicinity of an En-
       demic Focus of Yellow Fever in the Republic of Colombia.
       Proceedings of the Entomological Society of Washington, 38(4): 57-70.
       (Repr. No. 81)

108. KOMP, W. H. W.—1936.
      Anopheles (Anopheles) chiriquiensis, a New Species of *Anopheles* from
      Panamá (Diptera, Culicidae).
      Proceedings of the Entomological Society of Washington, *38*(7): 156-
      160. (Repr. No. 172)

109. KOMP, W. H. W.—1936.
      Description of Nine New Species of *Culex,* Seven from Panamá and
      Two from Venezuela (Diptera, Culicidae).
      Annals of the Entomological Society of America, *29*(2): 319-334. (Repr.
      No. 83)

110. KOMP, W. H. W.—1936.
      The Male and Larva of *Aedes dominicii* Rangel & Romero Sierra, and
      the Male of *Aedes pseudo-dominicii* sp. nov., Representatives of a New
      Sub-genus *(Soperia)* of the Genus *Aedes,* from Colombia.
      Proceedings of the Entomological Society of Washington, *38*(4): 71-75.
      (Repr. No. 82)

111. KOMP, W. H. W., and CLARK, H. C.—1936.
      A Fifth Year's Observations on Malaria in Panamá, with Reference to
      the Failure of Atabrine to Control an Epidemic.
      American Journal of Tropical Medicine, *16*(2): 109-131. (Repr. No. 61)

112. KOMP, W. H. W., and OSORNO, E.—1936.
      The Male and Larva of *Anopheles (Kerteszia) boliviensis* Theobald
      (Diptera, Culicidae).
      Annals of the Entomological Society of America, *29*(3): 415-419.
      (Repr. No. 173)

113. McCOY, O. R.—1936.
      Filarial Parasites of the Monkeys of Panamá.
      American Journal of Tropical Medicine, *16*(4): 383-403. (Repr. No. 75)

114. ROZEBOOM, L. E.—1936.
      The Larva and Adult of *Culex rooti* Rozeboom.
      Annals of the Entomological Society of America, *29*(2): 266-267.
      (Repr. No. 84)

115. ROZEBOOM, L. E.—1936.
      The Life Cycle of Laboratory—Bred *Anopheles albimanus* Wiedemann.
      Annals of the Entomological Society of America, *29*(3): 480-489.
      (Repr. No. 90)

116. ROZEBOOM, L. E.—1936.
      The Rearing of *Anopheles albimanus* Wiedemann, in the Laboratory.
      American Journal of Tropical Medicine, *16*(4): 471-478. (Repr. No. 85)

117. ROZEBOOM, L. E.—1936.
      Triatoma dimidiata Latr., Found Naturally Infected with *Trypanosoma
      cruzi* Chagas in Panamá.
      American Journal of Tropical Medicine, *16*(4): 481-484. (Repr. No.
      86)

118.   TALIAFERRO, W. H., and CANNON, P. R.—1936.
        The Cellular Reactions During Primary Infections and Superinfections
        of *Plasmodium brasilianum* in Panamanian Monkeys.
        Journal of Infectious Diseases, *59*: 72-125. (Repr. No. 73)

1937

119.   CLARK, H. C.—1937.
        The First Twelve Months of Infancy as a Test for the Community Inci-
        dence of Initial Attacks of Malaria. (Symposium on Malaria-Part 1).
        Southern Medical Journal, *30*(8): 848-850. (Repr. No. 103)

120.   CLARK, H. C.—1937.
        Periodic Ophthalmia.
        Horse, *18*(6): 14-15. (Repr. No. 99a)

121.   CLARK, H. C.—1937.
        Recent Research on Prophylaxis and Treatment of Malaria. Report
        for 1936.
        Southern Medical Journal, *30*(8): 850-853. (Repr. No. 105)

122.   CLARK, H. C.—1937.
        Moon Blindness (Periodic Ophthalmia). A Preliminary Report. [A
        Survey of Thoroughbred Horse Farms of Virginia and Kentucky for
        Recurrent Ophthalmia]
        The Veterinary Record, *49*(42): 1322-1324. (Repr. No. 99b)

123.*   CLARK, H. C., and KOMP, W. H. W.—1937.
        A Sixth Year's Report on Malaria in Panamá (Chagres Valley) with
        Reference to Drug Control.
        American Journal of Tropical Medicine, *17*(1): 59-77. (Repr. No. 93)

124.   DUNN, E. R.—1937.
        Notes on Tropical Lampropeltis.
        Occasional Papers of the Museum of Zoology—University of Michigan
        —No. 353, 1-11, April 28. (Repr. No. 99c)

125.   DUNN, E. R.—1937.
        The Snake Genus *Enulius* Cope.
        Proceedings of the National Academy of Sciences (Philadelphia), *89*:
        415-418. (Repr. No. 101b)

126.   FOSTER, A. O.—1937.
        The Occurrence of *Trichostrongylus axei* (Cobbold) in Equines of
        Panamá.
        The Journal of Parasitology, *23*(6): 573-574. (Repr. No. 94a)

127.   FOSTER, A. O.—1937.
        A Relationship in Equines Between Age of Host and Number of
        Strongylid Parasites.
        American Journal of Hygiene, *25*(1): 66-75. (Repr. No. 94)

128.* FOSTER, A. O., and CHITWOOD, B. G.—1937.
A New Nematode, *Habronema clarki,* n. sp. (Spiruridae), from *Hydrochoerus isthmius* Goldman.
Proceedings of the Helminthological Society of Washington, *4*(2): 63-65. (Repr. No. 101)

129. FOSTER, A. O., and CLARK, H. C.—1937.
Verminous Aneurysm in Equines of Panamá.
American Journal of Tropical Medicine, *17*(1): 85-99. (Repr. No. 95)

130. FOSTER, A. O., and CORT, W. W.—1937.
The Stability of the Cat and Dog Strains of *Ancylostoma caninum.*
Journal of Parasitology, *23*(1): 83-93. (Repr. No. 96)

131.* FOSTER, A. O., and ORTIZ O., P.—1937.
A Further Report on the Parasites of a Selected Group of Equines in Panamá.
Journal of Parasitology, *23*(4): 360-364. (Repr. No. 102)

132.* HAKANSSON, E. G.—1937.
Dientamoeba fragilis: Some Further Observations.
American Journal of Tropical Medicine, *17*(3): 349-362. (Repr. No. 98)

133. HILDEBRAND, S. F.—1937.
The Tarpon in the Panamá Canal.
Scientific Monthly, *44*: 239-248. (Repr. No. 101a)

134.* JOHNSON, C. M., and KELSER, R. A.—1937.
The Incidence of Chagas' Disease in Panamá as Determined by the Complement-Fixation Test.
American Journal of Tropical Medicine, *17*(3): 385-392. (Repr. No. 97)

135. KOMP, W. H. W.—1937.
Anopheles acanthotorynus, a New Species of the Subgenus *Stethomyia* from Perú (Diptera, Culicidae).
Annals of the Entomological Society of America, *30*(2): 358-360. (Repr. No. 99)

136.* KOMP, W. H. W.—1937.
The Nomenclature of the Thoracic Sclerites in the Culicidae, and their Setae.
Proceedings of the Entomological Society of Washington, *39*(9): 241-252. (Repr. No. 109)

137. KOMP, W. H. W.—1937.
Notes on the Identification of *Anopheles pseudo-punctipennis* Theobald (Diptera, Culicidae).
Proceedings of the Entomological Society of Washington, *39*(6): 157-163. (Repr. No. 100)

138. KOMP, W. H. W.—1937.
The Species of the Subgenus *Kerteszia* of *Anopheles* (Diptera, Culicidae).
Annals of the Entomological Society of America, *30*(3): 492-529. (Repr. No. 107)

139.   LANDSBERG, J. W., and FOSTER, A. O.—1937.
The White Cell Picture in Hookworm Disease in Dogs.
The American Journal of Hygiene, *25*(1): 141-149. (Repr. No. 94b)

140.* ROZEBOOM, L. E.—1937.
The Egg of *Anopheles pseudopunctipennis* in Panamá.
Journal of Parasitology, *23*(5): 538-539. (Repr. No. 106)

141.   ROZEBOOM, L. E.—1937.
Identification of Anopheline Mosquitoes of Panamá.
Mimeographed by the Health Department of the Panamá Canal and
Chief Health Office of the Republic of Panamá for Local Distribution
Among the Field Sanitary Forces. (Repr. No. 168)

142.* ROZEBOOM, L. E.—1937.
On *Anopheles albitarsis* Lynch Arribalzaga in Panamá.
Southern Medical Journal, *30*(9): 950-951. (Repr. No. 104)

143.   WILSON, C. B.—1937.
Some Parasitic Copepods from Panamá Bay.
Journal of the Washington Academy of Sciences, *27*(10): 423-431.
(Repr. No. 108)

1938

144.   BOYD, M. F., CARR, H. P., and ROZEBOOM, L. E.—1938.
On the Comparable Susceptibility of Certain Species of Nearctic and
Neotropical Anophelines to Certain Strains of *P. vivax* and *P. falciparum*
from the Same Regions.
The American Journal of Tropical Medicine, *18*(2): 157-168. (Repr.
No. 112a)

145.   BRITTON, S. W., and ATKINSON, W. E.—1938.
Poikilothermism in the Sloth.
Journal of Mammalogy, *19*(1): 94-99. (Repr. No. 109a)

146.   BRITTON, S. W., SILVETTE, H., and KLINE, R. F.—1938.
Adrenal Insufficiency in American Monkeys.
American Journal of Physiology, *123*(3): 705-711. (Repr. No. 118b)

147.* CLARK, H. C.—1938.
The Development of International Transportation and its Effects on
the Practice of Tropical Medicine.
American Journal of Tropical Medicine, *18*(1): 1-7. (Repr. No. 110)

148.* CLARK, H. C.—1938.
Review of Recent Research on Medical Prophylaxis and Treatment of
Malaria. (Symposium on Malaria—Part 2).
Southern Medical Journal, *31*(8): 933-938. (Repr. No. 118)

149.   CLARK, H. C., and KOMP, W. H. W.—1938.
A Seventh Year's Observations on Malaria in Panamá.
American Journal of Tropical Medicine, *18*(3): 271-288. (Repr. No.
116)

150.   HAKANSSON, E. G.—1938.
On the Effectiveness of Carbarsone as a Remedy for Amoebiasis.
American Journal of Tropical Medicine, 18(3): 245-269. (Repr. No.
115)

151.   HILDEBRAND, S. F.—1938.
A New Catalogue of the Fresh-Water Fishes of Panamá. Zoological
Series.
Field Museum of Natural History, 22(4): 219-359. (Repr. No. 118a)

152.*   JOHNSON, C. M.—1938.
Cardiac Changes in Dogs Experimentally Infected with *Trypanosoma
cruzi.*
American Journal of Tropical Medicine, 18(2): 197-206. (Repr. No.
112)

153.*   JOHNSON, C. M.—1938.
A New Method for Stripping Venomous Snakes.
American Journal of Tropical Medicine, 18(4): 385-386. (Repr. No.
117)

154.   KOMP, W. H. W.—1938.
Aedes leucotaeniatus, a New Species of *Aedes* Allied to *A. leucocelaenus*
D. & S.; and Descriptions of the Male and Larva of *A. leucocelaenus*
D. & S. (Diptera, Culicidae).
Proceedings of the Entomological Society of Washington, 40(9): 260-
266. (Repr. No. 121)

155.   KOMP, W. H. W.—1938.
Censo Estegómico (Aédico) en Guayaquil.
Boletín de la Oficina Sanitaria Panamericana, 17(7): 619-620. (Repr.
No. 120a)

156.   KOMP, W. H. W., and KUMM, H. W.—1938.
A New Species of *Haemagogus mesodentatus,* from Costa Rica, and a
Description of the Larva of *Haemagogus anastasionis* Dyar (Diptera,
Culicidae).
Proceedings of the Entomological Society of Washington, 40(9): 253-
259. (Repr. No. 120)

157.   ROZEBOOM, L. E.—1938.
The Eggs of the *Nyssorhynchus* Group of *Anopheles* (Culicidae) in
Panamá.
American Journal of Hygiene, 27(1): 95-107. (Repr. No. 111)

158.   ROZEBOOM, L. E.—1938.
The Role of Some Common Anopheline Mosquitoes of Panamá in the
Transmission of Malaria.
American Journal of Tropical Medicine, 18(3): 289-302. (Repr. No.
114)

159.   WISLOCKI, G. B.—1938.
The Topography of the Hypophysis in the Xenarthra.
Anatomical Record, 70: 451-471. (Repr. No. 121a)

160. WRIGHT, H. E.—1938.
Further Observation on the Incidence of *Hepaticola (Capillaria) hepatica* Ova in Human Feces.
American Journal of Tropical Medicine, *18*(3): 329-330. (Repr. No. 113)

1939

161. BLACKIE, W. J., and COWGILL, G. R.—1939.
Occurrence of Carotene in the Oil of *Attalea gomphococca* Mart. and its Relation to Vitamin A Potency.
Food Research, *4*(2): 129-133. (Repr. No. 122a)

162. BRITTON, S. W., and KLINE, R. F.—1939.
Augmentation of Activity in the Sloth by Adrenal Extract, Emotion and other Conditions.
American Journal of Physiology, *127*(1): 127-130. (Repr. No. 129b)

163. BRITTON, S. W., and KLINE, R. F.—1939.
Emotional Hyperglycemia and Hyperthermia in Tropical Mammals and Reptiles.
The American Journal of Physiology, *125*(4): 730-734. (Repr. No. 129a)

164. BRITTON, S. W., and KLINE, R. F.—1939.
On Deslothing the Sloth.
Science, *90*(2323): 16-17, 7 July. Repr. No. 129c)

165.* CLARK, H. C.—1939.
Review of Recent Research on Drug Prophylaxis and Treatment of Malaria.
Southern Medical Journal, *32*(7): 685-689. (Repr. No. 127)

166.* CLARK, H. C., and KOMP, W. H. W.—1939.
An Eighth Year's Observations on Malaria in Panamá.
American Journal of Tropical Medicine, *19*(1): 33-46. (Repr. No. 119)

167. DEMPSEY, E. W.—1939.
The Reproductive Cycle of New World Monkeys.
American Journal of Anatomy, *64*: 381-405. (Repr. No. 131b)

168. DUNN, E. R.—1939.
Mainland Forms of the Snake Genus *Tretanorhinus*.
Copeia, No. 4, 212-217. (Repr. No. 131c)

169. DUNN, E. R., and BAILEY, J. R.—1939.
Snakes from the Uplands of the Canal Zone and of Darién.
Bulletin of the Museum of Comparative Zoology (Harvard University), *86*(1): 1-22. (Repr. No. 131a)

170. FAIRCHILD, G. B.—1939.
Notes on the Genus *Acanthocera Macquart* (Diptera: Tabanidae).
Revista de Entomologia, *10*(1): 14-27. (Repr. No. 126a)

349

171.* FAIRCHILD, G. B.—1939.
Two New Species of *Chrysops* (Diptera: Tabanidae) from Panamá.
Proceedings of the Entomological Society of Washington, *41*(9): 257-260. (Repr. No. 131)

172.* FOSTER, A. O.—1939.
Some Helminthic Parasites Recovered from Domesticated Animals (excluding equines) in Panamá.
Proceedings of the Helminthological Society of Washington, *6*(2): 101-102. (Repr. No. 129)

173.* FOSTER, A. O.—1939.
Some Helminths of the Wooly Opossum in Panamá.
Transactions of the American Microscopical Society, *58*(2): 185-198. (Repr. No. 126)

174.* FOSTER, A. O., and ALICATA, J. E.—1939.
Notes on Parasites of Horses in Hawaii.
Proceedings of the Helminthological Society of Washington, *6*(1): 4-8. (Repr. No. 123)

175.* FOSTER, A. O., and JOHNSON, C. M.—1939.
An Explanation for the Occurrence of *Capillaria hepatica* Ova in Human Faeces Suggested by the Finding of Three New Hosts Used as Food. Transactions of the Royal Society of Tropical Medicine and Hygiene, *32*(5): 639-644. (Repr. No. 122)

176.* FOSTER, A. O., and JOHNSON, C. M.—1939.
A Preliminary Note on the Identity, Life-Cycle and Pathogenicity of an Important Nematode Parasite of Captive Monkeys.
American Journal of Tropical Medicine, *19*(3): 265-277. (Repr. No. 124)

177. HILDEBRAND, S. F.—1939.
The Panamá Canal as a Passageway for Fishes, with Lists and Remarks on the Fishes and Invertebrates Observed.
Zoologica (New York Zoological Society), *24*(Part 1): 15-45. (Repr. No. 122b)

178.* SAPERO, J. J.—1939.
Clinical Studies in Non-Dysenteric Intestinal Amebiasis.
American Journal of Tropical Medicine, *19*(6): 497-514. (Repr. No. 130)

179. SAPERO, J. J.—1939.
Observations Upon the Transmission of Amebiasis.
Proceedings of the Sixth Pacific Science Congress, *5*: 1-5. (Repr. No. 155)

180. SAPERO, J. J., and JOHNSON, C. M.—1939.
Endamoeba histolytica and other Intestinal Parasites. Incidence in Variously Exposed Groups of the Navy.
United States Naval Medical Bulletin, *37*(2): 279-287. (Repr. No. 128)

181.* SAPERO, J. J., and JOHNSON, C. M.—1939.
An Evaluation of the Role of the Food Handler in the Transmission of Amebiasis.
American Journal of Tropical Medicine, *19*(3): 255-264. (Repr. No. 125)

182. WISLOCKI, G. B.—1939.
Observations on Twinning in Marmosets.
American Journal of Anatomy, *64*(3): 445-483. (Repr. No. 122c)

1940

183. BOYD, M. F., and JOBBINS, D. M.—1940.
Further Observations on the Comparative Susceptibility of Nearctic and Neotropical Anophelines to Coindigenous Strains of *Plasmodium falciparum*.
American Journal of Tropical Medicine, *20*(3): 423-429. (Repr. No. 175)

184. CALERO M., C., ORTIZ O., P., and DE SOUZA, L.—1940.
Helminths in Rats from Panamá City and Suburbs.
Journal of Parasitology, *36*(5): 426. (Repr. No. 225)

185.* CLARK, H. C.—1940.
Review of Recent Research on Drug Prophylaxis and Treatment of Malaria. A Report to the National Malaria Committee. (Symposium on Malaria).
Southern Medical Journal, *33*(8): 879-882. (Repr. No. 134)

186.* CLARK, H. C., KOMP, W. H. W., and JOBBINS, D. M.—1940.
A Ninth Year's Observations on Malaria in Panamá, with Reference to the Occurrence of an Epidemic Following Continued Treatment with Atabrine and Plasmochin.
American Journal of Tropical Medicine, *20* (1): 47-67. (Repr. No. 132)

187. DUNN, E. R.—1940.
New and Noteworthy Herpetological Material from Panamá.
Proceedings of the Academy of Natural Sciences (Philadelphia), *92*: 105-122. (Repr. No. 132a)

188. DUNN, E. R.—1940.
Some Aspects of Herpetology in Lower Central America.
Transactions of the New York Academy of Sciences, *2*(2): 156-158. (Repr. No. 144)

189.* FAIRCHILD, G. B.—1940.
A Note on the Early Stages of *Lepiselaga crassipes* Fab. (Diptera, Tabanidae).
Psyche, *47*(1): 8-13. (Repr. No. 133)

190. FAIRCHILD, G. B.—1940.
Notes on the Simuliidae of Panamá (Diptera, Nematocera).
Annals of the Entomological Society of America, *33*(4): 701-719. (Repr. No. 137)

191.   FAIRCHILD, G. B.—1940.
       Notes on Tabanidae (Diptera) from Panamá. I. The Genera *Chloro-tabanus* and *Crytotylus*.
       Revista de Entomologia (Rio de Janeiro), *11*(3): 713-722. (Repr. No. 139)

192.   FAIRCHILD, G. B.—1940.
       Notes on Tabanidae (Diptera) from Panamá. II. The Genus *Dichelacera* Macquart and Related Genera.
       Annals of the Entomological Society of America, *33*(4): 683-700. (Repr. No. 136)

193.   KOMP, W. H. W.—1940.
       The Occurrence of *Anopheles darlingi* Root in British Honduras and Guatemala.
       United States Public Health Reports, *55*(16): 693-695. (Repr. No. 137a)

194.   KUMM, H. W., KOMP, W. H. W., and RUIZ, H.—1940.
       The Mosquitoes of Costa Rica.
       American Journal of Tropical Medicine, *20*(3): 385-422. (Repr. No. 174)

195.   SAPERO, J. J.—1940.
       The Hookworm Problem. Some General and Military Aspects. A Report of the Examination of 1169 Naval Recruits.
       United States Naval Bulletin, *38*(1): 136-143. (Repr. No. 133a)

196.* TALIAFERRO, W. H., and KLUVER, C.—1940.
       The Hematology of Malaria *(Plasmodium brasilianum)* in Panamanian Monkeys. I. Numerical Changes in Leucocytes. II. Morphology of Leucocytes, and Origin of Monocytes and Macrophages.
       Journal of Infectious Diseases, *67*: 121-176. (Repr. No. 135)

197.   TRAGER, W.—1940.
       A Note on the Problem of Acquired Immunity of Argasid Ticks.
       Journal of Parasitology, *26*(1): 71-74. (Repr. No. 135a)

1941

198.   BRITTON, S. W.—1941.
       Form and Function in the Sloth.
       Quarterly Review of Biology, *16*: 13-34. (Repr. No. 143a)

199.* CLARK, H. C.—1941.
       Review of Recent Research on Drug Prophylaxis and Treatment of Malaria. (Symposium on Malaria—Part 1).
       Southern Medical Journal, *34*(7): 703-708. (Repr. No. 140)

200.   CLARK, H. C., and KOMP, W. H. W.—1941.
       A Summary of Ten Years of Observations on Malaria in Panamá with Reference to Control with Quinine, Atabrine, and Plasmochin, without Anti-Mosquito Measures. (A Symposium on Human Malaria. . .).
       Publication No. 15 of the American Association for the Advancement of Science, pp. 273-284. (Repr. No. 141)

201.   CLARK, H. C., KOMP, W. H. W., and JOBBINS, D. M.—1941.
       A Tenth Year's Observations on Malaria in Panamá, with Reference to
       the Occurrence of Variations in the Parasite Index, During Continued
       Treatment with Atabrine and Plasmochin.
       American Journal of Tropical Medicine, *21*(2): 191-216. (Repr. No.
       151)

202.   FAIRCHILD, G. B.—1941.
       A New *Acanthocera* (Diptera, Tabanidae) from Central America.
       Annals of the Entomological Society of America, *34*(3): 647-648.
       (Repr. No. 146)

203.* FAIRCHILD, G. B.—1941.
       Notes on Tabanidae (Diptera) from Panamá. IV. The Genus *Leuco-
       tabanus* Ad. Lutz.
       Annals of the Entomological Society of America, *34*(3): 629-638.
       (Repr. No. 148)

204.   FAIRCHILD, G. B.—1941.
       Notes on Tabanidae (Diptera) from Panamá. VI. The Genus *Fidena*
       Walker.
       Annals of the Entomological Society of America, *34*(3): 639-646.
       (Repr. No. 147)

205.   JOBBINS, D. M.—1941.
       Methods Directed Against Adult Mosquitoes in the Control and Eradi-
       cation of Malaria. (A Symposium on Human Malaria. . .).
       Publication No. 15 of the American Association for the Advancement
       of Science, pp. 302-307. (Repr. No. 142)

206.   JOHNSON, C. M.—1941.
       Bovine Trypanosomiasis in Panamá.
       American Journal of Tropical Medicine, *22*(2): 289-297. (Repr. No.
       150)

207.* JOHNSON, C. M.—1941.
       Observations on Natural Infections of *Endamoeba histolytica* in *Ateles*
       and *Rhesus* Monkeys.
       American Journal of Tropical Medicine, *21*(1): 49-61. (Repr. No. 138)

208.   KOMP, W. H. W.—1941.
       The Classification and Identification of the *Anopheles* Mosquitoes of
       México, Central America, and the West Indies. (A Symposium on Hu-
       man Malaria. . .).
       Publication No. 15 of the American Association for the Advancement
       of Science, pp. 88-97. (Repr. No. 143)

209.   KOMP, W. H. W.—1941.
       The Occurrence of *Anopheles darlingi* Root in Central America.
       American Journal of Tropical Medicine, *21*(5): 659-670. (Repr. No.
       145)

210.　KOMP, W. H. W.—1941.

The Species of *Nyssorhynchus* Confused Under *tarsimaculatus* Goeldi and a New Name, *A. emilianus,* for One Species Found in Pará, Brazil (Diptera, Culicidae).

Annals of the Entomological Society of America, *34*(4): 791-807. (Repr. No. 149)

211.　KUMM, H. W., and KOMP, W. H. W.—1941.

Aedes (Howardina) allotecnon, a New Species of *Aedes* from Costa Rica, and a Description of the Larva, Adult, and Male Terminalia of *Aedes quadrivillatus* Coq.

Proceedings of the Entomological Society of Washington, *43*(2): 17-25. (Repr. No. 176)

1942

212.　CHAPIN, R. W., and MILLS, C. A.—1942.

Dental Caries in the Panamá Canal Zone.

Journal of Dental Research, *21*(1): 55-59. (Repr. No. 161a)

213.　CLARK, H. C.—1942.

Relapsing Fever in Panamá. (A Symposium on Relapsing Fever in the Americas).

Publication No. 18 of the American Association for the Advancement of Science, pp. 29-34. (Repr. No. 161)

214.　CLARK, H. C.—1942.

Review of Recent Publications on the Prophylaxis and Treatment of Malaria (A Report to the National Malaria Committee).

The Journal of the National Malaria Society, *1*(1): 113-124. (Repr. No. 178)

215.　CLARK, H. C.—1942.

Venomous Snakes. Some Central American Records. Incidence of Snake-Bite Accidents.

American Journal of Tropical Medicine, *22*(1): 37-49. (Repr. No. 153)

216.　DUNN, E. R.—1942.

New or Noteworthy Snakes from Panamá.

Notulae Naturae of the Academy of Natural Sciences of Philadelphia, No. 108, September 17th. (Repr. No. 162a)

217.　DUNN, E. R.—1942.

Survival Value of Varietal Characters in Snakes.

The American Naturalist, *76*(762): 104-109. (Repr. No. 162b)

218.　FAIRCHILD, G. B.—1942.

Biting and Stinging Arthropods of Panamá.

Mimeographed Documents Prepared for the Use of the United States Army, 14 Pages. (Repr. No. 165)

219. FAIRCHILD, G. B.—1942.
Notes on Tabanidae (Diptera) from Panamá. III. The Genus *Chrysops* Meigen.
Proceedings of the Entomological Society of Washington, *44*(1): 1-8. (Repr. No. 152)

220. FAIRCHILD, G. B.—1942.
Notes on Tabanidae (Diptera) from Panamá. V. The Genus *Tabanus,* Subgenus *Bellardia* Rondani.
Psyche, *49*(1-2): 8-17. (Repr. No. 157)

221. FAIRCHILD, G. B.—1942.
Notes on Tabanidae (Diptera) from Panamá. VII. Subgenus *Neotabanus* Ad. Lutz.
Annals of the Entomological Society of America, *35*(2): 153-182. (Repr. No. 158)

222. FAIRCHILD, G. B.—1942.
Notes on Tabanidae (Diptera) from Panamá. VIII. The Genera *Pityocera, Scione* and *Esenbeckia.*
Annals of the Entomological Society of America, *35*(2): 183-199. (Repr. No. 159)

223. FAIRCHILD, G. B.—1942.
Notes on Tabanidae (Diptera) from Panamá. IX. The Genera *Stenotabanus* Lutz, *Lepiselaga* Macquart and Related Genera.
Annals of the Entomological Society of America, *35*(3): 289-309. (Repr. No. 160)

224. FAIRCHILD, G. B.—1942.
Notes on Tabanidae (Diptera) from Panamá. X. The Genus *Tabanus* Linn. and Resume of the Tabanidae of Panamá.
Annals of the Entomological Society of America, *35*(4): 441-474. (Repr. No. 163)

225. FAIRCHILD, G. B.—1942.
The Seasonal Distribution of Some Tabanidae (Diptera) in Panamá.
Annals of the Entomological Society of America, *35*(1): 85-91. (Repr. No. 154)

226. FAIRCHILD, G. B., and BRICEÑO-IRAGORRY, L.—1942.
Nota Sobre *Simulium lutzianus* (Descripción del Adulto).
Boletín del Laboratorio de la Clínica Luis Razetti, *3*(9): 159-160. *Also in* the same Boletín, *3*(10): 187-188, 1943. (Repr. No. 163a)

227. KOMP, W. H. W.—1942.
Anopheles clarki, a New Species of *Nyssorhynchus* of Wide Distribution in South America (Diptera: Culicidae).
Proceedings of the Entomological Society of Washington, *44*(9): 196-201. (Repr. No. 162)

228. KOMP, W. H. W.—1942.
The Anopheline Mosquitoes of the Caribbean Region.
National Institute of Health Bulletin, No. 179, pp. 1-195. (Repr. No. 177a)

229. KOMP, W. H. W.—1942.
A Technique for Staining, Dissecting, and Mounting the Male Terminalia of Mosquitoes.
Public Health Reports, 57(36): 1327-1333. (Repr. No. 177)

230. MILLS, C. A.—1942.
Climatic Effects on Growth and Development with Particular Reference to the Effects of Tropical Residence.
American Anthropologist, 44(1): 1-13. (Repr. No. 160a)

231. SAPERO, J. J., HAKANSSON, E. G., and LOUTTIT, C. M.—1942.
The Occurrence of Two Significantly Distinct Races of Endamoeba histolytica.
American Journal of Tropical Medicine, 22(3): 191-208. (Repr. No. 156)

1943

232. BRITTON, S. W., and KLINE, R. F.—1943.
The Pseudaffective State and Decerebrate Rigidity in the Sloth.
Journal of Neurophysiology, 8(1): 65-69. (Repr. No. 178b)

233. CLARK, H. C.—1943.
Review of Recent Research on Drug Prophylaxis and Treatment of Malaria (A Report to the National Malaria Society).
The Journal of the National Malaria Society, 2(1): 31-38. (Repr. No. 178a)

234. FAIRCHILD, G. B.—1943.
An Annotated List of the Bloodsucking Insects, Ticks and Mites Known from Panamá.
American Journal of Tropical Medicine, 23(6): 569-591. (Repr. No. 179)

235. JOHNSON, C. M.—1943.
American Trypanosomiasis.
Medical Clinics of North America, 27(3): 822-834. (Repr. No. 166)

236. CLARK, H. C.—1943.
Some Impressions of Medical Practice in the Tropics.
American Journal of Tropical Medicine, 23(1): 11-15. (Repr. No. 164)

1944

237. CLARK, H. C.—1944.
The Age Level for the Peak of Acquired Immunity to Malaria as Reflected by Labor Forces.
American Journal of Tropical Medicine, 24(3): 159-161. (Repr. No. 180)

238.   CLARK, H. C.—1944.
       Recent Research in Prophylaxis and Treatment of Malaria. Report for
       1942-1943.
       Journal of the National Malaria Society, *3*(2): 85-94. (Repr. No. 182)

239.   FAIRCHILD, G. B.—1944.
       Life History of the Mosquito.
       National Geographic Magazine, *85*(2): 180-195. (Repr. No. 179a)

240.* TALIAFERRO, W. H., and TALIAFERRO, L. G.—1944.
       The Effect of Immunity on the Asexual Reproduction of *Plasmodium
       brasilianum*.
       Journal of Infectious Diseases, *75*: 1-32. (Repr. No. 181)

1945

241.   HERTIG, M., and FISHER, R. A.—1945.
       Control of Sandflies with DDT.
       Bulletin of the United States Army Medical Department, No. 88, May,
       97-101. (Repr. No. 182b)

242.   TALIAFERRO, W. H., and BLOOM, W.—1945.
       Inflammatory Reactions in the Skin of Normal and Immune Canaries
       and Monkeys After the Local Injection of Malarial Blood.
       Journal of Infectious Diseases, *77*(2): 109-138. (Repr. No. 182a)

243.   WETMORE, A.—1945.
       A Review of the Forms of the Brown Pelican.
       The Auk, *62*: 577-586, October. (Repr. No. 184b)

1946

244.   CLAUSEN, R. T.—1946.
       Najas arguta in Central America and its Relationship to *N. Wrightiana*.
       Bulletin of the Torrey Botanical Club, *73*(4): 363-365. (Repr. No.
       193a)

245.* FAIRCHILD, G. B.—1946.
       Additional Notes on the Tabanidae of Panamá (Diptera).
       Annals of the Entomological Society of America, *39*(4): 564-575.
       (Repr. No. 193)

246.* FAIRCHILD, G. B., and BARREDA, E. A.—1946.
       DDT as a Larvicide Against *Simulium*.
       Journal of Economic Entomology, *38*(6): 694-699. (Repr. No. 183)

247.   GALINDO, P.—1946.
       Anopheles xelajuensis De León, a New Addition to the Known Anoph-
       eline Fauna of Panamá.
       The Pan Pacific Entomologist, *23*(1): 44. (Repr. No. 185a)

248.   MELVIN, R.—1946.
       A Note on the Culturing of Chiggers (Trombiculidae).
       Annals of the Entomological Society of America, *39*(1): 143-144.
       (Repr. No. 208a)

249.   MICHENER, C. D.—1946.
A Method of Rearing Chigger Mites (Acarina: Trombiculinae).
American Journal of Tropical Medicine, 26(2): 251-256. (Repr. No. 185)

250.   MICHENER, C. D.—1946.
Notes on the Habits of Some Panamanian Stingless Bees (Hymenoptera, Apidae).
Journal of the New York Entomological Society, 54: 179-197. (Repr. No. 184a)

251.*   MICHENER, C. D.—1946.
Observations on the Habits and Life History of a Chigger Mite, *Eutrombicula batatas* (Acarina: Trombiculinae).
Annals of the Entomological Society of America, 39(1): 101-118. (Repr. No. 184)

252.*   MICHENER, C. D.—1946.
Taxonomic and Bionomic Notes on Some Panamanian Chiggers (Acarina, Trombiculinae).
Annals of the Entomological Society of America, 39(3): 411-417. (Repr. No. 192)

253.*   MICHENER, C. D.—1946.
The Taxonomy and Bionomics of a New Subgenus of Chigger Mites (Acarina: Trombiculinae).
Annals of the Entomological Society of America, 39(3): 431-445. (Repr. No. 190)

254.*   MICHENER, C. D.—1946.
The Taxonomy and Bionomics of Some Panamanian Trombidiid Mites (Acarina).
Annals of the Entomological Society of America, 39(3): 349-380. (Repr. No. 191)

255.*   SHRAPNEL, B. C., JOHNSON, C. M., and SANDGROUND, J. H.—1946.
Oral Emetine in the Treatment of Intestinal Amebiasis. A Preliminary Report.
American Journal of Tropical Medicine, 26(3): 293-310. (Repr. No. 186)

256.*   TRAPIDO, H.—1946.
Observations on the Vampire Bat with Special Reference to Longevity in Captivity.
Journal of Mammalogy, 27(3): 217-219. (Repr. No. 187)

257.*   TRAPIDO, H.—1946.
The Residual Spraying of Dwellings with DDT in the Control of Malaria Transmission in Panamá, with Special Reference to *Anopheles albimanus*.
American Journal of Tropical Medicine, 26(4): 383-415. (Repr. No. 189)

258.*   TRAPIDO, H., and CROWE, P. E.—1946.
The Wing Banding Method in the Study of the Travels of Bats.
Journal of Mammalogy, 27(3): 224-226. (Repr. No. 188)

259. WETMORE, A.—1946.
The Birds of San José and Pedro González Islands, Republic of Panamá.
Smithsonian Miscellaneous Collection, *106*(1): 1-60, August 5. (Repr. No. 186a)

260. WETMORE, A.—1946.
The Birds of San José Island, Archipiélago de las Perlas, Republic of Panamá. By Alexander Wetmore with additional notes by Robert Cushman Murphy.
San José Project Report No. 90, 27 April 1946, pp. 1-35. (Repr. No. 186b)

261. WETMORE, A.—1946.
New Forms of Birds from Panamá and Colombia.
Proceedings of the Biological Society of Washington, *59*: 49-54, March 11. (Repr. No. 186c)

1947

262.* CALERO M., C., and ORTIZ O., P.—1947.
Actinomycosis in a *Hydrochoerus isthmius* Goldman (Isthmian Capybara or Poncho).
American Journal of Tropical Medicine, *27*(3): 377-381. (Repr. No. 194)

263.* FAIRCHILD, G. B., and HERTIG, M.—1947.
Notes on the *Phlebotomus* of Panamá (Diptera, Psychodidae). I. The Subgenus *Brumptomyia* Franca and Parrot 1921.
Annals of the Entomological Society of America, *40*(4): 610-616. (Repr. No. 199)

264.* FAIRCHILD, G. B., and HERTIG, M.—1947.
Notes on the *Phlebotomus* of Panamá (Diptera, Psychodidae). II. Description of Three New Species.
Annals of the Entomological Society of America, *40*(4): 617-623. (Repr. No. 198)

265. GALINDO, P.—1947.
Reporte Preliminar Sobre el Control de la Malaria en Panamá por Medio del DDT y de las Nuevas Drogas Antipalúdicas Aralen y Paludrina.
Boletín de la Asociación Médica Nacional de Panamá, *10*(3): 249-259. (Repr. No. 199b)

266. GALINDO V., P., and GALLARDO, C., M.—1947.
Nota Preliminar Sobre el Control de la Malaria en Panamá por Medio del Riegue Residual de Casas con DDT. Presentado a la Comisión de Estudios Antimaláricos, XII Conferencia Sanitaria Panamericana (Venezuela, Caracas). pp. 1-51. ("Ciencia y Sanidad." Publicaciones Especiales [de la] Sección de Bioestadística y Educación Sanitaria [del] Departamento de Salud Pública. Ministerio de Trabajo, Previsión Social y Salud Pública. República de Panamá). (Repr. No. 199a)

267.* HERTIG, M., and FAIRCHILD, G. B.—1947.
The Control of *Phlebotomus* in Perú with DDT.
American Journal of Tropical Medicine, *28*(2): 207-230. (Repr. No. 200)

268. INGRAM, W. M., and TRAPIDO, H.—1947.
Cypraea cervinetta Kiener and *Cypraea arabicula* Lamarck.
The Nautilus, *61*(1): 17-19. (Repr. No. 196b)

269. RODANICHE, E. C. DE, and RODANICHE, A.—1947.
Fiebre Q. Reporte de un Caso y Estudio del Agente Etiológico.
Archivos del Hospital Santo Tomás, 2: 327-348. (Repr. No. 207a)

270.* SHRAPNEL, B. C.—1947.
Oral Emetine in the Treatment of Intestinal Amebiasis.
American Journal of Tropical Medicine, *27*(5): 527-544. (Repr. No. 195)

271.* TRAPIDO, H.—1947.
DDT Residual Spray Control of Sandflies in Panamá.
Journal of Economic Entomology, *40*(4): 472-475. (Repr. No. 196)

272. TRAPIDO, H.—1947.
As the Effectiveness of DDT Residual House Spraying. . . (Comments by Readers). Science, *105*(2739): 432. (Repr. No. 196a)

273.* TRAPIDO, H.—1947.
The Isthmian Capybara in the Canal Zone.
Journal of Mammalogy, *28*(4): 408-409. (Repr. No. 197)

274. TRAPIDO, H.—1947.
Range Extension of *Hyla septentrionalis* in Florida.
Herpetologica, *3*(6): 190. (Repr. No. 196c)

275. WETMORE, A.—1947.
News and Notes [Notice of two Darién Expeditions].
Science, *106*(2745): 124. (Repr. No. 199c)

1948

276.* CALERO M., C.—1948.
Outbreak of Typhus of the Murine Type. First Report from the Isthmus of Panamá.
American Journal of Tropical Medicine, *28*(2): 313-321. (Repr. No. 201)

277. CALERO M., C., and ORTIZ O., P.—1948.
Presencia de Huevos de *Heterodera radicicola* Greef, en las Materias Fecales Humanas.
Boletín de la Asociación Médica Nacional de Panamá, *11*(2): 301-304. (Repr. No. 201a)

278. CLARK, H. C.—1948.
Equine Trypanosomiasis—Murrina of Panamá.
Proceedings of the Fourth International Congresses on Tropical Medicine and Malaria, Washington, D. C., pp. 1342-1348. (Repr. No. 211)

279. DUNN, E. R., TRAPIDO, H., and EVANS, H.—1948.
A New Species of the Microhylid Frog Genus *Chiasmocleis* from Panamá.
American Museum Novitates, No. 1376, June 15th. (Repr. No. 206a)

280.* FAIRCHILD, G. B., and HERTIG, M.—1948.
An Improved Method for Mounting Small Insects.
Science, *108*(2792): 20-21. (Repr. No. 203)

281. FAIRCHILD, G. B., and HERTIG, M.—1948.
Notes on the *Phlebotomus* of Panamá (Diptera, Psychodidae). III. *P. cruciatus* Coq., *P. trinidadensis* Newst and *P. gomezi* Nitz.
Annals of the Entomological Society of America, *41*(2): 247-257. (Repr. No. 205)

282.* FAIRCHILD, G. B., and HERTIG, M.—1948.
Notes on the *Phlebotomus* of Panamá (Diptera, Psychodidae). IV. *P. atroclavatus* Knab, *P. cayennensis* Floch and Abonnenc, *P. chiapanensis* Dampf and Some Related Forms from the West Indies and México.
Annals of the Entomological Society of America, *41*(4): 455-467. (Repr. No. 209

283. HERTIG, M.—1948.
A New Genus of Bloodsucking Psychodids from Perú (Diptera: Psychodidae).
Annals of the Entomological Society of America, *41*(1): 8-16. (Repr. No. 202)

284.* HERTIG, M.—1948.
Sandflies of the Genus *Phlebotomus*—A Review of their Habits, Disease Relationships, and Control.
Proceedings of the Fourth International Congresses on Tropical Medicine and Malaria, Washington, D. C., May 10-18, 1948. pp. 1609-1615. (Repr. No. 210)

285.* RODANICHE, E. C. DE—1948.
Cross—Immune Reactions Between Panamanian Strains of Q Fever and Endemic Typhus.
American Journal of Tropical Medicine, *28*(5): 683-686. (Repr. No. 204)

286. ROGNONI, M., and RODANICHE, E. C. DE—1948.
Pulmonía Atípica Primaria; Presentación de un Caso.
Archivos del Hospital Santo Tomás, *3*(3/4): 157-164. (Repr. No. 206b)

287.* TRAPIDO, H.—1948.
The Development of a Sprayer for Use with Water Suspensions of DDT in Rural Areas of Latin America.
American Journal of Tropical Medicine, *28*(5): 721-739. (Repr. No. 206)

1949

288. CALERO M., C.—1949.
Cutaneous Myiasis Due to *Chrysostomomyia bergi* (Blanchard).
Journal of Parasitology, *35*(5): 545. (Repr. No. 227)

289. CALERO M., C., and ORTIZ O., P.—1949.
Triquinosis en Panamá.
Revista del Instituto de Salubridad y Enfermedades Tropicales, *10*(4): 355-358. (Repr. No. 214c)

290.   CLARK, H. C.—1949.
          The Tropics and the White Man.
          American Journal of Tropical Medicine, *29*(3): 303-309. *Also* Same
          Title and Contents as Above, but a Shorter Article *in*: Your Health,
          4(7): 25-26, July 1947. (Repr. No. 214)

291.   CLARK, H. C., and TOMLINSON, W. J.—1949.
          The Pathologic Anatomy of Malaria. (Chapter 37, pp. 874-903). *In:*
          Malariology Vol. 2. Ed. by M. F. Boyd. Philadelphia, Saunders, 1949.
          (Repr. No. 214b)

292.   DUNN, E. R.—1949.
          Relative Abundance of Some Panamanian Snakes.
          Ecology, *30*(1): 39-56. (Repr. No. 208b)

293.*   FAIRCHILD, G. B.—1949.
          A New Fly Related to *Phlebotomus* from Panamá. (Diptera, Psycho-
          didae).
          Proceedings of the Entomological Society of Washington, *51*(2): 81-84.
          (Repr. No. 212)

294.   GALINDO, P., CARPENTER, S., and TRAPIDO, H.—1949.
          Notes on Forest Mosquitoes of Panamá. I. *Haemagogus spegazzinii*
          falco Kumm *et al., Haemagogus iridicolor* Dyar, *Anopheles (Lophopo-*
          domyia) squamifemur Antunes, and *Anopheles (Anopheles) fausti*
          Vargas, Four New Records for the Country.
          Proceedings of the Entomological Society of Washington, *51*(6): 277-
          278. (Repr. No. 220)

295.*   HERTIG, M.—1949.
          The Genital Filaments of *Phlebotomus* During Copulation (Diptera,
          Psychodidae).
          Proceedings of the Entomological Society of Washington, *51*(6): 286-
          288. (Repr. No. 219)

296.*   HERTIG, M.—1949.
          Phlebotomus and Residual DDT in Greece and Italy.
          American Journal of Tropical Medicine, *29*(5): 773-809. (Repr. No.
          216)

297.*   RODANICHE, E. C. DE—1949.
          Experimental Transmission of Q Fever by *Amblyomma cajennense*.
          American Journal of Tropical Medicine, *29*(5): 711-714. (Repr. No.
          215)

298.*   RODANICHE, E. C. DE, and PINZÒN, T. DE—1949.
          Spontaneous Toxoplasmosis in the Guinea-Pig in Panamá.
          Journal of Parasitology, *35*(2): 152-155. (Repr. No. 213)

299.*   RODANICHE, E. C. DE, and RODANICHE, A.—1949.
          Studies on Q Fever in Panamá.
          American Journal of Hygiene, *49*(1): 67-75. (Repr. No. 207)

300.*   TRAPIDO, H.—1949.
          Gestation Period, Young and Maximum Weight of the Isthmian Capy-
          bara, *Hydrochoerus isthmius* Goldman.
          Journal of Mammalogy, *30*(4): 433. (Repr. No. 217)

301.* TRAPIDO, H.—1949.
The Isthmian Capybara in the Tocumen Savannas, Panamá.
Journal of Mammalogy, *30*(1): 80. (Repr. No. 208)

1950

302. CLARK, H. C.—1950.
A Discourse on Jungle Medicine.
Industry and Tropical Health, *1*: 141-146. (Repr. No. 226a)

303.* FAIRCHILD, G. B.—1950.
The Generic Names for Tabanidae (Diptera) Proposed by Adolfo Lutz.
Psyche, *57*(3): 117-127. (Repr. No. 229)

304. FAIRCHILD, G. B.—1950.
Phlebotomus Sandflies in the West Indies.
Natural History Notes of the Natural History Society of Jamaica, No. 40, pp. 77-78, Jan. 1950. (Mimeographed for the Society). (Repr. No. 220a)

305.* FAIRCHILD, G. B., and HERTIG, M.—1950.
Notes on the *Phlebotomus* of Panamá (Diptera, Psychodidae). VI. *Phlebotomus shannoni* Dyar and Related Species.
Annals of the Entomological Society of America, *43*(4): 523-533. (Repr. No. 226)

306. FAIRCHILD, G. B., and TRAPIDO, H.—1950.
The West Indian Species of *Phlebotomus* (Diptera, Psychodidae).
Annals of the Entomological Society of America, *43*(3): 405-417. (Repr. No. 224)

307. GALINDO, P., TRAPIDO, H., and CARPENTER, S. J.—1950.
Observations on Diurnal Forest Mosquitoes in Relation to Sylvan Yellow Fever in Panamá.
American Journal of Tropical Medicine, *30*(4): 533-574. (Repr. No. 222)

308. HERTIG, M.—1950.
Observations on the Density of *Phlebotomus* Populations Following DDT Campaigns.
Bulletin of the World Health Organization, *2*: 621-628. (Repr. No. 221a)

309.* HERTIG, M.—1950.
The Type of *Phlebotomus mascittii* Grassi (Diptera, Psychodidae).
Bulletin of Entomological Research, *40*(4): 453-457. (Repr. No. 218)

310. HERTIG, M., and FAIRCHILD, G. B.—1950.
Notes on the *Phlebotomus* of Panamá. V. The Second Sternite as a Taxonomic Character (Diptera, Psychodidae).
Proceedings of the Entomological Society of Washington, *52*(2): 91-95. (Repr. No. 221)

311.* RODANICHE, E. C. DE, and RODANICHE, A.—1950.
Spotted Fever in Panamá; Isolation of the Etiologic Agent from a Fatal Case.
American Journal of Tropical Medicine, *30*(4): 511-517. (Repr. No. 223)

312.   WETMORE, A.—1950.
       An Additional Form of Pepper-Shrike from Western Panamá.
       Proceedings of the Biological Society of Washington, *63*: 61-72, May
       25. (Repr. No. 229a)

313.   WETMORE, A.—1950.
       Additional Forms of Birds from the Republics of Panamá and Colombia.
       Proceedings of the Biological Society of Washington, *63*: 171-174, De-
       cember 29. (Repr. No. 229b)

314.   WETMORE, A.—1950.
       The Identity of the American Vulture Described as *Cathartes burro-
       vianus* by Cassin.
       Journal of the Washington Academy of Sciences, *40*(12): 415-418, De-
       cember 15. (Repr. No. 229c)

1951

315.   CALERO M., C., ORTIZ O., P., and DE SOUZA, L.—1951.
       Helminths in Cats from Panamá City and Balboa, C.Z.
       The Journal of Parasitology, *37*(3): 326. (Repr. No. 231a)

316.* FAIRCHILD, G. B.—1951.
       Descriptions and Notes on Neotropical Tabanidae.
       Annals of the Entomological Society of America, *44*(3): 441-462.
       (Repr. No. 234)

317.   FAIRCHILD, G. B.—1951.
       Some Nomenclatorial Notes on Psychodidae (Diptera).
       Bulletin of the Brooklyn Entomological Society, *46*(1): 10-18. (Repr.
       No. 234a)

318.* FAIRCHILD, G. B., and HERTIG, M.—1951.
       Notes on the *Phlebotomus* of Panamá (Diptera, Psychodidae). VII. The
       Subgenus *Shannonomyina* Pratt.
       Annals of the Entomological Society of America, *44*(3): 399-421.
       (Repr. No. 233)

319.* FAIRCHILD, G. B., and HERTIG, M.—1951.
       Notes on the *Phlebotomus* of Panamá (Diptera, Psychodidae). VIII.
       Two New Species of *Warileya*.
       Annals of the Entomological Society of America, *44*(3): 422-429.
       (Repr. No. 236)

320.* GALINDO, P., CARPENTER, S. J., and TRAPIDO, H.—1951.
       Description of Two New Species of *Wyeomyia* and the Male of *Sabethes
       tarsopus* Dyar & Knab (Diptera, Culicidae).
       Proceedings of the Entomological Society of Washington, *53*(2): 86-96.
       (Repr. No. 230)

321.* GALINDO, P., CARPENTER, S. J., and TRAPIDO, H.—1951.
       Ecological Observations on Forest Mosquitoes of an Endemic Yellow
       Fever Area in Panamá.
       American Journal of Tropical Medicine, *31*(1): 98-137. (Repr. No.
       228)

322.* GALINDO, P., CARPENTER, S. J., and TRAPIDO, H.—1951.
Westward Extension of the Range of *Haemagogus spegazzinii falco*
Kumm *et al.* into Costa Rica (Diptera, Culicidae).
Proceedings of the Entomological Society of Washington, *53*(2): 104-
106. (Repr. No. 231)

323. HARTMAN, F. A., and ALBERTIN, R. H.—1951.
A Preliminary Study of the Avian Adrenal.
The Auk, *68*: 202-209. (Repr. No. 232a)

324. HERTIG, M.—1951.
Review of Dr. William B. Herms' Book: *Medical Entomology, with
Special Reference to the Health and Well-being of Man and Animals.*
4th ed. New York, Macmillan, 1950.
American Journal of Tropical Medicine, *31*(6): 859-860. (Repr. No.
236a)

325. LAVERGNE, J. A., and TRAPIDO, H.—1951.
La Identificación y el Uso del Sapo Macho Común Panameño (*Bujos
marinus* Linneus) en el Diagnóstico Precoz del Embarazo.
Boletín de la Asociación Médica Nacional de Panamá, *14*(1): 108-113.
(Repr. No. 235a)

326.* TRAPIDO, H.—1951.
Factors Influencing the Search for Anopheline Larvae in Sardinia.
Journal of the National Malaria Society, *10*(4): 318-326. (Repr. No.
235)

327.* TRAPIDO, H.—1951.
The Toxicity of DDT to *Anopheles claviger* (Meigen) in Sardinia and
on the Italian Mainland.
Journal of the National Malaria Society, *10*(3): 266-271. (Repr. No.
232)

328. WETMORE, A.—1951.
Additional Forms of Birds from Colombia and Panamá.
Smithsonian Miscellaneous Collection, *117*(2): 1-11, September 25.
(Repr. No. 228a)

329. WETMORE, A.—1951.
Four Additional Species for Panamá.
The Auk, *68*(4): 525-526, October. (Repr. No. 228b)

1952

330. CALVO, A. E., and GALINDO, P.—1952.
Epidemiología de la Fiebre Amarilla en Panamá (1949-1952). Symposium: Yellow Fever.
Primer Congreso Interamericano de Higiene, Habana, Sept. 26-Oct. 1,
1952. (Repr. No. 251)

CALVO, A. E., and GALINDO, P.—1952.
Epidemiology of Yellow Fever in Panamá (1949-1952).
A Symposium. First Inter-American Congress of Public Health Con-
voked by Resolution of the XIII Pan-American Sanitary Conference, in
Commemoration of the 50th Anniversary of the Pan-American Sanitary Bureau and as a Tribute to Carlos J. Finlay. Havana, Cuba, Sept.
26-Oct. 1, 1952. . . (Mimeographed, 14 p.) (Repr. No. 251a)

331.   CARPENTER, S. J., GALINDO, P., and TRAPIDO, H.—1952.
        Forest Mosquito Studies in an Endemic Yellow Fever Area in Panamá.
        Mosquito News, *12*(3): 156-164. (Repr. No. 246a)

332.   CLARK, H. C.—1952.
        Endemic Yellow Fever in Panamá and Neighboring Areas.
        American Journal of Tropical Medicine and Hygiene, *1*(1): 78-86.
        (Repr. No. 237)

333.   DRAHEIM, J. H., and RODANICHE, E. C. DE—1952.
        Herpes Simplex Encephalitis; Report of a Case.
        American Journal of Clinical Pathology, *22*: 1077-1080. (Repr. No.
        238a)

334.*   FAIRCHILD, G. B.—1952.
        Notes on *Bruchomyia* and *Nemopalpus* (Diptera, Psychodidae).
        Annals of the Entomological Society of America, *45*(2): 259-280. (Repr.
        No. 239)

335.*   FAIRCHILD, G. B.—1952.
        Notes on *Phlebotomus* from the Australasian Region (Dipt., Psycho-
        didae).
        Proceedings of the Linnean Society of New South Wales, *77*(3-4): 189-
        208. (Repr. No. 243)

336.*   FAIRCHILD, G. B., and HERTIG, M.—1952.
        Notes on the *Phlebotomus* of Panamá. IX. Descriptions of Seven New
        Species.
        Annals of the Entomological Society of America, *45*(4): 505-528.
        (Repr. No. 245)

337.   GALINDO, P., CARPENTER, S. J., and TRAPIDO, H.—1952.
        The Taxonomic Status of the *Aedes leucocelaenus* Complex with De-
        scriptions of Two New Forms (Diptera, Culicidae).
        Annals of the Entomological Society of America, *45*(4): 529-542.
        (Repr. No. 246)

338.*   RODANICHE, E. C. DE—1952.
        Survey of Live Forest Animals for Protective Antibodies Against Yel-
        low Fever in Panamá, R. P.
        American Journal of Tropical Medicine and Hygiene, *1*(5): 789-795.
        (Repr. No. 241)

339.*   RODANICHE, E. C. DE—1952.
        Susceptibility of Certain Species of Panamanian Monkeys to the Virus
        of Acute Anterior Poliomyelitis.
        American Journal of Tropical Medicine and Hygiene, *1*(2): 205-209.
        (Repr. No. 238)

340.*   RODANICHE, A., and RODANICHE, E. C. DE—1952.
        An Epidemic of Acute Anterior Poliomyelitis in Panamá in 1950-1951.
        American Journal of Tropical Medicine and Hygiene, *1*(5): 784-788.
        (Repr. No. 242)

        RODANICHE, A., and RODANICHE, E. C. DE—1952.
        (Same Title and Contents as Above but in Spanish).
        Archivos Médicos Panameños, *1*(3): 215-222. (Repr. No. 242a)

341.* TRAPIDO, H.—1952.
Modified Response of *Anopheles albimanus* to DDT Residual House
Spraying in Panamá.
American Journal of Tropical Medicine and Hygiene, *1*(5): 853-861.
(Repr. No. 240)

342. WETMORE, A.—1952.
The Birds of the Islands of Taboga, Taboguilla, and Uravá, Panamá.
Smithsonian Miscellaneous Collection, *121*(2): 1-32, December 2.
(Repr. No. 246b)

343.* WIMSATT, W. A., and TRAPIDO, H.—1952.
Reproduction and the Female Reproductive Cycle in the Tropical
American Vampire Bat, *Desmodus rotundus murinus*.
American Journal of Anatomy, *91*(3): 415-446. (Repr. No. 244)

1953

344. CALERO M., C., and JOHNSON, C. M.—1953.
Cutaneous Leishmaniasis in the Republic of Panamá. A Report of
Twenty-five Cases.
American Journal of Tropical Medicine and Hygiene, *2*(4): 628-633,
July. (Repr. No. 250a)

345.* FAIRCHILD, G. B.—1953.
Arboreal Tabanidae in Panamá (Diptera).
Proceedings of the Entomological Society of Washington, *55*(5): 239-
243. (Repr. No. 256)

346.* FAIRCHILD, G. B.—1953.
A Note on *Hertigia hertigi* Fairchild and Description of the Female
(Diptera, Psychodidae).
Proceedings of the Entomological Society of Washington, *55*(2): 101-
102. (Repr. No. 248)

347.* FAIRCHILD, G. B.—1953.
Notes on Neotropical Tabanidae (Diptera) with Descriptions of New
Species.
Annals of the Entomological Society of America, *46*(2): 259-280.
(Repr. No. 255)

348.* FAIRCHILD, G. B.—1953.
Tabanidae from the State of Chiapas, México, with Descriptions of
Two New Species (Diptera).
Psyche, *60*(2): 41-51. (Repr. No. 254)

349.* FAIRCHILD, G. B., and HERTIG, M.—1953.
Notes on the *Phlebotomus* of Panamá (Diptera, Psychodidae). X. *P.
aragaoi, P. barrettoi,* and Two New Species.
Annals of the Entomological Society of America, *46*(1): 21-34. (Repr.
No. 249)

350.* FAIRCHILD, G. B., and HERTIG, M.—1953.
Notes on the *Phlebotomos* of Panamá (Diptera, Psychodidae). XI. The
Male of *P. cruciatus* Coq. and Notes on Related Species.
Annals of the Entomological Society of America, *46*(3): 373-385. (Repr.
No. 257)

351.* PINZÒN, T. P. DE—1953.
BCG Vaccination in the Republic of Panamá.
American Review of Tuberculosis, *67*(4): 522-525. (Repr. No. 247)

352. RODANICHE, E. C. DE—1953.
Natural Infection of the Tick, *Amblyomma cajennense* with *Rickettsia rickettsii* in Panamá.
American Journal of Tropical Medicine and Hygiene, *2*(4): 696-699. (Repr. No. 250)

353.* TRAPIDO, H.—1953.
Biological Considerations. Appendix 2. (*In: The Sardinian Project: An Experiment in the Eradication of an Indigenous Malarious Vector*, pp. 353-374).
Ed. by J. A. Logan. Baltimore, Johns Hopkins Press, 1953. Also in: The American Journal of Hygiene Monographic Series No. 20. (Repr. No. 258)

354. TRAPIDO, H.—1953.
A New Frog from Panamá *Dendrobates galindoi*.
Fieldiana—Zoology, *34*(15): 181-187. (Repr. No. 252)

355.* TRAPIDO, H., and AITKEN, T. H. G.—1953.
Study of a Residual Population of *Anopheles l. labranchiae* Falleroni in the Geremeas Valley, Sardinia.
American Journal of Tropical Medicine and Hygiene, *2*(4): 658-676. (Repr. No. 253)

356. WETMORE, A.—1953.
Further Additions to the Birds of Panamá and Colombia.
Smithsonian Miscellaneous Collection, *122*(8): 1-12, December 17. (Repr. No. 250b)

1954

357.* AITKEN, T. H. G., MAIER, J., and TRAPIDO, H.—1954.
The Status of Anophelism and Malaria in Sardinia During 1951 and 1952.
American Journal of Hygiene, *60*(1): 37-51. (Repr. No. 262)

358. AJELLO, L.—1954.
Occurrence of *Histoplasma capsulatum* and other Human Pathogenic Molds in Panamanian Soil.
American Journal of Tropical Medicine and Hygiene, *3*(5): 897-904. (Repr. No. 263a)

359.* CLARK, H. C.—1954.
The Suppressive Treatment of Malaria in a Rural Village with Primaquine and Plaquenil.
American Journal of Tropical Medicine and Hygiene, *3*(2): 250-253. (Repr. No. 259)

360.* CLARK, H. C.—1954.
The Suppressive Treatment of Naturally Acquired Malaria in a Rural Village with Pyrimethamine (Daraprim).
American Journal of Tropical Medicine and Hygiene, *3*(5): 831-832. (Repr. No. 263)

361. GALINDO, P., and BLANTON, F. S.—1954.
      Nine New Species of Neotropical *Culex,* Eight from Panamá and One
      from Honduras (Diptera, Culicidae).
      Annals of the Entomological Society of America, *47*(2): 231-247.
      (Repr. No. 260a)

362.* GALINDO, P., BLANTON, F. S., and PEYTON, E. L.—1954.
      A Revision of the *Uranotaenia* of Panamá with Notes on other Ameri-
      can Species of the Genus (Diptera, Culicidae).
      Annals of the Entomological Society of America, *47*(1): 107-177.
      (Repr. No. 260)

363. HARTMAN, F. A.—1954.
      Cardiac and Pectoral Muscles of Trochilids.
      The Auk, *71*: 467-469. (Repr. No. 263b)

364. JUNGEBLUT, C. W., and RODANICHE, E. C. DE—1954.
      Selective Susceptibility of *Ateles* Monkeys to Infection with Type I
      Poliomyelitis and Col SK Virus.
      Proceedings of the Society for Experimental Biology and Medicine,
      86(3): 604-606. (Repr. No. 261)

365. MICHENER, C. D.—1954.
      Bees of Panamá.
      Bulletin of the American Museum of Natural History, *104*(1): 1-176.
      (Repr. No. 263c)

366.* RODANICHE, E. C. DE—1954.
      Spontaneous Toxoplasmosis in the Whiteface Monkey, *Cebus capucinus,*
      in Panamá.
      American Journal of Tropical Medicine and Hygiene, *3*(6): 1023-1025.
      (Repr. No. 266)

367.* RODANICHE, E. C. DE—1954.
      Susceptibility of the Marmoset, *Marikina geoffroyi* and the Night Mon-
      key, *Aotus zonalis,* to Experimental Infection with *Toxoplasma.*
      American Journal of Tropical Medicine and Hygiene, *3*(6): 1026-1032.
      (Repr. No. 265)

368. TRAPIDO, H.—1954.
      Recent Experiments on Possible Resistance to DDT by *Anopheles*
      albimanus in Panamá.
      Bulletin of the World Health Organization, *11*: 885-889. (Repr. No.
      264)

369. TRAUB, R., HERTIG, M., LAWRENCE, W., and HARRISS, T.—1954.
      Potential Vectors and Reservoirs of Hemorrhagic Fever in Korea.
      American Journal of Hygiene, *59*(3): 291-305. (Repr. No. 266a)

370. WIMSATT, W. A.—1954.
      The Fetal Membranes and Placentation of the Tropical American Vam-
      pire Bat *Desmodus rotundus murinus,* with Notes on the Histochemistry
      of the Placenta.
      Acta Anatómica (Basle), *21*(4): 285-341. (Repr. No. 264a)

1955

371. BLANTON, F. S., GALINDO, P., and PEYTON, E. L.—1955.
Report of a Three Year Light Trap Survey for Biting Diptera in Panamá.
Mosquito News, *15*(2): 90-93. (Repr. No. 268a)

372. BLOEDELL, P.—1955.
Observations on the Life Histories of Panamá Bats.
Journal of Mammalogy, *36*(2): 232-235. (Repr. No. 274a)

373. CALERO M., C., ORTIZ O., P., and DE SOUZA, L.—1955.
Trematodiasis en Gatos de Arraiján y Chorrera.
Archivos Médicos Panameños, *4*(1): 37-41. (Repr. No. 268b)

374. FAIRCHILD, G. B.—1955.
The Relationships and Classification of the Phlebotominae (Diptera, Psychodidae).
Annals of the Entomological Society of America, *48*(3): 182-196. (Repr. No. 273)

375. FAIRCHILD, G. B., and ORTIZ, I.—1955.
Algunos Tabanidae del Bajo Orinoco, Venezuela. Novedades Científicas (Contribuciones Ocasionales del Museo de Historia Natural La Salle, Caracas). Serie Zoológica, No. 16, pp. 3-7. (Repr. No. 267)

376.* GALINDO, P., and BLANTON, F. S.—1955.
An Annotated List of the *Culex* of Panamá (Diptera, Culicidae).
Proceedings of the Entomological Society of Washington, *57*(2): 68-74. (Repr. No. 268)

377. GALINDO, P., CARPENTER, S. J., and TRAPIDO, H.—1955.
A Contribution to the Ecology and Biology of Tree Hole Breeding Mosquitoes of Panamá.
Annals of the Entomological Society of America, *48*(3): 158-164. (Repr. No. 272)

378. GALINDO, P., and TRAPIDO, H.—1955.
Forest Canopy Mosquitoes Associated with the Appearance of Sylvan Yellow Fever in Costa Rica, 1951.
American Journal of Tropical Medicine and Hygiene, *4*(3): 543-549. (Repr. No. 270)

379. GRIFFIN, D. R., and NOVICK, A.—1955.
Acoustic Orientation of Neotropical Bats.
Journal of Experimental Zoology, *130*(2): 251-299. (Repr. No. 284a)

380. HARTMAN, F. A.—1955.
Heart Weight in Birds.
The Condor, *57*(4): 221-238. (Repr. No. 265a)

381. PEYTON, E. L., GALINDO, P., and BLANTON, F. S.—1955.
Pictorial Keys to the Genera of Panamá Mosquitoes.
Mosquito News, *15*(2): 95-100. (Repr. No. 310)

382. TRAPIDO, H., and GALINDO, P.—1955.
The Investigation of a Sylvan Yellow Fever Epizootic on the North Coast of Honduras, 1954.
American Journal of Tropical Medicine and Hygiene, *4*(4): 665-674. (Repr. No. 271)

383. TRAPIDO, H., GALINDO, P., and CARPENTER, S. J.—1955.
A Survey of Forest Mosquitoes in Relation to Sylvan Yellow Fever in the Panamá Isthmian Area.
American Journal of Tropical Medicine and Hygiene, 4(3): 525-542. (Repr. No. 269)

384. WEBER, N. A.—1955.
Pure Cultures of Fungi Produced by Ants.
Science, 121(3134): 109. (Repr. No. 268c)

385. Yellow Fever Conference. Washington, D. C., Dec. 21-22, 1954.
American Journal of Tropical Medicine and Hygiene, 4(4): 571-661, 1955. *Also in:* Scientific Publication No. 19, Pan American Sanitary Bureau. A Spanish Translation of these Proceedings Appeared *in:* Boletín de la Oficina Sanitaria Panamericana, 39(1): 1-82, July 1955. (Repr. No. 274)

1956

386. FAIRCHILD, G. B.—1956.
Synonymical Notes on Neotropical Flies of the Family Tabanidae (Diptera).
Smithsonian Miscellaneous Collection, 131(3): 1-38, January 11. (Pub. No. 4225). (Repr. No. 279)

387.* FAIRCHILD, G. B., and HERTIG, M.—1956.
Notes on the *Phlebotomus* of Panamá (Diptera, Psychodidae). XII. The Group *Anthophorus,* with Descriptions of Four New Species from Panamá and México.
Annals of the Entomological Society of America, 49(4): 307-312. (Repr. No. 282)

388. FAIRCHILD, G. B., PHILIP, C. B., MACKERRAS, I. M., and OLDROYD, H.—1956.
Proposed Use of the Plenary Powers to Validate the Generic Names *"Elaphella"* Bezzi, 1913 (Class Insecta, Order Diptera) and *"Lophiotherium"* Gervais, 1850 (Class Mammalia).
Bulletin of Zoological Nomenclature, 12(7-8): 195-199. (Repr. No. 282a)

389.* GALINDO, P., RODANICHE, E. C. DE, and TRAPIDO, H.—1956.
Experimental Transmission of Yellow Fever by Central American Species of *Haemagogus* and *Sabethes chloropterus.*
American Journal of Tropical Medicine and Hygiene, 5(6): 1022-1031. (Repr. No. 284)

390.* GALINDO, P., TRAPIDO, H., CARPENTER, S. J., and BLANTON, F. S.—1956.
The Abundance Cycles of Arboreal Mosquitoes During Six Years at a Sylvan Yellow Fever Locality in Panamá.
Annals of the Entomological Society of America, 49(6): 543-547. (Repr. No. 285)

391.* GALINDO, P., and TRAPIDO, H.—1956.
Descriptions of Two New Subspecies of *Haemagogus mesodentatus* Komp and Kumm, 1938, from Middle America (Diptera, Culicidae). Proceedings of the Entomological Society of Washington, *58*(4): 228-231. (Repr. No. 278)

392. JOHNSON, C. M., and FARNSWORTH, S. F.—1956.
Results of Recent Studies of Yellow Fever in Middle America. Preliminary Note.
Bulletin of the Pan American Sanitary Bureau, *61*(2): 182-183. (Repr. No. 281)

393.* PHILIP, C. B., and FAIRCHILD, G. B.—1956.
American Biting Flies of the Genera *Chlorotabanus* Lutz and *Cryptotylus* Lutz (Diptera, Tabanidae).
Annals of the Entomological Society of America, *49*(4): 313-324. (Repr. No. 283)

394.* RODANICHE, E. C. DE—1956.
Isolation of the Virus of Ilheus Encephalitis from Mosquitoes of the Genus *Psorophora* Captured in Honduras.
American Journal of Tropical Medicine and Hygiene, *5*(5): 797-801. (Repr. No. 280)

395.* RODANICHE, E. C. DE—1956.
Survey of Mosquitoes Captured in Honduras for Yellow Fever Virus.
American Journal of Tropical Medicine and Hygiene, *5*(3): 480-482. (Repr. No. 277)

396. TRAPIDO, H., and GALINDO, P.—1956.
The Epidemiology of Yellow Fever in Middle America.
Experimental Parasitology, *5*(3): 285-323. (Repr. No. 276)

397.* TRAPIDO, H., and GALINDO, P.—1956.
Genus *Haemagogus* in the United States.
Science, *123*(3198): 634. (Repr. No. 275)

398. WETMORE, A.—1956.
Additional Forms of Birds from Panamá and Colombia.
Proceedings of the Biological Society of Washington, *69*: 123-126, September 12. (Repr. No. 282b)

399. WETMORE, A.—1956.
The Muscovy Duck in the Pleistocene of Panamá.
Wilson Bulletin, *68*(4): 327, September 24. (Repr. No. 282c)

1957

400. FAIRCHILD, G. B., and HERTIG, M.—1957.
Notes on the *Phlebotomus* of Panamá. XIII. The *Vexator* Group, with Descriptions of New Species from Panamá and California.
Annals of the Entomological Society of America, *50*(4): 325-334. (Repr. No. 290)

401.* GALINDO, P.—1957.
A Note on the Oviposition Behavior of *Sabethes (Sabethoides) chloropterus* Humboldt.
Proceedings of the Entomological Society of Washington, *59*(6): 287-288. (Repr. No. 294)

402.   GALINDO, P.—1957.
        On the Validity of *Haemagogus spegazzinii falco* Kumm *et al*, 1946 (Diptera, Culicidae).
        Proceedings of the Entomological Society of Washington, *59*(3): 121-124. (Repr. No. 288)

403.*   GALINDO, P., and TRAPIDO, H.—1957.
        Forest Mosquitoes Associated with Sylvan Yellow Fever in Nicaragua.
        American Journal of Tropical Medicine and Hygiene, *6*(1): 145-152. (Repr. No. 287)

404.*   RODANICHE, E. C. DE—1957.
        Survey of Primates Captured in Panamá, R. P., During the Years 1952-1956 for Protective Antibodies Against Yellow Fever.
        American Journal of Tropical Medicine and Hygiene, *6*(5): 835-839. (Repr. No. 293)

405.   RODANICHE, E. C. DE, and GALINDO, P.—1957.
        Isolation of Ilheus Virus from *Sabethes chloropterus* Captured in Guatemala in 1956.
        American Journal of Tropical Medicine and Hygiene, *6*(4): 686-687. (Repr. No. 291)

406.*   RODANICHE, E. C. DE, and GALINDO, P.—1957.
        Isolation of Yellow Fever Virus from *Haemagogus mesodentatus, H. equinus,* and *Sabethes chloropterus* Captured in Guatemala in 1956.
        American Journal of Tropical Medicine and Hygiene, *6*(2): 232-237. (Repr. No. 289)

407.*   RODANICHE, E. C. DE, GALINDO, P., and JOHNSON, C.M.—1957.
        Isolation of Yellow Fever Virus from *Haemagogus lucifer, H. equinus, H. spegazzinii falco, Sabethes chloropterus* and *Anopheles neivai* Captured in Panamá in the Fall of 1956.
        American Journal of Tropical Medicine and Hygiene, *6*(4): 681-685. (Repr. No. 292)

408.   TRAPIDO, H., and GALINDO, P.—1957.
        Mosquitoes Associated with Sylvan Yellow Fever Near Almirante, Panamá.
        American Journal of Tropical Medicine and Hygiene, *6*(1): 114-144. (Repr. No. 286)

409.   WETMORE, A.—1957.
        The Birds of Isla Coiba, Panamá.
        Smithsonian Miscellaneous Collection, *134*(9): 1-105, July 8. (Repr. No. 290a)

410.   WETMORE, A.—1957.
        Species Limitation in Certain Groups of Swift Genus *Chaetura*.
        The Auk, *74*(3): 383-385, July (September, 23). (Repr. No. 290b)

1958

411.*   FAIRCHILD, G. B.—1958.
        Notes on Neotropical Tabanidae (Diptera). II. Descriptions of New Species and New Records for Panamá.
        Annals of the Entomological Society of America, *51*(6): 517-530. (Repr. No. 297)

412.*   FAIRCHILD, G. B., and HERTIG, M.—1958.
        Notes on the *Phlebotomus* of Panamá. XIV. (Diptera, Psychodidae).
        P. vespertilionis and Related Species.
        Annals of the Entomological Society of America, *51*(6): 509-516.
        (Repr. No. 298)

413.*   FAIRCHILD, G. B., and HERTIG, M.—1958.
        Notes on the *Phlebotomus* of Panamá. XV. Four Apparently New
        Synonymies (Diptera, Psychodidae).
        Proceedings of the Entomological Society of Washington, *60*(5): 203-
        205. (Repr. No. 296)

414.   GALINDO, P.—1958.
        Bionomics of *Sabethes chloropterus* Humboldt, a Vector of Sylvan
        Yellow Fever in Middle America.
        American Journal of Tropical Medicine and Hygiene, *7*(4): 429-440.
        (Repr. No. 295)

415.   WETMORE, A.—1958.
        Extralimital Records for the Eastern Kingbird, Tree Swallow, and Black-
        poll Warbler.
        The Auk, *75*(4): 467-468, October (January 2, 1959). (Repr. No. 298a)

1959

416.*   FAIRCHILD, G. B., and HERTIG, M.—1959.
        Geographic Distribution of the *Phlebotomus* Sandflies of Central
        America (Diptera, Psychodidae).
        Annals of the Entomological Society of America, *52*(2): 121-124.
        (Repr. No. 300)

417.   GALINDO, P., RODANICHE, E. C. DE, and JOHNSON, C. M.—1959.
        St. Louis Encephalitis in Panamá. I. Isolation of the Virus from Forest
        Mosquitoes and Human Blood.
        American Journal of Tropical Medicine and Hygiene, *8*(5): 557-560.
        (Repr. No. 301)

418.   HANDLEY, JR., C. O.—1959.
        A Review of the Genus *Hoplomys* (Thick-Spined Rats) with Descrip-
        tion of a New Form from Isla Escudo de Veraguas, Panamá.
        Smithsonian Miscellaneous Collection, *139*(4): 1-10, July 3. (Repr.
        No. 302)

419.   PIPKIN, S. B.—1959.
        Review of Ingo Krumbiegel's Book *Gregor Mendel und das Schicksal
        seiner Verebungsgesetze.* Stuttgart, Wissenschaftliche Verlagsgesell-
        schaft, 1957.
        Quarterly Review of Biology, *34*(4): 298-300. (Repr. No. 299a)

420.*   RODANICHE, E. C. DE, GALINDO, P., and JOHNSON, C. M.—1959.
        Further Studies on the Experimental Transmission of Yellow Fever by
        Sabethes chloropterus.
        American Journal of Tropical Medicine and Hygiene, *8*(2): 190-194.
        (Repr. No. 299)

421. SNYDER, T. E., WETMORE, A., and PORTER, B. A.—1959.
James Zetek, 1886-1959.
Journal of Economic Entomology, *52*(6): 1230-1232. (Repr. No. 302a)

422. WETMORE, A.—1959.
The Birds of Isla Escudo de Veraguas, Panamá.
Smithsonian Miscellaneous Collection, *139*(2): 1-27, July 8. (Repr. No. 302b)

423. WETMORE, A.—1959.
Description of a Race of the Shearwater *Puffinus lherminieri* from Panamá.
Proceedings of the Biological Society of Washington, *72*: 19-22, April 22. (Repr. No. 302c)

1960

424. FAIRCHILD, G. B., and AITKEN, T. H. G.—1960.
Additions to the Tabanidae (Diptera) of Trinidad, B. W. I.
Annals of the Entomological Society of America, *53*(1): 1-8. (Repr. No. 303)

425.* FAIRCHILD, G. B., and PHILIP, C. B.—1960.
A Revision of the Neotropical Genus *Dichelacera*, Subgenus *Dichelacera*, Macquart (Diptera, Tabanidae).
Studia Entomologica, *3*(1-4): 1-96. (Repr. No. 306)

426. HANDLEY, JR., C. O.—1960.
Descriptions of New Bats from Panamá.
Proceedings of the United States National Museum, *112*(3442): 459-479. (Repr. No. 309)

427.* JOHNSON, P. T.—1960.
A New Species of *Hoplopleura* from Australia (Anoplura: Hoplopleuridae).
Proceedings of the Entomological Society of Washington, *62*(2): 111-113. (Repr. No. 312)

428. JOHNSON, P. T.—1960.
The Anoplura of African Rodents and Insectivores.
Technical Bulletin No. 1211, U. S. Department of Agriculture. Washington, D. C., U. S. Government Printing Office, 1960. pp. 1-116. (Repr. No. 312a)

429.* MÉNDEZ, E., and ALTMAN, R. M.—1960.
A New Species of *Kohlsia* from Central America (Siphonaptera: Ceratophyllidae).
Proceedings of the Entomological Society of Washington, *62*(1): 45-50. (Repr. No. 304)

430.* PIPKIN, A. C.—1960.
Avian Embryos and Tissue Culture in the Study of Parasitic Protozoa. II. Protozoa other than *Plasmodium*.
Experimental Parasitology, *9*(2): 167-203. (Repr. No. 307)

431. PIPKIN, A. C., and COLES, W. C.—1960.
Growth of *Leishmania braziliensis* in Tissue Cultures of Rodent Cells.
Journal of Protozoology, 7 (Supplement): 24. (Repr. No. 308)

432. PIPKIN, S. B.—1960.
Sex Balance in *Drosophila melanogaster:* Aneuploidy of Long Regions
of Chromosome 3, Using the Triploid Method.
Genetics, *45*(9): 1205-1216. (Repr. No. 315)

1961

433.* FAIRCHILD, G. B.—1961.
The Adolpho Lutz Collection of Tabanidae (Diptera). I. The Described
Genera and Species, Condition of the Collection, and Selection of
Lectotypes.
Memorias do Instituto Oswaldo Cruz, *59*(2): 185-250. (Repr. No. 334)

434.* FAIRCHILD, G. B.—1961.
The Adolpho Lutz Collection of Tabanidae (Diptera). II. Status of
the Names Published without Description.
Memorias do Instituto Oswaldo Cruz, *59*(3): 279-295. (Repr. No. 335)

435.* FAIRCHILD, G. B.—1961.
Insecta Amapaensia—Diptera: Tabanidae.
Studia Entomologica, Río de Janeiro, *4*(1-4): 433-448. (Repr. No. 326)

436.* FAIRCHILD, G. B.—1961.
A Preliminary Check-List of the Tabanidae (Diptera) of Costa Rica.
Revista de Biología Tropical, *9*(1): 23-38. (Repr. No. 331)

437.* FAIRCHILD, G. B., and HARWOOD, R. F.—1961.
Phlebotomus Sandflies from Animal Burrows in Eastern Washington
(Diptera, Psychodidae).
Proceedings of the Entomological Society of Washington, *63* (4): 239-
245. (Repr. No. 330)

438.* FAIRCHILD, G. B., and HERTIG, M.—1961.
Notes on the *Phlebotomus* of Panamá. XVI. (Diptera, Psychodidae).
Descriptions of New and Little-Known Species from Panamá and Cen-
tral America.
Annals of the Entomological Society of America, *54*(2): 237-255.
(Repr. No. 314)

439.* FAIRCHILD, G. B., and HERTIG, M.—1961.
Three New Species of *Phlebotomus* from México and Nicaragua (Dip-
tera, Psychodidae).
Proceedings of the Entomological Society of Washington, *63*(1): 22-28.
(Repr. No. 316)

440.* GALINDO, P., and MÈNDEZ, E.—1961.
Descriptions of Four New Species of *Culex* from Panamá (Diptera,
Culicidae).
Annals of the Entomological Society of America, *54*(1): 1-4. (Repr.
No. 305)

441.* GALINDO, P., and RODANICHE, E. C. DE—1961.
    Birds as Hosts of Ilheus Encephalitis Virus in Panamá.
    American Journal of Tropical Medicine and Hygiene, *10*(3): 395-396.
    (Repr. No. 319)

442.* GALINDO, P., and RODANICHE, E. C. DE—1961.
    Isolation of the Virus of Ilheus Encephalitis from Mosquitoes Captured in Panamá.
    American Journal of Tropical Medicine and Hygiene, *10*(3): 393-394.
    (Repr. No. 318)

443.* HANSON, W. J.—1961.
    The Breeding Places of *Phlebotomus* in Panamá (Diptera, Psychodidae).
    Annals of the Entomological Society of America, *54*(3): 317-322.
    (Repr. No. 317)

444.* HERTIG, M., and JOHNSON, P. T.—1961.
    The Rearing of *Phlebotomus* Sandflies (Diptera: Psychodidae). I. Technique.
    Annals of the Entomological Society of America, *54*(6): 753-764.
    (Repr. No. 327)

445.* JOHNSON, P. T.—1961.
    Autogeny in Panamanian *Phlebotomus* Sandflies (Diptera, Psychodidae).
    Annals of the Entomological Society of America, *54*(1): 116-118.
    (Repr. No. 311)

446.* JOHNSON, P. T.—1961.
    A Revision of the Species of *Monopsyllus* Kolenati in North America (Siphonaptera: Ceratophyllidae).
    United States Department of Agriculture Bulletin No. 1227, pp. 1-69.
    (Repr. No. 323)

447. JOHNSON, P. T.—1961.
    The Sucking Lice (Anoplura) of Egypt. I. Species Infesting Rodents.
    Journal of the Egyptian Public Health Association, *35*(6): 203-228.
    (Repr. No. 324)

448.* JOHNSON, P. T., and HERTIG, M.—1961.
    The Rearing of *Phlebotomus* Sandflies (Diptera: Psychodidae). II. Development and Behavior of Panamanian Sandflies in Laboratory Culture.
    Annals of the Entomological Society of America, *54*(6): 764-776.
    (Repr. No. 328)

449.* JOHNSON, P. T., and LAYNE, J. N.—1961.
    A New Species of *Polygenis* Jordan from Florida, with Remarks on its Host Relationships and Zoogeographic Significance (Siphonaptera: Rhopalopsyllidae).
    Proceedings of the Entomological Society of Washington, *63*(2): 115-123. (Repr. No. 322)

450. PIPKIN, S. B.—1961.
    Taxonomic Relationships within the *Drosphila victoria* Species Group, Subgenus *Pholadoris* (Diptera: Drosophilidae).
    Proceedings of the Entomological Society of Washington, *63*(3): 145-161. (Repr. No. 329)

451.* QUATE, L. W., and FAIRCHILD, G. B.—1961.
Phlebotomus Sandflies of Malaya and Borneo (Diptera, Psychodidae). Pacific Insects, 3(2-3): 203-222. (Repr. No. 325)

452.* RODANICHE, E. C. DE, and JOHNSON, C. M.—1961.
St. Louis Encephalitis in Panamá. II. Survey of Human Blood for Antibodies Against St. Louis and Two Related Group B Viruses, Ilheus and Yellow Fever.
American Journal of Tropical Medicine and Hygiene, 10(3): 387-389. (Repr. No. 320)

453.* RODANICHE, E. C. DE, and GALINDO, P.—1961.
St. Louis Encephalitis in Panamá. III. Investigation of Local Mammals and Birds as Possible Reservoir Hosts.
American Journal of Tropical Medicine and Hygiene, 10(3): 390-392. (Repr. No. 321)

454.* TIPTON, V. J., and MÈNDEZ, E.—1961.
New Species of Fleas (Siphonaptera) from Panamá.
Annals of the Entomological Society of America, 54(2): 255-273. (Repr. No. 313)

1962

455.* FAIRCHILD, G. B.—1962.
Notes on Neotropical Tabanidae (Diptera). III. The Genus Protosilvius Enderlein.
Annals of the Entomological Society of America, 55(3): 342-350. (Repr. No. 332)

456.* GALINDO, P., and FAIRCHILD, G. B.—1962.
Notes on Habits of Two Bloodsucking Bugs, Triatoma dispar Lent, 1950, and Eratyrus cuspidatus Stal, 1859 (Hemiptera: Reduviidae). Proceedings of the Entomological Society of Washington, 64(4): 229-230. (Repr. No. 342)

457. HERTIG, M.—1962.
Research Problems in Connection with Leishmaniasis. In: Tropical Health. A Report on a Study of Needs and Resources. Washington, D. C., National Academy of Sciences-National Research Council, 1962, pp. 505-508. (Publication 996. Division of Medical Sciences). (Repr. No. 340a)

458.* JOHNSON, P. T.—1962.
Notes and Descriptions of African Lice (Anoplura).
Proceedings of the Entomological Society of Washington, 64(1): 51-56. (Repr. No. 333)

459.* JOHNSON, P. T.—1962.
Redescriptions of Two Cervid-Infesting Anoplura from Southeast Asia. Proceedings of the Entomological Society of Washington, 64(2): 107-110. (Repr. No. 339)

460.   JOHNSON, P. T.—1962.
        Review of the Monograph *The Siphonaptera of Japan,* by Kohei Saka-
        guti and E. W. Jameson, Jr. Honolulu, Bernice P. Bishop Museum,
        1962. pp. 1-169. (Pacific Insects Monograph No. 3).
        Proceedings of the Entomological Society of Washington, *64*(3): 154.
        (Repr. No. 340b)

461.*   JOHNSON, P. T.—1962.
        The Species of *Fahrenholzia* Kellogg and Ferris from Spiny Pocket Mice
        (Anoplura: Hoplopleuridae).
        Annals of the Entomological Society of America, *55*(4): 415-428.
        (Repr. No. 338)

462.*   JOHNSON, P. T.—1962.
        Three New Anoplura from African Rodents (Anoplura: Hoplopleuri-
        dae).
        Proceedings of the Entomological Society of Washington, *64*(3): 155-
        165. (Repr. No. 340)

463.*   JOHNSON, P. T., McCONNELL, E., and HERTIG, M.—1962.
        Natural and Experimental Infections of Leptomonad Flagellates in
        Panamanian *Phlebotomus* Sandflies.
        Journal of Parasitology, *48*(1): 158. (Repr. No. 336)

464.*   PIPKIN, S. B.—1962.
        Mesonotal Color Polymorphism in *Drosophila l. lebanonensis.*
        Genetics, *47*(9): 1275-1290. (Repr. No. 341)

465.*   PIPKIN, S. B.—1962.
        Sex Combs in Unbalanced Male Forms in *Drosophila melanogaster.*
        Journal of Heredity, *52*(6): 255-259. (Repr. No. 337)

466.   WETMORE, A.—1962.
        Systematic Notes Concerned with the Avifauna of Panamá.
        Smithsonian Miscellaneous Collection, *145*(1): 1-14, June 26. (Repr.
        No. 340c)

1963

467.*   FAIRCHILD, G. B.—1963.
        A New Genus and Species of Neotropical Horsefly (Diptera: Tabani-
        dae).
        Psyche, *70*(4): 193-196. (Repr. No. 353)

468.*   GALINDO, P.—1963.
        Culex Mosquitoes of *Melanoconion* and Related Subgenera as Hosts of
        Arboviruses.
        Anais de Microbiologia, *11*(Parte A): 83-87. (Repr. No. 355)

469.*   GALINDO, P., MÉNDEZ, E., and ADAMES, A. J.—1963.
        Banding of Migrant Thrushes in Almirante, Panamá.
        Bird-Banding, *34*(4): 202-209. (Repr. No. 350)

470.   HERTIG, M., and McCONNELL, E.—1963.
        Experimental Infection of Panamanian *Phlebotomus* Sandflies with
        Leishmania.
        Experimental Parasitology, *14*(1): 92-106. (Repr. No. 345)

471.* JOHNSON, P. T.—1963.
Two Rare Anoplura from Kenya.
Proceedings of the Entomological Society of Washington, 65(3): 226-229. (Repr. No. 349)

472. JOHNSON, P. T., McCONNELL, E., and HERTIG, M.—1963.
Natural Infections of Leptomonad Flagellates in Panamanian *Phlebotomus* Sandflies.
Experimental Parasitology, 14(1): 107-122. (Repr. No. 346)

473. LOFTIN, H.—1963.
Notes on Autumn Bird Migrants in Panamá.
Caribbean Journal of Science, 3(1): 63-68. (Repr. No. 350a)

474. LOFTIN, H.—1963.
Some Repeats and Returns of North American Migrants in Panamá.
Bird-Banding, 34(4): 219-221. (Repr. No. 350b)

475. LOFTIN, H., and OLSON, S. L.—1963.
Notes on Spring Migrants in Panamá (Aves).
Caribbean Journal of Science, 3(4): 191-195. (Repr. No. 350c)

476. McCONNELL, E.—1963.
Leptomonads of Wild-Caught Panamanian *Phlebotomus:* Culture and Animal Inoculation.
Experimental Parasitology, 14(1): 123-128. (Repr. No. 347)

477.* PIPKIN, S. B.—1963.
Mating Success in the *Drosophila victoria* Species Group, Subgenus *Pholadoris* (Diptera: Drosophilidae).
The American Naturalist, 97(895): 235-242. (Repr. No. 344)

478.* RODANICHE, E. C. DE, and GALINDO, P.—1963.
Ecological Observations on Ilheus Virus in the Vicinity of Almirante, Republic of Panamá.
American Journal of Tropical Medicine and Hygiene, 12(6): 924-928. (Repr. No. 357)

479.* THATCHER, V. E.—1963.
A New Species of *Westella* (Trematoda: Opisthogoniminae) from a Mexican Snake.
Journal of Parasitology, 49(1): 123-124. (Repr. No. 343)

480.* THATCHER, V. E.—1963.
Studies on the Trematodes of the Mexican Indigo Snake *(Drymarchon corais melanurus)* with Descriptions of Two New Species.
Transactions of the American Microscopical Society, 82(4): 351-380. (Repr. No. 351)

481. THATCHER, V. E.—1963.
The Trematodes of the Basilisk Lizard from Tabasco, México.
Anales del Instituto de Biología (México), 34(1-2): 205-216. (Repr. No. 354)

482.* THATCHER, V. E.—1963.
Trematodes of Turtles from Tabasco, México, with a Description of a New Species of *Dadaytrema* (Trematoda: Paramphistomidae).
The American Midland Naturalist, 70(2): 347-355. (Repr. No. 348)

483. WETMORE, A.—1963.
    An Additional Race of the Pileated Tinamou from Panamá.
    Proceedings of the Biological Society of Washington, *76*: 173, August 2. (Repr. No. 345a)

484. WETMORE, A.—1963.
    Additions to Records of Birds Known from the Republic of Panamá.
    Smithsonian Miscellaneous Collection, *145*(6): 1-11, December 16. (Repr. No. 345b)

1964

485.* FAIRCHILD, G. B.—1964.
    Notes on Neotropical Tabanidae (Diptera). IV. Further New Species and New Records for Panamá.
    Journal of Medical Entomology, *1*(2): 169-185. (Repr. No. 359)

486.* GALINDO, P., PERALTA, P. H., MacKENZIE, R. B., and BEYE, H. K.—1964
    St. Louis Encephalitis in Panamá: A Review and a Progress Report.
    American Journal of Tropical Medicine and Hygiene, *13*(3): 455. (Repr. No. 356)

487.* GALINDO, P., and RODANICHE, E. C. DE—1964.
    Surveillance for Sylvan Yellow Fever Activity in Panamá (1957-1961).
    American Journal of Tropical Medicine and Hygiene, *13*(6): 844-850. (Repr. No. 366)

488.* HERTIG, M.—1964.
    Laboratory Colonization of Central American *Phlebotomus* Sandflies.
    Bulletin of the World Health Organization, *31*(4): 569-570. (Repr. No. 368)

489. HERTIG, M.—1964.
    Bartonellosis. (Chapter 3, pp. 23-28). *In: Preventive Medicine in World War II.* Vol. 7: Communicable Diseases; Arthropod-Borne Diseases other than Malaria. Washington, D. C., Office of the Surgeon General—Dept. of the Army, 1964. (Repr. No. 364)

490.* HERTIG, M., and SABIN, A. B.—1964.
    Sandfly Fever (Pappataci, Phlebotomus, Three-Day Fever). Part I. History of Incidence, Prevention, and Control. (Chapter 9, pp. 109-132). *In: Preventive Medicine in World War II.* Vol. 7: Communicable Diseases; Arthropod-Borne Diseases other than Malaria. Washington, D. C., Office of the Surgeon General—Dept. of the Army, 1964. (Repr. No. 363)

491.* JOHNSON, C. M.—1964.
    American Leishmaniasis.
    Industrial Medicine and Surgery, *33*(5): 315-318. (Repr. No. 361)

492.* JOHNSON, P. T.—1964.
    The *Hoplopleurid* Lice of the Indo-Malayan Subregion (Anoplura: Hoplopleuridae).
    Miscellaneous Publications of the Entomological Society of America, *4*(3): 68-102. (Repr. No. 352)

493.* McCONNELL, E., and CORREA, M.—1964.
Trypanosomes and other Microorganisms from Panamanian *Phlebotomus* Sandflies.
Journal of Parasitology, *50*(4): 523-528. (Repr. No. 358)

494.* PIPKIN, S. B.—1964.
New Flower Breeding Species of *Drosophila* (Diptera: Drosophilidae).
Proceedings of the Entomological Society of Washington, *66*(4): 217-245. (Repr. No. 367)

495.* PIPKIN, S. B., and HEED, W. B.—1964.
Nine New Members of the *Drosophila tripunctata* Species Group (Diptera: Drosophilidae).
Pacific Insects, *6*(2): 256-273. (Repr. No. 362)

496.* RODANICHE, E. C. DE, ANDRADE, A. P. DE, and GALINDO, P.—1964.
Isolation of Two Antigenically Distinct Arthropod-Borne Viruses of Group C in Panamá.
American Journal of Tropical Medicine and Hygiene, *13*(6): 839-843. (Repr. No. 365)

497. ROWE, N. H., and JOHNSON, C. M.—1964.
A Search for the Burkitt Lymphoma in Tropical Central America.
The British Journal of Cancer, *18*: 228-232. (Repr. No. 360)

498. SHAW, J. J.—1964.
A Possible Vector of *Endotrypanum schaudinni* of the Sloth *Cholepus hoffmanni* in Panamá.
Nature, *201*(4917): 417-418, 25 January. (Repr. No. 359a)

499. THATCHER, V. E.—1964.
Estudios Sobre los Tremátodos de Reptiles de Tabasco, México; Lista de Huéspedes y sus Parásitos.
Anales de la Escuela Nacional de Ciencias Biológicas, *13*(1-4): 91-96. (Repr. No. 395)

500. WETMORE, A.—1964.
A Revision of the American Vultures of the Genus *Cathartes*.
Smithsonian Miscellaneous Collection, *146*(6): 1-18, August 14. (Repr. No. 359b)

1965

501.* BELKIN, J. N., SCHICK, R. X., GALINDO, P., and AITKEN, T. H. G.—1965.
Mosquito Studies (Diptera, Culicidae); I. A Project for a Systematic Study of the Mosquitoes of Middle America.
Contributions of the American Entomological Institute, *1*(2): 1-17. (Repr. No. 369)

502.* BELKIN, J. N., HOGUE, C. L., GALINDO, P., AITKEN, T. H. G., SCHICK, R. X., and POWDER, W. A.—1965.
Mosquito Studies (Diptera, Culicidae); II. Methods for the Collection, Rearing and Preservation of Mosquitoes.
Contributions of the American Entomological Institute, *1*(2): 19-78. (Repr. No. 370)

503.* FAIRCHILD, G. B.—1965.
Notes on Neotropical Tabanidae. VI. A New Species of *Lepiselaga*
Macq. with Remarks on Related Genera.
Psyche, *72*(3): 210-217. (Repr. No. 378)

504.* GALINDO, P., and MÉNDEZ, E.—1965.
Banding of Thrushes and Catbirds at Almirante, Panamá; Second Year
of Observations.
Bird-Banding, *36*(4): 233-239. (Repr. No. 375)

505.* KLITE, P. D., and KOURANY, M.—1965.
Isolation of *Salmonellae* from a Neotropical Bat.
Journal of Bacteriology, *90*(3): 831: (Repr. No. 374)

506. LEGLER, J. M.—1965.
A New Species of Turtle, Genus *Kinosternon,* from Central America.
University of Kansas Publications, *15*(13): 615-625. (Repr. No. 375a)

507.* PIPKIN, S. B.—1965.
The Influence of Adult and Larval Food Habits on Population Size of
Neotropical Ground-Feeding *Drosophila.*
The American Midland Naturalist, *74*(1): 1-27. (Repr. No. 373)

508. PIPKIN, S. B.—1965.
A Mesonotal Colour Polymorphism Apparently Dependent on Linkage
Disequilibrium.
Heredity, *20*(4): 523-536. (Reprint No. 524)

509. ROGERS, D. T.—1965.
Fat Levels and Estimated Flight-Ranges of Some Autumn Migratory
Birds Killed in Panamá During a Nocturnal Rainstorm.
Bird-Banding, *36*(2): 115-116. (Repr. No. 375b)

510.* SCHNEIDER, C. R.—1965.
Besnoitia panamensis, sp. n. (Protozoa: Toxoplasmatidae) from Pana-
manian Lizards.
The Journal of Parasitology, *51*(3): 340-344. (Repr. No. 371)

511.* SRIHONGSE, S., and JOHNSON, C. M.—1965.
Wyeomyia Subgroup of Arbovirus: Isolation from Man.
Science, *149*(3686): 863-864. (Repr. No. 372)

512.* SOUSA, O. E., and LOMBARDO, J. D.—1965.
Informe de un Caso de Hidatidosis en Sujeto Nativo Panameño. Primer
Caso Autóctono.
Archivos Médicos Panameños, *14*(2): 79-86. (Repr. No. 379)

513.* THATCHER, V. E., EISENMANN, C. DE, and HERTIG, M.—1965.
Experimental Inoculation of Panamanian Mammals with *Leishmania
braziliensis.*
The Journal of Parasitology, *51*(5): 842-844. (Repr. No. 376)

514.* THATCHER, V. E., EISENMANN, C. DE, and HERTIG, M.—1965.
A Natural Infection of Leishmania in the Kinkajou, *Potos flavus,* in
Panamá.
The Journal of Parasitology, *51*(6): 1022-1023. (Repr. No. 380)

515.   WETMORE, A.—1965.
       The Birds of the Republic of Panamá, Part 1—Tinamidae (Tinamous)
       to Rynchopidae (Skimmers).
       Smithsonian Miscellaneous Collection, *150*: 1-483, December 27. (Repr.
       No. 380a)

1966

516.* AITKEN, T. H. G., and GALINDO, P.—1966.
       On the Identity of *Culex (Melanoconion) portesi* Senevet & Abonnenc
       1941 (Diptera, Culicidae).
       Proceedings of the Entomological Society of Washington, *68*(3): 198-
       208. (Repr. No. 396)

517.   DUELLMAN, W. E., and TRUEB, L.—1966.
       Neotropical Hylid Frogs, Genus *Smilisca*.
       University of Kansas Publications, *17*(7): 281-375. (Repr. No. 387b)

518.* FAIRCHILD, G. B.—1966.
       A Checklist of the *Hippoboscidae* of Panamá (Diptera). *In: Ectopara-
       sites of Panamá.* Chicago, Field Museum of Natural History, 1966.
       pp. 387-392. (Repr. No. 415)

519.* FAIRCHILD, G. B.—1966.
       Introduction. *In: Ectoparasites of Panamá.*
       Chicago, Field Museum of Natural History, 1966. pp. 1-8. (Repr. No.
       411)

520.* FAIRCHILD, G. B., and HANDLEY, JR., C. O.—1966.
       Gazetteer of Collecting Localities in Panamá. *In: Ectoparasites of
       Panamá.* Chicago, Field Museum of Natural History, 1966. pp 9-22.
       (Repr. No. 412)

521.* FAIRCHILD, G. B.—1966.
       Notes on Neotropical Tabanidae (Diptera). V. The Species Described
       by G. Enderlein.
       Journal of Medical Entomology, *3*(1): 1-19. (Repr. No. 386)

522.   FAIRCHILD, G. B.—1966.
       Notes on Neotropical Tabanidae. VIII. The Species Described by J. C.
       Fabricius.
       Psyche, *73*(1): 17-25. (Repr. No. 388)

523.* FAIRCHILD, G. B.—1966.
       Notes on Neotropical Tabanidae. IX. The Species Described by Otto
       Krober.
       Studia Entomologica, *9*, Fasc. 1-4, 329-384. (Repr. No. 400)

524.* FAIRCHILD, G. B.—1966.
       Some New Synonymies in Tabanidae (Diptera).
       Proceedings of the Entomological Society of Washington, *68*(2): 94-96.
       (Repr. No. 390)

525.* FAIRCHILD, G. B.—1966.
       The Tabanid Fauna of the West Indies. *In: Proceedings of the First
       International Congress of Parasitology* (Roma, 21-26 September, 1964).
       Ed. by Augusto Corradetti. Milano, Edit. Tamburini, 1966. Vol. 2.
       pp. 993-995. (Repr. No. 510)

526.* FAIRCHILD, G. B., KHOLS, G. M., and TIPTON, V. J.—1966.
The Ticks of Panamá (Acarina: Ixodoidea). *In: Ectoparasites of Panamá.* Chicago, Field Museum of Natural History, 1966. pp. 167-219. (Repr. No. 413)

527.* GALINDO, P., and SOUSA, O. E.—1966.
Blood Parasites of Birds from Almirante, Panamá, with Ecological Notes on the Hosts.
Revista de Biología Tropical, *14*(1): 27-46. (Repr. No. 397)

528.* GALINDO, P., SRIHONGSE, S., RODANICHE, E. C. DE, and GRAYSON, M. A.—1966.
An Ecological Survey for Arboviruses in Almirante, Panamá, 1959-1962.
American Journal of Tropical Medicine and Hygiene, *15*(3): 385-400. (Repr. No. 384)

529.* HERRER, A., THATCHER, V. E., and JOHNSON, C. M.—1966.
Natural Infections of Leishmania and Trypanosomes Demonstrated by Skin Culture.
The Journal of Parasitology, *52*(5): 954-957. (Repr. No. 398)

530.   HICKS, D. L., ROGERS, JR., D. T., and CHILD, G. I.—1966.
Autumnal Hawk Migration Through Panamá.
Bird-Banding, *37*(2): 121-123. (Repr. No. 385b)

531.   LOFTIN, H., ROGERS, JR., D. T., and HICKS, D. L.—1966.
Repeats, Returns and Recoveries of North American Migrant Birds Banded in Panamá.
Bird-Banding, *37*(1): 35-44. (Repr. No. 385a)

532.* MYERS, C. W.—1966.
The Distribution and Behavior of a Tropical-Horned Frog, *Cerathyla panamensis* Stejneger.
Herpetologica, *22*(1): 68-71. (Repr. No. 387)

533.   MYERS, C. W.—1966.
Lygophis boursieri (Jan.), a Snake New to the Fauna of Colombia.
Copeia, No. 4, pp. 886-888. (Repr. No. 387a)

534.* MYERS, C. W.—1966.
A New Species of Colubrid Snake, Genus *Coniophanes,* from Darién, Panamá.
Copeia, No. 4: 665-668. (Repr. No. 399)

535.   PIPKIN, S. B., RODRÍGUEZ, R. L., and LEÓN, J. —1966.
Plant Host Specificity Among Flower-Feeding Neotropical *Drosophila* (Diptera: Drosophilidae).
The American Naturalist, *100*(911): 135-156. (Repr. No. 389)

536.* PORTER, JR., J. A., JOHNSON, C. M., and DE SOUSA, L.—1966.
Prevalence of Malaria in Panamanian Primates.
The Journal of Parasitology, *52*(4): 669-670. (Repr. No. 393)

537.* PORTER, JR., J. A., and YOUNG, M. D.—1966.
Susceptibility of Panamanian Primates to *Plasmodium vivax.*
Military Medicine, *131*(9): 952-958. (Supplement). (Repr. No. 392)

538.   ROGERS, JR., D. T., and ODUM, E. P.—1966.
         A Study of Autumnal Postmigrant Weights and Vernal Fattening of
         North American Migrants in the Tropics.
         Wilson Bulletin, *78*(4): 415-433. (Repr. No. 385c)

539.*   SCHNEIDER, C. R.—1966.
         Experimental Infection of Short-Tailed Bats, *Carollia perspicillata,*
         with *Besnoitia panamensis,* (Protozoa: Toxoplasmatidae).
         The Journal of Parasitology, *52*(4): 703. (Repr. No. 394)

540.*   SCHNEIDER, C. R., and HERTIG, M.—1966.
         Immunodiffusion Reactions of Panamanian Leishmania.
         Experimental Parasitology, *18*(1): 25-34. (Repr. No. 381)

541.*   SRIHONGSE, S.—1966.
         Rapid Identification of Venezuelan and Eastern Equine Encephalitis
         Viruses Using Infected Suckling Mouse Serum as the Hemagglutinating
         Antigen.
         American Journal of Tropical Medicine and Hygiene, *15*(3): 401-405.
         (Repr. No. 385)

542.*   SRIHONGSE, S., GALINDO, P., and GRAYSON, M. A.—1966.
         Isolation of Group C Arboviruses in Panamá Including Two New Mem-
         bers, Patois and Zegla.
         American Journal of Tropical Medicine and Hygiene, *15*(3): 379-384.
         (Repr. No. 383)

543.*   THATCHER, V. E., and HERTIG, M.—1966.
         Field Studies on the Feeding Habits and Diurnal Shelters of Some
         Phlebotomus Sandflies (Diptera, Psychodidae) in Panamá.
         Annals of the Entomological Society of America, *59*(1): 46-52. (Repr.
         No. 377)

544.*   THATCHER, V. E., and SOUSA, O. E.—1966.
         Echinococcus oligarthrus Diesing, 1863, in Panamá and Comparison
         with a Recent Human Hydatid.
         Annals of Tropical Medicine and Parasitology, *60*(4): 405-416. (Repr.
         No. 403)

545.*   TIPTON, V. J., and MÈNDEZ, E.—1966.
         The Fleas (Siphonaptera) of Panamá. *In: Ectoparasites of Panamá.*
         Chicago, Field Museum of Natural History, 1966. pp. 289-385. (Repr.
         No. 414)

546.   YOUNG, M. D.—1966.
         Malaria (Chapter 35, pp. 316-362). *In: A Manual of Tropical Medicine,*
         by George W. Hunter, William W. Frye, and J. Clyde Swartzwelder.
         4th ed. Philadelphia, Saunders, 1966. (Repr. No. 438)

547.   YOUNG, M. D.—1966.
         Scientific Exploration and Achievement in the Field of Malaria.
         The Journal of Parasitology, *52*(1): 2-8. (Repr. No. 382)

548.   YOUNG, M. D., PORTER, JR., J. A., and JOHNSON, C. M.—1966.
         Plasmodium vivax Transmitted from Man to Monkey to Man.
         Science, *153*(3739): 1006-1007. (Repr. No. 391)

1967

BELKIN, J. N., SCHICK, R. X., GALINDO, P., and AITKEN, T. H. G.—1967.

Estudios Sobre Mosquitos (Diptera, Culicidae). Ia. Un Proyecto Para un Estudio Sistemático de los Mosquitos de Meso-América.
Contributions of the American Entomological Institute, *1*(2a): 1-17. (Repr. No. 369a)

BELKIN, J. N., HOGUE, C. L., GALINDO, P., AITKEN, T. H. G., SCHICK, R. X., and POWDER, W. A.—1967.

Estudios Sobre Mosquitos (Diptera, Culicidae). IIa. Métodos Para Coleccionar, Criar y Preservar Mosquitos.
Contributions of the American Entomological Institute, *1*(2a.): 19-89. (Repr. No. 370a)

[The two articles listed above are Spanish translations of our publication numbers 501 and 502 respectively]

549.* DALY, J. W., and MYERS, C. W.—1967.

Toxicity of Panamanian Poison Frogs *(Dendrobates):* Some Biological and Chemical Aspects.
Science, *156*(3777): 970-973. (Repr. No. 419)

550.* FAIRCHILD, G. B.—1967.

Notes on Neotropical Tabanidae (Diptera). VII. The Species Described by C. R. W. Wiedemann.
Pacific Insects, *9*(1): 73-104. (Repr. No. 404)

551.* FAIRCHILD, G. B.—1967.

Notes on Neotropical Tabanidae (Diptera). X. The Species Described by J. R. Schiner and others.
Pacific Insects, *9*(2): 243-256. (Repr. No. 410)

552.* FAIRCHILD, G. B.—1967.

Notes on Neotropical Tabanidae (Diptera). XI. *Stenotabanus staryi* n. sp. from Cuba.
Psyche, *74*(3): 208-211. (Repr. No. 431)

553.* GALINDO, P.—1967.

Preliminary Observations on the Colonization and Bionomics of the Crab-Hole Breeding Mosquito *Deinocerites pseudes* Dyar and Knab, 1909.
Mosquito News, *27*(2): 187-190. (Repr. No. 406)

554.* GALINDO, P., and SRIHONGSE, S.—1967.

Evidence of Recent Jungle Yellow-Fever Activity in Eastern Panamá.
Bulletin of the World Health Organization, *36*(1): 151-161. (Repr. No. 409)

555.* GALINDO, P., and SRIHONGSE, S.—1967.

Transmission of Arboviruses to Hamsters by the Bite of Naturally Infected *Culex (Melanoconion)* Mosquitoes.
The American Journal of Tropical Medicine and Hygiene, *16*(4): 525-530. (Repr. No. 416)

556.* GALINDO, P., and TRAPIDO, H.—1967.
Description of *Haemagogus aeritinctus,* a New Species from British Honduras, with a Note on the Validity of *Haemagogus lucifer* (H. D. and K.) (Diptera, Culicidae).
Proceedings of the Entomological Society of Washington, *69*(2): 103-111. Repr. No. 421)

557.* GRAYSON, M. A., SRIHONGSE, S., and GALINDO, P.—1967.
Isolation of St. Louis Encephalitis Virus from *Deinocerites pseudes* in Panamá.
Mosquito News, *27*(2): 204. (Repr. No. 407)

558.* GUEVARA, J. F., and JOHNSON, C. M.—1967.
Vectocardiografía.
Archivos Médicos Panameños, *16*(1): 3-13. (Repr. No. 427)

559. HICKS, D. L.—1967.
First Record of the White-Eyed Vireo in Panamá.
Condor, *69*(1): 90. (Repr. No. 425a)

560.* HICKS, D. L., MÉNDEZ, E., and LOFTIN, H.—1967.
Additions to the Avifauna of Panamá: The Palm Warbler and the Connecticut Warbler.
The Condor, *69*(3): 319-320. (Repr. No. 408)

561. HUFF, C. G., and WETMORE, A.—1967.
Blood Parasites of Birds Collected in Four Successive Years in Panamá.
Bulletin of the Wildlife Disease Association, *3*: 178-181, October. (Repr. No. 420a)

562. LOFTIN, H.—1967.
Hawks Delayed by Weather on Spring Migration Through Panamá.
Florida Naturalist, *40*: 29. (Repr. No. 425c)

563. LOFTIN, H., CHILD, G. I., and BONGIORNO, S.—1967.
Returns in 1965-66 of North American Migrant Birds Banded in Panamá.
Bird-Banding, *38*(2): 151-152. (Repr. No. 425b)

564.* MÉNDEZ, E.—1967.
Description of a New Genus and Species of Trimenoponidae from Panamá (Mallophaga).
Proceedings of the Entomological Society of Washington, *69*(3): 287-291. (Repr. No. 428)

565.* MÉNDEZ, E.—1967.
A New Species of *Gyropus* (Mallophaga: Gyropidae) from the Arboreal Spiny Rat *Diplomys labilis* in Panamá.
Annals of the Entomological Society of America, *60*(3): 555-557. (Repr. No. 402)

566.* PORTER, JR., J. A., and YOUNG, M. D.—1967.
The Transfer of *Plasmodium falciparum* from Man to the Marmoset *Saguinus geoffroyi.*
The Journal of Parasitology, *53*(4): 845-846. (Repr. No. 424)

567.* SCHNEIDER, C. R.—1967.
Besnoitia darlingi (Brumpt, 1913) in Panamá.
The Journal of Protozoology, *14*(1): 78-82. (Repr. No. 405)

568.* SCHNEIDER, C. R.—1967.
Cross-Immunity Evidence of the Identity of *Besnoitia panamensis* from Lizards and *B. darlingi* from Opossums.
Journal of Parasitology, *53*(4): 886. (Repr. No. 423)

569.* SCHNEIDER, C. R.—1967.
The Distribution of Lizard Besnoitiosis in Panamá, and its Transfer to Mice.
Journal of Protozoology, *14*(4): 674-678. (Repr. No. 430)

570.* SCHNEIDER, C. R.—1967.
Susceptibility of the Marmoset, *Saguinus geoffroyi* Pucheran, to Intraperitoneal and Oral Infections with *Besnoitia* (Protozoa: Toxoplasmea).
The Journal of Parasitology, *53*(6): 1135-1139. (Repr. No. 429)

571.* SRIHONGSE, S., and GALINDO, P.—1967.
The Isolation of Eastern Equine Encephalitis Virus from *Culex (Melanoconion) taeniopus* Dyar and Knab in Panamá.
Mosquito News, *27*(1): 74-76. (Repr. No. 401)

572.* SRIHONGSE, S., and JOHNSON, C. M.—1967.
The Isolation of Ilheus Virus from Man in Panamá.
The American Journal of Tropical Medicine and Hygiene, *16*(4): 516-518. (Repr. No. 418)

573.* SRIHONGSE, S., and JOHNSON, K. M.—1967.
Production of Hemagglutinins of Group C Arboviruses in Adult Hamsters.
Bacteriological Proceedings, 167. (Repr. No. 422)

574.* SRIHONGSE, S., SCHERER, W. F., and GALINDO, P.—1967.
Detection of Arboviruses by Sentinel Hamsters During the Low Period of Transmission.
The American Journal of Tropical Medicine and Hygiene, *16*(4): 519-524. (Repr. No. 417)

575.* THATCHER, V. E.—1967.
Paragonimus in Some Wild and Domestic Animals of Panamá.
Transactions of the American Microscopical Society, *86*(3): 335-336. (Repr. No. 420)

576.* THATCHER, V. E., and SOUSA, O. E.—1967.
Echinococcus oligarthrus (Diesing, 1863) from a Panamanian Jaguar (*Felis onca* L.).
The Journal of Parasitology, *53*(5): 1040. (Repr. No. 426)

577.* WALTON, B. C., and SOUSA, O. E.—1967.
Trypanosomes of the Lesser Anteater, *Tamandua tetradactyla,* from Panamá.
The Journal of Parasitology, *53*(5): 956-961. (Repr. No. 425)

578. WETMORE, A.—1967.
Further Systematic Notes on the Avifauna of Panamá.
Proceedings of the Biological Society of Washington, *80*: 229-242, December 1. (Repr. No. 430a)

1968

579.* COMER, R. D., YOUNG, M. D., PORTER, JR., J. A., GAULD, J. R., and MERRITT, W.—1968.
Chloroquine Resistance in *Plasmodium falciparum* Malaria on the Pacific Coast of Colombia.
American Journal of Tropical Medicine and Hygiene, *17*(6): 795-799. (Repr. No. 508)

580. DUELLMAN, W. E.—1968.
Description of New Hylid Frogs from México and Central America.
University of Kansas Publications, *17*(13): 559-578. (Repr. No. 432a)

581.* GRAYSON, M. A., and GALINDO, P.—1968.
Epidemiologic Studies of Venezuelan Equine Encephalitis Virus in Almirante, Panamá.
American Journal of Epidemiology, *88*(1): 80-96. (Repr. No. 501)

582.* JOHNSON, C. M.—1968.
Cycloguanil Pamoate in the Treatment of Cutaneous Leishmaniasis. Initial Trials in Panamá.
American Journal of Tropical Medicine and Hygiene, *17*(6): 819-822. (Repr. No. 509)

583.* MÈNDEZ, E.—1968.
Las Especies Panameñas de Venados.
Revista Panameña de Biología, *1*(1): 1-9. (Repr. No. 503)

584.* MÈNDEZ, E.—1968.
Scolopsyllus colombianus, New Genus and Species of the Family *Rhopalopsyllidae* (Siphonaptera) from Colombia.
Journal of Medical Entomology, *5*(3): 405-410. (Repr. No. 437)

585.* PIPKIN, A. C.—1968.
Domiciliary Reduviid Bugs and the Epidemiology of Chagas' Disease in Panamá (Hemiptera: Reduviidae: Triatominae).
Journal of Medical Entomology, *5*(1): 107-124. (Repr. No. 432)

586. PIPKIN, S. B.—1968.
Introgression Between Closely Related Species of *Drosophila* in Panamá.
Evolution, *22*(1): 140-156. (Repr. No. 504)

587. ROGERS, JR., D. T.—1968.
Energy Expenditures of Caged Postmigrants in Panamá.
Bird-Banding, *39*: 60-61. (Repr. No. 435a)

588.* SCHNEIDER, C. R.—1968.
Hepatozoon procyonis Richards, 1961, in a Panamanian Raccoon, *Procyon cancrivorus panamensis* (Goldman).
Revista de Biología Tropical, *15*(1): 123-135. (Repr. No. 507)

589.* SCHNEIDER, C. R.—1968.
Immunodiffusion Studies on a Skin-Inhabiting Leishmania from the Tropical Porcupine, *Coendou rothschildi* Thomas.
The Journal of Parasitology, *54*(3): 638-639. (Repr. No. 434)

590.* SRIHONGSE, S., and SHOPE, R. E.—1969.
The Patois Group of Arboviruses.
Acta Virológica, *12*(5): 453-456. (Repr. No. 505)

591.* THATCHER, V. E.—1968.
Arboreal Breeding Sites of Phlebotomine Sandflies in Panamá.
Annals of the Entomological Society of America, *61*(5): 1141-1143.
(Repr. No. 502)

592.* THATCHER, V. E.—1968.
Studies of Phlebotomine Sandflies Using Castor Oil Traps Baited with
Panamanian Animals.
Journal of Medical Entomology, *5*(3): 293-297. (Repr. No. 500)

593.* THATCHER, V. E., and PORTER, JR., J. A.—1968.
Some Helminth Parasites of Panamanian Primates.
Transactions of the American Microscopical Society, *87*(2): 186-196.
(Repr. No. 433)

594.* THATCHER, V. E., SOUSA, O. E., and CROSS, J. H.—1968.
Echinococcus oligarthrus (Diesing, 1863) Developing in a United States
Zoo.
Journal of Parasitology, *54*(4): 847-848. (Repr. No. 506)

595.* TIPTON, V. J., and MÉNDEZ, E.—1968.
New Species of Fleas (Siphonaptera) from Cerro Potosí, México, with
Notes on Ecology and Host Parasite Relationships.
Pacific Insects, *10*(1): 177-214. (Repr. No. 435)

596.* WALLACE, F. G., and HERTIG, M.—1968.
Ultrastructural Comparison of Promastigote Flagellates (Leptomonads)
of Wild-Caught Panamanian *Phlebotomus*.
The Journal of Parasitology, *54*(3): 606-612. (Repr. No. 436)

597. WETMORE, A.—1968.
The Birds of the Republic of Panamá, Part 2—Columbidae (Pigeons)
to Picidae (Woodpeckers).
Smithsonian Miscellaneous Collection, *150* (Part 2): 1-605, September
27. (Repr. No. 435b)

598. WETMORE, A.—1968.
[On the Indigo Bunting in Panamá]. *In:* Taber, W., and Johnston, D.
W., *Passerina cyanea* (Linnaeus), Indigo Bunting. Published in *Life
Histories of North American Cardinals, Grosbeaks, Buntings, Towhees,
Finches, Sparrows, and Allies; Order Passeriformes: Family Fringillidae.*
Part One. Genera Richmondena through Pipilo (part), [by] Arthur
Cleveland Bent and Collaborators. Comp. and Ed. by Oliver L. Austin,
Jr.
United States National Museum Bulletin, *237*: 105-106. (Repr. No.
435c)

1969

599.* BAERG, D. C., PORTER, JR., J. A., and YOUNG, M. D.—1969.
Sporozoite Transmission of *Plasmodium vivax* to Panamanian Primates.
The American Journal of Tropical Medicine and Hygiene, *18*(3): 346-
350. (Repr. No. 516)

600.* BAERG, D. C., and YOUNG, M. D.—1969.
Susceptibility of Mosquitoes to Human Malaria Induced in Panamanian
Monkeys.
Military Medicine, *134*(10): 772-779, September. (Repr. No. 529)

601.* BLANDÒN, R., GUEVARA, J. F., and JOHNSON, C. M.—1969.
Tránsito Esofágico en Pacientes con Enfermedad de Chagas en Panamá.
Arquivos de Gastroenterologia, *6*(4): 189-196, Oct.-Nov. (Repr. No.
541)

602.   CHILD, G. I.—1969.
A Study of Non-Fat Weight in Migrating Swainson's Thrushes *(Hylo-
cichla ustulata)*.
Auk, *86*: 327-338. (Repr. No. 516c)

603.* CHRISTENSEN, H. A., HERRER, A., and TELFORD, JR., S. R.—1969.
Leishmania brasiliensis s. lat. Isolated from *Lutzomyia panamensis* in
Panamá.
The Journal of Parasitology, *55*(5): 1090-1091, October. (Repr. No.
532)

604.* FAIRCHILD, G. B., LEE, V., and BARRETTO, P.—1969.
Artrópodos Hematófagos del Río Raposo, Valle, Colombia. III. Tabani-
dae.
Caldasia, *10*(49): 441-458. (Repr. No. 535)

605.* FAIRCHILD, G. B.—1969.
Climate and the Phylogeny and Distribution of Tabanidae.
Bulletin of the Entomological Society of America, *15*(1): 7-11. (Repr.
No. 512)

606.* FAIRCHILD, G. B.—1969.
Notes on Neotropical Tabanidae. XII. Classification and Distribution,
with Keys to Genera and Subgenera.
Arquivos de Zoologia (Sao Paulo), *17*(4): 199-255. (Repr. No. 515)

607.* FURMAN, D. P., and SOUSA, O. E.—1969.
Morphology and Biology of a Nest-Producing Mite, *Bakerichela chanayi*
(Acarina: Cheyletidae).
Annals of the Entomological Society of America, *62*(4): 858-863, July.
(Repr. No. 525)

608.* GALINDO, P.—1969.
Notes on the Systematics of *Culex* (Melanoconion) *taeniopus* Dyar and
Knab and Related Species, Gathered During Arbovirus Investigations in
Panamá.
Mosquito Systematics Newsletter, *1*(4): 82-89, November. (Repr. 533)

609.* GRAYSON, M. A., and GALINDO, P.—1969.
Ecology of Venezuelan Equine Encephalitis Virus in Panamá.
Journal of the American Veterinary Medical Association, *155*(12):
2141-2145, December 15. (Repr. No. 540)

610.* HERRER, A., and TELFORD, JR., S. R.—1969.
Leishmania braziliensis Isolated from Sloths in Panamá.
Science, *164*(3886): 1419-1420, June 20. (Repr. No. 519)

611.	KIRMSE, P.—1969.
Cnemidocoptiasis (Scaly-Leg) in a Buff-Throated Saltator (Saltator maximus) from Panamá.
Bird-Banding, 40(1): 51-52, January. (Repr. No. 516a)

612.	KIRMSE, P., and LOFTIN, H.—1969.
Avian Pox in Migrant and Native Birds in Panamá.
Bulletin of the Wildlife Disease Association, 5: 103-107. (Repr. No. 516b)

613.*	KOURANY, M., and PORTER, JR., J. A.—1969.
A Survey for Enteropathogenic Bacteria in Panamanian Primates.
Laboratory Animal Care, 19(3): 336-341, June. (Repr. No. 518)

614.*	KOURANY, M., and VÀSQUEZ, M. A.—1969.
Enteropathogenic Bacteria Associated with Diarrhea Among Infants in Panamá.
The American Journal of Tropical Medicine and Hygiene, 18(6): 930-935, November. (Repr. No. 537)

615.*	KOURANY, M., and VÀSQUEZ, M. A.—1969.
Housing and Certain Socioenvironmental Factors and Prevalence of Enteropathogenic Bacteria Among Infants with Diarrhea Disease in Panamá.
The American Journal of Tropical Medicine and Hygiene, 18(6): 936-941, November. (Repr. No. 538)

616.	MENDEZ, E.—1969.
Una Breve Introducción a las Aves de Panamá.
Panamá, Editora Unión, 1969. pp. 1-56. (Repr. No. 517)

617.*	MÈNDEZ, E.—1969.
Four New Species of Gyropidae (Mallophaga) from Spiny Rats in Middle America.
Pacific Insects, 11(3-4): 497-506. (Repr. No. 530)

618.*	MYERS, C. W.—1969.
The Ecological Geography of Cloud Forest in Panamá.
American Museum Novitates No. 2396, December 5. (Repr. No. 536)

619.*	MYERS, C. W.—1969.
Snakes of the Genus Coniophanes in Panamá.
American Museum Novitates No. 2372, pp. 1-28. (Repr. No. 514)

620.*	MYERS, C. W., and RAND, A. S.—1969.
Checklist of Amphibians and Reptiles of Barro Colorado Island, Panamá, with Comments on Faunal Change and Sampling.
Smithsonian Contributions to Zoology No. 10, Washington, D. C., Smithsonian Institution Press, 11 p. (Repr. No. 531)

621.*	PORTER, JR., J. A.—1969.
Hematology of the Night Monkey Aotus trivigatus.
Laboratory Animal Care, 19(4): 470-472, August. (Repr. No. 521)

622.*	RABSON, A., EDGCOMB, J. H., LEGALLAIS, F. Y., and TYRELL, S. A.—1969.
Isolation and Growth of Rat Cytomegalovirus in Vitro.
Proceedings of the Society for Experimental Biology and Medicine, 131(3): 923-927, July. (Repr. No. 522)

623.*   SOUSA, O. E., and THATCHER, V. E.—1969.
        Observations on the Life-Cycle of *Echinococcus oligarthrus* (Diesing,
        1863) in the Republic of Panamá.
        Annals of Tropical Medicine and Parasitology, *63*(2): 165-175, June.
        (Repr. No. 520)

624.*   SRIHONGSE, S.—1969.
        Vesicular Stomatitis Virus Infections in Panamanian Primates and other
        Vertebrates.
        The American Journal of Epidemiology, *90*(1): 69-76, July. (Repr.
        No. 523)

625.*   SRIHONGSE, S., and JOHNSON, K. M.—1969.
        Hemagglutinin Production and Infectivity Patterns in Adult Hamsters
        Inoculated with Group "C" and other New World Arboviruses.
        American Journal of Tropical Medicine and Hygiene, *18*(2): 273-279.
        (Repr. No. 511)

626.*   TELFORD, JR., S. R.—1969.
        A New Saurian Malarial Parasite *Plasmodium balli* from Panamá.
        The Journal of Protozoology, *16*(3): 431-437, August. (Repr. No.
        527)

627.*   TELFORD, JR., S. R.—1969.
        The Ovarian Cycle, Reproductive Potential, and Structure in a Popu-
        lation of the Japanese Lacertid *Takydromus tachydromoides*.
        Copeia, No. 3, 548-567, August 29. (Repr. No. 526)

628.*   YOUNG, M. D., and BAERG, D. C.—1969.
        Experimental Infections of *Plasmodium falciparum* in *Cebus capucinus*
        (White Faced Capuchin) Monkeys.
        Military Medicine, *134*(10): 767-771, September. (Repr. No. 528)

629.*   YOUNG, M. D., and PORTER, JR., J. A.—1969.
        Susceptibility of *Ateles fusciceps, Ateles geoffroyi* and *Cebus capucinus*
        Monkeys to *Plasmodium vivax*.
        Transactions of the Royal Society of Tropical Medicine and Hygiene,
        63(2): 203-205. (Repr. No. 513)

630.*   YOUNG, M. D., and ROSSAN, R. N.—1969.
        Plasmodium falciparum Induced in the Squirrel Monkey *Saimiri sciureus*.
        Transactions of the Royal Society of Tropical Medicine and Hygiene,
        63(5): 686-687, October. (Repr. No. 534)

AUTHOR INDEX

(Numbers following the names of authors refer to GML publication number)

SUBJECT HEADINGS INDEX

(Numbers below the headings refer to GML publication number)

With a few minor adaptations (like *Animals, Wild* to describe some Panamanian species used for medical research at GML), Subject Headings used in this List are those authorized by the *Medical Subject Headings—1969* of the National Library of Medicine and the Library of Congress *Subject Headings,* 7th edition.

Acarina see MITES

ACTINOMYCOSIS
262

Aedes see CULICIDAE

AMEBIASIS see also
ENTAMOEBA HISTOLITYCA   PROTOZOAN INFECTIONS

AMEBIASIS
15, 16, 19, 28, 29, 150, 178, 179, 181, 225, 270

AMOEBA
82

Amphibia see HERPETOLOGY

ANCYLOSTOMA see also HOOKWORMS

ANCYLOSTOMA
80, 130

ANEMIA
99

ANIMALS, DOMESTIC see also
ANIMALS, LABORATORY   ANIMALS, WILD

ANIMALS, DOMESTIC
35, 72, 79, 80, 98, 100, 126, 127, 129, 130, 131, 152, 172, 174, 184, 575

ANIMALS, LABORATORY see also
ANIMALS, DOMESTIC
ANIMALS, WILD
BATS
FROGS
LIZARDS
MONKEYS
SNAKES

ANIMALS, LABORATORY
26, 298, 453, 555, 569, 570, 573, 574, 625

ANIMALS, WILD see also
ANIMALS, DOMESTIC
ANIMALS, LABORATORY
BATS
FROGS

BATS
25, 27, 38, 53, 73, 104, 105, 256, 258, 343, 370, 372, 379, 426, 505, 539

BCG VACCINATION
351

BEES
250, 365

BEHAVIOR, ANIMAL
50, 94, 239, 251, 252, 254, 401, 414, 448, 507, 532, 543, 553

BESNOITIA
510, 539, 567, 568, 569, 570

BIOGRAPHY
421

BIRD-BANDING
469, 473, 474, 475, 504, 531, 563, 612

BIRDS
24, 242, 243, 259, 260, 261, 275, 312, 313, 314, 323, 328, 329, 342, 356, 363, 380, 398, 399, 409, 410, 415, 422, 423, 441, 453, 466, 469, 473, 474, 475, 483, 484, 500, 504, 509, 515, 527, 530, 531, 538, 559, 560, 561, 562, 563, 578, 587, 597, 598, 602, 611, 612, 616

BLOOD CELLS, MONKEYS
118, 196, 621

BOOK-REVIEWS
324, 419, 460

BRUCELLOSIS, BOVINE
30

BURKITT'S LYMPHOMA
497

Capybaras see ANIMALS, WILD

Capillaria Hepatica see TRICHUROIDEA

CARBOHYDRATES
84

CAROTENE
161

Chagas' Disease see TRYPANOSOMIASIS, SOUTH AMERICAN

Chloroquine see ANTIMALARIALS

CLIMATOLOGY, MEDICAL
147, 230, 236, 290

COPEPODA
143

CULEX
31, 32, 90, 91, 93, 109, 114, 361, 376, 468, 440, 516, 555, 571, 608

CULICIDAE see also ANOPHELES

CULICIDAE
6, 68, 89, 90, 107, 110, 136, 154, 155, 156, 194, 205, 211, 229, 239, 294, 307, 320, 321, 322, 331, 337, 362, 377, 378, 381, 382, 383, 389, 390, 391, 394, 395, 397, 401, 402, 403, 405, 406, 407, 408, 414, 417, 420, 442, 501, 502, 553, 556, 557, 600

DDT see INSECTICIDES

Deinocerites see CULICIDAE

DENTAL CARIES
212

DIARRHEA
614, 615

DIENTAMOEBA
101, 132

DROSOPHILA
432, 450, 464, 465, 477, 494, 495, 507, 508, 535, 586

DRUG RESISTANCE
579

Drugs see ANTIMALARIALS

ECHINOCOCCOSIS
512, 544, 576, 594, 623

ECOLOGY
321, 437, 478, 528, 595, 618

ECTOPARASITES see also
    FLEAS
    LICE
    MITES
    TICKS

ECTOPARASITES
24, 518, 519, 520, 526, 545

EMETINE
255, 270

ENCEPHALITIS, ST. LOUIS
417, 452, 453, 486, 557

ENCEPHALITIS VIRUSES see also
    ARBOVIRUS   ENCEPHALITIS, ST. LOUIS

ENCEPHALITIS VIRUSES
333, 394, 405, 441, 442, 478, 572

ENCEPHALOMYELITIS, EQUINE
541, 571, 581, 609

HELMINTHS
54, 76, 77, 78, 172, 173, 184, 277, 289, 315, 575, 593

HEMATOLOGY
621

Hemorrhagic Fever see EPIDEMIC HEMORRHAGIC FEVER

HERPETOLOGY see also
FROGS	LIZARDS	SNAKES

HERPETOLOGY
187, 188, 506, 620

HOOKWORMS
79, 99, 195

HORSE DISEASES
34, 35, 75, 96, 98, 100, 120, 122, 126, 127, 129, 131, 174, 278

Hydatidosis see ECHINOCOCCOSIS

ILHEUS VIRUS see also ENCEPHALITIS, ST. LOUIS

ILHEUS VIRUS
394, 405, 441, 442, 478, 572

IMMUNITY
80, 237, 240, 242

INSECT CONTROL
6, 205, 241, 246, 257, 265, 266, 267, 271, 272, 296, 308, 353, 355, 371

INSECTICIDES
241, 246, 257, 265, 266, 267, 271, 272, 287, 296, 308, 327, 341, 353, 355

INSECTICIDES RESISTANCE
368

Intestinal Diseases, Parasitic see
AMEBIASIS
ANCYLOSTOMA
ENTAMOEBA HISTOLYTICA
HELMINTHS
HOOKWORMS
HORSE DISEASES
STRONGYLOIDES
TRICHUROIDEA
TRICHOSTRONGYLOIDEA

INTESTINAL SECRETIONS
59

LABORATORY INFECTION
8, 9, 29, 62, 63, 65, 66, 67, 94, 104, 118, 152, 158, 242, 297, 339, 364, 367, 389,420, 463, 470, 476, 513, 537, 539, 548, 555, 566, 569, 570, 599, 600, 628, 630

LABORATORY TECHNIQUES
24, 26, 45, 46, 64, 82, 86, 115, 116, 134, 153, 229, 248, 249, 258, 280, 287, 325, 444, 448, 476, 488, 541

LEISHMANIA see also LEISHMANIASIS

LEISHMANIA
431, 470, 513, 540, 603

LEISHMANIASIS, MUCOCUTANEOUS
344, 457, 491, 514, 529, 582, 589, 610

LEPROSY
103

LICE
234, 427, 428, 447, 458, 459, 461, 462, 471, 492, 564, 565

LIZARDS
481, 510, 568, 569, 626, 627

MALARIA see also
  ANTIMALARIALS
  MALARIA, MONKEYS
  MONKEY DISEASES
  MONKEYS
  PLASMODIUM BRASILIANUM
  PLASMODIUM FALCIPARUM
  PLASMODIUM VIVAX

MALARIA
2, 8, 21, 22, 33, 49, 61, 62, 63, 65, 66, 67, 71, 89, 92, 94, 95, 111, 118, 119, 121, 123, 144, 148, 149, 158, 165, 166, 183, 185, 186, 196, 199, 200, 201, 205, 214, 233, 237, 238, 240, 242, 291, 353, 357, 359, 360, 536, 537, 546, 547, 548, 566, 579, 599, 600, 626, 628, 629, 630

MALARIA, MONKEYS
8, 33, 62, 63, 65, 66, 67, 118, 196, 242, 536, 537, 548, 566, 599, 600, 628, 629, 630

MEDICAL PRACTICE
147, 236

Melanoconion see CULEX

MITES
234, 248, 249, 251, 252, 253, 254, 607

Mochlostyrax see CULEX

MOLLUSKS
268

MONKEY DISEASES see also
  MALARIA, MONKEYS   PLASMODIUM BRASILIANUM

MONKEY DISEASES
1, 7, 8, 9, 13, 29, 33, 43, 62, 63, 65, 66, 67, 78, 83, 113, 118, 146, 176, 196, 207, 242, 339, 364, 366, 367, 404, 536, 537, 548, 566, 570, 593, 599, 613, 624, 629

MONKEYS see also MONKEY DISEASES

MONKEYS
5, 167, 182, 621

Mosquitoes see CULICIDAE

MYIASIS
3, 288

NEMATODA
13, 77, 78, 100, 113, 128, 176

PAPPATACI FEVER
490

PARASITES, BLOOD
1, 7, 527, 561

PHLEBOTOMUS see also PSYCHODIDAE

PHLEBOTOMUS
234, 241, 263, 264, 267, 271, 281, 282, 284, 293, 295, 296, 304, 305, 306, 308, 309, 310, 318, 319, 335, 336, 346, 349, 350, 374, 387, 400, 412, 413, 416, 437, 438, 439, 443, 444, 445, 448, 451, 463, 470, 472, 476, 488, 493, 543, 591, 592, 596

PLANTS
56, 244

Plaquenil see ANTIMALARIALS
Plasmochin see ANTIMALARIALS

PLASMODIUM BRASILIANUM
8, 33, 63, 65, 66, 118, 196, 240

PLASMODIUM FALCIPARUM
62, 67, 144, 183, 566, 579, 628, 630

PLASMODIUM VIVAX
94, 144, 537, 548, 599, 629

PNEUMONIA
286

POLIOMYELITIS
339, 340, 364

PROTOZOA see also PROTOZOAN INFECTIONS

PROTOZOA
84, 430, 499, 567, 568, 626

PROTOZOAN INFECTIONS
15, 19, 29, 43, 83, 101, 180, 181, 373, 539, 569, 570, 588

Psorophora see CULICIDAE

PSYCHODIDAE see also PHLEBOTOMUS

PSYCHODIDAE
234, 283, 293, 305, 317, 334

Pyrimethamine (Daraprim) see ANTIMALARIALS
Q FEVER see also
    RICKETTSIA RICKETTSII   ROCKY MOUNTAIN SPOTTED FEVER

Q FEVER
269, 285, 297, 299

Quinine see ANTIMALARIALS

RATS
184, 289, 418, 617

REDUVIIDAE
36, 55, 117, 234, 456, 585

RELAPSING FEVER
9, 41, 213

RICKETTSIA RICKETTSII
352

ROCKY MOUNTAIN SPOTTED FEVER
311

Sabethes Chloropterus see CULICIDAE

SALMONELLAE see also BACTERIA, PATHOGENIC

SALMONELLAE
60, 505

Sandflies see PHLEBOTOMUS

SIMULIUM
190, 226, 246

Sloths see TROPICAL ANIMALS-PHYSIOLOGY

SNAKES
37, 74, 96, 124, 125, 153, 168, 169, 215, 216, 217, 274, 292, 479, 480, 533, 534, 619, 620

Spotted Fever see ROCKY MOUNTAIN SPOTTED FEVER

STRONGYLOIDES
4, 14, 127

SYPHILIS
69

TABANIDAE
170, 171, 189, 191, 192, 202, 203, 204, 219, 220, 221, 222, 223, 224, 225, 234, 245, 303, 316, 345, 347, 348, 375, 386, 393, 411, 424, 425, 433, 434, 435, 436, 455, 467, 485, 503, 521, 522, 523, 524, 525, 550, 551, 552, 604, 605, 606

TAXONOMY
252, 253, 337, 450

TICKS
12, 39, 40, 41, 51, 58, 197, 234, 297, 352, 526

TISSUE CULTURE
430, 431

TOXOPLASMOSIS
298, 366

TREMATODA
373, 479, 480, 481, 482, 500, 575

Triatominae see REDUVIIDAE

TRICHOSTRONGYLOIDEA
126

TRICHUROIDEA
160, 175

TROPICAL ANIMALS-PHYSIOLOGY
145, 146, 159, 162, 163, 164, 198, 232

TROPICAL MEDICINE
15, 47, 147, 230, 236, 290, 302

TRYPANOSOMA see also
TRYPANOSOMIASIS, BOVINE   TRYPANOSOMIASIS, EQUINE
TRYPANOSOMIASIS, SOUTH AMERICAN

TRYPANOSOMA
27, 51, 152, 493, 529, 577

TRYPANOSOMIASIS, BOVINE
35, 72, 206

TRYPANOSOMIASIS, EQUINE
25, 27, 34, 64, 75, 104, 105, 278

TRYPANOSOMIASIS, SOUTH AMERICAN
18, 20, 36, 55, 87, 106, 117, 134, 235, 585, 601

TUBERCULOSIS
48

TYPHUS
276, 285

Uranotaenia see CULICIDAE

VECTOCARDIOGRAPHY
558

VENOMS
153, 215

VETERINARY HELMINTHOLOGY
13, 76, 77, 79, 97, 98, 99, 100, 113, 126, 127, 129, 130, 131, 172, 174, 176, 315

VITAMIN "A"

161

WARBLE-FLIES

3, 57

YAWS

68, 69

YELLOW FEVER

107, 307, 321, 322, 330, 331, 332, 338, 378, 382, 383, 385, 389, 390, 392, 395, 396, 403, 404, 406, 407, 408, 414, 420, 487, 554

ZOOLOGY, CLASSIFICATION

388

INDEX OF INDIVIDUALS

411

INDEX OF SUBJECTS

419

H